POLYESTERS

AND

THEIR APPLICATIONS

By

BJORKSTEN RESEARCH LABORATORIES, INC.
Madison, Wisconsin

JOHAN BJORKSTEN
President

HENRY TOVEY
Chief, Literature Division

BETTY HARKER
Administrative Assistant

JAMES HENNING
Administrative Assistant

REINHOLD PUBLISHING CORPORATION
NEW YORK

CHAPMAN & HALL, LIMITED, LONDON
1956

91223
2-57

REINHOLD PUBLISHING CORPORATION

Also publishers of "Materials & Methods," Chemical Engineering Catalog, Chemical Materials Catalog, "Progressive Architecture," and "Automatic Control"; Advertising Management of American Chemical Society

DEDICATION

This book is dedicated to the staff of the Classification Group of the U. S. Patent Office, whose painstaking work in classifying the patent literature has been of immeasurable benefit in preparing it.

PREFACE

For many years we have been assembling data on polyesters. This task seems nearly endless. Several times when we thought the data were up to date and suitable for presentation in book form, some new advances in the art made it necessary to rewrite the manuscript completely. When this rewriting was completed, there were new advances which required still further work.

In order to terminate this potentially endless process of improvement, we decided to print the data as available June 1, 1954. (Some pertinent references published after this date are listed at the end of the bibliography.)

It is the intention of the authors to publish supplements to this book periodically. We will therefore greatly appreciate any comments and particularly suggestions for improvements or extensions of the present material.

We have to the best of our ability followed and reported on the best practice available today from published sources. Beyond this we can accept no responsibility.

Bjorksten Research Laboratories, Inc.

Madison, Wis.
March 1, 1956

TABLE OF CONTENTS

THEORETICAL CONSIDERATIONS

A detailed exposition of the theory of high polymers (1203) is beyond the scope of this book. In this chapter the concepts necessary for an understanding of high polymers are presented briefly. The thermoplastic and thermosetting characteristics of resins are interpreted on the basis of the functionality theory. The reactions leading to the formation of high polymers and the mechanisms of these reactions are described. Degree of polymerization, average molecular weight, and methods for determination of these values are discussed.

Polyesters, both saturated and unsaturated, are discussed extensively in a separate section. The fiber-forming characteristics of the linear polyesters and cross-linking reactions of the unsaturated polyesters are described.

GENERAL CONCEPTS

Functionality Theory

High polymers are formed by continuous reaction of simple molecules. The molecules that can partake in the reactions leading to the formation of high polymers must possess certain characteristics. R. H. Kienle, whose work on alkyds contributed greatly to an understanding of the formation of high polymers, proposed the functionality theory (1176, 1177). According to this theory only molecules which contain at least two active centers (two reactive groups) can react to form a polymer. Thus, a monohydroxy alcohol may react with a monocarboxylic acid to form an ester, but no polymeric molecule will be produced by such a reaction. A dibasic acid, however, may react with a dihydroxy alcohol to form a macromolecule of a polyester:

$$\underset{\substack{\displaystyle \|\\ \displaystyle O}}{HOC} -(CH_2)_n - \underset{\substack{\displaystyle \|\\ \displaystyle O}}{COH} + HO -(CH_2)_m - OH \rightarrow$$

$$\underset{\substack{\displaystyle \|\\ \displaystyle O}}{HOC} -(CH_2)_n - \underset{\substack{\displaystyle \|\\ \displaystyle O}}{CO} -(CH_2)_m - \underset{\substack{\displaystyle \|\\ \displaystyle O}}{OC} -(CH_2)_n - \underset{\substack{\displaystyle \|\\ \displaystyle O}}{CO} \cdots + H_2O$$

This type of reaction Kienle called a $2:2$ polymerization, thus indicating that each of the monomeric molecules partaking in the reaction has a functionality of 2.

1

However, not all the bifunctional molecules will form polymers (1136). Stereochemical factors, such as the shielding of functional groups by other groups, are important. If in a 2:2 reaction it is possible for the two reactants to form a six-membered ring by intraesterification, in general almost no polymer will form. Polymerization in solution, particularly in dilute solution, will also favor ring formation (1136). The solvent molecules separate the reactant molecules, so that the chance of the ends of the same molecules coming together is greater than that of their contacting other molecules.

Addition Polymerization

W. H. Carothers' work, which eventually led to the discovery of nylon, also contributed to our understanding of the high polymers (1208, 1212). Carothers proposed a division of the high polymers according to the mechanism of reaction by which they are formed. Some monomers polymerize by addition through their unsaturated bonds, and the process is called A-polymerization or addition polymerization. The polyvinyls, the polymethacrylates, and the polystyrenes are representative of polymers formed by this type of polymerization. For example, a molecule of styrene $\left(\bigcirc CH = CH_2 \right)$ contains a vinyl double bond. Polystyrene is formed by styrene molecules adding on to each other at their double bonds, and thus it contains no unsaturation:

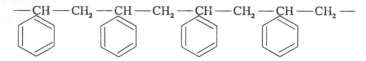

Free Radical Mechanism. The addition polymerization reaction has been the subject of much study (1119, 1122, 1128, 1140, 1196, 1197, 1198, 1213, 1214). It is now known that addition polymerization proceeds by a free radical mechanism (1119).

Free radicals can be produced by the decomposition of labile molecules by heat, light, or fast nuclear particles or formed in the course of a chemical reaction. Benzoyl peroxide is an example of a compound that decomposes to give free radicals:

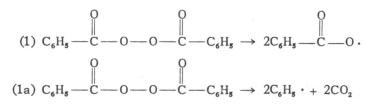

Free radicals, as produced in reactions 1 and 1a, attack the double bond of a monomer and add on to it:

$$(2) \quad C_6H_5 \overset{\overset{O}{\|}}{-C} -O \cdot + H_2C{=}CHX \rightarrow C_6H_5 \overset{\overset{O}{\|}}{-C} -O-CH_2-CHX \cdot$$

The dimer formed remains activated, attacks another double bond, and a chain macromolecule grows.

The chain formation is terminated when the molecule is inactivated. The inactivation occurs, according to some authorities, only when there is a collision between two activated molecules (1223):

$$(3) \quad C_6H_5 \overset{\overset{O}{\|}}{-C} -O-CH_2 \cdots CHX \cdot + C_6H_5 \overset{\overset{O}{\|}}{-C} -O-CH_2 \cdots CHX \cdot \rightarrow$$

$$C_6H_5 \overset{\overset{O}{\|}}{-C} -O-CH_2-CHX \cdots CHX-CH_2-O \overset{\overset{O}{\|}}{-C} -C_6H_5$$

Others say that the chains are terminated when an activated molecule collides with another activated molecule, an unactivated monomer molecule, or a molecule of solvent (1223).

The rate of formation of the chain molecule is very rapid. The concentration of the monomer may still be fairly large when a number of long chains are present. There are some indications that the gel points of the polymers depend on the rate of diffusion of the polymer molecules, as well as on the rate of the polymer chain growth (1249). Any effect of diffusion rate on gel points may be questioned, however, in view of the fact that the reaction rate does not show any dependence on viscosity, but the diffusion rate does (1149).

Catalysts. Substances promoting the formation of free radicals are commonly used during addition polymerization reactions. They are called "catalysts" by the trade, though because they take part in the reaction and appear chemically combined with the resulting polymers they are not "catalysts" as the chemist usually understands this term. The Commission on Nomenclature of the International Union of Pure and Applied Chemistry (IUPAC) proposed that these substances be called "initiators" inasmuch as they initiate addition polymerization (1116).

Benzoyl peroxide is a popular polymerization "catalyst." A description of how this compound breaks down to give free radicals which initiate addition polymerization is given on page 2. More detailed information on the effects of various "catalysts" on addition polymerization is given in the chapter on catalysis and inhibition (p. 46).

Condensation Polymerization

Some monomers polymerize with elimination of water. They are said by Carothers to partake in a C-polymerization or polycondensation. The phenolics, polyamides, and polyesters are examples of the products of this type of polymerization.

In the synthesis of nylon, a dicarboxylic acid condenses with a diamine in a typical 2:2 polycondensation, giving a long, chainlike polyamide. Water is formed as a by-product.

$$HO\overset{\overset{O}{\|}}{C}-(CH_2)_n-\overset{\overset{O}{\|}}{C}OH\ +\ H_2N-(CH_2)_m-NH_2\ \rightarrow$$

$$HO\overset{\overset{O}{\|}}{C}-(CH_2)_n-\overset{\overset{O}{\|}}{C}NH-(CH_2)_m-NH\overset{\overset{O}{\|}}{C}-(CH_2)_n-\overset{\overset{O}{\|}}{C}NH\cdots\ +\ H_2O$$

The mechanism of the polycondensation reaction is similar to that of any normal condensation reaction (1144). Unlike the addition polymerization, the polycondensation reaction proceeds in a steplike fashion. At any state of the reaction most of the material reaches the same level of polymerization before further polymerization occurs. For example, most of the monomeric substances present change to dimer form before higher polymers are formed to any great extent. Thus, the polymer is formed gradually.

Since this reaction is by-product forming and reversible, its progress is greatly affected by the rate of removal of the by-product (1225).

Catalysts are sometimes used in this reaction. The esterification catalysts are discussed in the chapter on catalysis and inhibition (p. 46).

Thermoplastic High Polymers

The 2:2 type of polymerization results in a long chainlike molecule. These molecules form the so-called linear polymers, which are essentially thermoplastic, that is, are capable of indefinite, inelastic deformation at elevated temperatures.

Enough energy is usually supplied by heating thermoplastic material to counteract the effect of intermolecular forces and to permit the molecules to slip past each other. The intermolecular forces vary for chemically different polymers, however. They are stronger, for example, for highly polar molecules, such as polystyrene, where they are augmented by electrical forces, than for those with no polarity, such as butadiene-styrene synthetic rubber. The sterical structure of the molecules also affects the intermolecular forces; a more symmetrical and ordered arrangement results in partial crystallinity and greater strength.

Thermosetting High Polymers

High polymers produced by reaction between compounds whose functionality is greater than 2 are not thermoplastic (1151). If at least one of the monomers partaking in the reaction has an active functionality of 3 or higher, a space network (or three-dimensional) type of high polymer may result. In a completely cured polymer of this type, the whole structure is, in effect, one enormous molecule in which each carbon atom is bound to any other carbon atom by primary valence bonds.[1] The phthalic anhydride-glycerol polycondensation is an example of a 2:3 reaction resulting in such a polymer:

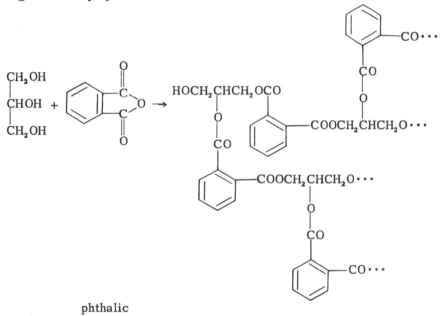

glycerol   phthalic anhydride   glyceryl phthalate

A compound with such a structure has little flexibility and is thermosetting, that is, once cured it cannot be softened by heating and reformed. Even at high temperatures the cured plastic is incapable of much deformation and is infusible and insoluble.

Various phases of reaction are possible. The phenolics, for example, pass through three stages during polymerization. Stage A represents the monomeric stage; stage B, the partially polymerized but not completely cured (thermosetting) stage; and stage C, the completely cured (thermo-

[1] H. P. Staudinger, who first championed the theory that high polymers are single molecules in which the atoms are connected with primary valence bonds, was given the Nobel Prize for Chemistry in 1953 in recognition of his work.

set) stage. In fabrication of the phenolic plastics, the manufacturer makes the resin and polymerizes it to stage B, when it may be formed into pellets, etc. The molder then forms the resin into the final desired shape and cures it to the C stage.

Degree of Polymerization

Both the degree of polymerization (average number of base units per molecule, e.g., number of styrene units in a molecule of polystyrene) and the degree of polymerization distribution (relative amounts of low- and high-molecular-weight macromolecules) greatly affect the properties of a plastic material.

A minimum degree of polymerization (DP), ranging from 40 to 80, is necessary to obtain mechanical strength (1204). The mechanical strength[2] rises with the DP until the latter reaches about 250. Then the proportionality is less direct, but the strength still rises with the DP up to a DP of about 600. Above this value the mechanical strength has little relation to the DP.

The degree of polymerization is important for flexural or bending strength. J. J. Lamb *et al.* performed a series of tests on the flexural strength of glass fabric reinforced unsaturated polyester laminates and found that it changed as the temperature was raised from $-70°$ to $+200°F$. (1194). The authors emphasize that the change may have been a function of further cure.

The mechanical strength of a plastic depends not only on the average molecular weight of the macromolecules it contains, but on the range of distribution of high- and low-molecular-weight macromolecules in it. Thus, the DP distribution is important for plastics since they are codispersed systems in which macromolecules of different molecular weights are dispersed in each other (1118). For example, a resin in which one-half of the macromolecules have a molecular weight of 200,000 and the other half a molecular weight of 100 would be vastly different in properties from a resin in which all the macromolecules have a molecular weight of 100,000.

Solubility characteristics are also affected by the DP distribution. Some solvents will dissolve only compounds of a low degree of polymerization; but they may attack a plastic that contains some low polymerization products. The resulting mixture of solvent with the low polymerization products is a better solvent for the higher polymerization products, and thus solvation of the plastic may occur by a stepwise process.

Although these are extreme examples, uniformity of molecular weight is generally preferable. In addition, the higher the average molecular weight,

[2]See the chapter on testing for mechanical strength tests (p. 233).

the better generally speaking will be the toughness and strength of the resin, but the lower will be its solubility.

Determination of Molecular Weight

The determination of the molecular weight of high polymers is important not only from the theoretical point of view but also for practical applications in the manufacture of resins (p. 44).

The principal methods for the determination of molecular weight are based on the following definitions (1207):

(1) The number average molecular weight, $\overline{M_n}$, defined as

$$\overline{M_n} = \frac{\Sigma M_i N_i}{\Sigma N_i}$$

where M_i is the molecular weight of particles of chain length i, and N_i is the number of particles of chain length i.

(2) The weight average molecular weight, $\overline{M_w}$, defined as

$$\overline{M_w} = \frac{\Sigma M_i^2 N_i}{\Sigma M_i N_i}$$

(3) The sedimentation average molecular weight (or z average molecular weight), $\overline{M_s}$, defined as

$$\overline{M_s} = \frac{\Sigma M_i^3 N_i}{\Sigma M_i^2 N_i}$$

If a resin were composed of macromolecules of identical molecular weight, all of the preceding formulas would give the same results. For example, assume a sample of resin composed of 50 molecules, each having a molecular weight of 10,000; then

$$(1)\ \overline{M_n} = \frac{10,000 \times 50}{50} = 10,000$$

$$(2)\ \overline{M_w} = \frac{10,000^2 \times 50}{10,000 \times 50} = 10,000$$

$$(3)\ \overline{M_s} = \frac{10,000^3 \times 50}{10,000^2 \times 50} = 10,000$$

However, no one has been able, as yet, to prepare a highly polymeric resin composed of molecules of identical weight. Resins are actually composed of mixtures of macromolecules whose molecular weights vary over a wide range. For this reason the various methods of determining average molecular weight give results that differ considerably.

We can assume, for the sake of simplicity, that a given sample of resin contains 50 molecules of only three different molecular weights:

$$N_i' = 15 \text{ molecules of molecular weight } M_i' = 15,000$$
$$N_i'' = 30 \text{ molecules of molecular weight } M_i'' = 10,000$$
$$N_i''' = 5 \text{ molecules of molecular weight } M_i''' = 7,500$$

(1) The number average molecular weight will be

$$\overline{M_n} = \frac{\Sigma M_i N_i}{\Sigma N_i} = \frac{M_i'N_i' + M_i''N_i'' + M_i'''N_i'''}{N_i' + N_i'' + N_i'''} =$$

$$\frac{(15,000 \times 15) + (10,000 \times 30) + (7,500 \times 5)}{15 + 30 + 5} = 11,240$$

(2) The weight average molecular weight will be:

$$\overline{M_w} = \frac{\Sigma M_i^2 N_i}{\Sigma M_i N_i} = \frac{[(M_i')^2 N_i'] + [(M_i'')^2 N_i''] + [(M_i''')^2 N_i''']}{(M_i'N_i') + (M_i''N_i'') + (M_i'''N_i''')} =$$

$$\frac{(15,000^2 \times 15) + (10,000^2 \times 30) + (7,500^2 \times 5)}{(15,000 \times 15) + (10,000 \times 30) + (7,500 \times 5)} = 11,834$$

(3) The sedimentation average molecular weight will be:

$$\overline{M_s} = \frac{\Sigma M_i^3 N_i}{\Sigma M_i^2 N_i} = \frac{[(M_i')^3 N_i'] + [(M_i'')^3 N_i''] + [(M_i''')^3 N_i''']}{[(M_i')^2 N_i'] + [(M_i'')^2 N_i''] + [(M_i''')^2 N_i''']} =$$

$$\frac{(15,000^3 \times 15) + (10,000^3 \times 30) + (7,500^3 \times 5)}{(15,000^2 \times 15) + (10,000^2 \times 30) + (7,500^2 \times 5)} = 12,429$$

The example was chosen so that the weight average molecular weight was larger than the number average molecular weight, as is usually the case. In actual experience, the difference in results is much larger than found here, since the greater the polydispersity (or size range of the various molecules), the greater is the disparity between the different types of average molecular weight (1233).

Determination of Number Average Molecular Weight. The experimental methods which result in determination of the number average molecular weight all depend on estimating the number of molecules present in a sample of given weight. These methods include the cryoscopic and ebullioscopic methods, the methods which utilize osmotic pressure measurements, and the methods which depend on estimation of end groups by chemical analysis.

Cryoscopic and Ebullioscopic Methods. The cryoscopic and ebullioscopic methods are seldom used for polymers of molecular weight of over 5,000. They depend on the changes in the melting and boiling points of pure compounds effected by the presence of the molecules of the polymer. Since these changes depend on the number of molecules in the small amount of solute in the mixture, the giant molecules of the higher polymers exert an effect too minute to be measured conveniently.

Osmotic Pressure. The osmotic pressure method also depends on the number of macromolecules in the solvated sample of the polymer (1226). Because it gives excellent results, it is often used for basic studies on high polymers. Because of the difficulties in using semipermeable membranes for nonaqueous solvent systems and the rather involved procedures, however, other methods are usually favored in the production plant.

End-Group Analysis. Estimation of the terminal groups gives good results in a much shorter time than the osmotic pressure method. The "acid number" test is often used in polyester manufacture. In this method free carboxyl groups in the resin are determined by titration to give an indication of the extent of polyesterification and the molecular weight of the resin.

Other applications of end-group analysis are the quantitative addition of bromine to the double bond of styrene, the use of the "iodine number" for the determination of the molecular weight of cellulose, and the measurement of the Raman spectra of double bonds (1217).

Some of the errors incident to end-group analysis methods are discussed by P. J. Flory (1150).

Determination of Weight Average Molecular Weight. Viscometric, light scattering, and sedimentation or diffusion velocity methods give the weight average molecular weight.

Viscometric Method. The viscometric method depends on Staudinger's basic formula relating the viscosity of a solution of a high polymer to its molecular weight (1226):

$$\eta_{sp} = KcM_w$$

where M_w is the molecular weight, c is the concentration of the solution, K is a constant, and η_{sp} is the specific viscosity of the solution. This relation depends on the length of the molecules. Kuhn modified it to

$$\eta_{sp} = K_1 cM^{0.8 \text{ or } 0.9}$$

asserting that the molecules are coiled and therefore actually longer than measurements indicate (1162). Houwink postulated an even more coiled structure and proposed

$$\eta_{sp} = K_1 cM^{0.6}$$

as the equation giving the actual molecular weight (1162). He stated that the adoption of this formula would bring the results obtained by the viscometric method nearer to those obtained by osmotic determinations.

Other discussions of the viscometric method are given by Krüger and Broser (1193) and Flory (1150, 1152).

G. N. Chelnokova *et al.* obtained the same results for average molecular weight by the viscometric, cryoscopic, and end-group titration methods for polyesters prepared from stoichiometric amounts of adipic acid and ethylene glycol (1135).

Light Scattering. The light scattering method for determination of molecular weight depends on the fact that the presence of foreign particles in a solution greatly increases the power of the solution to scatter light (1252). P. Debye related the scattering (or turbidity) constant to the weight average molecular weight, M_w, by the equation:

$$Hc/\tau = 1/M_w + 2Bc$$

where τ is the turbidity constant, c is the concentration of the solution, and H and B are constants (1138, 1139). The turbidity constant τ is defined as

$$\tau \doteq (1/l)\ln(I/I_0)$$

where l is the length of the path of light through the solution, I_0 is the initial intensity of the light, and I is the intensity of the transmitted light.

Sedimentation Velocity. Sedimentation (or diffusion) velocity is another method which gives the weight average molecular weight. This determination can be done in an ultracentrifuge. As the sample of the solvated polyester is rotated, a boundary between pure solvent and the solution becomes apparent. In polydispersed systems, since molecules of various weights will not move at the same speed under the centrifugal force, the boundary will not be clear-cut. Its shape indicates the degree of polydispersity: The more uniform the sample, the clearer is the boundary.

The rate at which the boundary moves away from the center is determined and correlated with the weight average molecular weight, M_w, by the following equation prepared by T. Svedberg (1242):

$$M_w = \frac{RTs}{D(1 - V\rho)}$$

where R is the gas constant, T is the absolute temperature, D is the diffusion constant, V is the partial specific volume of the solute, ρ is the density of the solution, and s is the sedimentation rate constant.

Sedimentation Average Molecular Weight. Also using an ultracentrifuge, but at a lower number of revolutions per minute, it is possible to observe the final equilibrium between sedimentation and diffusion. This equilibrium permits determination of the molecular weight of the solute according to the following equation (1241):

$$M_s = \frac{2RT \ln (c/c_0)}{(1 - V\rho)\omega^2 (x^2 - x_0^2)}$$

where R, T, V, and ρ have the same meaning as in previous equations, c_0 and c are the equilibrium solute concentrations at the distances x_0 and x from the axis of rotation, respectively, ω is the angular velocity of the centrifuge, and M_s is the sedimentation (or z) average molecular weight.

Birefringence. The birefringence (double refraction) of macromolecules in solution has been studied as a means for determining the size and shape of molecules in solution (1188). Doty and Mark discuss this method, as well as most of the other methods previously mentioned in reference (1142).

Other reviews on the determination of molecular weight are given by G. V. Schulz (1223) and Losev and Trostyanskaya (1199).

POLYESTERS

Many classifications have been proposed for plastics, but the term "polyesters" is still applied to many different types of resins (1297, 1322). We shall define polyesters as the polycondensation products of dicarboxylic acids with dihydroxy alcohols. These compounds may be modified by monocarboxylic acids, monohydroxy alcohols, and even small amounts of polycarboxylic acids or polyhydroxy alcohols. This definition does not include materials commonly known as alkyds, which are usually modified by fatty acids and drying oils. Unsaturated polyesters, which are produced when any of the reactants contain nonaromatic unsaturation, can be cross-linked or copolymerized with another unsaturated copolymerizable monomer.

The kinetics of polyesterification reactions were studied extensively by P. J. Flory and his coworkers (1278). Flory reports that the rate of polyesterification is independent of both the molecular weight increase and the increase in viscosity that occur during this reaction (1149).

The effect of varying proportions of reactants in a polycondensation of glycol with adipic acid was studied by V. V. Korshak et al. (1295). At stoichiometric proportions the average molecular weight of the polymer was 3,800; at 20% excess of acid it went down to 1200, and at 80 to 100% excess of acid, to below 500. Analogous results were obtained with excess glycol. When the polyester was heated with either excess acid or glycol, a cleavage occurred, and low-molecular-weight compounds were formed in proportion to the excess acid or glycol used. It is possible that esterification and ester cleavage occur simultaneously in the polycondensation reactions.

Unsaturated Polyesters

The major portion of polyesters now in production contain unsaturation. The unsaturation is usually introduced by the use of unsaturated dicarboxylic acids, such as maleic and fumaric acids. It can also be introduced by the use of unsaturated alcohols (1273).

The unsaturated polyesters are usually cross-linked by dissolving them in a monomeric copolymerizable compound, such as styrene, and heating (curing) the mass (1317).

"Drying" Properties. In the late 1930's, when all the polyesters were lumped together under "alkyds," work began on the clarification of the "drying" properties of the unsaturated polyesters (1265). It was noted that the unsaturated polyesters are converted by oxygen, heat, and light to insoluble, infusible structures. T. F. Bradley extended the theories of Carothers and Kienle to this "drying" phenomenon, and discovered that the main requirement for "drying" is not the ability to oxidize, but the possession of a unit molecule with a sufficient number and proper type of reactive centers to permit unrestricted growth in all directions (1267, 1268). "In other words, the simplest monomeric unit should be capable of joining with more than two other units."

H. L. Vincent continued this line of investigation and found that linear polyesters from glycols and maleic, fumaric, and citraconic acids undergo gelation through their double bonds (1323). A mixed ester containing 10% of maleic acid and 90% of succinic acid showed full convertability to an insoluble, infusible state. Kropa, Bradley, and Johnston experimentally established that the convertability is connected with the double bond by experiments with triethylene glycol and succinic acid and the glycol and maleic anhydride (1270). They discovered that addition polymerization (cross-linking) is accelerated by heat, ultraviolet light, and the presence of minute amounts of oxygen, but will not occur unless the molecule contains at least two carbon-to-carbon double bonds. Soluble cobalt salts accelerate the reaction, but antioxidants such as hydroquinone inhibit it.

In the preparation of unsaturated polyesters it is necessary to conduct the first or polycondensation step under conditions that will prevent, or at least substantially reduce, the tendency of the double bonds to polymerize (1291). Control of temperature during the polycondensation and the use of inhibitors of addition polymerization are essential. Oxygen should be excluded during the polycondensation in order to get the reaction to proceed far enough to give a resin of low acid number and still of low viscosity. The reaction therefore is usually carried out in an atmosphere of inert gas, such as nitrogen or carbon dioxide.

Cross-Linking. Thermosetting resins are obtained by cross-linking of unsaturated polyesters. In this reaction it is vital to balance properly the amounts of catalyst, inhibitors, and promoters, to regulate the temperature, and to consider the reactivity of the resin, particularly as it affects the speed and temperature of the reaction. An excellent review of the cross-linking reaction is given by Patterson and Robinson (1310). These authors discuss the exothermic curve in terms of the four parts of the curing cycle: the induction period, the initiation period, the peak temperature, and the reduction temperature.

It is possible, by activating the double bonds in the unsaturated polyesters, to cause the unsaturated residues in the polycondensate to polymerize by addition polymerization among themselves (1270). For example, prolonged heating of the linear unsaturated polyester obtained from ethylene glycol and maleic anhydride

$$-R-CH=CH-R-CH=CH-R-$$

$$[R \text{ is } -OCOCH_2CH_2OCO-]$$

will cause a certain amount of reaction between double bonds resulting in the formation of a cross-linked structure

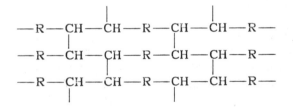

The unsaturated polyesters are more commonly cross-linked with unsaturated monomers, usually styrene. One type of cross-linking which can occur is illustrated by the following formula, which represents the compound formed when styrene cross-links the double bonds in the linear ethylene glycol maleate of the preceding example:

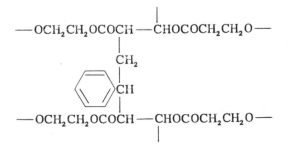

The structure of the cross-linked unsaturated polyesters is very much like that of the space network type of polymers (p. 5). The cross-linked resins are thermosetting and, when fully cured, are insoluble and infusible.

The extent of cross-linking can be controlled by varying (1) the amount of unsaturation in the polyester, for example, by the proportion of maleic and adipic acids and (2) the amount of cross-linking agent. It is easier to vary the unsaturation, since most common polyesters contain 30% of styrene but need only 16% to become thermoset. Catalytic systems and reaction conditions will also affect the extent of the reaction. There is no exact parallel, however, to the three stages exhibited by phenolic resins, unless the linear stage, before addition polymerization takes place, be called stage B. Of course, there is a similarity between the B stage in phenolics and the preimpregnated polyester plastics (p. 112), particularly those in which diallyl phthalate is used as the cross-linking agent. The reason for the lack of stages is the difficulty encountered in stopping the exothermic cross-linking reaction once it is started.

Nevertheless the cross-linked polyesters hold a big advantage over the space network type of phenolic polymers inasmuch as the cross-linking reaction is an addition polymerization and produces no by-products which could evaporate, forming pores. This advantage is utilized commercially, for example, by the coating industry in the so-called "solventless" varnishes, and it is the key to the success of polyesters in electrical applications (p. 182). In the production of the phenolics the polycondensation reaction carries the resin through all three stages and produces by-products. In the final molding step, high pressures and high temperatures must be used to hold the gaseous by-products in solution.

Saturated Polyesters

The polyesters prepared from saturated compounds are an example of a typical 2:2 polycondensation product. They are linear, chainlike structures that are soluble and, depending on their degree of polymerization and their individual components, range from viscous liquids to solids.

To be sure, these linear polymers can be made to cross-link. W. O. Baker reports that compounds which break down with the formation of free radicals, such as benzoyl peroxide, can cause the linear polyundecanoates to become thermoset (1259). He suggests that the free radicals activate the polyester by removing a hydrogen from the $-CH_2-$ (methylene) group alpha to the ester group. The active $-\overset{\cdot}{C}H-$ group formed can combine with another active $-\overset{\cdot}{C}H-$ group or attack another methylene group.

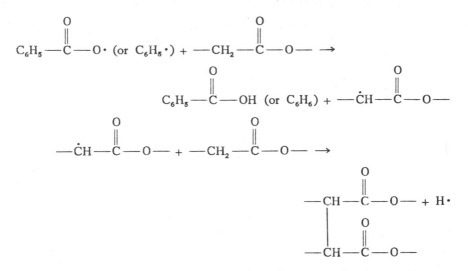

This free radical reaction is suggested as the cause of aging, oxidation, and similar phenomena occuring in the high polymers that contain little or no polythenic unsaturation. The linear polyesters, however, do not cross-link under ordinary conditions.

Fiber-Forming Polyesters. Many high polymers of the thermoplastic type are microcrystalline. Plastics composed of these polymers can be stretched, so that the molecules become alined with their chains more or less parallel to each other. An actual straightening of the chains on stretching is suggested for polymethylene glycol polyesters by changes in diffraction patterns (1266). Such an arrangement increases the strength of the plastic in the direction of the stretch, and in general, gives it fiber-forming characteristics.

The stretched or oriented polymers are anisotropic and exhibit different properties when tested along different axes. Boyer and Spencer suggest that below the transition temperature $(T_m)^3$ the polymer chains can expand sideways but not lengthwise (1266). At T_m, the parallel expansion becomes prominent, and there is a sudden increase in thermal expansion.

Crystallinity. Crystalline areas contribute high strength to fibers; therefore, factors that influence the tendency of polymers to crystallize are important (1306). Polyesters derived from polymethylene glycols and polymethylene dicarboxylic acids are more crystalline than those prepared from compounds containing hetero atoms, unsaturated carbon-to-

[3] The "second-order transition" is the discontinuity in thermal expansion, specific heat, and other physical properties that occurs over a relatively small temperature range and that is characteristic of any plastic composition.

carbon bonds, and side-chain constituents, particularly of unsymmetrical type (3, 1278). For example, crystalline polyesters can be prepared from fumaric acid if a symmetrical glycol, such as ethylene glycol, is used. If diethylene glycol, which contains an odd oxygen atom, is introduced into the polymer, however, an amorphous product is obtained (1278). On the other hand, if the fumaric acid is wholly or partly replaced by adipic acid, which is saturated, crystallinity is increased. Polyethylene adipate is highly crystalline and fiber-forming. Even with adipic acid, however, noncrystalline polymers may be obtained if an unsymmetrical glycol is used. Polypropylene adipate, in which one of the hydrogen atoms of the glycol portion of the polymer chain is randomly replaced by a methyl group, is a very viscous syrup (1312).

The length of the polymethylene chain also affects the crystallinity. For example, polyisopropylene succinate does not become highly crystalline, even when as much as 50% of the isopropylene glycol is replaced by ethylene glycol. However, if only about 30% of the isopropylene glycol in polyisopropylene sebacate is replaced by ethylene glycol, a polyester of a relatively high degree of crystallization is obtained (3).

"Another factor influencing crystallinity, aside from the molecular structure of the individual constituents, is the degree of order in the polyester molecule. The most ordered molecules, having the most regular polar group spacing, all other factors being equivalent, are the most crystalline" (3). The greater the number of acids and of glycols used, the lesser is the tendency to crystallize.

Melting Point. The main difficulty encountered in the utilization of linear polyesters in fibers is the low melting point of such compounds. Carothers experimented with polyesters, but, discouraged by their low melting point, turned to polyamides for fiber-forming.

One way to increase the melting point of polyesters is to introduce ring compounds (aromatic rings) in the structure. In 1949 Fisher and Lincoln obtained patents on the use of *trans*-quinitol in the formation of polyesters (4, 6). They state that this compound increases the melting point to such a degree that a polymethylenic dicarboxylic acid may be used for polyester production without lowering the melting point considerably. If acids containing aromatic nucleii are used, thus also contributing to the high melting point, some glycol may be used instead of the *trans*-quinitol.

Another way to make fibers higher melting, as well as stronger, and less soluble, is to introduce into the linear resin some unsaturation and then cross-link the double bonds. If prolonged heating is required for esterification, however, the cross-linking may make the resin very viscous and may even cause gelation during the polycondensation reaction.

J. B. Howard discloses a method for shortening the time of esterification by the use of catalysts ($ZnCl_2$), continuous agitation, and a large excess of glycol (2). The excess of glycol is maintained until substantially complete esterification is obtained and no further water is evolved. At this point, the reaction mixture consists largely of low-molecular-weight polyesters. Further polymerization, to produce chains of sufficient length for fiber-forming, proceeds by ester interchange. Removal of the free glycol produced is necessary and is accomplished by applying a vacuum.

H. A. Pohl found that the thermal stability of polyethylene terephthalate resin is increased by replacing the hydrogen on the methylene group two carbons removed from either oxygen of the carboxyl in the polyethylene glycol by a methyl (CH_3) group (1311).

Edgar and Hill concluded that in polyethylene terephthalate the para-phenylene linkage itself has an elevating effect on the melting point (1277). It reduces the possibilities of change of shape available to a given length of chain, resulting in a low entropy of crystallization and a high melting point.

In terephthalates increasing the distance between the ester groups, as in the trimethylene, tetramethylene, and hexamethylene polymers, has but little effect on the melting point (1277). In isophthalates, however, the effect is very marked, the tetramethylene derivatives having by far the most favorable properties (5).

E. F. Izard has made excellent studies of the effects of variation in chemical structure on the physical properties of linear polyesters (1168, 1169).

Commercial Fibers. The linear polyesters from which commercially available fibers are made are those made from terephthalic acid and ethylene glycol. These polyesters were discovered in England, and were first produced there, under the trade name of Terylene, by Imperial Chemical Industries, Ltd. (ICI). Recently, production of films from polyethylene terephthalates was started by ICI.

The American counterparts of the English-made polyethylene terephthalate fibers and films (Terylene) are "Dacron"[4] fibers and "Mylar"[4] film produced by E. I. du Pont de Nemours & Co., Inc. The terephthalates are discussed more fully in the chapter on linear fiber-forming polyesters (p. 199).

There is no definite, accepted nomenclature in use for man-made fibers. A classification based on the raw materials and methods of preparation of the fibers was proposed by H. D. Smith (1321). He proposes *rayon* for

[4]Du Pont trademarks.

fibers made from a natural cellulosic base; *synthons* for fibers made from organic substances that have been synthesized from simple raw materials; and *prolons* for fibers from natural protein bases. Glass and miscellaneous fibers made from natural bases other than cellulose or protein would be named according to the base. Such fibers as nylon and Dacron would therefore be classified as *synthons*.

UNSATURATED POLYESTERS

I. RAW MATERIALS

The materials used in the production of polyester resins are discussed in this chapter. The compounds most widely used and various methods for their manufacture are described in some detail. Other compounds which are not widely used are described less extensively. Compounds which have been suggested as raw materials for polyesters are listed. Production volumes and other economic considerations are included for all of the important raw materials.

The basic raw materials in polyester manufacture are dicarboxylic acids and dihydroxy alcohols. If any of the reactants used are unsaturated, the polyesters produced may be unsaturated and are then usually cross-linked with compatible unsaturated monomers. Inert gases are generally used in the manufacturing process, and solvents are used in some cases. Addition-polymerization inhibitors and esterification catalysts are considered in the chapter on catalysis and inhibition (p. 46). Glass fibers and other fillers are also considered in a separate chapter (p. 73). The effects of variation in ingredients on the properties of polyesters are discussed in the chapter on tailor-making polyesters (p. 156).

ACIDS

The most important unsaturated acids used in the manufacture of polyesters are maleic and fumaric acids. Saturated acids used in large volumes are phthalic, terephthalic, and adipic acids. The acid anhydrides are often used when available and applicable. Terephthalic acid is used principally in the production of saturated polyesters and is discussed in the chapter on linear fiber-forming polyesters (p. 199).

Maleic Acid

Chemistry. Maleic acid ($HOOCCH=CHCOOH$) is the *cis* form of a four-carbon, alpha,beta-unsaturated dicarboxylic acid. Both carboxyl groups in maleic acid can be easily esterified, and addition polymerization is possible through the reactive double bond. The form·most widely used in polyester manufacture is the anhydride.

Synthesis and Production. Commercial production of maleic anhydride, which is a purely synthetic product, began in 1933. The first production method used was the catalytic oxidation of benzene, which still accounts for over three-fourths of the total maleic anhydride production. In this process, a mixture of benzene vapor and air is passed over a vanadium catalyst at a temperature of approximately 450°C. (1368).   Yields of about 65% are reported.

Experiments on some variables in the benzene oxidation process have been reported by Takikawa (1369).

Maleic anhydride is also recovered commercially as a by-product from the production of phthalic acid or anhydride. The yield is about 5%, based on the phthalic anhydride produced. This method was announced by Gibbs and Conover in 1916, but commercial production did not begin until 1934 (1368). In this process the maleic anhydride is separated from the crude phthalic anhydride by crystallization or by scrubbing the tail gases from the condenser system (1334). A method for improving yields of maleic and phthalic anhydrides, which utilizes the effluent reaction vapors as cooling media for the catalyst chamber, is described by F. Porter (42).

Other methods of producing maleic anhydride are:

(1) By the oxidation of butenes or butadiene in the presence of a vanadium catalyst at temperatures up to 400°C. This process gives yields in excess of 25% of the theoretical, but has not been successful commercially (1368).

(2) By the controlled oxidation of haloaliphatic compounds containing at least four carbon atoms in a straight chain, using an oxide of vanadium, molybdenum, tungsten, chromium, or uranium as the catalyst. The temperature of operation is 300° to 550°C. Either maleic anhydride or fumaric acid can be produced by properly controlling the reaction conditions (36).

(3) By the vapor-phase oxidation of butyrolactone, using vanadium oxide or copper oxide as the catalyst at a temperature of 220° to 250°C. (38).

(4) By the vapor-phase oxidation of furfural, using a catalyst comprising vanadium and molybdenum oxides. This process yields from 71 to 81% of both maleic anhydride and maleic acid (43).

(5) By warming malic acid with acetyl chloride, or dehydrating malic acid by heating. The first method yields maleic anhydride, and the second yields both maleic and fumaric acids. They are convenient labora - tory methods of preparation.

Physical Properties. Maleic anhydride is produced in the form of white crystals which melt at 53°C. It is soluble in water and very slightly soluble in alcohol and chloroform.

Fumaric Acid

Chemistry. Fumaric acid ($HOOCCH == CHCOOH$) is the *trans* form of the four-carbon, alpha,beta-unsaturated dicarboxylic acid. Both carboxyl groups in fumaric acid are easily esterified. Polyesters formed from it are reported to be more crystalline than those prepared from maleic anhydride, because the *trans* structure produces a more linear polymer. An important reason for the use of fumaric acid in the preparation of polyesters is that it is less corrosive than maleic acid as indicated by a comparison of their primary dissociation constants [fumaric, 1×10^{-3}; maleic, 1.5×10^{-2} (1356)]. No anhydride is possible for fumaric acid.

Synthesis and Production. Although fumaric acid is found in nature, it is made synthetically in commercial production. The raw material most generally used is maleic acid, which is easily converted to the more stable fumaric acid by heat alone, or by the use of catalysts. One method of preparation involves separating monosodium maleate from the scrub liquor from the phthalic anhydride plant, heating it in a hydrochloric acid solution, and separating the fumaric acid (44).

In another method the converter gases from the oxidation of benzene are passed into a hydrochloric acid solution. The fumaric acid produced by this method may be crystallized to a purity of 99.6 to 99.8% (40). Fumaric acid may be recovered from aqueous fermentation products by a somewhat similar method (66).

Fumaric acid may also be prepared by heating a 50% solution of maleic acid in maleic anhydride. (An equimolar mixture of maleic anhydride and water may be used as the equivalent of maleic acid.) The yield after filtering the hot dispersion is about 80%. Recycling the filtrate for continuous production provides an efficiency of 95%. This process prevents the formation of malic acid as a by-product (45).

Catalysts for the conversion of maleic acid to fumaric acid are described by W. Scott. They include thiazoles and bithiocarbamates. Yields of approximately 80%, based on the maleic acid used, are obtained (41). Fumaric acid may also be obtained by the catalytic oxidation of a fraction separated at $60°-71°$ C. from the reaction products of the pyrolytic conversion of dichlorobutane to butadiene (35).

Physical Properties. Fumaric acid is sold commercially in the form of white to yellowish crystals which have a melting point of $287°$ C. It is slightly soluble in cold alcohol (5.8 grams in 100 grams of alcohol).

Other Unsaturated Dibasic Acids

None of the other unsaturated dibasic acids are used in the polyester resin industry in large volume. Generally, no advantages are obtained by their use, and the expense of these compounds limits their commercial value.

Endomethylene tetrahydrophthalic acid (or anhydride),[1] the Diels-Alder reaction product of maleic anhydride and cyclopentadiene, is noteworthy,

[1]This compound is sold by Carbide & Carbon Chemicals Co. under the trade name of Carbic Anhydride (1333). The resins produced with it are sometimes called Carbic Resins.

however. It is used as an ingredient in polyesters to obtain better air-drying properties (1355). Preparation of this type of compound is described by Carter and Plimmer (65).

Hexachloroendomethylene tetrahydrophthalic acid,[2] the Diels-Alder reaction product of maleic anhydride and hexachlorocyclopentadiene, is also of special interest. This compound possesses over 50% of its weight of stable chlorine and is used to obtain polyester resins[2] with a very high degree of flame resistance (1342). Preparation of hexachloroendomethylene tetrahydrophthalic acid and similar compounds is described by Herzfeld, Lidov, and Bluestone (51). The anhydride of this acid picks up moisture and slowly converts to the acid.

The double bonds in both endomethylene and hexachloroendomethylene tetrahydrophthalic acids are not reactive under the usual conditions for producing polyesters. They are therefore used in combination with maleic anhydride or fumaric acid in order to obtain unsaturated polyesters which can be cross-linked.

Phthalic Anhydride

Chemistry. Phthalic acid $[C_6H_4(COOH)_2]$ has two carboxyl groups directly attached to a benzene nucleus in the ortho position. Both carboxyl groups may be esterified, but the molecule contains no unsaturation which is capable of double-bond polymerization. Since the carboxyl groups are in the ortho position, the anhydride of this compound is prepared with ease. It is the form of the commercial product.

The main functions of phthalic anhydride in polyesters are to reduce the amount of unsaturation present (provide flexibility) and to increase the compatibility of the polyesterification product with the aromatic cross-linking monomer. Tetrachlorophthalic anhydride is one of the principal raw materials used to make flame-resistant polyesters (1357).

Synthesis and Production. The most important commercial process for the production of phthalic anhydride is the controlled oxidation of naphthalene (1334). Crude naphthalene is vaporized and fed, with a large excess of pressurized air, into the converter. With a supported heavy metal oxide as the conversion catalyst, a contact time of 0.1 second is sufficient for conversion. A fluid catalyst of very finely powdered vanadium pentoxide may also be used. The vapor emerging from the converter is cooled to just above the dew point by a vapor cooler and condensed in a series of three condensers. The crude product is transferred to a melt tank and purified by distillation.

---

[2]This compound is used under the trade name of HET acid by Hooker Electrochemical Co. to produce flame-resistant polyesters with the trade name of Hetron resins.

The yield of phthalic anhydride is 70 to 80% based on the naphthalene used. Maleic anhydride is obtained as a by-product. The commercial phthalic anhydride from this process contains 0.25 to 0.4% of maleic anhydride (1334).

The production of phthalic anhydride from other coal tar fractions and higher aromatics has been investigated. A fraction separated at 200° to 225° C. from crude coal tar gave a 75% yield of high-purity phthalic anhydride when a silica-base vanadium oxide catalyst was used (1359).

Physical Properties. Phthalic anhydride is produced in the form of translucent, white, crystalline needles or flakes. It melts at 131° C. and is soluble in alcohol, slightly soluble in ether and very slightly soluble in water.

Adipic Acid

Adipic acid $[HOOC(CH_2)_4COOH]$ is a six-carbon, saturated dicarboxylic acid. Both carboxyl groups are capable of esterification. Adipic acid is widely used in the preparation of flexible polyester resins.

This acid is produced commercially by the oxidation of cyclohexanol. It is sold in the form of white crystals which melt at 150° to 153° C. and are very soluble in alcohol.

Other Saturated Acids

Other saturated acids which are sometimes used in polyesters are malonic, succinic, glutaric, pimelic, sorbic, and similar acids. Consumption of these compounds by the polyester resin industry is not large, however, and no detailed discussion of their syntheses is given here. Dibasic rosin acids have been suggested for polyesters but not yet used.

ALCOHOLS

The alcohols used in large volume in polyester manufacture are dihydroxy alcohols or glycols. This class of compounds is capable of polymer formation through the reaction of both hydroxy groups. A long-chain linear compound may be built up by reacting these compounds with dibasic acids. The saturated glycols most generally used are ethylene, propylene, diethylene, and dipropylene glycols.

Allyl alcohol, which is unsaturated, has been used in quantity in polyester preparation. This compound is mostly used with a dibasic acid to produce a "trimer" (two allyl alcohol molecules and one dibasic acid molecule) which is capable of further addition polymerization. For example, diallyl phthalate is frequently used as a cross-linking agent for polyesters (p. 31).

Ethylene Glycol

Ethylene glycol $[C_2H_4(OH)_2]$ is the first member of the glycol series which, as the formula indicates, contains no double-bond unsaturation. This compound is widely used in polyester manufacture and was used almost exclusively before the higher members of the glycol series became more readily available.

Commercially, ethylene glycol is prepared from ethylene. The intermediate steps involve the synthesis of ethylene chlorohydrin, the dehydrochlorination of this compound to ethylene oxide, and hydrolysis of the oxide to the glycol (1463).

Another method involves the catalytic hydrogenation of hydroxyacetic acid and its derivatives (110).

Ethylene glycol is sold as a liquid which boils at 197°C. It is miscible with water and alcohol in all proportions.

Propylene Glycol

Two isomers of propylene glycol exist, namely, 1,3-propanediol and 1,2-propanediol. The 1,2-propanediol ($CH_3CHOHCH_2OH$) is commercially available. Propylene glycol became commercially available later than ethylene glycol, but is currently used in production of polyesters as a single glycol constituent and with other glycols. Propylene glycol polyesters, especially propylene glycol fumarate polyesters, tend to be less crystalline and more soluble in styrene than their ethylene glycol counterparts.

Propylene glycol is prepared commercially from propane.

Commercial propylene glycol is sold as a liquid that boils at 189°C. and is miscible with water and alcohol in all proportions.

Diethylene Glycol

Diethylene glycol ($HOCH_2CH_2OCH_2CH_2OH$) reacts similarly to ethylene and propylene glycols in that both hydroxyl groups are easily esterified. The oxygen bridge or ether linkage is reasonably stable and polyesters prepared from this compound tend to be more flexible and less crystalline than those prepared from ethylene glycol. Because of the oxygen bridge, however, they tend to be more water-sensitive, and to have less favorable electrical characteristics.

Diethylene glycol is prepared commercially from ethylene glycol.

Diethylene glycol is sold commercially as a liquid that boils at 245°C. and is soluble in water, alcohol, and ether.

Dipropylene Glycol

Polyesters prepared from dipropylene glycol $[(CH_3CHOHCH_2)_2O]$ are not so sensitive to water as those prepared from diethylene glycol. Dipropylene glycol is prepared from propylene glycol. It is sold as a liquid which boils at 232°C. and is soluble in toluene and water.

Other Saturated Glycols

The higher saturated glycols have not been extensively used for polyesters on a commercial scale. Their use in polyesters generally imparts increasing flexibility with the increasing length of the hydrocarbon chain between the hydroxyl groups. The expense of these compounds prohibits their use, except in instances where special properties might be desired. Flexibility is imparted to a resin more economically by use of adipic acid in the formulation.

Allyl Alcohol

Allyl alcohol (CH_2=$CHCH_2OH$) is used to prepare monomers that may be used to cross-link unsaturated polyesters and polymers closely related to the polyester resins. This compound, which is an unsaturated monohydroxy alcohol, cannot form a linear long-chain molecule by esterification, but forms instead a monoester or diester with a monocarboxylic or dicarboxylic acid. These esters may be polymerized with themselves or copolymerized with other compounds; in the latter case they may be used to cross-link the polyester resins.

Allyl alcohol is prepared commercially from allyl chloride by hydrolysis:

$$CH_2=CHCH_2Cl + H_2O \rightleftarrows CH_2=CHCH_2OH + HCl$$

Another method for the preparation of allyl alcohol is the electrolytic reduction of acrolein (111).

Allyl alcohol is sold as a liquid that boils at 97°C., and is miscible with water, alcohol, and ether in all proportions.

Unsaturated Glycols

It is possible to make unsaturated polyesters from saturated and unsaturated dibasic acids and some unsaturated glycols. The use of both unsaturated acids and glycols permits additional cross-linking and produces a more rigid cured resin. Until recently, unsaturated glycols have not been readily available to industry. The development of acetylene chemistry, however, is likely to increase commercial sources of such glycols (1374). Unsaturated glycols which are commercially available include 2,5-dimethyl 3-hexyne-2,5-diol; 3,6-dimethyl 4-octyne-3,6-diol; and 2-butene-1,4-diol (1371, 1373, 1377).

Another type of compound that might be used in polyesters is the reaction product between an alpha,gamma-dialkyl crotonaldehyde and formaldehyde. The preparation of this type of compound is described in U.S. patent 2,418,290 (106).

CROSS-LINKING AGENTS

Compounds containing double-bond unsaturation are used with a linear unsaturated polyester to achieve a three-dimensional structure when the resin is cured. There are, of course, many compounds that can be used for this purpose, but the ones most commonly used are styrene and diallyl phthalate. Certain other allyl derivatives have been used to achieve special effects in the final polymer. The use of triallyl cyanurate to prepare resins with exceptional heat resistance is a recent and important development.

Styrene

Styrene ($C_6H_5CH = CH_2$), also called vinylbenzene, contains the requisite double bond for the addition polymerization which is involved in the cross-linking of the polyester resins. It is the most widely used cross-linking agent because of its availability, cheapness, and speed of reaction, and because it gives certain desirable properties to the final product, such as rigidity, light color, and resistance to aging.

Synthesis and Production. Ninety percent of the styrene produced in this country is made all or in part by the ethylbenzene process. This process consists of three steps (1419):

(1) The reaction between benzene and ethylene in the presence of aluminum chloride to give ethylbenzene.

(2) The catalytic dehydrogenation of the ethylbenzene in the presence of steam to produce styrene.

(3) The purification of the product.

In the first step, the reaction is carried out at 190°F. and 15 pounds gage pressure. Seventy-five to 100 pounds of ethylbenzene are produced per pound of aluminum chloride catalyst, and 80% of the spent catalyst can be recovered. A grade of benzene having a 2°F. boiling range can be used without a detrimental effect on the quality of the product. Sulfur or small amounts of unsaturates do not have to be removed from the benzene (1404). Ethyl chloride may be added along with ethylene (1402, 1423).

The dehydrogenation step is carried out in the presence of steam and a catalyst. Copper-chromium or chromia-alumina catalyst systems are used (1398, 1399, 1417). If the crude ethylbenzene from the first phase is washed and distilled to 99% purity before dehydrogenation, the styrene produced is of higher purity (1426).

The styrene is purified by removing the ethylbenzene, crystallizing the styrene, and washing the crystals, or by polymerizing the styrene, separating it from the ethylbenzene, and depolymerizing the polystyrene at 350° to 500°C. (1427). Recovered ethylbenzene may be recycled to the dehydrogenation apparatus. The styrene may be distilled to remove tars and some hydrocarbons, such as toluene. Sulfur is often used as a polymerization inhibitor during the distillation, and other inhibitors, such as tertiary-butyl catechol, may be added to the styrene product to inhibit polystyrene formation during storage (1402).

Methods for separating styrene from ethylbenzene are:

(1) Extraction with aqueous silver nitrate and pentane in a two-stage operation (131).

(2) Fractional distillation and crystallization (138).

Processes for the production of styrene from ethylbenzene using variations in catalysts and the hydrocarbon feed mixture are described in references (130, 133, 135, 144, 154, 159, 1429).

Styrene has also been produced from various hydrocarbon fractions by the following methods:

(1) Conversion of a butadiene dimer (142).

(2) Extraction of an alkylated benzene fraction with furfural and dehydrogenation of the extract (136).

(3) "Relatively homogeneous cracking" of a primarily naphthenic petroleum product (134).

(4) Dehydrogenation of a solvent naphtha (155).

(5) Cracking of hydrocarbons in the presence of coke (151).

Some processes for production of styrene that use other starting compounds are:

(1) From ethyl alcohol via acetophenone. This process was used by Carbide & Carbon Chemicals Co. during World War II, but is not believed to be competitive with the ethylbenzene process under market conditions as of June 1, 1954.

(2) From the vapor-phase dehydration of methylphenyl carbinol, using a titania catalyst (143).

(3) From the reaction of chloromethylbenzene and trichloromethane, using a magnesium iodide complex as catalyst (149).

(4) From the pyrolysis of isopropylbenzene and alpha-methylstyrene (148).

(5) From passing vapors of ethylcyclohexane over a catalyst composed of aluminum, chromium, and magnesium oxides (139).

Further reviews, discussions, or descriptions of styrene production are given in references (1396, 1410, 1462, 1469).

Styrene is toxic. Its principal biological action is irritation of the lungs and skin, although more damage could result from concentrated or prolonged exposure. The danger of overexposure to styrene during production may be lessened by enclosing only the control room and leaving other equipment out-of-doors. Safety precautions used in styrene manufacture are described in references (1405, 1422).

Physical Properties. Styrene is a liquid which boils at 146° C. and is soluble in all proportions in alcohol and ether and very slightly soluble in water.

Styrene Stabilizers

Styrene will polymerize under storage conditions. If styrene is exposed to air and sunlight at room temperature, polymerization commences slowly, but it is soon accelerated by peroxides formed by auto-oxidation in air. The raw material supplier must therefore stabilize the monomer before shipping it to the resin manufacturer or storing it.

The stabilizing agents for styrene are many, and since a number of books and articles on styrene and styrene inhibition are available, we shall not attempt to list them all. Sulfur, hydroquinone, pyrogallol, mono-, di- and tri-nitrobenzenes, picramide, para-aminophenol compounds, triphenyl compounds, certain phenolic sulfides, hydroxylamine hydrochloride, hexamine, hematoxylin, hematein, and phenylacetylene are some of them (120, 121, 122, 123, 132, 146, 152, 157, 158). Alkoxy derivatives of polyhydroxy aromatic compounds are claimed by E. R. Ericson to protect the monomer during distillation as well as storage (156). T. S. Chambers uses very volatile dienes and acetylenes as styrene inhibitors and thus obtains the additional benefit of using a gaseous system (150). The conventional way to store styrene is to dilute it with an inert low-boiling solvent, add hydroquinone, and keep under a nitrogen atmosphere (270).

Alpha- and beta-conidendrols, which are not commonly used inhibitors, were evaluated by Mack and Bickford. They report that the inhibiting action of the conidendrols is equal or even surpasses that of such popular stabilizers as phenyl beta-naphthylamine or ditertiary-butyl para-cresol (1415). Frank and Adams, who determined the relative efficiency of 12 inhibitors, also found that some of the widely used ones, such as tertiary-butyl catechol and phenyl beta-naphthylamine, are not so effective as those less known, such as picric acid and trinitrobenzene (1408).

The removal of polymerization inhibitors is usually done in the manufacturer's plant, if it is done at all. It is usually accomplished by distillation. G. Goldfinger boiled styrene with carbon black to absorb the inhibitor (147). E. W. Gluesenkamp purified stored styrene by refluxing it with an amine (126).

Additional references to styrene inhibition will be found in references (1396, 1401, 1407, 1409, 1411, 1418, 1425).

Other Vinyl Derivatives of Benzene

Other vinyl derivatives of benzene, such as divinylbenzene and alpha-methylstyrene, have been used as cross-linking agents for polyesters, but only in small quantities. The ready availability and low price of styrene outweigh any advantages that these compounds might give to the final product. In addition, divinylbenzene is difficult to blend with the resin without gelling the product.

Chloro- and fluoro-styrenes might impart better heat resistance and electrical properties to the final products. The preparation of some of these derivatives is given in U. S. patent 2,406,319 (145).

For tracer experiments with polyesters and other styrene resins, tritium-labeled styrene might be used. The method of preparation of this compound is given by Berstein *et al* (1400).

Vinyltoluene is a new monomer that is expected to compete in price and uses with styrene (1394). It is similar in chemical behavior to styrene.

Diallyl Phthalate

Diallyl phthalate $[C_6H_4(COOCH_2CH=CH_2)_2]$ is sometimes used as a cross-linking agent with unsaturated polyesters. Since it is less easily polymerized than styrene, polyesters containing diallyl phthalate are slower curing and tend to be more flexible than those containing styrene. This compound offers certain advantages as a cross-linking agent, however. With diallyl phthalate the polymerization reaction may be arrested in the gel stage if desired. In addition, diallyl phthalate has a very low vapor pressure and thus is less likely to evaporate in wet lay-up processes.

Diallyl phthalate is prepared by esterifying one mole of phthalic anhydride with two moles of allyl alcohol. It is sold in the forms of a monomer, a monomer plus low-molecular-weight polymer, and a partial polymer.

Other Cross-Linking Agents

Methyl methacrylate has been used as a cross-linking agent in polyesters. It offers the advantages of fast reaction and low viscosity of the unreacted mixture of cross-linking agent and resin. Possible disadvantages are its low boiling point and high expense. Methyl methacrylate is used with phosphonates to obtain resins having refractive indices matched to those of glasses for making transparent laminates.

Resins which retain many of their room-temperature physical properties when exposed to temperatures as high as 500° F. for prolonged periods have been prepared with triallyl cyanurate as the cross-linking agent (1438, 1439, 1440). This compound, which has three allyl groups attached to a triazine nucleus, forms extremely stable cross-links that make the polyester resins resistant to heat and chemicals. Because it contains three polymerizable groups, triallyl cyanurate can be incorporated into a wide variety of resins. Triallyl cyanurate can be prepared from cyanuric chloride and allyl alcohol (187).

Allyl diglycolate has also been used as a cross-linking agent for polyesters. It may be prepared from diglycolic anhydride and allyl alcohol (175, 203). One reason for the use of allyl diglycolate is that it has a high index of refraction, which influences the index of refraction of the cured resin. Laminates that are almost transparent have been made from glass fibers and polyester resins cross-linked with allyl diglycolate. Diallyl phenyl phosphonate has been used similarly in glass fabric laminates (1445).

Other allyl compounds may be used as cross-linking agents for the unsaturated polyester resins. (In fact, almost any monomer capable of addition polymerization could be used.) R. D. Bright gives an interesting discussion of allyl polymers and copolymers, including the cross-linking of polyester resins (1436).

Unsaturated compounds for cross-linking may be prepared from phosgene, an unsaturated alcohol, and a glycol. Among these are diethylene glycol bis(allyl carbonate) (131, 180) and 1,2-propylene glycol bis(allyl carbonate) (169). Phosgene may also be used with an unsaturated ester that has an available hydroxyl group to prepare similar unsaturated compounds, such as bis(allyl lactate) carbonate (189, 190) and bis(allyl glycolate) carbonate (162).

Other compounds that might be used for cross-linking are allyl carbonate (179); 1,4-bis(allyl carbonato) 2,3-dichlorobenzene and similar compounds (196); diallyl isopropylidene bis(para-phenoxyacetate) (176); allyl succinyl allyl glycolate (181); and methallyl maleate (170).

SOLVENTS

Solvents are occasionally used in the preparation of polyester resins to form azeotropes with water and thereby aid in its removal. When used with maleic anhydride polyesters, they perform the additional service of diluting the corrosive acid vapors. They also reduce corrosion by minimizing the corrosive activity of water traces held in the mix during the reaction. The solvents most generally used are cyclic hydrocarbons, such as xylene or toluene, which may be obtained from petroleum fractions.

INERT GASES

An inert gas is used during polyester manufacture to prevent oxidation and discoloration of the resin. The gases most commonly used are carbon dioxide, nitrogen, and combustion gas, although any gas that would exclude oxygen could be used.

Commercial nitrogen is sometimes not sufficiently free from oxygen and should be checked in this regard before use. For this reason it is usually not used alone but as a diluent for carbon dioxide. Nitrogen is produced by distillation of liquid air.

Carbon dioxide, which is more expensive, may be diluted with nitrogen to reduce plant expense. Commercial carbon dioxide gas contains little oxygen and is produced from solidified carbon dioxide. It may be purchased by the plant in cylinders or produced there with a carbon dioxide generator.

Combustion gas is produced in the plant with a combustion gas generator. This system is widely used because of the low cost of the inert gas obtained. In some processes, however, a question might exist as to possible catalytic effects of traces of nitrogen oxides which might be present in the combustion gas.

ECONOMICS

Production of polyester resins, particularly for use in resin-glass fiber products, is expanding at a rate of roughly 60% a year. It is predicted that by 1958, the demand for polyesters will be more than triple the production in 1952, which was around 19 million pounds (1450).

Of course, a limiting factor in the expansion of this field is the supply of raw materials. Production figures for the more important raw materials are given in table No. 1.

Table No. 1.—*Production of raw materials used in manufacture of polyester resins**

Raw material	Production			
	1950	1951	1952	1953
	Pounds	*Pounds*	*Pounds*	*Pounds*
Fumaric acid	......	4,655,000	......	3,829,000
Maleic anhydride	15,978,000	23,718,000	17,838,000	......
Phthalic anhydride	216,206,000	248,042,000	228,576,000	226,646,000
Diethylene glycol	......	49,913,000	64,191,000	47,436,000
Dipropylene glycol	4,304,000	5,928,000	5,570,000	4,227,000
Ethylene glycol	519,013,000	596,737,000	760,959,000	624,324,000
Propylene glycol	78,964,000	88,712,000	90,626,000	59,646,000
Styrene	539,379,000	706,780,000	699,666,000	798,433,000

*Source: U. S. Tariff Commission (1465, 1466, 1467, 1479a, 3239).

New plants and plant expansion are lifting production capacity for phthalic anhydride toward the 425-million-pound mark (1473). By comparison, current consumption for polyester resins—about 5 million pounds— seems very small, but these products may ultimately become tonnage consumers as they move into larger markets.

Maleic anhydride consumption for polyester resins is also about 5 million pounds a year. The consumption of fumaric acid for these resins is about 2 million pounds a year (1337). The supply of both maleic anhydride and fumaric acid can be expanded to meet any requirements foreseeable as of June 1, 1954.

Current production rates for ethylene glycol exceed future estimated needs (1449). For example, the estimated consumption in 1962 will be 800 million pounds; at the end of 1952 the estimated production rate had already reached 810 million pounds annually, and production goals for 1955 are set at 850 million pounds. Nearly 70% of the total ethylene glycol production is sold directly for use as antifreeze. The remaining 30% is used for a miscellany of uses, of which Dacron[3] polyester fiber (p. 217). is among the top three. In 1953 5.4 million pounds of ethylene glycol was used for Dacron (a polyester of terephthalic acid and ethylene glycol) (1456).

The supply of styrene monomer seems adequate to take care of any anticipated expansion of polyester resin production in the predictable future. Of the total yearly styrene production in this country, only about $1\frac{1}{2}$% is used in polyester resins (1421). Nearly 90% of the total styrene production goes into two products—GR-S synthetic rubber and polystyrene (1456).

Vinyltoluene is now in volume production (1394). New processes have also been developed for production of methyl homalogs of styrene (1416). These materials will give manufacturers a wider choice of vinyl type of cross-linking agents.

[3]Du Pont trade name.

II. RESIN MANUFACTURE

The manufacture of polyester resins at present is still a batch process carried out in two steps (1490). In the first step the acids and alcohols are condensed to a fusible, soluble resin. The next step consists of the blending of this product with a polymerizable monomer. A flow sheet for the manufacture of polyester resins is given in figure No. 1.

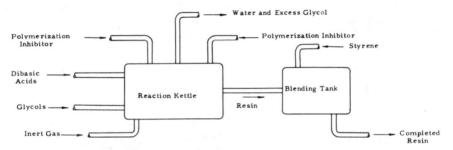

Figure No. 1.—Flow sheet for manufacture of styrene-polyester resins.

EQUIPMENT

Condensation Reaction

Kettle. The condensation (or polyesterification) reaction is carried out in a stainless steel or glass-lined kettle, which is insulated to prevent heat loss and resulting variations in temperature. This kettle is equipped with various attachments (fig. No. 2). These attachments, and the reasons for their use, are discussed in the following paragraphs.

Manhole. Since the same kettle can be used for making polyesters from various reactants, it is not economical to have individual permanent pipelines for the introduction of the reactants. The reasons for this are:

(1) The pipes would require cleaning after various reactants had been added, unless a very large number of pipes were available.

(2) Introduction of solids of various consistencies (phthalic anhydride is in flake form, fumaric acid is in powder form, etc.) would necessitate expensive equipment.

(3) It is also sometimes necessary for a worker to enter a kettle—to clean it, to check the extent of corrosion, to dry out the inside, or to check the internal equipment, such as the blades and shaft of the agitator.

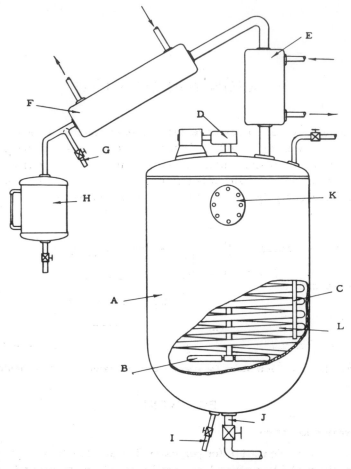

Figure No. 2.—Equipment for condensation reaction in manufacture of poly-ester resins: *A*, reaction kettle; *B*, propeller stirrer; *C*, inert gas inlet; *D*, pro-peller driving mechanism; *E*, reflux condenser; *F*, total condenser; *G*, distillate sampling tube; *H*, distillate receiver; *I*, resin sampling tube; *J*, resin removal tube; *K*, manhole; *L*, heating and cooling coils.

For these reasons the kettle is equipped with a manhole large enough to admit a man and to permit easy addition of ingredients. The manhole is covered with a hinged, gasketed top, which is bolted in place by swing bolts.

Heating and Cooling Coils. A heat-exchange system is necessary be-cause the temperature of the reaction must be controlled. The reactants must be heated initially to increase the reaction rate and to maintain the ingredients in a liquid condition. During the reaction, they must be held at a specified temperature that will insure the most efficient rate of reaction but that is not high enough to cause double-bond polymerization, discoloration, gelation, and excessive vaporization of the ingredients. When the desired degree of condensation has been attained, the product must be cooled, both to prevent premature gelation and to save time—no inhibitor known would prevent gelation if the polyester were blended with the monomer at the reaction temperature.

The usual heat-exchange system consists of stainless steel coils spirally mounted on the internal walls of the kettle, going from near the bottom up to about three-quarters of its height. The coils must be designed so that they provide a large enough surface for efficient heat exchange between the heat-exchange medium and the reaction mixture. A popular heat-exchange medium, Dowtherm, is made by Dow Chemical Co. (1482).

It is possible to utilize other methods, such as direct flame or electrical resistance, for heating the reaction mixture. It is necessary, then, to provide also for the cooling of the system. If direct flame or radiant heating is used, excellent agitation is required to avoid hot spots and discoloration of the resin.

Agitator. The reaction mixture must be thoroughly mixed to provide for even temperatures throughout the mixture, to avoid local overheating, to aid in water removal, and to keep the reactants in contact. The kettles are therefore usually provided with a marine type of propeller-agitator, which is positioned with its shaft in the center of the kettle and its blades within 3 feet from the bottom. Turbo-type mixers are also employed.

The agitator must be powerful enough to mix viscous liquids with little splashing. Splashing must be avoided because:

(1) It may be necessary to add reactants to the kettle while the reaction is in progress, and the manhole is not far enough from the liquid surface to prevent the splashes from reaching the operator.

(2) When half batches are made, some of the splashed mixture may fall on the exposed upper coils, overcure, char, fall down, and discolor the whole batch.

(3) Very excessive splashing may cause the resin to carry over into the condenser and gum up the system.

Inert Gas Inlet. An inert gas such as nitrogen or carbon dioxide diluted with nitrogen is introduced to keep out oxygen, which may cause discoloration and gelation of the resin; to assist in the removal of reaction by-products, such as water; and towards the end of the reaction, to assist in the removal of some of the unesterified reactants, if desired. For small-scale production it is also valuable for agitation.

The inlet pipe for the inert gas is positioned on the kettle so that the gas is introduced near the bottom. The flow of the gas is regulated by a valve at a flow meter. It is important that the inert gas used be entirely free from oxygen; even traces of oxygen cause discoloration. When two kettles are used in tandem so that the inert gas passes through both kettles, the second kettle almost invariably produces a lighter colored product.

View-Port. Because it is sometimes desirable to check the contents of the kettle visually, a view-port may be provided. This view-port usually consists of two walls of heat-treated glass plate. It is usually positioned in the top part of the kettle.

Sampling Tube. Since the progress of the reaction must be followed directly, a "sampling tube" is located on the bottom part of the kettle. It consists of a valve with a short length of small-diameter pipe.

Vapor Removal and Condensation. To carry the reaction to the desired degree, the by-product water must be removed. The inert gas must also have an outlet. A vapor outlet pipe is therefore provided on top of the reactor. This pipe is fairly wide (4 to 8 inches), is constructed of stainless steel, and leads to a two-condenser system.

Reflux Condenser. A considerable amount of glycol may be found in the vapors leaving the kettle through the vapor outlet pipe. Since it is advisable to keep the reactants in original proportions (and glycols cost money), it is necessary to return the glycol to the kettle. This is the function of the first, or reflux, condenser. This condenser is operated at a temperature intermediate between the boiling point of the glycol used in the reaction and the boiling point of water. It may be packed for more efficient separation of glycol.

Total Condenser. The water vapor and the inert gases pass on into the water-cooled total condenser, where the water condenses. Glycol not removed by the reflux condenser will condense along with the water. The amount of glycol in the condensate is determined by refractive index measurements.

Condensate Sampling and Receiving. To obtain samples for the refractive index measurements, a valved sampling tube may be placed in the line leading from the total condenser to the receiver. The receiver is a tank equipped with a gage to indicate the water level, a vent pipe on the top for the removal of the inert gases, and a valve on the bottom for disposal of the water. The amount of water collected indicates the stage of the reaction, and it is therefore necessary—at the beginning—to calibrate the water-level gage. The gases, before release into the atmosphere, may be scrubbed to remove noxious acid vapors.

Solvents Handling. In the manufacture of maleic anhydride polyesters, it is desirable to dilute the corrosive acid vapors with a solvent. This solvent is so chosen that it forms an azeotrope with water, and thus helps to remove it from the reaction mixture. It must also have a boiling point lower than the reaction temperature.

If a solvent is used, it is necessary to condense the vapors, trap the water, and return the solvent to the kettle.

Use of Vacuum. A vacuum may be employed near the end of the condensation reaction to remove the residual water and solvent.

Blending Equipment

When a polycondensation is completed, the products are blended with a suitable cross-linking agent. Although blending could conceivably be done in the same reactor, for many reasons it is not. First of all, it is usually desirable to add the hot polycondensation product to the cross-linking agent, to minimize vaporization of the latter and splattering. Then, the volume of the kettle may not be sufficient for the total amount of resin. Also, the blending tanks may serve as temporary storage tanks, before the various batches are mixed to form a uniform lot.

Transfer of Polyester. The polycondensation product is removed from the reactor through a valved pipe on the bottom. This pipe, which leads to the blender, is usually of stainless steel and 2 to 4 inches in inside diameter. A pump must be provided to move the resin at a rate of from 15 to 30 gallons per minute, and since the polyester may be very viscous, the pump must be powerful.

The transfer pipe introduces the polycondensation product into the blending tank at a point near the top of the tank. If the cross-linking agent is to be introduced into the polyester, another inlet is necessary. This inlet delivers the cross-linking agent into the polyester just below the resin level, to prevent splashing and flash vaporization, and to provide initial contact for more efficient blending.

Blending Tank. The blending tank is usually constructed from stainless steel or stainless steel-clad materials. Its capacity is from two to four times that of the reactor. The stirring mechanism, which is of the same type as the one in the reactor, is used to mix the polyester intimately with the cross-linking agent, or to mix several batches into one lot.

Insulation of the blending tank is imperative only in the special case of the polycondensation product being difficultly soluble in the cross-linking agent. In this case, it may be necessary to maintain higher temperatures while blending. If the tank is insulated, sufficient cooling coils should be installed to permit an efficient cycle of operations.

The blending tank is provided with a manhole similar to the one in the reactor and with an inert gas inlet tube. It has an outlet in the bottom, through which the finished resin is transferred into drums for shipping and storage.

Instrumentation

The instrumentation used in the manufacture of polyester resins need not be elaborate. For observing the temperature of the reaction, recording thermocouples are generally used. An additional thermocouple should be placed in the condenser system line right after the reflux condenser, to check the temperature of emergent vapors. Thermocouples are also employed in the heat-exchange system.

The rate of flow of the inert gas is determined by a flow meter in the line.

Other Equipment

Equipment used to cure and fabricate polyester resins is discussed in the chapters on shaping (p. 97) and finishing (p. 124).

PROCEDURE

Ingredients Handling

The raw materials for the production of polyesters are brought to the manufacturing plant in drums, bags, and other containers. The materials are weighed and added to the reaction kettle in the following manner: The alcohols are poured in first. The amount of glycol is usually somewhat in excess of the amount required stoichiometrically. This is done to ensure a sufficient amount of glycol, since not all of this compound may be returned by the reflux condenser system. Solvents may be added at this point if desired. The usual quantity is about 10% of the total weight of the reactants. The liquid ingredients are then heated up to about 100°C., while the agitator is started and the inert gases are passed into the mix. The solids (acids, etc.) are then added gradually, and the mixture is further agitated and heated.[1]

Among the solids may be added 0.01 to 0.2% of polymerization inhibitors, to prevent premature gelation, and esterification catalysts. The latter are usually not employed, because the reaction proceeds at a satisfactory rate without them, and their removal from the reaction products is difficult.

[1] Ready-made esters can be charged to the resin kettle, rather than the individual alcohols and acids, for greater convenience in handling and reduced processing time (1481).

The volume occupied by all the reactants usually should not exceed 80% of the total volume of the reactor, because the water is removed very rapidly initially and there is danger of foaming.

Initial Reaction Phase

The rate at which the temperature is raised depends on the boiling point of the glycol used, and, above all, on the efficiency of the glycol separation and the reflux condenser.

At the beginning of the reaction a large volume of water results from the initial esterification. This water is vaporized faster if the rate of heating is rapid, but the water vapor will carry with it glycol vapor. The glycol vapor will be more concentrated the lower the boiling point of the given glycol, and the faster the rate of heating. For a fast rate of heating, therefore, it is imperative that the reflux condenser system be efficient enough to separate the glycol from this initial large volume of vapor.

A high rate of heating will give fast cycles, which are economically desirable. Thus, the rate of temperature increase must be a compromise. Of course, it is assumed that the heating system can easily provide the necessary heat, and that the mixing system can evenly distribute the heat.

Reaction Temperature

The temperature of the reaction mixture is raised at the chosen rate up to 190° to 200°C. and held at this point until the desired degree of polyesterification has been obtained. Here again, the maximum temperature is a compromise between the demand for economic efficiency, which requires a high temperature for fast reaction, and the danger of discoloration and premature gelation, which would occur at temperatures higher than 200°C.

Of course, some compounds used in the manufacture of special polyesters are heat sensitive and would discolor at standard operating temperatures. When they are used, the maximum temperatures must therefore be much lower. Such heat-sensitive ingredients include certain of the chlorine-containing acid components used for producing fire-resistant resins (p. 165).

Reaction Time

The time of reaction at the maximum temperature depends on the following factors:

(1) *The nature of the reactants.* Each acid reacting with each glycol has a rate of reaction peculiar to itself.

(2) *The desired extent of reaction.* It is usually desirable to complete the reaction as far as possible without gelling the product. This, of course, depends on the amount of double-bond unsaturation present. The smaller the amount of unsaturation present, the lesser is the danger of forming three-dimensional polymers and of gelation. Therefore, if less unsaturation is present, the reaction may be carried safely to a greater degree of polyesterification. A longer polyesterification time will be required, however. For example, diethylene glycol maleate resin requires a total heating period of approximately 6 hours; propylene glycol adipate-maleate (adipic, 6 moles, maleic, 1 mole) requires about 16 hours. The acid number that can be safely attained in the first case is about forty; in the second case it is possible to go as far as five.

(3) *Amount of glycol lost.* If the amount of glycol lost is appreciable, the danger of gelation is increased, and the heating time must therefore be cut down.

(4) *Efficiency of excess acid removal.* In some cases, the resin mix will approach the desired viscosity, but the acid number of the mix will remain undesirably high. The acid number may be decreased by passing inert gas through the mixture at a higher rate, with the result that free monomeric acid is removed from the reaction mixture. This process is variable, depending on the rate of passage of the inert gas, and may prolong the heating time.

Process factors that reduce the time cycle include: use of vacuum, strong flow of inert gas, direct-heated kettle, and surface agitation of the batch (but not enough to cause splashing).

Cooling and Blending

When the desired extent of reaction has been reached, the product should be cooled and blended with the cross-linking agent. The excess solvent is trapped and removed at this point, or just before it. The reaction mixture is cooled as rapidly as possible to prevent undue loss of time. The temperature to which it is cooled varies widely, depending on the type of inhibitor system used in blending.

The mixture is mixed until uniform—usually for 2 to 4 hours. Individual batches may then be mixed together to form "lots." The characteristics of the lot are determined and, if necessary, adjusted to meet specifications.

Inhibitor System

The blending procedure is flexible and producers use widely different techniques. The determining factor is the choice of inhibitor, which in turn determines the highest possible temperature of blending.

The necessity for an inhibitor system during the blending stems from economic considerations. The blending could be done at room temperature, but the resin is then difficult to dissolve in the cross-linking monomer. The solubility increases with increasing temperature, but at higher temperatures there is the danger of a premature reaction between the resins and the cross-linking agent. To assure a higher rate of solvation, the higher temperatures are used—and inhibitors, such as hydroquinone and tertiary-butyl catechol, are used to prevent cross-linking. [Inhibitors of addition polymerization are discussed in the chapter on catalysis and inhibition (p. 46).]

The Naugatuck Chemical Division of the U. S. Rubber Co. uses hydroquinone as the inhibitor in the preparation of a general-purpose polyester resin (1483). In this case, the resinous products are cooled to $100°$ C., and the hydroquinone is added; the batch is then cooled further to $70°$ C., and the blending operation takes place at this temperature. The resin is transferred to the blending tank, and styrene is pumped into the tank through a cloth filter, entering at a point just below the surface of the polyester resin.

Storage and Shipping

After the blending operation the resin is transferred into drums for shipment and storage. The product may be filtered when drummed to remove solid particles. A filter-aid, such as Celite, may also be added to the resin to help clarify the product.

An interesting procedure for granulating solid polyester resins was invented by B. W. Lew (219). He kneads the polyester with water at a temperature slightly below its melting point. Other methods for producing granular resins are given by E. M. Beavers (211) and M. Baer (212, 215).

PROCESS AND PRODUCT CONTROL

This section mentions some of the tests used for controlling the quality of the raw materials, the manufacturing process itself, and the quality of the final product. Details of these tests are given in the chapter on testing (p. 233).

Raw Materials

Most of the raw materials arriving at the manufacturing plant have passed the standard specifications established for their use, and generally can be utilized without much further checking.

The one exception to this rule is the cross-linking agents, which are less stable than the other ingredients and should therefore be tested for polymer formation. Styrene, for example, is tested for the presence of insoluble polystyrene.

Glycols may be checked visually or colorimetrically against standards for clarity and color.

Reaction Progress

The next product control tests are run on the reaction mix in the reactor. The object of these tests is to determine the extent of polyesterification.

The quantity of water removed from the reaction is indicative of the stage of polyesterification. It is not generally accepted as an independent production control but is used in conjunction with other determinations.

The viscosity of the resin is related to the weight average molecular weight; the acid number of the resin is related to the number average molecular weight. Hence, both are indicative of the extent of reaction. Viscosity determinations are usually reserved for higher-viscosity resins, and as a final product (polyester plus cross-linking agent) control. The usual tests of the mix in the reactor are acid number tests made on samples removed from the kettle at periodic intervals.

On resins that are cooked to an acid number below 20, it is advisable to use viscosity determinations to check the progress of the reaction. At low acid numbers the accuracy of the acid number test is not good and the mix may gel rapidly.

Finished Resin Testing

Additional tests are conducted on the finished resin to assure its compliance to specifications. Specific gravity is determined by the usual methods. The length of storage life is determined experimentally, sometimes by using accelerated weathering conditions. Gel times at peak exotherm, or the maximum temperature reached by the resin during cure, are also determined.

The refractive index is determined by refractometer measurements. The color and clarity of the resin and the presence of foreign material in it are determined by visual inspection.

OUTLOOK IN RESIN MANUFACTURE

Before polyester resin production can approach a mass-production basis, continuous methods for manufacture of these resins will have to be adopted. Already, the Dacron[2] and Mylar[2] types of terephthalate polyester fibers and films are made in continuous operation. In these cases

[2]Du Pont trade names.

the adoption of a continuous method was facilitated because large quantities of a single formulation are needed, and the high surface-to-volume ratio of the ultimate product favors water removal and thus completion of the condensation reaction.

When continuous processes for making laminating polyester resins are developed, they will no doubt utilize every known expedient to speed the reaction without the use of destructive heat. These will include a high surface-to-volume ratio during the reaction, which could be achieved by working in thin films, or by using gas dispersion techniques, such as those worked out for ore flotation or submerged culture in fermentation. An unusually high vacuum will be used to accelerate water removal. The entire process no doubt will be governed by a series of automatic viscometers, which will control the rate of feed and movement of raw materials so as to secure an outgoing flow of closely controlled viscosity. Automatic blending equipment is available for continuous mixing and blending of two-component resin systems such as polyester-styrene resins.

III. CATALYSIS AND INHIBITION

This chapter is concerned with the use of catalysts and inhibitors in the manufacture and fabrication of polyester resins. This subject is discussed before the chapter on shaping because the catalyst is added to the resin before fabrication, although its action usually occurs during or after the shaping operations.

Although there are no hard and fast rules for catalyzing polyesters, certain basic principles have been discovered. It is now possible to choose an appropriate catalytic system for various methods of fabrication without too extensive experimentation. The practical aspects of catalysis—the choice of the proper catalyst and the concentration used—are discussed here in detail. Theoretical considerations are limited to those necessary for a basic understanding of the action of catalytic agents used. The limitations of various catalytic systems are listed in order to aid in the selection of a system suited to given cases.

DEFINITIONS

The word "catalyst" in the preceding paragraph is used in the sense in which it is used in the plastics industry. As in the chemical industry, substances added in very small quantities for the purpose of changing the rates of various reactions are called catalysts in the plastics industry. This analogy is misleading, however. The "catalysts" used in the plastics industry actually take part in the various reactions and are consumed in the process. Indeed, it has been proposed to use the distinctive ultraviolet light absorption characteristics of fragments of peroxide catalysts in polymers for study of the mechanism of addition polymerization (1519).

The International Union of Pure and Applied Chemistry, through its Commission on Nomenclature, recently proposed a set of terms for the field of high polymers, but the old terminology is still used almost universally in the industry. The proposed nomenclature, however, has considerable merit, and if adopted would bring about a much needed standardization.

The terms "catalyst," "accelerator," and "promoter" are now used almost interchangeably. The same is true for "stabilizer," "inhibitor," and "retardant." This practice often results in confusion and misunderstanding.

The IUPAC names catalytic substances in accordance with the mechanism of their action, and not merely in accordance with their effect on the reaction. The term "catalyst" is reserved for substances that are not consumed as they speed the process. Substances used to initiate addition polymerization, such as peroxides, are called "initiators." Compounds which activate the initiators are called "activators." If the activator acts by reduction, as for example by reduction of the peroxide initiator, it is called a "reduction activator," and the initiator-activator system a "redox system."

For further information on the proposed nomenclature the reader is referred to the Commission's report (1116). Although we wish for the change, it cannot be accomplished suddenly, and to avoid confusion this text will, as a rule, refer to the compounds described in terms used in the original references. The IUPAC terms will be inserted in the text occasionally for the purpose of familiarizing the public with them.

POLYESTERIFICATION CATALYSIS

The polyesterification of compounds commonly used in the manufacture of polyesters proceeds readily without catalysis. Catalysts therefore are seldom used in this process, particularly since their removal presents difficulties.

When catalysts are used the object is to help reduce the well-known reversibility of the reaction between alcohol and acid and force the reaction to completion. This is done mainly by removal of water from the reaction mixture by mechanical means. [A detailed description of the apparatus is given in the chapter on manufacture of resins (p. 38).] The catalysts used for this purpose are water-removing agents, such as sulfuric acid, gaseous hydrochloric acid, and anhydrous zinc chloride. The same substances which catalyze simple esterifications catalyze polyesterifications as well.

In general, acidic substances are used in most large-scale operations. Para-toluenesulfonic acid seems to be the most popular catalyst in the manufacture of polyesters. Other compounds that have found the favor of polyester manufacturers are hydroquinone, gaseous hydrochloric acid, tannic acid, pyrogallol, sodium hydrogen sulfate, and aromatic amines such as aniline or phenylenediamine.

The effectiveness of the catalytic agent used must be established for each particular case since it will vary for different materials. For example, the usual polyesterification catalysts, such as sulfuric acid, sodium hydrogen sulfate, and zinc chloride, cause the reaction between unsaturated alcohols and unsaturated acids to become too violent. Alkali metal silicates are suggested as catalysts for this reaction (170). No definite proportions can be given in which polyesterification catalysts are to be used. In general, amounts ranging from 0.5 to 2% of the total weight of the reactants are sufficient.

An important consideration in the choice of catalyst is the ease of its removal. If a catalyst is not removed or destroyed, its continued presence may lead to overpolymerization, discoloration, and impairment of impact strength and other mechanical properties. Gaseous or highly volatile compounds are preferred as catalysts since they can be easily "topped off." Thermally unstable catalysts are destroyed by heating. The catalysts, of course, must not have a deleterious effect on the final properties of the resin.

Inhibitors of addition polymerization are often added to the reaction mixture to prevent premature cross-linking. This step is discussed under a separate heading.

INITIATORS OF ADDITION POLYMERIZATION

Substances used in the polyester industry to initiate addition polymerization are commonly called "catalysts." When these "catalysts" decompose free radicals are formed. In the presence of unsaturated carbon-to-carbon double bonds, the free radicals cause addition polymerization to start as explained in the chapter on theoretical considerations (p. 3). The formation of free radicals is illustrated by the following equations for the decomposition of benzoyl peroxide:

$$C_6H_5 - \overset{\overset{\displaystyle O}{\|}}{C} - O - O - \overset{\overset{\displaystyle O}{\|}}{C} - C_6H_5 \rightarrow 2C_6H_5 - \overset{\overset{\displaystyle O}{\|}}{C} - O \cdot$$

$$C_6H_5 - \overset{\overset{\displaystyle O}{\|}}{C} - O - O - \overset{\overset{\displaystyle O}{\|}}{C} - C_6H_5 \rightarrow 2C_6H_5 \cdot + 2CO_2$$

Peroxide Initiators for Polyesters

Since some peroxide catalysts (initiators) decompose at higher temperatures than others, the choice of an appropriate catalyst depends on the intended molding temperature. Benzoyl peroxide, for example, starts to decompose at a considerable rate at about 50°C., and is therefore used mainly for resins which are cured at higher temperatures. Methylethyl ketone peroxide is a popular initiator for lower temperatures, particularly in conjunction with cobalt naphthenate.

The dissociation of peroxides can be accelerated by various reducing compounds and metallic salts, or retarded by certain substances. The action of accelerators and retardants is discussed in detail in other sections.

Some of the commonly available peroxide catalysts for polyester resins are listed in table No. 2.

Table No. 2. — *Composition, form, and suppliers of peroxide catalysts for polyesters*

Trade name	Composition	Physical form	Peroxide assay	Supplier*
			%	
......	Benzoyl peroxide	Granules	96	2
......	Benzoyl peroxide	Fine granules	96	2
......	Benzoyl peroxide purified	Fine crystals	99	2
Lucidol	Benzoyl peroxide	Fine granules	96	1
Luperco ATC	Benzoyl peroxide compounded with tricresyl phosphate	Thick paste	50	1
Cadox BTP	Benzoyl peroxide compounded with tricresyl phosphate	Thick paste	50	2
Cadox BDP	Benzoyl peroxide compounded with dibutyl phthalate	Thick paste	50	2
Luperco CDB	2,4-Dichlorobenzoyl peroxide compounded with dibutyl phthalate	Thick paste	50	1
Lupersol DDM	Methylethyl ketone peroxide in dimethyl phthalate	Liquid	60	1
Cadox MDP	Methylethyl ketone peroxide in dimethyl phthalate	Liquid	60	2
......	Cyclohexanone peroxide (mixed ketone peroxides)	Granules	96	1
Luperco JDB	Cyclohexanone peroxide compounded with dibutyl phthalate	Thick paste	50	1
......	Cumene hydroperoxide	Liquid	73 (as hydroperoxide)	3

*Supplier: (1) Lucidol Division, Wallace and Tiernan Inc., Buffalo, N. Y.
(2) McKesson & Robbins, Inc., Chemical Division, New York, N. Y. (distributors for Cadet Chemical Corp., Buffalo, N. Y.)
(3) Hercules Powder Co., Naval Stores Department, Wilmington, Del.

Other peroxide catalysts mentioned in the polyester patent literature are bis(para-bromobenzoyl) peroxide, bis(phthalyl) peroxide, bis(para-chlorobenzoyl) peroxide, bis(succinyl) peroxide, acetylbenzoyl peroxide, bis(chloroacetyl) peroxide, bis(acetyl) peroxide, tertiary-butyl perbenzoate, tertiary-butyl hydroperoxide, bis(dichlorobenzoyl) peroxide, ozonides such as di-isopropylene ozonide and di-isobutylene ozonide, peracetic acid, perbenzoic acid, benzoyl peracetate, and peroxycarbonates such as ethyl peroxydicarbonate.

Ditertiary-butyl peroxide and 2,2-bis(tertiary-butylperoxy) butane have been proposed for use as polymerization catalysts at temperatures above 100° C. They are liquids and are therefore more readily soluble in polyesters (1514, 1534). Ditertiary-alkyl peroxides (246) are claimed to be more suitable as polymerization catalysts than the usual peroxide catalysts because they are relatively stable and do not discolor the resin (1527).

The National Bureau of Standards has determined the order of activity of peroxides in polymerizing a special casting resin developed by the Bureau (1515) (table No. 3).

Table No. 3.—*Order of activity of peroxides in polymerizing NBS casting resin**

Peroxide	Concentration, parts /100 as—		Percentage of polymer after 17 hours at 25° C. plus—	
	Pure peroxide	Commercial product	2 hours at 50°C.	24 hours at 50°C.
Cumene hydroperoxide	0.12	0.17	75	98–100
Uniperox 60 ($C_7H_{13}OOH$)	0.13	0.21	75	96
Dichlorobenzoyl peroxide	0.24	0.48	60	98–100
Tertiary-butyl hydroperoxide	0.06	0.10	59	98–100
Benzoyl peroxide	0.16	0.16	20–30	98–100
Tertiary-butyl perbenzoate	0.16	0.17	20–30	95
Acetyl benzoyl peroxide	0.12	0.13	<25	98
Caprylyl peroxide	0.19	0.21	<25	98–100
Lauroyl peroxide	0.27	0.31	<25	97
Hydroxyheptyl peroxide	0.19	0.20	....	87
Methylethyl ketone peroxide	0.06	0.17	....	80
1-Hydroxycyclohexyl hydroperoxide-1	0.086	0.095	....	74
Ditertiary-butyl perphthalate	0.11	0.11	....	70
Dibenzaldiperoxide	0.08	0.16	....	61
Tertiary-butyl peroxide	0.09	0.091	....	<35
2,2-(Tertiary-butylperoxy) butane	0.08	0.11	....	24

*Source: P. J. Franklin, D. M. French, and W. C. Nyberg, "Development of the National Bureau of Standards Casting Resin," National Bureau of Standards Circular No. 493 (1950).

Although the NBS resin is not a polyester, the order of activity of peroxides in it is nearly the same as that found in unsaturated polyester resins by Rybolt and Swigert (1530), if the aldehyde and ketone peroxides and peroxides containing hydroxyl groups are considered separately. The order of decreasing activity for this classification in both the NBS resin and polyester resins was: hydroxyheptyl peroxide, methylethyl ketone peroxide, 1-hydroxycyclohexyl hydroperoxide-1, dibenzaldiperoxide (1515).

For other peroxides, the order of decreasing activity was as follows (1515):

In NBS casting resin	*In polyester resins*
Dichlorobenzoyl peroxide	Dichlorobenzoyl peroxide
tert.-Butyl hydroperoxide	*tert.*-Butyl hydroperoxide
Benzoyl peroxide	Lauroyl peroxide
tert.-Butyl perbenzoate	Benzoyl peroxide
Lauroyl peroxide	*tert.*-Butyl perbenzoate
ditert.-Butyl perphthalate	*ditert.*-Butyl perphthalate

Catalysts for Polymerization in Presence of Copper

The electrical industry uses a large volume of "solventless varnishes" for embedding condensers, coils, and similar apparatus. Polyesters are ideal for this application, and have indeed made possible great savings in weight in electrical equipment because, in addition to their insulating value, they also assume a mechanical function, thus reducing the amount of structural metal necessary.

One factor which must be noted, however, is that organic copper salts are inhibitors for polymerization. Therefore, prolonged contact of copper electrical equipment with polyester resins before cure should be avoided. Goggin and Boyer inhibit the formation of aldehydes, which cause the formation of the polymerization-inhibiting organometallic compounds, by addition of para-tertiary-butyl catechol to the resin (1518). According to Nordlander and Loritsch, discoloration and inhibition of the resin are also caused by the benzoyl peroxide initiator commonly used in polyesters. They disclosed experimental evidence that the use of secondary- or tertiary-butyl hydroperoxide as initiator solves the problem (270).

A method of stabilizing polyesters with an organic complex of a drier metal, such as zinc or lead, so that they can be used in coatings for copper wire, is disclosed by a British patent (358).

Other Polymerization Catalysts

Peroxides are not the only polymerization catalysts, although the field is predominantly theirs. According to M. Hunt, organic azo compounds are better polymerization catalysts than peroxides because they do not affect the color of dyes used and will not oxidize the resin (261).

Ascaridol is said to polymerize unsaturated polyester-vinyl monomer mixtures exclusively; it does not catalyze addition polymerization of vinyl compounds alone (235).

Other types of polymerization catalysts are described in references (250, 251, 260, 264, 265, 305, 314, 1535).

INHIBITION OF ADDITION POLYMERIZATION

Unsaturated polyesters, and particularly mixtures of unsaturated polyesters with polymerizable monomers, are not stable and will polymerize on standing, even at room temperature. This problem has been given considerable attention, and although the first polyesters had to be shipped in dry ice (1541), the useful life of most commercial polyester resins is now longer than 6 months.

An early polyester patent gave special emphasis to the problem of stability. C. Ellis discovered that various fillers, such as cellulose, asbestos, chalk, and ground glass, will prevent premature gelation of the resin (316). Even completely inert fillers, however, will affect the cure characteristics of the filler-resin mix, acting simply as diluents of the resin. [The role of inert fillers in curing polyester resins is discussed in the chapter on fillers (p. 94).]

Some pigments and dyes also affect the cure of polyesters. Not enough systematic work has been done on this subject, however, and the effect of pigments, fillers, and dyes must still be evaluated by a trial and error method.

The use of fillers as inhibiting agents for polyesters would greatly limit the applications of these resins. Therefore, research in this field has been concerned mainly with developing inhibitors for unfilled resins.

Two main types of inhibitors have been developed for polyester resins. The inhibitors of one type are often called "retardants," and their inhibiting effect is directly proportionate to their concentration in the resin. The inhibitors of the second type are called "stabilizers" in the patent literature to distinguish them from the "retardants." They have the advantage of losing their inhibiting effect at higher temperatures and thus permitting the economically important fast-cure cycles.

Retardants

The inhibitors belonging to the retardant group are usually reducing agents which are capable of donating hydrogen atoms in a reaction. Their inhibiting effect depends on the suppression of free-radical formation, and can perhaps best be illustrated by the reactions:

(1) $C_4H_9 - O - OH \rightarrow C_4H_9O \cdot + OH \cdot$

(1a) $C_4H_9 - O - OH \rightarrow C_4H_9 \cdot + H \cdot + O_2$

(2) $C_4H_9O \cdot + OH \cdot + HO - C_6H_4 - OH \rightarrow C_4H_9OH + H_2O + O = C_6H_4 = O$

(2a) $C_6H_9 - O - OH + HO - C_6H_4 - OH \rightarrow C_4H_9OH + H_2O + O = C_6H_4 = O$

Reactions 1 and 1a show the products of the disintegration of tertiary-butyl hydroperoxide in the absence of hydrogen-donating retardants. The products of these reactions are free radicals, which initiate addition poly-merization. Reactions 2 and 2a show how hydroquinone, a popular re-tardant, prevents the formation of free radicals by donating two hydrogen atoms to the disintegration products of the peroxide.

Other retardants of this type are phenols, particularly di- or poly-hydroxy-phenols; phenolic resins; aromatic amines, particularly symmetrical alpha,beta-naphthyl para-phenylenediamine; antioxidants, such as pyro-gallol, tannic acid, and ascorbic acid; benzaldehyde; alpha-naphthol; re-sorcinol; and sulfur compounds (353). The proportions used are usually less than 1%, based on the total weight of the resin; the preferred re-tardants give satisfactory inhibition when used in the proportion of 0.01%.

The retarding action of these inhibitors is independent of the tempera-ture of the reacting mass. Of course, an increase in the temperature of the resin will result in an increase in the rate of disintegration of the peroxide, and any given amount of the retardant will be used up faster. But at any temperature a given amount of the retardant will "neutralize" a given amount of the peroxide initiator. To achieve a fast and complete cure, even at the higher temperatures of molding, peroxide must therefore be added in considerable excess of the amount which can be "neutralized" by the retardant. Thus, a certain amount of the peroxide initiator, when used in conjunction with these retardants, is always wasted. Furthermore, the initiator must be added to the resin shortly before it is used, so that the amount will be large enough to overcome the inhibiting action of the retardant and still be sufficient to permit a complete cure. Polymeriza-tion will start as soon as the retardant is used up.

Attention therefore has been directed toward developing inhibitors that are continuously active at all temperatures. Such inhibitors belong to the stabilizer group.

Stabilizers

Inhibitors which stabilize the resin at room temperature and yet permit fast and complete cure at molding temperatures have many advantages over the retardants. A longer storage life and a longer pot life for the resin (the terms "tank life," "shelf life," "pot life," and "bench life" all refer to the useful life of a resin to which a catalyst has been added) are their principal advantages. The only information about these com-pounds is in recent patent disclosures, and since it is only necessary for the inventor to say how a compound acts, and not why it has this action, there is no information available on the mechanism of their action.

Salts of substituted hydrazines (331), quaternary ammonium salts (333), and substituted para-benzoquinones (336) are compounds which can be classified in this group.

Salts of Substituted Hydrazines. The salts of substituted hydrazines are claimed to stabilize uncatalyzed polyesters at room temperatures, yet permit an easy and fast cure at higher temperatures. These claims of the inventor, E. E. Parker of the Pittsburgh Plate Glass Co., are substantiated by the data in table No. 4.

Table No. 4.—*Gel time of various resins with and without substituted hydrazine salts as stabilizers*

Resin	Gel time at 150°F.	Gel time at 70°F.
	Days	*Days*
Propylene maleate phthalate-diethylene glycol bis(allyl carbonate)	1	30
Propylene maleate phthalate-diethylene glycol bis(allyl carbonate) with 0.015% phenylhydrazine hydrochloride	18	6 months
Propylene maleate phthalate-methyl methacrylate	Less than 1	30
Propylene maleate phthalate-methyl methacrylate with 0.015% phenylhydrazine hydrochloride	More than 40	More than 180
Propylene maleate phthalate-vinyl acetate	1	30
Propylene maleate phthalate-vinyl acetate with 0.015% phenylhydrazine hydrochloride	More than 40	More than 180
Diethylene fumarate-diethylene glycol bis(allyl carbonate)	1	30
Diethylene fumarate-diethylene glycol bis(allyl carbonate) with 0.015% phenylhydrazine hydrochloride	More than 50	180
Propylene maleate-diethylene glycol bis(allyl carbonate)	1	30
Propylene maleate-diethylene glycol bis(allyl carbonate) with 0.01% phenylhydrazine hydrochloride	More than 50	180

A resin stabilized in this way can be cured by incorporating 0.1–5% of a peroxide catalyst (initiator) and heating to about 93°C. At 75°C. it takes about an hour for the resin to set, and it can then be hardened by baking at 125° to 150°C.

Quaternary Ammonium Salts. More recently Parker disclosed that quaternary ammonium salts retard high-temperature cure less than other commonly used inhibitors (333). Parker's experiments also prove that these compounds prevent the cracks and discolorations that commonly occur in the resins when other inhibitors are used. For example, a propylene maleate phthalate-styrene polyester, inhibited with 0.1% of trimethyl benzyl ammonium chloride and catalyzed with 0.5% of tertiary-butyl hydroperoxide, gelled on heating at 100°F. for 1 hour; three other samples of the same resin, catalyzed in the same manner but inhibited with 0.1% of para-benzyl aminophenol, 0.1% of di-beta-naphthyl para-phenyldiamine, and 0.0168% of hydroquinone did not gel in this time. On further heating at 110°F., all samples gelled, but the latter three were discolored and severely fractured.

A further comparison of results obtained with various inhibitors is given in table No. 5. The resin used was prepared from 2.2 moles of propylene glycol, 1 mole of maleic anhydride, and 1 mole of phthalic anhydride; 2 parts of this resin were combined with 1 part of styrene.

Some of the inhibitors in this disclosure have the very important property of prolonging the pot life of the resin. This property is particularly important for fabricating large objects, where the time required by the various complex lay-ups is fairly long. Trimethyl benzyl ammonium oxalate has this property in a very high degree. When the following inhibitors were used in a concentration of 0.1% in the propylene maleate phthalate-styrene resin, the pot life of the resin at 77°F., with 1.5% of benzoyl peroxide added, was more than 100 hours:

> Trimethyl benzyl ammonium acid oxalate
> Di(trimethyl benzyl ammonium) oxalate
> Trimethyl benzyl ammonium maleate
> Di(trimethyl benzyl ammonium) maleate
> Trimethyl benzyl ammonium tartrate
> Di(trimethyl benzyl ammonium) tartrate
> Trimethyl benzyl ammonium lactate
> Trimethyl benzyl ammonium glycolate

Substituted Benzoquinones. A third class of stabilizing agents—the substituted para-benzoquinones disclosed by T. F. Anderson of the Libbey-Owens-Ford Glass Company (336)—is of great economic importance. The stabilizers of this class have the important advantage of preventing premature gelation of polyester resins which have been precatalyzed with peroxide initiators without proportionately decreasing the curability of the compositions at higher temperatures. They do not "use up" the peroxide while the resin is in storage, and moldings prepared from precatalyzed stored resin stabilized with them have the hardness and water and heat resistance of moldings prepared from freshly catalyzed resins. The manufacturer, rather than the fabricator, can then mix in the catalyst. He is usually better equipped to mix in the catalyst evenly, so that the resin will develop no hard centers, and no lumps of hardened resin are likely to be found in molds.

To test the effectiveness of these stabilizers Anderson designed a special procedure in which a resin was tested for stability at the rather severe conditions of 90°F. and 30% to 50% relative humidity. The resin tested was an ethylene phthalate maleate-diallyl phthalate resin (32.8 parts) containing 1.3 parts of Luperco ATC catalyst (50% benzoyl perox-

Table No. 5.—*Effect of various inhibitors on the gel time of a polyester resin*

Inhibitor	At 150°F. No catalyst	At 77°F. Benzoyl peroxide added	At 77°F. 0.1% of tertiary-butyl hydroperoxide added	At 77°F. 0.5% of tertiary-butyl hydroperoxide added	Test E*
	Days	Hours	Hours	Hours	Minutes
0.1% Lauroyl pyridinium chloride	8	11–15	4.5	2	3.2
0.1% Cetyl trimethyl ammonium bromide	8	4–8	4	2	3.1
0.1% Phenyl trimethyl ammonium chloride	8	17	4	2	2.9
0.1% Trimethyl benzyl ammonium chloride	8	11–15	4	1.5	3.5
0.1% Trimethyl benzyl ammonium chloride with 0.0012% quinone	9	…	7	2	…
5% Trimethyl benzyl ammonium hydroxide	1.5	…	…	…	…
0.1% Hydroquinone	8	192	216	192	29.3
0.1% 4-Tertiary-butyl catechol	8	192	216	72	26.7
0.1% Catechol	8	192	216	72	7
0.1% Ascorbic acid	Gelled at once	…	Gelled at once	Gelled at once	…
0.1% Alpha-naphthol	0.5	…	34	34	…
0.1% Tertiary-butyl catechol with n-butylamine	9	…	72	72	…
0.1% Di-beta-naphthyl para-phenylene-diamine	9	48–120	34	34	17.4

*Test E was run in the following manner: A series of samples were prepared containing 1.5% by weight of benzoyl peroxide as catalyst, and containing gelation inhibitors. Test tubes 16 millimeters in diameter, containing the mixture to a depth of 3 inches, were placed in a water bath at a temperature of 190° F. The temperatures of the mixtures during the curing operations were determined by means of conventional thermocouples, and the time in minutes required for the temperatures of the samples to rise from 150° F. to the maximum (which was termed the "peak exotherm") was observed and recorded. This test constitutes a good indication of the rate at which the catalyzed mixtures will cure when heated.

ide and 50% tricresyl phosphate). Seven different stabilizers were added to separate samples of this resin, and one sample was used as a control. The results were as follows:

Inhibitor	Days stable
0.12% Para-xyloquinone	18
0.1% Para-toluquinone	44
0.04% Quinone dioxime	26
0.1% Thymoquinone	40
0.08% 2,6-Dichloroquinone	109
0.15% 2,6-Dibromoquinone	23
0.08% Thymoquinone monoxime	21
Control	8

Oxygen as an Inhibitor

The inhibiting effect of oxygen on the addition polymerization of polyesters is only too well known to anyone who has tried to cure them in air. (See pp. 63 and 163 for means of reducing air inhibition.) This effect can also serve a useful purpose, however; it can be used to stabilize resins.   H. L. Gerhart bubbled oxygen through a diethylene maleate-styrene resin catalyzed with benzoyl peroxide and made it stable in storage (326).   T. F. Anderson disclosed that N-aryl-hydroxy-3-naphthamides, such as N-para-tolyl-2-hydroxy-3-naphthamide, prevent gelation if the resin is permeated with air (328). Dearing and Howald dispose with adding inhibitors to the resin, and prevent premature gelation of precatalyzed polyesters simply by permeating them with air (340,341).

In all cases the air inhibition seems to disappear on heating, and the resins are readily moldable to hard objects resistant to water and elements.

To permit the resins to be in continuous contact with air they must be prepared in an appropriate physical state. This can be accomplished by the use of a filler that imparts a leathery texture to the mix and prevents the chopped pieces of the filled polyester from sticking to each other (340). Metallic-base compounds can be similarly used. Another way of assuring air permeation is to use compounds that give crystalline resins, which can be powdered and will stay dry (341).

Inhibitors for Thixotropic Polyesters

Thixotropic polyesters have a tendency to skin[1] in storage. They can be stabilized with tertiary-butyl catechol, but this inhibitor, when used in conjunction with peroxide initiators, destroys the thixotropy of the resin.

[1]Form a scum or "skin" on the top of the resin.

According to R. E. Burnett, a small amount of quinone, added together with the tertiary-butyl catechol, preserves the thixotropy of the resin (337). General Electric Co., the assignee of Burnett's patent, is said to grant nonexclusive licenses under this patent.

Effect of Physical State of Resin on Stability

The physical state of the resin influences the degree of its stability. Solid resins even in the presence of catalysts are slow to cure. Advantage is taken of this property, for example, in the manufacture of preimpregnated glass fabrics or mats. Polyesters which are crystalline at room temperature, such as fumaric acid-ethylene glycol polyesters, are used. These resins, because of their solid state, are sufficiently inhibited to be mixed with a catalyst and used for impregnating glass fiber or mat that will be stored several weeks and even months before use. The resin-catalyst mixture is activated by molding at elevated temperatures.

ACCELERATORS AND PROMOTERS

It is not easy to obtain a good cure with polyesters catalyzed with peroxide initiators alone. Too much peroxide may result in a very fast cure, giving polymers of comparatively low molecular weight and poor properties. Too little peroxide results in too long cure times, which are economically undesirable; attempts to speed the cure with heat can result in a product full of bubbles and cracks. A partial answer to this problem is provided by accelerators and promoters, which activate the initiator.

J. A. Loritsch obtained a number of patents on mixtures of resins with oxygen-releasing peroxide catalysts and a reducing substance capable of being oxidized by accepting an oxygen atom (273, 274). The following reactions, all of which have been used previously to illustrate principal reactions, will serve us once more:

$$(1) \quad C_6H_5 - \overset{\overset{\displaystyle O}{\|}}{C} - O - O - \overset{\overset{\displaystyle O}{\|}}{C} - C_6H_5 \;\rightarrow\; 2C_6H_5 - \overset{\overset{\displaystyle O}{\|}}{C} - O \cdot$$

$$(1a) \quad C_6H_5 - \overset{\overset{\displaystyle O}{\|}}{C} - O - O - \overset{\overset{\displaystyle O}{\|}}{C} - C_6H_5 \;\rightarrow\; 2C_6H_5 \cdot + 2CO_2$$

$$(2a) \quad C_4H_9 - O - OH \;\rightarrow\; C_4H_9O \cdot + OH \cdot$$

$$(2b) \quad C_4H_9 - O - OH \overset{2H}{\rightarrow} C_4H_9OH + H_2O$$

$$(2c) \quad C_4H_9 - O - OH \;\rightarrow\; C_4H_9 \cdot + H \cdot + O_2$$

Reactions 1 and 1a show the dissociation of benzoyl peroxide. No oxygen is formed. Reactions 2a, 2b, and 2c show the dissociation of tertiary-butyl hydroperoxide, which can go in three directions: a, in which only free radicals are produced; *b*, in which the dissociating peroxide accepts two hydrogen atoms and no free radicals are formed; and *c*, in which both free radicals and oxygen are produced.

Loritsch's invention consists of introducing into the reaction a compound that accepts the atomic oxygen readily, thus forcing the reaction to proceed by route *c*, with the production of free radicals. The IUPAC term for accelerators of this type is "reduction activator."

Phosphorus compounds, such as phenyl phosphinic acid, in which oxygen is attached directly to phosphorus, and in which the phosphorus is capable of increasing its valence by adding on another oxygen, are used as reduction activators (273). Similar organic sulfur compounds are also used (273), as are ascorbic and isoascorbic acids (274). Tables Nos. 6 and 7 illustrate the effectiveness of accelerators of this type. In each case a diethylene maleate-diallyl phthalate resin was used.

Table No. 6.—*Effect of phenyl phosphinic acid accelerator on the gel time of a polyester resin catalyzed with various catalysts*

Catalyst	Phenyl phosphinic acid content	Average gel time at room temperature
	%	*Hours*
1% Benzoyl peroxide	0	120
1% Benzoyl peroxide	2	160
1% Diheptanol peroxide	0	About 340
1% Diheptanol peroxide	2	1
1.5% Tertiary-butyl perbenzoate	0	50
1.5% Tertiary-butyl perbenzoate	1.5	4
1.5% Ditertiary-butyl diperphthalate	0	55
1.5% Ditertiary-butyl diperphthalate	1.5	4
1.5% Tertiary-butyl perfuroate	0	79
1.5% Tertiary-butyl perfuroate	1.5	5
1.5% Ditertiary-butyl diperadipate	0	55
1.5% Ditertiary-butyl diperadipate	1.5	7
1.5% Ditertiary-butyl dipersuccinate	0	85
1.5% Ditertiary-butyl dipersuccinate	1.5	12
1.5% 1-Hydroxycyclohexyl hydroperoxide-1	0	300
1.5% 1-Hydroxycyclohexyl hydroperoxide-1	1	12
1% Tertiary-amyl hydroperoxide	0	320
1% Tertiary-amyl hydroperoxide	1	12
1.5% Diacetyl peroxide	0	20
1.5% Diacetyl peroxide	2	3
1.5% 1-Acetyl benzoyl peroxide	0	20
1.5% 1-Acetyl benzoyl peroxide	1.5	6
1.5% Ditertiary-butyl peroxide	0	90
1.5% Ditertiary-butyl peroxide	1.5	94
None	0	96
None	2	More than 1,080

Table No. 7.—*Effect of various accelerators on the gel time of a polyester resin catalyzed with tertiary-butyl hydroperoxide*

Accelerator	Amount of catalyst in resin	Average gel time at room temperature
	%	*Hours*
None	1	340
None	1	216
None	1.5	144
2% Tertiary-butyl catechol	1	More than 384
2% Guaiacol	1	More than 384
2% Quinone	1	More than 384
2% Phenyl phosphinic acid	1	12
2% n-Butyl sulfite	1	12
2% Diphenyl hydroxyphosphine	1	60
1% Diphenyl phenylphosphine	1.5	5

Catalytic Systems for High-Speed Molding Cycles

According to R. R. Harris the use of inorganic reducing agents with peroxide initiators, while effective for acceleration of the polymerization of linear unsaturated polyesters with polymerizable monomers at room temperature, has not been effective in reducing the cure time of polyester resins at high temperatures (271). Hydrochloric acid, sulfuric acid, oxalic acid, and sulfonic acid have all been proposed as cure promoters, but have no appreciable effect.

Harris uses 0.03 to 0.3% of an aromatic sulfonic acid as a promoter with a phenolic type of inhibitor and a peroxide initiator to accelerate the cure of polyester resins at high temperatures. The acid is added as a 30% solution in ethylene glycol.

Table No. 8 gives cure time data for a resin composed of 3.6 moles of ethylene glycol, 3 moles of diethylene glycol, 4 moles of fumaric acid,

Table No. 8.—*Effect of various amounts of para-toluenesulfonic acid promoter on the cure time of a polyester resin*

Amount of para-toluenesulfonic acid added to resin	Stability of accelerated mix	Time at 70°C. necessary to set	Time at 70°C. necessary to cure
%	*Hours*	*Minutes*	*Minutes*
0	3	63	74
0.03	More than 24	38	43
0.03	More than 24	42	47
0.06	More than 24	14	19
0.06	More than 24	18	21
0.12	More than 24	40	18

and 2 moles of phthalic anhydride and diluted with one-half of its weight of styrene. The resin was stabilized with 0.01% of hydroquinone and contained 0.5% of benzoyl peroxide. Various amounts of para-toluene sulfonic acid were added as promoter.

This invention is particularly suitable for polyester resins that are stabilized with phenolic type of inhibitors in concentrations of from 0.01% to 0.1%.

Catalytic Systems for Laminating of Complex Shapes (Low-Temperature Cure)

For polyester molding compounds it is desirable to develop a catalytic system that keeps the resin stable at room temperature and permits high-speed curing at the higher temperatures of molding. Polyesters used for laminating must have different cure characteristics, however. For example, in one method for laminating large objects, resin-impregnated filler is laid up in the mold and the mold is heated. Temperatures of about 125°C. are often necessary to cure the resin, which usually contains an inhibitor and a peroxide initiator. At these high temperatures the resin becomes less viscous than at room temperatures and tends to flow down, leaving so-called "starved spots," particularly in the upper parts of the molded article. This behavior results in a spotty and weakened molding.

The U. S. Rubber Co. is the assignee of a number of patents designed to overcome this difficulty. Catalytic systems that permit fast gelation at temperatures below 50°C., at which the resin is not thin enough to flow, were developed by E. C. Hurdis (252, 253, 257, 263). He incorporated methylene poly(N,N-dialkylarylamines), aliphatic polyamines, N-monoalkyl mono(monocyclic aryl) monoamines, and dialkyl monoaryl tertiary amines as promoters in the inhibited resin together with a peroxide initiator. C. F. Fisk used sulfhydryl promoters, such as dodecyl mercaptan (256). The following data show the effect of promoters of these types on the gelling time at 25°C. of a diethylene maleate-styrene resin; the resin contained 0.01% of para-tertiary-butyl catechol and 2% of benzoyl peroxide.

Promoter	Gel time at 25°C. Minutes
2.0% 4,4-(Tetramethyl diamino) diphenylmethane	12
0.4% 1,2-Propylenediamine	11
0.2% N-ethyl-meta-toluidine	4
0.2% Diethylaniline	9
0.1% Dodecyl mercaptan	23
None	50 hours

Hoover, Paulsen, and Landgraf used hydrazine or aromatic hydrocarbon substituted hydrazine in concentrations of 0.01 to 0.5% to get a peroxide-catalyzed unsaturated polyester to gel at room temperature. The final cure was still necessary and was done at 175° to 250°F. (249, 309).

Another method of curing laminates of complex shapes without heating the resin so that it flows away from high spots is given by D. A. Swedlow. He irradiates cellophane-covered lay-ups of resin-impregnated reinforcing fabrics with light until the structure is rigid. The cure is then completed at higher temperatures (310).

Other Room-Temperature Catalytic Systems

Room-temperature cure is also obtainable by the use of oxides and hydroxides of metals in Group 2A of the Periodic Table, e.g., barium, strontium, magnesium, and calcium. According to V. J. Frilette, no external heat is necessary to convert a stabilized, unsaturated polyester-styrene mixture to a solid if 0.5 to 5% of calcium hydroxide is added to it with a conventional peroxide catalyst (277).

Phosphines were disclosed by M. M. Lee for use as promoters with a peroxide catalyst to cure inhibited polyester-monomer resins at room temperature. Dimethyl phenylphosphine (0.15 to 0.5%) gelled such a resin in 7 minutes at room temperature. A hard, fracture-free solid was formed within 30 minutes (269).

M. M. Levine uses triethanolamine or tri-isopropanolamine as promoter with a conventional peroxide catalyst (254). With this type of promoter a polyester-styrene-acrylate resin gelled in 10 minutes and hardened in 22 minutes at room temperature. Without the promoter, the gelling time was 5 days.

Meta-toluidine, diethylenetriamine, and piperidine are also useful promoters, but require external heat to cure fully (254).

Other accelerators that gel polyester resins at room temperature but require further heating at higher temperatures for a complete cure are disclosed by H. L. Gerhart (278). These are aldehyde amines, or other rubber vulcanizers of this type.

Multivalent metals in a lower state of oxidation ($SnCl_2$, for example) are used by R. R. Harris to speed up peroxide-catalyzed polymerization at room temperature (295).

Fraser and Park obtained haze-free transparent castings from polyester-polymerizable monomer copolymers when 0.01 to 1% of an alkali metal sulfonate of organic compounds was included with the conventional peroxide catalyst (332).

Metallic salt driers have been used with peroxide initiators to promote gelation of polyesters at room temperature, but a complete cure cannot be obtained. If organic hydroperoxides and peracids containing an easily oxidized hydrogen group are used with the metallic driers, a complete cure can be obtained overnight at room temperature, or in about 1 hour at 40°C. The larger the proportion of the drier, the faster the cure, but the softer the final product (272). A fraction of 1% of cobalt naphthenate used with benzoyl peroxide catalyst accelerated the curing rate of a diethylene glycol maleate-polymerizable monomer resin 5 to 6 times (1517).

Many of the metallic accelerators color the resins. Cobalt naphthenate, for example, colors the resin purple red. These colors, however, can be easily masked with pigments and other coloring agents.

A catalytic system which inhibits the formation of excess heat, and thus permits embedding of delicate biological specimens, is disclosed by G. L. Fraser (268). It consists of tertiary-butyl catechol (0.005 to 0.1%), cobalt or manganese naphthenate (0.0002 to 0.002%), and 1-hydroxycyclohexyl hydroperoxide-1 (0.25 to 5%) in ethylene maleate phthalate-styrene polyester resin. This resin is clear, transparent, tough, and resilient, and is fully cured to a hard product in 2 to 5 hours at room temperature.

D. M. French uses a catalytic system containing an accelerator that can combine with oxygen (an organic reducing agent) to prevent air inhibition of polyester polymerization (1516). Dodecyl mercaptan, used in an unsaturated polyester resin with tertiary-butyl hydroperoxide and manganese naphthenate, permits full, nontacky cure even if the resin is not protected from air.

Hydrogen halides, when used with peroxide catalysts, prevent discoloration sometimes caused by the peroxide (322).

An interesting method of polymerization of unsaturated compounds is given in a British patent assigned to Shell Development Co. The polymerization rate is increased without increasing the total catalyst amount, and without raising the temperature, by using two or more catalysts that have their maximum catalytic effectiveness at different temperatures (303).

ADDITION OF CATALYTIC SUBSTANCES

The addition of the catalytic substances to the polyester resin must be done carefully. For example, a serious explosion can be caused by adding a peroxide catalyst with an accelerator. An expensive molding can be spoiled by using a resin that has developed hard centers because the initiator has not been dispersed in it properly.

Inhibitors

Polymerization retarders are often put into the reaction kettle during or before the polyesterification reaction. Although the bulky molecules of linear polyesters do not cross-link by addition through their unsaturated carbon-to-carbon bonds easily, the high temperature of the reaction may cause some cross-linking. The additional advantage of introducing inhibitors at this point is that some inhibitors would not be readily soluble in the polyester. Of course, the danger exists that some parts of the inhibitor will attach themselves to the resin and decrease some of the desirable properties of the final product.

Additional amounts of inhibitors are often introduced just before the linear polyester is combined with the copolymerizable monomer. Since this operation is also done in the manufacturing plant, with large batches of resin, thorough distribution of the inhibitor in the resin is assured.

Initiators and Promoters

Most resin manufacturers conduct extensive studies on the effect of the various catalytic systems they recommend, and it is usually advisable to follow the procedure they prescribe. Little trouble is experienced with the newer precatalyzed-stabilized resins, since with these the whole job is done by the resin manufacturer. If the fabricator needs to introduce the initiator himself, the situation is not so easy.

One way out is to buy the initiator in a form which is fairly easily soluble in the resin. Various pastes and even liquid initiators are available. But the economy-minded fabricator, who prefers to buy his peroxide in the dry state, must first weigh it out in exact proportions. Since the catalysts are used in minute amounts, this requires care. The usual procedure for adding benzoyl peroxide is to soak it in its own weight of styrene for about 10 minutes. The mixture should then be used right away and completely, because it can explode if left for too long a time.

Promoters should never be added together with peroxide initiators. Some prefer to add the initiator first, mix it in well, and then add the promoter shortly before use. Another method is to divide the total amount of resin into two parts, one of which is usually larger than the other. The initiator is mixed into the larger part, and the promoter into the smaller. The two parts are combined shortly before use.

The initiator, the promoter, or any other catalytic substance must be evenly and thoroughly distributed throughout the resin to avoid local saturation and resulting hard spots. At the same time the agitation must not be so violent as to introduce air into the resin. Entrapped air will result in voids in the final product.

Gerhart and Lycan obtained a patent on a method of introducing peroxide catalyst into polyester resins (275). They prepared a fluid, unsaturated polyester paste containing 10 to 80% of a peroxide catalyst. This paste can be put in a tube, similar to a toothpaste tube, from which it is easily pushed out in the form of a ribbon. Since the length of the ribbon can be measured on a ruler and a weight of initiator-length of ribbon ratio easily established, the cumbersome weighing of the initiator is eliminated.

CURING

Three factors are important in the curing of polyester resins: (1) the time and (2) the temperature necessary to cure the resin, and (3) the shrinkage that takes place in the resin during curing. Since these factors are interdependent, the fabricator can obtain the type of cure which is most appropriate for his application by the proper choice of resin, catalyst, and curing conditions.

Elevated Temperatures

All polyesters liberate heat during cure. The *amount* of heat liberated, or exotherm, is constant for any type of resin, and depends on the amount of unsaturation in the polyester and the type of monomer copolymerized with it. The *rate* of liberating the heat, however, may be varied by catalysts, inhibitors, accelerators, and cure temperatures. Thus, if a catalytic system is used which causes very fast cure at a given temperature ("trigger" system), all the heat is liberated at once, and the temperature of the resin rises very fast. Since the resin shrinks on polymerization, and the rising temperature causes the polymer to extend, two opposing forces are always at work during the cure, and strains and cracks may result.

Curing time is inversely proportional to the curing temperature. For economic reasons it is desirable to make the curing time as short as possible to permit fast cure cycles and fast production. But high temperatures of cure cannot be used for some applications—for example, for very large objects or for objects that must be strain-free. Therefore, a number of factors must be considered when deciding whether high-temperature cure can be used.

(1) *The total mass of resin.* A polyester resin is a poor conductor of heat. As the mass of the resin increases the heat generated by the cure increases, and since it is not conducted away, the danger of cracks is proportionately greater. As the size of the batch increases, therefore, the temperature of cure must be lowered, and a catalytic system must be chosen which will spread the exotherm over a longer period of time.

(2) *The nature of the resin.* The more unsaturation a resin contains the more heat it will give off during polymerization, and the more it will shrink. Resins with a large amount of unsaturation, therefore, must be cured at low temperatures, and the catalytic systems chosen for them must be designed to avoid very rapid cure.

(3) *The amount and type of filler.* Most fillers are inactive and, at any rate, do not contribute to the exotherm. Their effect is therefore that of inert diluents, and the greater the ratio of filler to binding resin, the faster the cure can be without danger of cracking. This means that both higher temperatures and "trigger" catalytic systems can be used.

(4) *The type of mold.* Since heat should not be permitted to build-up excessively within the molded part, the thermal conductivity of the mold is very important. In metal molds, which conduct the exothermic heat away easily, polyesters can be cured at higher temperatures and in a shorter time than in molds composed of wood, plaster, or other nonconducting materials. Metalizing of a nonmetal mold is helpful, as is the introduction of a circulating liquid or gas for heat transfer near the surface of the mold.

Room Temperature

When the mass of resin is large, and it is necessary to avoid high strain concentration and cracks, it is advisable to spread the exotherm over a longer period of time and to avoid high-temperature cure. In other applications it is not possible (or economical) to provide the external heat necessary for high-temperature cure. Room-temperature cure may be used in these cases if the usual peroxide initiators are supplemented with accelerators and promoters that activate the initiators.

Cobalt naphthenate is often used to accelerate gelation at room temperature. It should be used with a hydroperoxide type of catalyst such as Lupersol DDM, not with a peroxide. The proportions employed vary from 0.006 to 0.12% of cobalt. If commercial products are used, the amounts should be calculated on the basis of the cobalt content. For example, Nuodex (made by Nuodex Products, Inc.), which contains 6% of cobalt metal, is used in proportions ranging from 0.1 to 2% (1503).

Many prefer to add the cobalt to the resin first, because the mixture is stable for several months. The hydroperoxide is added shortly before use. (Never add the two together!)

By a proper selection and ratio of catalyst and promoter, it is possible to achieve a cure in which the exotherm results in only a 5° to 10°C. increase in temperature. Since some of the room-temperature casting applications utilize wax molds, it is obvious that the allowable heat build-up cannot be very high.

Pot Life

The pot life of the catalyzed resin (time the resin will stay liquid at room temperature after all catalysts are added) is another important consideration in fabrication of polyesters. It must be at least long enough to permit the fabricator to perform all the necessary operations in making up molds. In most cases, the pot life is determined by the choice of resin and catalyst system.[2]

For example, by using a very active hydroperoxide catalyst, such as methylethyl ketone peroxide, and cobalt naphthenate accelerator with certain resins, a pot life of only 30 minutes may be obtained (1506). By decreasing the concentration of the accelerator the pot life can be pro-

Table No. 9. — *Gel time of Paraplex P-43 resin with various catalyst systems**

Catalyst	Accelerator	Gel time at 25°C.
1% Benzoyl peroxide	......	6 days
1% Methylethyl ketone peroxide	......	15 hours
2% Methylethyl ketone peroxide	......	7 hours
1% Methylethyl ketone peroxide	1.6% Cobalt naphthenate solution (6% metal)	50 minutes
1% Methylethyl ketone peroxide	0.16% Cobalt naphthenate solution (6% metal)	4 hours
1% Cumene hydroperoxide	......	48 hours
1% Methylethyl ketone peroxide	1% Accelerator B**	20 minutes
1% Cumene hydroperoxide	1% Accelerator B**	60 minutes
1% Cumene hydroperoxide	1.6% Cobalt naphthenate solution (6% metal)	35 hours

*Source: Rohm & Haas booklet on Paraplex "P" Series Resins.
**Accelerator B is an organic liquid accelerator supplied by Rohm & Haas Co.

Table No. 10. — *Storage life of Laminac resins with and without catalyst and accelerator**

Resin**	Resin temperature	Storage life		
		Uncatalyzed (minimum)	With cobalt, but uncatalyzed (minimum)	With 0.004% cobalt and 0.5% Lupersol DDM
	°C.	Days	Days	Hours
Laminac 4116	25	90	90	3.5-4.0
	52	18-21	18-21	......
75% Laminac 4116 with 25%	25	90	90	3.5-4.0
Laminac 4134	52	18-21	18-21	......

*Source: American Cyanamid booklet on "Casting with Laminac Resins."
**As manufactured, both Laminac resins 4116 and 4134 contain 0.04% cobalt, as metal.

[2]For some coating applications it is possible to prolong the pot life of a resin by adding to it about 10% of methyl alcohol.

longed up to 6 to 8 hours without losing the characteristic of complete cure at room temperature.

Table No. 9 lists some typical pot lives obtainable with Paraplex[3] P-43 resin with various catalyst systems (1506).

Table No. 10 gives the storage life of Laminac[4] resin 4116 and a mixture of this resin with Laminac flexible resin 4134 with and without a catalyst and an accelerator (1495).

The manufacturers of the various accelerators on the market, usually indicate what gel times can be expected from any given concentration of their product. In general, the smaller the amount of accelerator used, the longer is the gel time.

Table No. 11 and figure No. 3 show the gel times, with varying amounts of methylethyl ketone peroxide catalyst and cobalt accelerator, for polyester resins made by Bakelite Co., and General Electric Co., respectively (1496, 1498).

Table No. 11.—*Gel time of Bakelite resin BRS-193 with various amounts of catalyst and accelerator* *

Amount of methylethyl ketone peroxide catalyst**	Amount of cobalt naphthenate accelerator***	Gel time	Time until set hard
%	%	*Minutes*	*Minutes*
2	0.5	10	12
1	0.5	20	25
0.5	0.25	40	55
0.5	0.15	80	90
0.25	0.10	120	130

*Source: Booklet on "Polyester Resins for Reinforced Plastics." (Courtesy of Bakelite Co.)

**Solution of methylethyl ketone peroxide in dimethyl phthalate. Peroxide assay: 60%.

***6% cobalt, as metal.

Figures Nos. 4, 5, 6, and 7 show the peak exotherms obtained with various Laminac resins (American Cyanamid Co.) and different amounts of methylethyl ketone peroxide catalyst and cobalt accelerator (1495). When all other variables are kept constant, increasing the amount of cobalt used increases the peak exotherm (highest temperature reached by the resin during cure) and decreases the time of cure; keeping the amount of cobalt constant and increasing the amount of catalyst has the same effect.

[3]Trade name of Rohm & Haas Co.
[4]Trade name of American Cyanamid Co.

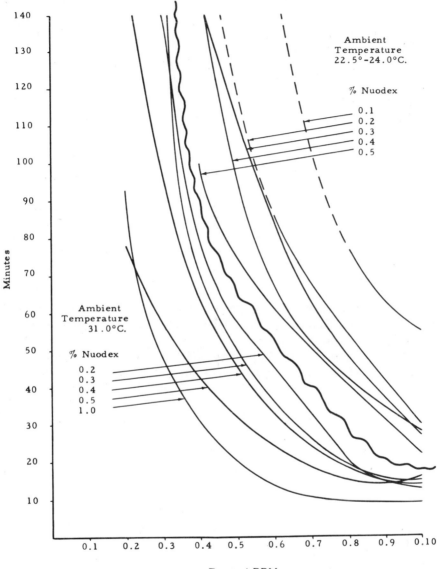

Figure No. 3.—Gel time curves for a typical polyester resin catalyzed with Lupersol DDM and Nuodex cobalt naphthenate accelerator (courtesy of General Electric Co.).

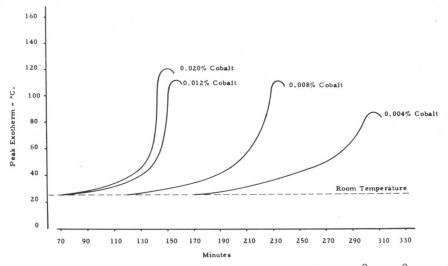

Figure No. 4.——Exotherm curves for Laminac resin 4116 at 25°C. (77°F.) with 0.75% Lupersol DDM (courtesy of American Cyanamid Co.).

In addition to the catalytic system and the nature of the resin, the pot life is considerably affected by the temperature. An increase in temperature of about 10°C. will approximately double the rate of polymerization and cut the pot life in half.

Pot life is also shortened by ultraviolet light, which accelerates polymerization and eventually causes gelation of the resin. Therefore, the

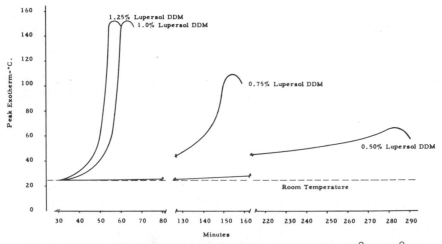

Figure No. 5.——Exotherm curves for Laminac resin 4116 at 25°C. (77°F.) with 0.012% cobalt (courtesy of American Cyanamid Co.).

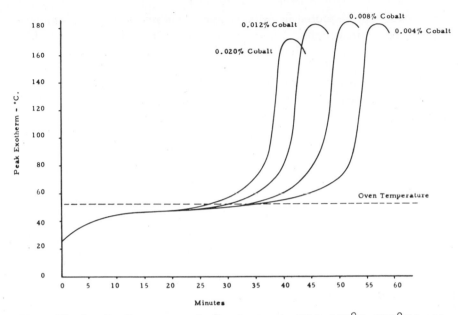

Figure No. 6.—Exotherm curves for Laminac resin 4116 at 52°C. (125°F.) with 0.5% Lupersol DDM in a forced draft oven (courtesy of American Cyanamid Co.).

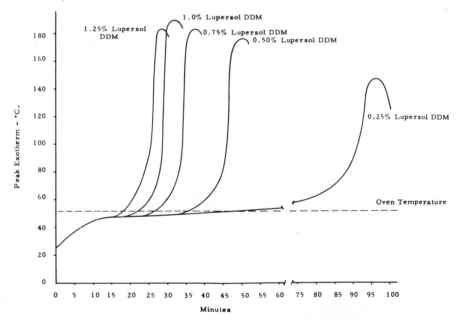

Figure No. 7.—Exotherm curves for a blend of 75% Laminac resin 4116 and 25% Laminac resin 4134 at 52°C. (125°F.) in a forced draft oven (courtesy of American Cyanamid Co.).

resin should not be stored in ordinary glass containers, but in containers that protect it from light. Impurities in the resin, particularly metallic impurities, can also accelerate polymerization and considerably shorten its pot life.

The age of the resin also affects pot life. Since the inhibitor put in the resin by the manufacturer is gradually used up on standing, the older the resin, the less active inhibitor is present. When the catalyst is added it has then but little inhibitor to overcome and may cause almost instant polymerization.

Evaluation of State of Cure

The state of cure of a resin is related to its hardness and is usually determined by hardness tests, such as the Barcol or Rockwell tests for rigid resins and the Shore A hardness test for flexible resins. Specific gravity and solvent-resistance tests are also used for determination of the degree of cure. Methods for these tests are given in the chapter on testing (p. 239).

IV. FILLERS AND REINFORCEMENTS

Fillers are substances added to the catalyzed polyester resin before curing and shaping to enhance various properties of the final product or to reduce its cost. For the purpose of this chapter, fillers are divided into three broad groups: reinforcing (fibrous), bulk, and special.

Reinforcing fillers include such fibrous materials as glass, quartz, cotton, nylon, asbestos, ramie, and sisal. They are usually incorporated into the resin to improve strength, particularly impact and flexural strengths. They also may improve temperature resistance, electrical properties, and many other properties of the resin.

Bulk fillers, such as silicates, carbonates, and clays, are used to decrease the cost of the final products, give better flowing characteristics to the resin, give it enough consistency to support suspended fibers, and provide a smoother surface on the finished laminate. Another advantage of bulk fillers in most cases is that they absorb some of the exothermic heat of the curing reaction. This lessens internal strains and settling effects due to extreme viscosity changes, which might cause a more porous surface, and reduces thermal expansion and shrinkage (1608).

Special fillers include metals added for special effects. For example, metallic powders may be used to weight bases of objects by allowing the powders to settle to the bottom of the mix in the mold. Patterns and decorative effects can be obtained by the use of embossed metallic foils (1699). Coloring matter, added for decorative purposes, also may be classed as a special filler. Other fillers in this classification are those which are used to increase the electrical properties or fire resistance of the final products beyond properties obtained by using fibrous or bulk fillers.

Several fillers are combined when a combination of the properties they contribute is desired.

REINFORCING FILLERS

Fillers used for reinforcing polyester resins are generally fibrous. They may be used as short staple fibers, continuous fibers, woven cloth, or in other forms. The primary aim in using reinforcing fillers is to increase the strength of the final product, although several other advantages are obtained with their use. The most outstanding filler used for reinforcing polyester resins is glass fiber, because of the high strength values that are possible with this material. Since the use of glass is so widespread, major attention is paid to its manufacture, uses, and forms in this chapter. Other materials are discussed to less extent.

Manufacture of Glass Fiber

Glass fiber is made in two basic forms: wool and textile (1660). The wool form is used mainly for insulation and filtering purposes and is not used in reinforcing polyesters to any great extent. There are two types of textile fibers: staple fibers, which are 8 to 15 inches long, and continuous filaments. The continuous filaments are widely used as a filler for polyester resins. The staple fibers offer certain advantages for possible use in the laminating field.

Glass Wool. The production of wool-like glass fibers is a batch process. The raw materials are mixed in a rotary mixer and melted and refined in furnaces that have a capacity of 40 tons or more. After melting and refining, the glass reaches a forehearth where it flows through perforated bushings in thin streams. As the streams emerge from the orifices high-pressure steam jets force them to thin down into long, resilient fibers. The fibers are gathered on a traveling conveyor at the bottom of the forming chamber. This type of fiber forming lends itself to the production of glass mat.

The diameter and length of the fibers are controlled by the viscosity and temperature of the glass, the size of the orifices, and the steam pressure. The depth of the mass on the conveyor is controlled by the belt speed (1634).

Staple Fibers. In one method for the manufacture of staple fibers the raw materials are mixed and melted in small furnaces, and the melt is formed into small marbles $\frac{5}{16}$ inch in diameter. These marbles are examined for impurities that might impair the fiber quality. Those passing inspection are remelted in small electric furnaces. The furnaces contain electrically heated platinum orifices in the base through which the molten glass flows by gravity (1639).

Another method eliminates the marble-forming operation. In this method the raw materials are melted in one part of a furnace and flow to a forehearth that contains the orifice plates (1594). Here, as in glass wool manufacture, the fibers are drawn by jets of high-pressure steam. A "blowing plate" has been used to aid in the drawing of the fibers (1639).

After the fibers are drawn they are sprayed with a "size," which prevents the fibers from breaking or abrading one another in subsequent handling operations. The fibers then fall on a revolving, perforated drum that is under a slight vacuum, from which they are removed in "sliver" form and wound on tubes (1604). When a "blowing plate" is used, it is adjusted so that the glass fibers remain parallel, and these fibers are carried away on a belt conveyor and cross-wound on a bobbin before twisting and weaving operations (1647).

The diameters of staple fibers are controlled by the size of the orifices (the usual orifice diameter is 0.04 to 0.08 inch), the temperature and viscosity of the batch, and the speed of flowing (1652). The latter is the simplest method of control, a high speed producing a fine fiber and a low speed a coarser fiber (1639).

Staple fibers have not been widely used in laminates. They have been used, however, to build up thickness between layers of continuous filament glass cloth. In combination with continuous filament yarns, they have been woven into cloth with increased hairiness, which increases resistance to delamination in rubber laminates (1604).

Staple fibers offer certain advantages for use in the laminating field. This type of yarn is cheaper than continuous filaments. Better adhesion in laminates has been claimed because of more surface area extending into the resin. [This advantage is of little importance, however, since the introduction of modern bonding finishes (p. 86).] More uniform bulk, because the fiber concentration is spread over a larger area, and less surface shrinkage, crazing, and blooming might also be obtained from the use of staple fiber fabrics (1602).

The use of staple fibers as reinforcing material for polyester laminates is presently being examined by at least one yarn producer (1594). There is a question, however, whether the filament strength of staple yarn can ever equal that of continuous filaments, which are cooled under tension.

Continuous Filaments. The first steps in the manufacture of continuous filaments are similar to those in the manufacture of staple fibers.

The raw materials are combined and made into marbles which are inspected for impurities and remelted in electric furnaces. The orifice plates in the bottom of the furnaces usually contain 102 or 204 holes. The molten glass filaments are drawn from these holes mechanically, sprayed with a "size," and combined into strands at the same time they are wound on a revolving drum or spindle (1626).

Spinning directly from a melt tank is also possible, but inspection is more difficult than in the marble-forming method.

Some patents relating to the manufacture and the equipment used in the manufacture of glass fibers are given in references (403, 404, 405, 406, 407). Glass filaments may be colored by incorporating pigments in the batch (1633).

The diameter of the glass filaments produced by the continuous process depends on the speed of drawing, which varies from 5,000 to over 10,000 feet per minute, the orifice size, and the temperature and viscosity of the molten glass (1583).   Continuous filaments were originally made as thin as possible, because it was recognized that the smaller the filaments the greater is their ability to bend without fracture (1627). Recently, however, in an attempt to reduce cost the filaments have been made in larger diameters.   It is now possible to buy at least four grades of yarn in which the filament diameter in each progressive grade is 10% larger than the previous filament size (1602).

Filament sizes are designated by letters indicating the filament diameter: "D"—0.00023 inch, "E"—0.00028 inch, "G"—0.00038 inch, and "K"—0.00053 inch.   Two hundred and four filaments usually make a single strand of yarn, although yarns of 102 filaments are made and used.   Yarn sizes are designated by a yarn number, which multiplied by 100 equals the number of yards it takes to make a pound (1635).   The "D" yarns are usually called 450's, the "E" yarns 225's, the "G" yarns 150's, and the "K" yarns 75's; thus, 45,000, 25,000, 15,000 and 7,500 yards, respectively, are required to make a pound of these yarns.

The types of fabrics made from the coarser yarns can be used in laminates without undue loss in strength properties.   Consequently, the laminating industry is today veering away from an ultimate strength basis toward the use of more practical and economical fibers and fabrics (1602).

Forms of Glass Fiber Reinforcing Materials

The strands produced by the continuous process provide the basic material for the glass threads used as fillers in the polyester resins. The reinforcing materials made from these basic strands may be in the form of reinforcing cloth, yarns, mats, rovings, milled fibers, parallel strands, or surfacing mats.   A fairly new development is the incorporation of very short glass fibers that would otherwise be waste or chopped rovings in molding compounds for compression or transfer molding (p. 108).

The following is a partial list of suppliers of glass fiber reinforcing materials:

Bigelow-Sanford Carpet Co., Fiber Glass Products Division, New York, N. Y.
Cheney Bros., Textiglas Division, New York, N. Y.
Coast Manufacturing & Supply Co., Livermore, Calif.
Deering Miliken Co., New York, N. Y.
Ferro Corp., Glass Fiber Division, Nashville, Tenn.
Glass Fibers, Inc., Toledo, Ohio
Hess, Goldsmith & Co., Inc., New York, N. Y.
Libbey-Owens-Ford Glass Co., Fiber Glass Division, Toledo, Ohio
Modigliani Glass Fibers, Inc., Lancaster, Ohio
Owens-Corning Fiberglas Corp., Toledo, Ohio
Pittsburgh Plate Glass Co., Fiber Glass Division, Pittsburgh, Pa.
St. George Textile Corp., New York, N. Y.

J. P. Schwebel & Co., New York, N. Y.
Soule Mill, New Bedford, Mass.
J. P. Stevens & Co., New York, N. Y.
Strandcote Corp., Los Angeles, Calif.
Texas Glass Fiber Corp., Grandview, Texas
United Merchants Industrial Fabrics, New York, N. Y.
U. S. Glass Fiber Co., Manchester, Ohio

Parallel Reinforcing Strands. Parallel reinforcing strands are produced by winding the basic strands directly from the fiber-forming operation on cellophane-covered drums, using a traverse winding mechanism. The number of strands per inch can be varied by varying the speed of the traverse; 400 strands of 204 filaments each is usual. The strands may be impregnated with the laminating resin by brushing or dipping as they are wound. After the strands have been applied to the full width of the drum, the mat is cut and removed from the drum while still wet and flexible and laid out to dry at room temperature.

Utilization of glass fibers in this way eliminates the textile operations necessary in preparing the other forms of reinforcing materials. Other advantages are that the maximum glass content in the laminate is more easily achieved by the use of parallel strands, and that reinforcement in the direction of the load is possible. A disadvantage in the use of parallel strands is that the strands separate during lamination with resulting cracks and fissures in the laminate. In addition, there are many handling operations after the mat is removed from the drum, and the process is a batch operation. Consequently, more time and effort have been devoted to the development of the other reinforcing materials than to ironing out the present disadvantages in this method.

Reinforcing Yarns. Reinforcing yarns are usually made by unwinding the "forming packages" or bobbins containing the basic strands, twisting these strands on a standard "textile bobbin," and winding the twisted strands in multiple wound packages. Yarns have also been made in which the strands are not twisted, but held together by a binder (1569).

Reinforcing yarns are used for the reinforcement of plastics, mainly in rod form, and as electrical insulating material (1624, 1629, 1650, 1655). The twisted strands should have received, somewhere in the process, a surface treatment or finish to promote adhesion between the glass and plastic (p. 85).

Reinforcing Rovings. Reinforcing rovings are made by running together a number of strands from the forming package, or a number of yarns, into multiple wound "roving packages" (1569, 1583). Usually 60 ends of the basic strands are used to make a 35- to 40-pound ball or roving package (1580). The bundles of fibers are held together by a binder (p. 117).

The roving packages are a convenient form for shipping glass or for use in preforming, rod fabrication, and formation of parallel strand mats (1583).

Milled Fibers. The textile strands may be hammer-milled into short individual fibers which vary in length from $\frac{1}{32}$ to $\frac{1}{4}$ inch (1580). Fibers that might otherwise be wasted may be used to make this type of reinforcement. The short milled fibers may be used with mat or cloth reinforcing material (361, 365, 366, 1640). Their use promotes interlaminar strength and gives better surface characteristics to laminates (365, 1640).

Surfacing Mat. Filament types of random distribution mats are made by laying rather coarse filaments on a belt (1604). They are used with other types of reinforcing material to produce a smooth surface on a molding (1580).

Reinforcing Mats. Glass fibers are frequently used in the form of mats for reinforcing polyester resins. There are presently two basic types of reinforcing mats available, the chopped strand mat and the continuous strand mat.

The continuous strand mat is made by laying continuous filament strands on a moving belt in either a random-coil fashion or a diamond pattern (378). The random-coil mat is infrequently made and has been replaced by the chopped strand mat. The diamond mat is made by laying continuous strands in a uniform pattern and is used as a substitute for unidirectional cloth where cost is a factor. Both the coiled and diamond mats are held together by a binder (p. 117).

Chopped strand mats are made by depositing 2- to 3-inch lengths of chopped yarn or strands on an endless moving belt in a random fashion. Variations in the amount of fiber per unit area are possible, and the distribution of glass can be made very uniform (1604). A powdered or liquid binder (p. 117) is usually used to hold the mat together for subsequent handling operations (1580). This binder may or may not be soluble in the resin. Soluble or partially soluble binders provide light transmission in the finished laminate but also may allow the fibers to flow, so that an uneven distribution of glass in the laminate may result. Recently, a mat held together by stitching or needling instead of a binder has been made (1603). The use of this product, which could be provided with a commercial polyester finish for better adhesion, should result in mat laminates with higher strength values.

It is also possible to introduce continuous strands in a chopped strand mat to provide better orientation of the strength values in one or more directions (1603).

Mats are used in the laminating and molding of many products, particularly of trays and boxes. They are used in large amount in the manufacture of corrugated wall paneling and awnings (1546, 1604).

REINFORCING CLOTH

The first market for woven glass fabric was in the electrical equipment field. At this time, the type "D" filament (0.00023 inch in diameter) was used because of the belief that the coarser fibers would be unsuited to weaving. When the type "E" filament was developed, however, it was found to be entirely suitable for cloth, and specifications were soon established for its use. The type "G" filament came into production in 1943 and was also thought to be too coarse for weaving. But in 1947 it was woven into fabrics that duplicated the weaves of the type "E" and that were entirely suitable for reinforcing laminates. The type "K" yarns are under evaluation for use in fabrics.

The fabrics presently used in laminating and molding are designated by numbers and are 112, 128, 162, 120, 181, 182, and 183 (1566). The numbers used indicate the type of weave and may also indicate other relevant data. The 112, 128, and 162 fabrics are "plain" or "square" weaves (p. 81); the 120, 181, 182, and 183 fabrics are long-shaft "satin" weaves that differ in thickness (p. 81).

Manufacture of Reinforcing Glass Cloth

Twisting and Plying. Reinforcing fabrics are seldom woven from single strand yarn. Usually, one or more strands of the basic yarns are twisted and the twisted strands are plied together to form plied yarns, which are woven into fabric. The twisting and plying are usually done in opposite directions. Twisting is usually held to a minimum for better resin penetration during lamination.

The plied yarn is designated by a number that shows the original number of yards to make a pound, followed by a fraction. The numerator of the fraction indicates the number of strands twisted, and the denominator shows the number of twisted strands plied together. For example, the yarn used in weaving the standard 181 cloth is designated "225-1/3." This means that in the first operation one strand of 225's yarn is twisted, and in the second operation three ends of twisted strands are plied together to make the final yarn. The number of yards per pound of the plied yarn is obtained by dividing the yards per pound of the original yarn by the number of plies multiplied by the number of twisted strands in each ply, e.g., for the 181 cloth, dividing 22,500 by 3 (1594). The yarns used in weaving other laminating fabrics are as follows: 112 fabric, 450-1/2; 128 fabric, 225-1/3; 162 fabric, 225-2/5; 120 fabric, 450-1/2; 182 fabric, 225-2/2; 183 fabric, 225-3/2 (1566).

Weaving. Weaving of glass fabrics is done on standard textile equipment, and the fabrics are produced in many patterns or weaves. Factors that affect the cost of the weave and the fabric produced are the thread count and the yarn size.

Thread Count. The threads in the various weaves run in two directions; the "warp" threads or "ends" run along the length of the cloth, and the "filling" threads or "picks" or "weft" threads run across the fabric perpendicular to the "warp." The thread count of a fabric is expressed as the number of threads running in each direction per inch, and the number of "warp" threads is expressed first. For example, a 42 by 32 count fabric has 42 threads per inch running lengthwise and 32 threads per inch running across the fabric.

The number of threads per inch determines to a great extent the breaking strength of a fabric; generally, the more threads per inch, the higher the breaking strength. The warp and filling threads, however, have a shearing action on one another. In the case of a fabric with about the same number of threads in each direction, the higher the thread count the lower the breaking strength on a weight basis.

The cost of weaving is usually based on the number of filling threads per inch. Although the optimum would be a cloth with warp threads only (which is no longer a woven fabric), a certain number of filling threads are required to hold the warp together (1594). Of course, a fabric with a minimum of filling threads would have strength in only one direction in a laminate, but this type of fabric could be cross-laminated, or the plies could be arranged to give strength in many directions.

Yarn Size. The yarn size determines the thickness of a fabric; the higher the ply of the yarn, the greater the thickness of the fabric (1594). Except for impact strength, the strength of a laminate, especially its compressive strength, decreases with increasing cloth thickness. Impact strength increases with increasing cloth thickness (1604).

The yarn size also affects the cost of the fabric. If the same thread count is maintained, the higher the yarn size, the lower the cost per pound. The cost is also reduced if the thread count is lowered but larger yarns are used to maintain the same weight. A compromise is usually effected involving the lowest cost possible with the yarn size and the amount of flexibility in the fabric and the strength values necessary in the laminate.

Type "D" yarns are not generally used in laminating; type "E" yarns are widely used, but are slowly being replaced by type "G" yarns, which cost less.

Recently, fabrics have been woven from rovings that offer high strength at substantially reduced cost (1556).

Types of Weaves of Glass Cloth. Many of the weaves of glass cloth in current production are not used for reinforcing plastics because of obvious disadvantages, and many are used for surface applications only. Two of the basic weave patterns that have been used extensively in laminating are the "plain" or "square" weave and the "satin" weave (1604).

Plain Weave. In the plain weave the same number of threads per inch are used in each direction, and each thread passes over one thread and under the next. This results in a uniform close-packed weave in which the threads are crimped (waved) to a great extent (1604).

A modification of the plain weave is the "leno" weave, in which the warp threads are used in pairs and cross each other after passing around each filling thread. This results in an open type of weave in which the fibers hold their positions and do not slip on the cross threads (1602). A further modification of the plain weave is the "mock leno" weave, which resembles a leno weave in that an open pattern is formed, but the fibers are held together in the open pattern by a system of interlacings, rather than by the warp threads crossing over one another.

Basic plain weave fabrics are used in applications where uniform strength is required in two directions, easy removal of entrapped air is necessary, and in the case of thicker cloths, where considerable drawing properties are needed (1604). Other advantages of the plain weave are the closer control of glass-to-resin content permitted by the uniform weave; the high impact strength of laminates prepared from this cloth, since the "crimp" absorbs the impact, and the stability of the warp and weft threads (1594, 1602).

The plain weave fabrics are not used where high compressive strength is required, because the crimped columns of fibers collapse under edge-wise pressure. This effect is less in the thinner cloths than it is in the thicker cloths (1604). Other disadvantages of the plain weave are low pliability and, since this weave contains a maximum number of interlac-ings and the fibers abrade one another, lower flexural and tensile strength than other weaves (1594).

Leno weaves, which produce a uniform fabric whose glass content and price approach a minimum, have shown promise in the reinforcing of thin glass sheaths (1602). Because of their lower glass content, these weaves are not generally used where high laminate strength values are essential.

Satin Weave. In the satin weave the warp and weft threads go under one thread and over three, five, or seven threads, depending on the "shaft" or "harness" of the weave prepared. Thus, in an eight-shaft or eight-harness satin weave (type 181 fabric), each warp and filling thread passes over one thread and under seven threads (1604). In the "crowfoot" or four-shaft satin weave, the interlacings are over one thread and under three threads (1594).

The eight-shaft satin weave has been widely used to reinforce poly-esters, second in volume only to the plain weave (1602). It is best suited for applications requiring high strength in all directions combined with light weight and a minimum of lay-up time; high strength coupled with a low material cost; or where its excellent surfacing and decorative characteristics may be used to advantage (1604).

The straightness of the fibers and the small number of interlacings in the satin weave are factors contributing to high laminate strength. Since the elimination of "crimp" also allows the fabric to lie flatter, more layers of fabric can be packed into a smaller space, which, in turn, gives better strength values for the same thickness as compared to the plain weave. This factor may also reduce the cost of the laminates somewhat, since fewer layers are necessary to achieve the desired strength values (1594).

In the satin weave the threads may slip over one another, which is generally an advantage but might be a disadvantage in some cases. The advantage of this property is that the cloth may be formed around curves to a certain degree. Porosity cannot be maintained evenly, however, and laminates prepared from satin weave fabrics often exhibit nonuniform strength unless the cloth is handled carefully before lamination (1594). This disadvantage can be reduced by higher thread counts, which, however, also reduce the flexibility of the cloth (1594). A recent development is a "stretchable" glass fabric that is more suited to compound curves or deep draw applications than the ordinary eight-shaft weave (1571). In this weave, the thread alinement plays up, and yet controls, the slippage of the fibers to give a fabric that is "stretchable" (1571).

An outgrowth of the satin weave is a unidirectional weave in which there are the minimum number of filling threads necessary to hold the cloth together and the maximum number of warp threads. The filling threads are usually of smaller diameter than the warp threads (1602).

The advantages of fabrics of unidirectional weave are that they allow reinforcement to be limited to necessary directions, that they can be cross-laminated to meet predetermined directional load requirements, and that they can be used as a cheap means of spot reinforcing for structures requiring additional localized strength (1604). The unidirectional weave uses the minimum number of interlacings, so that the abrasion of the fibers by each other is reduced to a minimum. The laminate strength values obtained from fabrics of this type are excellent. The weight of the fabrics is low, and they give higher strength values than the plain weaves for the same laminate thickness (1602).

Other Weaves. Glass cloth is woven into other weaves, such as the "twill" variety, but these weaves have not been used so widely in laminating as the plain and satin weaves. The twill weaves have not been examined thoroughly as a reinforcement for polyesters. They possess a high degree of abrasion resistance, which might make them desirable in some instances (1602).

PROPERTIES OF GLASS FIBERS, YARNS, AND FABRICS

At one time glass fibers were used as reinforcement for high-pressure laminates, but the pressure used crushed the glass or made it flow and created a nonuniform molding. The abrasive effect of the glass also caused excessive mold wear when high pressures were used (1645). It is possible to mold with glass under very high pressure if the mold is designed to permit escape of the resin. The resin is then added in sufficient quantity to stop compression before the glass is crushed. This technique gives very good surfaces and good impregnation of the resin in the glass reinforcing material.

The change from high-pressure to low-pressure laminating made some of the more desirable properties of resin-glass combinations apparent. These properties depend, for the most part, on the properties of the glass fibers. The functions of the resin in the laminate are to support the glass fibers, to distribute any applied load evenly, and above all to separate the fibers to reduce their abrasive effect on one another—thus, to help the glass approach its inherent high strength properties (1638). A comparison of the strength of glass in the fibrous and solid forms is given by G. Slayter (1653).

The most outstanding property of glass fibers is their tensile strength, which is generally over 250,000 pounds per square inch and may reach the range of 2,000,000 pounds per square inch in very fine fibers (1663). The electrical insulation value of glass fibers is also high; the dielectric strength with proper impregnation has been reported as 1,200 volts per mil (1658). Other valuable properties are high temperature resistance, resistance to most acids and milder alkalies, high thermal insulation value, and resistance to rot, germs, and mildew (1591, 1663).

Possible disadvantages in the use of glass fibers are their present high cost and their higher density as compared to natural or organic fibers (1614, 1623).

Glass fabrics contribute certain advantages to polyester resin laminates that stem from properties in the basic fibers and yarn. Glass yarns have "greater tensile strength, stiffness, heat resistance, plus less elongation than any other textile yarns now available in commercial quantities" (1625). Glass fabrics also provide a means for obtaining consistent and reproducible results in laminating. Ease of handling is another advantage of this form of glass fibers (1604). The higher cost of glass fabrics as compared to mats or rovings may prohibit their use in some instances.

SIZING AND FINISHING OF GLASS FIBERS

Important phases of glass fiber manufacture and the use of glass fibers for reinforcing plastic materials are "sizing" and "finishing." A "size" is usually applied to glass fibers right after they emerge from the orifices in the manufacturing process. The main function of a size is to lubricate the fibers to prevent them from abrading and consequently weakening each other during the subsequent handling and weaving operations. A "finish," at present, is generally applied to the fibers after fabrication or weaving. However, application of the finishing agent as the glass fibers are formed is practiced to some extent and will undoubtedly find increasingly wider use. The prime function of a finish is to bond the glass to the laminating resin.

The ideal glass treatment, of course, would be one that combines the advantages of a size, permitting the glass fibers to be woven, and the advantages of a finish, providing good chemical bonding between the glass and the resin (1583, 1584, 1585).

Improvement of Handling Characteristics. Sizes especially designed to impart good handling characteristics to glass fibers usually contain the following ingredients: water, an emulsifier, a film-forming constituent, and a lubricant. The film-forming ingredient must be tough enough to bond the fibers together in a strand and prevent abrasion of the fibers, and flexible enough to permit winding and processing operations without cracking or otherwise destroying its protection. The lubricant enables the fibers to move freely over surfaces during processing. These ingredients must be balanced so that the strand has the proper degree of "integrity, pliability, lubricity, and high abrasion resistance" (1583, 1584).

The "Dutch oil" size has been popular in the past for imparting good handling characteristics to textile fibers. This size consists of water, an emulsifying agent, starch as the film-former, and a vegetable oil as the lubricant. Additional ingredients have been used, such as gelatin or a vinyl polymer to aid the film-forming characteristics and a softener with the lubricant (1583, 1584). A similar size is given in U. S. patent 2,343,180 (362). It improves handling characteristics but does not promote adhesion between the glass surface and the laminating resin.

Size Removal. Since relatively poor adhesion is obtained from sizes of the lubricating type, the usual practice is to remove them after the fibers have been fabricated and before lamination.

Carmelization. A partial removal of the lubricating size by heating the fibers or cloth to 200° to 300° C. for a short time effects some improvement in bond strength (367, 1651). A treatment of this nature on cloth is designated as 111, V11, or V11A finish (1594). The cloth subjected to this operation is brown, and the laminate strength, although better than that obtained with the starch-oil size, is poor when compared to the strength obtained with more recently developed finishes. This finish, however, is inexpensive because it requires little equipment for additional treatment; other finishes require fairly extensive machinery. It is used currently in high-pressure melamine or phenolic laminates and in some special low-pressure work (1594).

Heat Cleaning. The lubricating size can be completely removed from the fabric by washing or by heat cleaning. The preferred method is heat cleaning because no traces of detergent, soap, or organic matter are left on the fabric (1585). It is usually accomplished commercially by heating the glass at 500° to 600°F. for 50 to 60 hours. This treatment, which is known commercially as 112 or V12 finish, is used before most finishes applied to glass reinforcement for polyesters, because it leaves the glass free of all previous sizing materials. Cloth prepared with this finish may be used in some specialized applications without further finishing (1594). Heat cleaning impairs the handling characteristics of the fibers, however, so that care should be taken to avoid loss of strength from fiber breakage (1618).

Other Methods. Sizes can be removed by treatment with starch-splitting enzymes, followed by an emulsifier or detergent wash to remove oil constituents. E. Balz has found that treatment with a urea solution or treatment with a chlorate solution followed by a heat treatment will also remove lubricating sizes (401).

Chemical Bonding Finishes

Several finishes have been developed that promote adhesion between the glass surface and the polyester resins used for laminating. The oldest of these is the 114 finish, which, on its development, represented a substantial improvement over the starch-oil finish previously used. This finish involves the treatment of the heat-cleaned glass surface with a methacrylate-chrome complex solution (363, 375, 382). It was the first commercial finish specifically designed to improve the bond between the glass and the resin.

In military as well as commercial applications, however, the 114 finish was limited by its sensitivity to moisture. On continuous exposure to high humidity, laminates with this finish lost 40 to 50% of their flexural strength, with corresponding impairment in other mechanical as well as electrical properties. This was taken in account in the prevailing military specifications. To compensate for the loss in strength, a 40 to 50% excess of weight and material had to be used in all laminated parts that might be exposed to high humidity. For this reason, the Materials

Laboratory, Research Division, Wright Air Development Center,[1] initiated a study to improve the moisture resistance of laminated glass-polyester plastics (1670).

Vinyl Silane Treatments. Working under an Air Force contract, L. L. Yaeger and his co-workers proceeded on the assumption that a vinyl group which was copolymerizable with the styrene in the polyester system and tied to the glass with a silicon atom should effect an anchorage resistant to any moisture condition. They found that treatment of glass (or other filler material) with vinyl trichlorosilane, followed by a quick water wash, produced a filler that when laminated retained its original strength properties even on unlimited exposure to moisture or immersion in water (1669, 1670).

The vinyl trichlorosilane can be applied either in the liquid phase, from a solution in mineral spirits, carbon tetrachloride, or other organic solvents, or in the gaseous or vapor phase. Modification of the vinyl trichlorosilane with beta-chloroallyl alcohol before application results in higher strength values (1670).

Several adaptations of the principle of the vinyl silane treatment were made by industry, to provide the most convenient means for binding the vinyl group, via silicon, to the glass. Owens-Corning Fiberglas Corp. introduced the 136 finish, which is said to be vinyl trichlorosilane hydrolyzed with an alkali and applied from an acidic water solution. Linde Air Products Co. introduced a silicone size GS-1, which on heating deposits a film of vinyl silicone on the glass (1619). A third proprietary finish, the Garan finish of Libbey-Owens-Ford Co., is generally classed with the silane finishes, although its composition has not been disclosed (1657). (Also see references 372, 376.)

The steric effects of the various vinyl structures employed in chemical finishes have been investigated by Erickson and Silver (1606). They report favorable results with a finish comprising, for example, an unsaturated alkyl trichlorosilane reacted with glycidyl methacrylate and triphenylamine.

Modification of 114 Finish. Yaeger found that the moisture resistance imparted to glass fabrics by the vinyl silane treatment is greatly enhanced if application of the finishing chemical is followed by a thorough afterwash with water (1669). This finding was applied in a modification of the 114 finish, called the Volan A finish (1616, 1661). Although the results with this treatment fall short of those obtained with the vinyl silane finishes, they nonetheless represent a marked improvement in moisture resistance over those obtained with the 114 finish.

[1] Wright-Patterson Air Force Base, Ohio.

Other Finishes. Some finishes that are applicable to glass fibers but that are not specifically designed toward the improvement of strength in polyester laminates have been reported. Various compositions containing formaldehyde with other compounds are claimed to improve the strength of laminates made from glass fibers and urea-formaldehyde, phenolic, and similar resins (364, 369). The use of an amino polymer as a coating for glass fibers has been proposed (377). For polyester resins, these finishes now have only historical interest.

Comparison of Finishes. The optimum properties of a polyester laminate are obtained by the vinyl trichlorosilane treatment as originally disclosed (1636). The commercial variations of this treatment entail a compromise, in which some sacrifice in moisture resistance (about 5 to 10%) has been made to gain ease in applicability.

Table No. 12 gives a comparison of the properties of glass fabric-polyester laminates made from 181 fabric with the following finishes: starch-oil size, heat cleaned, methacrylato-chromic chloride, sodium vinylsiloxanolate, and vinyl trichlorosilane modified with beta-chloroallyl alcohol (1585). The methacrylato-chrome and siloxanolate finishes were commercial finishes applied from water solution.

Flexural strength values in excess of 85,000 pounds per square inch have been reported for laminates prepared from glass cloth finished with vinyl trichlorosilane (1606). After immersion for 3 hours in boiling water the laminates retained 96% of their original strength. These tests were made with Selectron 5003[2] resin. For laminates made with resins other than Selectron 5003, flexural strength values ranging from 58,600 to 74,000 pounds per square inch have been reported (1586). Strength retention for these laminates after 3 hours in boiling water ranged from 81 to 99%.

Much less laminating pressure is required to obtain translucent, clear laminates of optimum strength if the glass fabric has a vinyl type finish rather than a 114 finish. This is due to the more favorable wetting behavior of polyester resins toward the vinyl finishes. Press settings established with 114 type finishes will therefore have to be revised for the vinyl finishes.

Outlook in Finishes and Sizes

The trend in finishes undoubtedly will favor gas-phase application to the virgin fiber as it is formed. This type of application has the advantages of absolutely uniform application, lowest material cost, and ease of bonding to a virgin glass surface. Vinyl chlorosilane has been applied

[2]Pittsburgh Plate Glass Co. trade name.

Table No. 12—*Properties of glass fabric-polyester laminates made from 181 fabric with various finishes.**

Fabric finish	Flexural strength		Modulus of elasticity in flexure		Compressive strength		Impact strength (edge)	Water absorption (24-hr. immersion)
	Dry	Wet**	Dry	Wet**	Dry	Wet**	Ft.-lb.	%
	10^3 psi	10^3 psi	10^6 psi	10^6 psi	10^3 psi	10^3 psi		
Starch-oil size	37	22	2.7	2.4	16	10	***35	0.54
Heat cleaned	52	20	3.2	2.5	25	10	17	1.00
Methacrylato-chromic chloride	73	57	3.4	3.1	35	29	21	0.14
Sodium vinylsiloxanolate	80	69	3.7	3.6	34	32	25	0.17
Vinyl trichlorosilane (modified)	80	77	3.8	3.7	46	41	25	0.10

*Source: L. P. Biefeld and T. E. Philipps, "Finishes for Glass Fabrics for Reinforcing Polyester Plastics," *Industrial and Engineering Chemistry* 45, 1281–6 (1953) (reprinted by permission).

**Tested wet after immersion in boiling water for 2 hours.

***The poor fiber-to-plastic adhesion of laminates made from fabrics with starch-oil size permits fiber slippage, high strain distribution, and fabric-plastic delamination over a wide area. Since these changes absorb considerable impact energy, high impact strength values are obtained.

in gas phase on a laboratory and pilot-plant scale with results as satisfactory as those obtained by liquid application. The gas-phase application, however, will require special provisions for corrosion-resistant
equipment, ventilation, and spacing, which may make it necessary to
await the construction of specially designed plant facilities for its
adoption.

As a lubricating and parting size for glass fibers, a resin emulsion
might be developed that is compatible with the laminating resin and thus
would not have to be removed before laminating. Such a size could be
applied over a gas-phase-applied bonding finish.

Recently, a technique was developed by which a vinyl ethoxysilane
bonding agent can be applied to glass rovings by inclusion in the impregnating resin (1637). This method eliminates the need for separate
application of vinyl silane finishes, but must be carefully controlled to
produce roving fibers with good mechanical properties.

The chemical bonding finishes are being extended to non-glass materials, including fibrous organic materials and bulk fillers. The bulk
fillers are particularly adapted for gas-phase treatment, and such treatment should materially improve the properties, particularly moisture
resistance, of laminates made with them.

OTHER REINFORCING MATERIALS

Because of the outstanding properties of glass fiber reinforced polyesters, the investigation and the utilization of other types of reinforcing
materials have not received much attention in the United States.

Asbestos

Asbestos has been used extensively as a filler in England because of
its cheapness and availability. Some English sources claim that asbestos
gives laminates of higher elastic modulus than those obtained from glass
fibers, but other sources dispute this claim (Discussion, *Reinforced
Plastics Division, Society of the Plastics Industry Conference, 7th
Annual*, 1952, Section 8, p. 5). Asbestos is used, mainly with phenolic
resins, in the preparation of laminates having high heat resistance and
good electrical properties (1612).

Cotton

Cotton fillers are used where cost may be a factor but have not been
extensively used with polyester resins because of their poor water resistance (Discussion, *Reinforced Plastics Division, Society of the Plastics
Industry Conference, 6th Annual*, 1951, Section 4, p. 11). They are usually
laminated with phenolic resins. Cotton fillers lend themselves well to

use in preforms and thus serve well in high-speed compression molding
(1612). They have also been used in bag molding (1607). A method for
reducing the flammability of cotton laminates has been disclosed (1667).

Other Fillers

Ramie, sisal, cellulose, nylon, rayon, and other fibers have been
suggested as fillers (368, 408, 1612) but, as far as published literature
indicates, have not been widely used because they cost more, have higher
water absorption, or are less available than other fillers (1612; Discussion, *Reinforced Plastics Division, Society of the Plastics Industry
Conference, 6th Annual,* 1951, Section 4, p. 11). The high resilience of
these fibers, and consequent stress distribution over a wide area, might
be an advantage in laminates. Application of sizing procedures for glass
to these materials might greatly reduce the moisture sensitivity of some
of them.

High-strength paper has been used to a small degree with polyester
resins but is used mostly with phenolic resins (370, 1623). A discussion
of the choice of paper for laminates is given in reference (1582). The
difficulty of poor bonding between resins and paper seems to have been
overcome to some degree (1615).

BULK FILLERS

Properties Required

Bulk fillers do not chemically combine with the resin but may be added
to increase the volume of the final mix or for other reasons. A bulk filler
should possess the following properties: minimum oil absorbency; a
particle size of 1 to 3 microns for easy dispersion in the resin; low metal
content to reduce cure variations; a specific gravity of less than 1.50 for
good bulking characteristics; a white or neutral color to produce good
coloring backgrounds; low solubility in water to maintain low water absorption in the laminate; and for particular applications the desired effect
on the curing cycle (1676, 1677, 1679). No one bulk filler is known that
meets all of these requirements.

Types of Bulk Fillers

The bulk fillers most often used with polyester resins are clays, silicates, and carbonates. Wood products have been suggested as fillers
(430, 1517), but have not been generally used because of their high water
absorption (1699). The following is a partial list of bulk fillers used
with polyester resins and their suppliers:

Filler	*Supplier*
	CARBONATES
Atomite	Thompson-Weinman Co., New York, N. Y.
Carbonate of magnesia	Whittaker, Clark, & Daniels, Inc., New York, N. Y.
Cliffstone Whiting	Whittaker, Clark, & Daniels, Inc., New York, N. Y.
Kalite	Diamond Alkali Co., Cleveland, Ohio
Keystone Filler	Whittaker, Clark, & Daniels, Inc., New York, N. Y.
Lesamite	Thompson-Weinman Co., New York, N. Y.
Precipitated Chalk	Whittaker, Clark, & Daniels, Inc., New York, N. Y.
Purecal	Wyandotte Chemical Corp., New York, N. Y.
Snow Flake White	Thompson-Weinman Co., New York, N. Y.
Surfex	Diamond Alkali Co., Cleveland, Ohio
Suspenso	Diamond Alkali Co., Cleveland, Ohio
Terra Alba	Whittaker, Clark, & Daniels, Inc., New York, N. Y.

SILICA AND SILICATES

Aluminum Flake	Aluminum Flake Co., Akron, Ohio
Asbestine	W. H. Loomis Talc Corp., Gouverneur, N. Y.
Cab-o-sil	Godfrey L. Cabot, Inc., Boston, Mass.
Celite	Johns-Manville Corp., New York, N. Y.
Grey Slate Flour	Parsons Manufacturing Co., Pen Argyl, Pa.
Magnesium silicate	Whittaker, Clark, & Daniels, Inc., New York, N. Y.
Mica	Mitchell-Rand Insulation Co., Inc., New York, N. Y.
Mineralite	Mineralite Sales Corp., New York, N. Y.
Microsil Super	Standard Silica Corp., Chicago, Ill.
Nuca	Harshaw Chemical Co., New York, N. Y.
Quartz	Whittaker, Clark, & Daniels, Inc., New York, N. Y.
Silene	Columbia Chemical Division, Pittsburgh Plate Glass Co., Pittsburgh, Pa.
Silica Super White	C. K. Williams & Co., Easton, Pa.
Talc	Whittaker, Clark, & Daniels, Inc., New York, N. Y.
Wollastonite	Godfrey L. Cabot, Inc., Boston, Mass.

CLAYS

ASP Clay	Edgar Brothers Co., Metuchen, N. J.
Georgia Clay	Albion Kaolin Unit, Interchemical Corp., Hephsibah, Ga.
Ideal Clay No. 2	Witco Chemical Co., New York, N. Y.
	R. T. Vanderbilt Co., New York, N. Y.

Three of the main reasons for the use of bulk fillers in laminates are to improve appearance, to improve water resistance, and to lower cost (1555). A proper choice of filler can also reduce crazing and tendency to shrink in molded parts (1676). Bulk fillers are used to thicken resins so that reinforcing fibers can be incorporated in the same mass without settling out.

At this time the data are inconclusive concerning the action of different types of bulk fillers. This discussion of bulk fillers will therefore be restricted to the end results obtained by their use.

Cost Reduction

The reduction in material cost obtained from the use of bulk fillers is often less than might be expected (1677, 1679). For example, assume that a typical resin costing $0.40 per pound and a filler costing $0.05 per pound are used; 25 cubic centimeters of the resin weigh 1 ounce, and 10 cubic centimeters of the filler weigh the same. With a ratio of resin to filler of 3 to 1 by weight we obtain 1,360 cubic centimeters of a mix costing $1.25. The same volume of resin, without filler, would cost $1.36. Therefore, if the resin-filler mixture could be substituted for the unfilled resin volume for volume, the cost saving in raw materials (aside from labor, handling, and other expenses, which may be substantial) would be only 8%. On a weight for weight basis the cost would be 22% less but the reduction in volume of 15% with the resin-filler mixture makes substitution on this basis impractical.

It is not usually possible to substitute a resin-filler mix for a resin on an equal volume basis, because the reduction in strength that usually occurs may make it necessary to use more of the resin-filler mix, thereby reducing the cost differential (1677). If a resin-filler mix, using the filler of the previous example at 30% concentration, is substituted for one particular resin, the dry tensile strength of the molded parts is reduced from approximately 8,500 pounds per square inch to 5,500 pounds per square inch (1677). However, substitutions on a volume basis resulting in cost reductions of up to 18% have been reported with no detrimental effects on the molded part (1676).

The tendency today in the use of bulk fillers is to concentrate on attaining the other more obvious advantages rather than a cost saving at a possible reduction in quality (1677).

In some speciality applications, fillers may actually be employed to cause weakness, for example, expendable structures in movie scenes that are easy to destroy as well as to make.

Improvement of Water Resistance

A distinct decrease in water absorption is obtained, in most cases, through the use of bulk fillers. In tests on some fillers, increases in tensile strength for resin-filler mixtures were reported after immersion for 16 hours in water at $160°$ F., 4 hours in boiling water, and 20 hours in water at room temperature (1677). The strength results for the resin-filler mixtures were less, however, than the original dry strength of the unfilled resin, but could be improved by the addition of fibrous fillers.

Other results have been reported in which a 40% filled resin had higher original strength values than the unfilled resin and excellent strength retention after water immersion for periods up to 14 days (1676). Improved water resistance is also attributed to the use of bulk fillers with silicate fibers (416).

Treatment of bulk fillers with a size, preferably vinyl chlorosilane applied in gas phase, would undoubtedly lower water absorption considerably.

Improvement of Appearance

The addition of bulk fillers to resins reduces surface "crazing" of molded parts and produces a smoother surface with reduced porosity (1676).

Reduction in surface "crazing" may be due in part to the reduction in exotherm noted with the use of fillers (1677). The slower cure and reduction in peak heat reduce strains and are very helpful in eliminating surface or internal flaws due to extreme variations in internal heat. The improvements in other surface characteristics might be due in part to the fine size and even distribution of the filler, which would tend to "hold" the resin and reduce flow in molds.

Fillers improve the appearance of pigmented parts because they impart opacity and thus increase the hiding power of the pigments. The whiteness of many bulk fillers also makes coloration in the resin more apparent.

Improvement of Other Properties

Bulk fillers are used to improve the handling characteristics of a resin for hand lay-ups, to change the flow characteristics of a resin in a mold, and to improve the hardness of a cured resin (1679). Improvements in handling and flow characteristics are due, in part, to the increase in viscosity obtained by loading the resin with filler, which reduces its tendency to flow. Thixotropy, or resistance to flow except under stress, can be obtained in resins by the use of flocculated suspensions of fillers (1683). Resins with this property are of special value in gel coating, spray molding, hand lay-ups, and matched metal die molding.

Effect on Strength Properties

The available information on the effect of fillers on the strength properties of polyester resins is scanty and in poor agreement. In some cases the published results are even contradictory. Testing programs are underway, however, to compile more reliable data on the effects of fillers (1677, 1678). The conclusions at present are that the effect of fillers on strength depends on the type and particle size of the filler and on the particular resin used.

The present practice in industry is to incorporate up to 40% of filler in a reinforced polyester resin. Higher concentrations are commonly believed to cause reduction in product properties, as well as difficulties in processing (1681).

One series of tests indicates the following effects of filler concentration on the strength properties of a glass mat reinforced polyester molding: Flexural and impact strengths remain constant up to 40% filler; the compressive strength is raised about 2,000 pounds per square inch by 10% filler, and this value remains almost constant up to about 50% filler; the tensile strength is lowered about 1,000 pounds per square inch over the range of from 0 to 40% filler; the flexural modulus remains constant for from 0 to 30% filler, and then increases from 1.5×10^6 to 2×10^6 as the filler concentration increases from 30% to 50% (1676).

Parker and Whittaker determined a correlation between the reciprocal of the particle size of the filler and the compressive strength and cross-breaking strength of mineral filler bonded with resins (1680).

Effect on Curing Characteristics

Some fillers may have a profound effect on the curing characteristics of the resin. The gel time, using a controlled amount of catalyst, may be raised from about 15 minutes to about 425 minutes, and even further, by the choice of filler. Other fillers, such as Witco Clay No. 2, lower the peak exotherm, which is sometimes useful in production molding or for producing objects with less internal strains (1677, 1678). Carbon black retards the cure of polyesters catalyzed by organic peroxides, but accelerates cure in the presence of certain peroxide-promoter combinations (3235).

Use of Bulk Fillers

Bulk fillers have been most often used in consumer products rather than military items. In consumer products a reduction in peak strength values is less important since it may be counter-balanced by the improvement in appearance, and perhaps a reduction in cost.

SPECIAL FILLERS

Coloring of Polyester Resins

It is advantageous, especially in the consumer field, to color polyester resin products for better appearance and sales appeal. The coloring of polyester resins may be done in two ways: internally and externally. The external application of coloring material is considered a finishing process (p. 129). This section is concerned with the internal or "filler" type of coloring agent.

Methods of Coloring. Coloring agents used may or may not be soluble in the polyester resins. The pigmentation of plastics with the insoluble variety of pigments can be improved by milling the pigment with a small amount of a polyester oil, dispersing the pigment in the monomer (or mixture of monomer and polymer) to be used, and polymerizing the mixture (431). This method could be used with polyester resins but would probably necessitate having on hand a supply of the polyester without the cross-linking agent added. A careful working of the pigment with the potential cross-linking agent might be used, however. The prevalent method of coloring polyester resins involves merely mixing a suitable amount of pigment and resin.

P. Fram et al. found that a rigidly adhered-to procedure of resin formulation and fabrication is required in order to obtain consistent and reproducible color with pigments in low-pressure laminates (1693). Variation in nearly any phase of procedure can produce great changes in the final color of the laminate. For example, in producing flesh-colored laminates for artificial limbs, an increase in the concentration of promoter caused a marked red-to-yellow shift. High oven temperatures as well as premature oven treatment caused an increase in both yellow content and luminous reflectance. During the early stages of gelling of the resin-pigment mix, the color is highly sensitive to a rapid increase in temperature. It is therefore recommended that partial polymerization be allowed to occur at room temperature before laminates are placed in ovens for heat curing.

Properties of Pigments. Pigments used for polyester resins should exhibit heat and light fastness and chemical stability (1695). The gel characteristics of the resin should not be affected, neither should the long-range characteristics of the cured article. Some red pigments have caused difficulty after the resin has been cured (1676). A copolymerizing pigment would undoubtedly change the cure characteristics of the resin; oil reds retard gelation; and titanium or zinc oxides accelerate the cure (434, 1698).

Other Special Fillers

Fillers have been added to polyesters and other resins to improve various specific characteristics, but usually at the expense of some other characteristics of the cured resin. Mica has been added to enhance the dielectric properties of the finished product, as has silica gel (415, 1612). The machinability of products in which mica has been used is poor, and the silica gel would probably reduce the hardness of the finished product.

Antimony trioxide is used to increase the fire resistance of general-purpose polyester resins. It also imparts opacity, increases softness, and may change the cure characteristics of the resin. Most commercial fire-resistant polyester resins, however, are made by a change of ingredients in the original mix; for example, in some resins chlorinated phthalic anhydride is substituted in equal proportions for phthalic anhydride. Recently, fire-resistant resins were developed by the Hooker Electrochemical Co. in which hexachloroendomethylene tetrahydrophthalic acid is the key ingredient (p. 000).

Metallic powders or foils may be used to give interesting effects, add weight to bases, or provide additional decorative aspects (1699). Since this type of filler is generally incompatible with the resin, it will settle in the product, which may be desirable in some cases where base weight is desired, but undesirable in others. Adhesion difficulties resulting in delamination in the product may result from the use of metallic foils.

V. SHAPING

The fabrication or shaping of polyester resins into final products differs somewhat from fabrication of other thermosetting resins in that little, and sometimes no, pressure may be used. Low-pressure molding and laminating are possible because no by-products that must be enclosed are formed during the cure of the resins.

Tooling costs for the low-pressure fabrication processes used for polyesters are considerably lower than those for high-pressure processes. It was this possibility for a very low capital investment that initially stimulated the entry of many small operators into the polyester field. The resultant sharp competition and insufficient capitalization and facilities contributed to the drop in polyester sales that followed World War II (p. 194). Even in 1954, the industry was still made up of nearly 200 fabricators and molders, dividing up a market of approximately $45 million. Fewer than a dozen of these companies had sales of more than a million dollars (1978).

Steps are being taken, however, to eliminate the main industrial weakness of polyester fabrication—the absence of a mass production technique. The present trend is toward larger installations, preferably continuous operation, and high-pressure presses to obtain parts which need few finishing operations. The introduction of preimpregnated polyester-glass fiber molding and laminating materials (p. 112) eliminates separate handling of the glass and resin, and thus a good part of the handwork involved in polyester fabricating processes.

Since little or no heat is necessary in most cases for curing polyester resins, they have been used widely for one-piece molding of large objects that are not easily made from other plastics. Polyester resin-filler combinations are also adaptable for most standard molding and laminating procedures.

Subjects covered in this chapter are: molds and mold making; methods of molding and laminating; preforming; casting; and postforming; including examples, equipment, and production variables. The fabrication of honeycombs and foamed plastics is also included.

MOLDS AND MOLDMAKING

Mold Cost and Materials

One of the principal advantages derived from the low pressure and temperature necessary to shape polyester resins is the low mold cost.

The cost is lower because molds may be made from less expensive material than molds for high-pressure work (although polished steel molds may be used economically for large-volume production). Polyester resin laminates have therefore been used widely in molding of large articles in low volume. In this field the low tooling expense offsets the relatively high material cost and provides a saving over the high tooling expense necessary for other materials (1996). This saving is particularly great when the object to be fabricated is curved in more than one direction. When this is the case, polyester laminates are cheaper than steel of the same strength, unless the cost of dies for fabricating steel can be distributed over a long run, say, of more than 20,000 items.

Molds for reinforced polyester resins may be constructed from wood, plaster, plastics, or metal, depending on the size, shape, and number of the articles to be molded and the molding operation to be used. For some purposes flexible molds have been used (1738).

The reinforced plastics industry has recognized that reinforced plastics themselves offer many advantages as tooling materials (1725). These advantages include not only cost reduction, but wear resistance, reduction in weight, and ease of manufacture and repair. Laminators and molders are using molds and dies, as well as trim and check fixtures, drill jigs, assembly jigs, and other special tools, made from reinforced polyesters in increasing volume for fabricating their own polyester products.

For long-production runs, metal dies are generally used. The lower end cost of quantity-produced items will usually make up for the higher tooling cost.

A general discussion of mold making is given by D. A. Dearle (1720). Some factors affecting mold designs are discussed by W. V. Prince (1734, 1735). Examples of molds that may be applicable to polyester resin fabrication are given in references (435, 437, 445, 446).

Master Patterns and Matrices

The first step in the fabrication of a mold is the construction of a "master" pattern. The pattern can be made of many materials, but usually wood, plaster, plastic, or metal is used (1721, 1741). After it is shaped accurately, the pattern is finished, smoothed, and its surface treated with a sealing agent, such as waxes or various resins (p. 113), to reduce porosity. The sealing treatment is particularly necessary for patterns made of wood or plaster; plastic molds usually need no surface sealer (1741). The master pattern is usually a male mold (1716).

Before the master mold is used to make other molds, its surface is coated with a mold release agent. The materials which may be used for this purpose include waxes (1732), vaseline, light lubricating oils, stearic acid mixed with kerosene, or lard oil if plaster molds are to be made (1741); polyvinyl alcohol is often used for releasing plastic molds (1716). Other mold release agents are discussed on page 113.

One-piece molds can be made directly from the master mold by building up plaster or reinforced plastics over it.

Plaster castings may be reinforced with hemp fibers, metal, or wood bars (1741).

If reinforced plastics are used, a thin layer of quick-setting resin is first applied to the pattern to provide a smooth finish on the final laminate. A resin for this purpose is described by J. J. Coleman (1718). Glass cloth reinforcement is then applied over the surface coat, impregnated with resin by brushing or spraying (wet lay-up can also be used), and allowed to cure.

Glass mat may also be used as a reinforcing material in making one-piece molds, such as those used for boat manufacture. The process is the same as that used with glass cloth—a male master is made (usually of wood) and the female mold of mat reinforced polyester is taken from it. The mold is then polished smooth (1711).

Matrices are a sort of intermediate pattern used in preparing both one- and two-piece molds. They usually duplicate the master pattern or the dimensions of the part to be molded. Matrices may be made of plaster (1716, 1729) or reinforced plastics (1724, 1732). Before the master pattern is used to make a matrix, it should be coated with a mold-release agent, as is done in making molds directly from the pattern.

A matrix for a one-piece model can be made by "splashing" plaster directly on the master mold, allowing the plaster to set, and removing the cast. A reinforced plastic "splash" can also be made by applying glass fabric saturated with catalyzed resin to the master layer by layer until sufficient thickness is built up. Final molds can be made directly from the "splash." A more complicated but more accurate method, however, uses a female "splash" obtained from a male master to prepare a reinforced plastic male matrix (1724). This matrix is a precise duplication of the master mold and is used for making the final female mold.

When male and female molds are prepared, the plastic or plaster matrix is built up over the male mold to the thickness of the part to be molded (1716, 1732). In preparing a reinforced plastic matrix, care must be taken to exclude air from between the plies and to finish the lay-up before the resin gels, in order to stay within the accepted tolerances for the molded part (1732). When the matrix has set or cured, its surface is sanded smooth and a parting agent is applied. More plaster or layers of resin-saturated glass cloth are then built up to the desired thickness on the matrix to form the female mold section.

Polyester resins reinforced with clay and chopped glass have been used for small development molds in research on plastic items (1716). A wooden box or flask is placed around the pattern, which also may serve as a male mold during molding. Copper tubes for heating are bent to the shape of the pattern and suspended around it in the flask. The reinforced plastic mixture is poured in until the flask is filled and allowed to harden. Air pockets found on the mold surface can be filled with an epoxy resin-clay mixture, and the surface sanded smooth.

Metalized Molds

Metalized molds are used in production where the size and number of parts to be made are sufficiently large to justify this expense. For example, radomes are shaped in metalized molds. There are two methods of making these molds: electrodeposition and metal spraying. At present, spraying is more widely used.

Electrodeposition. In the electrodeposition method, a female plaster "splash" is taken from the master, and a matrix (male) of reinforced plastic (polyester or phenolic) is made from the plaster "splash." The matrix is lowered into the electroplating bath. Nickel, copper, or iron may be used for plating. Nickel gives the greatest strength, and therefore is used for larger parts. After a suitable thickness of metal has deposited [from $\frac{1}{4}$ to $\frac{1}{2}$ inch in most cases (1723)], the matrix and metal mold are removed together, the metal mold is reinforced and mounted on a frame, and the matrix is removed. The metal female mold may then be finished by buffing to a high gloss (1733).

A male metal mold may be made by using a male plaster "splash," taken from the female "splash," to make a female plastic matrix which can be metalized.

Metal Spray. Metal-spray molds, which were more recently developed for polyesters (1723), have been used mainly in making large-area moldings. In this method a female "splash" is taken from the male master. Reinforced polyesters are used for the "splash" if a large-size mold is to be made (1724); a plaster "splash" may be used for small molds (1716). The "splash" is coated with a separating agent, and a male reinforced polyester matrix is made from it. The male matrix is reinforced with metal framework. Its surface is sanded smooth, all pinholes are removed and refilled, and a coat of primer is applied to prevent volatilization during the spray process.

Metal is sprayed on the surface of the matrix rapidly to prevent overheating; one side of the mold may be allowed to cool while the other is being sprayed. Several metals may be applied during the spraying process. For example, zinc can be applied first to give heat protection and low shrinkage; aluminum next, followed by Metco Spramold[1] wire, which is a very dense metal, to seal the porous aluminum, and finally a bronze spray to give rigidity and density.

After the spraying process the mold may be backed up with layers of glass cloth reinforced polyester and an iron framework. It is then removed from the matrix. As a final step the surface is polished to a high gloss.

Sprayed metal molds may be made in male and female pairs and used in compression molding in some cases (1716). They have the advantages of a high-luster mold surface, fast and even heat transfer, and comparatively low cost. They are considered permanent molds and require little maintenance (1716).

Metal Molds

When low-pressure lamination was originated, emphasis was placed on low-cost tooling. As production volume increased, however, more expensive tooling proved necessary in order to maintain quality, as well as economical when end costs were considered. According to W. B. Goldsworthy, cheaper plastic or plaster tooling is adequate for short runs, but metal should be used for large-production dies (1723). [Reinforced plastics should not be discounted entirely. Reinforced polyester dies used for cutting and molding steel take a terrific beating, yet stand up well (1710). In the automotive industry, reinforced plastic tooling has won wide acceptance (1710, 1726). Die runs of over 20,000 parts at more than 300 per hour have been made.]

Metals and Alloys. Various metals and alloys have been used for dies, including aluminum, Meehanite and other steel alloys, and Kirksite, a zinc base alloy. Kirksite can be hobbed or cast and lends itself to low-cost tooling for low-volume production (1737). It does not meet all the requirements, however, for the positive-pressure dies used in large-scale production.

Cast aluminum dies are used for large reinforced plastic parts, such as automobile bodies, aircraft wing sections, radomes, and large tanks (1719). Aluminum sheet dies have also been made (436). The recommendation has been made, however, that aluminum dies be used only for low-volume production or for experimental work (1740). Aluminum has the disadvantage of being very porous, and surfaces of articles molded with aluminum dies are fairly rough (1740). Finishing of articles molded in such dies is likely to be expensive unless a suitable surface coating can be applied.

For large-scale production of reinforced polyester items, positive-pressure matched metal dies are used. These dies are generally made of

---

[1]Trade name of Metallizing Engineering Co., Long Island, N. Y.

steel, nickel iron castings, Meehanite, or chill-cast iron. They may be cast or a plate may be used (1736). Various types of steel for use in dies are discussed by O. Mirt and by G. B. Thayer (1730, 1739). The advantages and disadvantages of matched metal dies are discussed on pages 111–112.

Die Making. Matched metal dies are machined so that they hold the molding material in the desired thickness of the molded part at all points. Any projection or reinforcing ribs are machined exactly in the dies. Positive pressure means that the dies are constructed so that the plastic is confined within the dies and is under the full pressure of the press throughout the cure (1731, 1988). This type of die must telescope, one inside the other, with a minimum clearance between the upper and lower dies. This is in contrast to flash types of molds, which are made with stops or lands that absorb part of the pressure. In order to maintain pressure on the plastic, the mold must be overcharged. Excess material is "flashed" out when pressure is applied (1988).

Three methods of forming positive-pressure matched metal dies are: casting, "coring" or machining of the cavity (1736), and hobbing, which involves pressing out the cavity in a soft metal block or sheet with a hardened steel master and subsequently hardening the cavity (1737). The dies are generally made with flame-hardened pinch-offs (sealing points) and case-hardened guide pins and bushings (1731). The die surfaces can be polished and chrome plated if desired (1740). A wet-blasting technique was recently developed that is said to save costs involved in manual polishing of dies (1706).

HEATING EQUIPMENT AND METHODS

Three basic types of heating which may be used during molding operations are: heated air (gas-fired heating), electric, and circulating hot liquid or vapor (1746).

Gas-Fired Heating

Gas-fired heating is cheap to operate and only moderately expensive to install. The efficiency of the system is low, however, and temperature distribution is unequal (1752). This type of heating is therefore impractical for most molds for reinforced polyesters (1748).

Electric Heating

Electric heating systems are easy and relatively inexpensive to install. The heat applied is exactly and easily controlled, and in metal dies may be much more evenly distributed than heat supplied by gas-fired systems. Further advantages of electric heating are the possibilities of localizing heat at needed points, so that the entire room won't be heated up and become unpleasant for working, and of using separate units that may be repaired individually (1752). In dies and molds for polyesters that are not of metal, however, and even in metal dies, "hot spots" may be created by electric systems.

Many applications for electric heat exist in the molding plant in addition to heating dies. It is used for controlled heating of the oil reservoirs of the hydraulic presses, which eliminates variations in oil viscosity and flow, and consequently in press closure time (1752). Infrared ovens are used for drying glass mat, curing plastics in continuous lamination processes, drying preforms, and preheating plastics for punching or postforming operations (1752).

High-frequency heating is a fairly recent development and has not been widely used for polyesters. It depends on the fact that electrical waves or impulses impinging on a nonconducting material cause a molecular disturbance which creates heat (1756). Although a short cure time may be obtained with high-frequency heating systems (1754), they are expensive to install (1901) and have been used mostly for high-temperature preheating of preforms for compression molding (1744, 1747, 1757). High-frequency heating is further discussed by T. Hazen and by P. N. Lategan (1751, 1991).

Fluid Heating

The most important types of fluid heating are hot oil heat, hot water heat, and steam heat. Other fluids, such as molten alloys or wax, have been used, but are restricted to special uses (449). Hot oil is infrequently used because the temperatures usually necessary for molding are within the range of steam or hot water heating units.

Steam heat is widely used. The cost of installation of either a steam or hot water system is high as compared to electricity, but operating costs are lower. Both the water-based systems and the electric systems provide even heating (in metal dies), but temperatures are more difficult to vary in the water-based systems and they have less flexibility in operation (1752).

Supertherm systems (hot water circulated under pressure) are more expensive to install than steam systems, but they eliminate the corrosion difficulties associated with the condensation apparatus that is necessary with steam heat (1748). These systems are most adaptable to low-pressure molding operations where nonmetallic or sprayed metal dies or molds are used. Both steam and supertherm systems have the disadvantage of "heating the whole plant" in addition to the presses (1752).

A circulating-liquid heating medium is recommended for use in a container for heating molds (448).

PRESSES FOR MOLDING

Hydraulically operated presses are generally used in the low-pressure laminating field. They are used mainly for large production runs, with metal dies. For other types of low-pressure laminating which require no pressure or little pressure, vacuum or autoclave techniques are used.

Some hydraulic presses for low-pressure laminating are described by Brinkema and Wilkins, Hastings, Muller, and Powell (1764, 1765, 1766, 1767).

MOLDING AND LAMINATING METHODS

Low-pressure laminating and molding were first tried with phenolics, with fair success (1849), but the polyesters have somewhat overshadowed them. The polyesters give no by-products during polymerization, and are perhaps more suited to this field (1823) except in high-temperature and some specialty applications. The versatility of low-pressure molding in the different end products that can be produced has been pointed out by D. Swedlow (1892), one of the most resourceful pioneers in this field.

Fabrication processes first used for polyesters used little or no pressure. Contact pressure was considered sufficient, although higher pressures sometimes were applied (462, 1880). From the first use of the "hat-press" technique, in which a rubber plunger was used to apply pressure, the field has expanded to include many methods of laminating and molding. The methods used today include vacuum or pressure bag molding, no-pressure molding, such as the "Marco" or double-mold vacuum injection process, progressive or single mold lamination, continuous lamination, conventional compression and transfer molding with chopped glass reinforced polyesters, and matched metal die molding (1580, 1842, 1859, 1884, 1891). At the present time matched metal die molding is the process most widely used for large-volume production.

Hat-Press Techniques

The hat-press process, which was adopted from the felt hat industry, utilizes a metal female mold and a rubber plunger to apply pressure (1868, 1873, 1894). It was one of the first methods used to shape polyesters. Now, however, matched metal positive-pressure dies are chosen more frequently than the hat-press technique, because they produce a more desirable product and are better suited to production molding. The hat-press method utilizes inexpensive equipment, and the articles produced are satisfactory for many uses (1899). Glass mat or cloth is usually used as reinforcing material. The previously catalyzed resin is applied to the reinforcement during the lay-up, with any additional filler if desired. In another type of lay-up wet resin-impregnated fillers are used.

The plunger is lowered, and the pressure is then applied. Cure time may be varied by varying the heat, pressure, and catalyst.

One item made by this method is a bread tray cover. The lay-up for the cover, either wet or dry, is stamped to a metal strengthening frame. The assembly is then placed over a rubber plug and into a metal die, and cured at 250° F. and a pressure of 100 pounds per square inch for 3 minutes (1845).

Bag Molding

Bag molding is a process in which a flexible bag or blanket is used to apply pressure against a lay-up while it cures. A single mold, either male or female, is used. This method is useful for items of relatively large area but not too complex shape (1830). Low-cost tooling is used. Bag molding is therefore widely used for low-volume production, where a very smooth surface is not required (1607).

Bag molding can be divided into two types: vacuum bag molding and pressure bag molding. In vacuum bag molding, the bag or blanket is pulled over the lay-up in the mold and clamped down, and the air is evacuated from between the bag and the mold. Atmospheric pressure on the bag presses it down against the lay-up. In pressure bag molding, additional pressure is applied to the bag, either by placing a pressure plate over the mold to make an air-tight enclosure and admitting pressure or by placing the assembly in an autoclave (1858). Stronger molds are required for pressure bag molding.

Bag molding can be applied equally well to parts cured at room temperature or at higher temperatures (1858). Heat cures can be obtained by placing the complete lay-up in an oven or autoclave, equipping the mold with heating facilities, such as steam pipes or electric blankets, or using heat lamps or heating blankets on the bag side of the lay-up.

Either wet or dry lay-up can be used. In the wet method, resin-saturated reinforcement is laid-up on the mold. In the dry method the reinforcement is laid-up dry, then saturated with resin. Presaturated reinforcement can also be used (p. 112). In pressure bag molding, make-up can be facilitated by making the lay-up on a light mold, allowing it to gel, and transferring it to a heavy mold for cure (443).

Materials used for bags include cellophane, polyvinyl alcohol, polyvinyl chloride, and neoprene and other rubbers. Polyvinyl chloride is the most widely used material in the vacuum bag molding field. Neoprene is recommended for pressure bag molding if steam is used for both pressure and heat. Inhibition of the cure of polyester resins by neoprene can be prevented by placing a cellophane sheet as a barrier between the neoprene and the lay-up or by hand rubbing the neoprene with a silicone grease. If air pressure is used with heated molds, specially compounded rubbers should be used rather than neoprene, which ages rapidly and becomes brittle (1858).

Several molds designed for bag molding are described in references (436, 438, 443).

Continuous Lamination

Flat sheets and reinforced pipe are made by the continuous lamination process. This process offers the highest speed of production.

Flat Sheets. The production of flat sheets by continuous laminating actually involves several operations performed essentially as one continuous operation: (1) application of resin to the reinforcing material, (2) combining of resin-impregnated reinforcing material into a laminate, and (3) curing of the laminate under heat and pressure (1863).

The webs of reinforcing material can be impregnated by passing them through a tank of low-viscosity resin and squeezing off the excess resin. Some reinforcing materials such as dense paper or closely woven fabrics are difficult to saturate by this method. These materials can be coated with sufficient high-viscosity resin for saturation and then stored in roll form until saturation is complete (1863).

Several resin-impregnated webs are passed between two rolls to laminate them into a single sheet. The gap between the rolls determines the final thickness of laminate produced (1863). As the laminates emerge from the rolls, it is encased, top and bottom, with cellophane sheets in order to exclude air and prevent surface tackiness. The cellophane-encased laminate is then carried to the heating section of the laminator for cure.

The contraction of the cellophane during heating provides lateral pressure on the laminate. Longitudinal pressure may be supplied by running the rolls at each end of the heating oven at different speeds (1870). Pressure may also be supplied during the heating cycle by moving steel belts which clamp and press down on the web (461), as in the Rotocure[2] machines (1793).

A continuous-lamination apparatus has been described that uses hydrostatic pressure to cure insulating covering for wire (453).

In continuous lamination, it is necessary to use a resin with a short pot life and a low exotherm for accurate control of the process (1842). The process is economical for high-volume but not low-volume production. It can be used to produce thin laminates that are not economically feasible by any other method, but thick laminates are not practical in any reasonable length of machine (1863).

[2]Trade name of Boston Woven Hose & Rubber Co.

Reinforced Pipe. Reinforced polyester pipe is currently made by an essentially continuous process (1791, 1809). All operations occur in sequence on a rotating mandrel that moves vertically in the plant building. The fabrication apparatus requires a tower about 75 feet high (1862).

In the first step of the pipe-making operation, one or more thicknesses of glass fiber tape, made from 10-mil surfacing mat bonded together with 22 roving ends per inch, are passed through a resin bath and spirally wound on the mandrel at an angle. Three layers of resin impregnated rovings are applied next: The first and second layers are spirally wound on the mandrel, the first layer in the same direction as the surfacing layer and the second layer in the opposite direction. In the third layer equally spaced strands are applied parallel to the axis of the mandrel. Next, two thicknesses of glass fiber tape are spirally wound under tension to squeeze out excess resin. [Preimpregnated glass fiber materials (p. 112) can also be used in this process (1907).] A double layer of cellophane is then applied under tension, and the lay-up is cured to the gel state. The pipe is removed from the mandrel in this state and heated in an oven to full cure.

Polyester pipe has been made in lengths up to 20 feet by this process, and in diameters up to 12 inches, although most commercial pipe is from 2 to 6 inches in internal diameter (1791, 1809).

A method developed in Sweden permits continuous production of polyester pipe of unlimited length and without seams. The equipment is relatively simple and inexpensive. Although the method was developed primarily for small-diameter pipe, it should be applicable to large-diameter pipe as well. A Swedish-developed polyester resin that is not inhibited by air is used in the process, which eliminates the need for cellophane or other air-excluding materials.

Centrifugal casting and extrusion have also been used to fabricate pipe, although neither method has proven as satisfactory as the mandrel wrapping method. Pipe made by centrifugal casting has been successfully used for gasoline distribution. Pipe 7 inches in diameter in 10-foot lengths for pressures up to 700 pounds has been made by the extrusion method (1862). Reinforced plastic raw stock of tube, bar, angle, channel, and other structural shapes can be produced on a single "continuous extrusion" machine which permits quick changeovers from one cross-sectional shape to another. The production of raw stock by this machine is also believed to be applicable to pipe manufacture (1847). Reinforced plastics shaped in this machine are cured by radio-frequency heating.

Ducting is made on a machine similar to cable wrapping machines in which glass tape is wound around a mandrel by a rotating creel (450, 451). The number of bobbins holding the tape on the creel, and thus the thickness of the part, can be varied. Two contrarotating creels provide for winding in opposite directions for strength (1852).

Compression and Transfer Molding

In compression molding, the molding material is charged directly into the heated mold cavity, the mold is closed, and pressure is applied. In transfer molding, the molding material is heated in a separate pressure chamber and forced into the closed, heated mold. Transfer molding, which is the newer method, is also called closed-mold or plunger molding. Further descriptions of these methods are given by Borro, Donohue, Hantz, and Otero (1826, 1839, 1848, 1871).

Until recently, polyester resins were not used in these processes. The materials most commonly used were thermoplastics and the thermosetting phenolics, melamines, and ureas, which require high pressure during molding in order to retain volatile by-products in the polymerization product. The polyesters give off no by-products, with the exception of some styrene vapors, during polymerization. In addition, the glass fiber reinforcement commonly used with polyesters is difficult to use successfully at high pressures (1900).

To enable fabricators to use standard molding equipment for polyesters, new glass-polyester molding compounds have been developed that may be compression or transfer molded. These compounds are mixtures of chopped glass fibers, usually ¼ to ¾ inch long, polyester resins, and inert mineral fillers (1799, 1838, 1860, 1883, 1900). The chopped fibers used may be material that would otherwise be scrap, such as chopped glass cloth or glass mat left as trimmings from laminating operations. Most commercially available premixes, however, contain chopped rovings. For optimum strength and water resistance, the fillers and glass fibers used should be sized, for example, by a vapor-phase treatment with vinyl trichlorosilane (p. 86).

Resins cross-linked with diallyl or polyallyl esters, such as diallyl phthalate, diallyl diglycol carbonate, or triallyl cyanurate, are used more commonly than resins cross-linked with styrene, which has a low boiling point. The fact that no volatile by-products are produced in polymerization of polyester molding compounds has proved to be an advantage in closed molds, because blistering and gassing is avoided (1770).

The glass-polyester premixes tend to fall into two general classes: the putty type, which has a low glass content (under 20%), and the straw type, which has a high glass content (over 20%). The low glass mixes generally are less expensive, give less trouble with cracking during rapid curing, but may give more trouble with flow into complex shapes. They have lower physical properties but tend to have excellent dimensional, electrical, and chemical stability. The high glass mixes are generally much more difficult to handle in preforming and molding and may yield erratic results, but they give outstanding physical properties. Parts molded from premixes have extraordinary impact resistance, although contrary to general opinion, they are not high in tensile strength (1900).

One of the major problems in the use of glass-polyester premixes is the tendency toward strongly directional fiber orientation due to the flow characteristics of the mix (1883, 1900). Random orientation of the fibers is particularly difficult to obtain in transfer molding (1878). The flow characteristics of the mix are also an important factor in producing undesirable resin-rich areas in which there is little or no glass present. The straw-type mixes offer an advantage here, since in loading the glass is well distributed throughout the mold cavity, due to the large bulk factor of these mixes. When the piece is molded, very little flow is required to produce uniform distribution of the mix in the mold (1883).

High-glass mixes are usually formed into a loose wad, ball, or other preform shape by hand and placed in the mold cavity. Low-glass mixes are more commonly used in the form of extruded rope, sausages, or slugs. Pressures used in compression molding of premixes are relatively low; usually 500 to 2,000 pounds per square inch is adequate (1900). Much higher pressures are used in transfer molding, with usual values being 6,000 to 8,000 pounds per square inch (1878).

No-Pressure Molding

In no-pressure (or contact-pressure) molding of reinforced polyester parts, glass cloth or mat is laid up in layers on a mold, impregnated with resin, and cured at room temperature using a special catalyst system but no external pressure. No-pressure methods use either one mold or matched molds, depending on whether smooth surfaces are required on both sides or on one side of the part. They are best suited to making large moldings such as boats and tanks (1856, 1861) or to surfacing of reinforced polyester parts.

An important no-pressure molding method is the Marco[3] or vacuum injection process (1732, 1776, 1855). Two molds are used, with the male mold mounted in a trough and the female having one or more vacuum outlets at the top. The molds may be made of metal, plaster, or reinforced plastic, but they must be nonporous and have very smooth internal surfaces. For this reason, reinforced plastic molds are often given a sprayed-metal coating.

A dry lay-up of the reinforcing cloth or mat is made on the male mold (preforms may also be used), and the female mold is lowered over it.

[3]Trade name of Celanese Corp. of America.

Resin is placed in the trough running around the bottom of the male mold and is drawn up into the lay-up by a vacuum applied on the top. Thorough impregnation may be obtained by leveling off the vacuum periodically and allowing the resin to saturate the reinforcing material (1732). The best wetting is obtained with glass reinforcement having a vinyl silane finish. When impregnation is completed and all entrapped air is removed from the lay-up, the vacuum is turned off and the resin is allowed to set until hard.

The no-pressure methods are particularly useful in molding boats from reinforced polyesters. One-piece hulls as large as 36 feet have been made for landing craft with sheet steel molds. Buoyancy was provided by initially molding carefully sealed blocks of Styrofoam[4] into the hulls (1864). Boat hulls 24 feet long have been molded using a "one-shaft" plaster male mold only. Cure time, in this case, was accelerated by placing a box containing infrared heating elements over the lay-up (1827).

Glass fiber reinforcing with quick-curing resin has been used to patch boat hulls and to make them impervious to water. A no-pressure process is used: The glass cloth is placed over the sanded hull, to which a coat of resin has been applied, more resin is brushed on, and the smoothed surface is allowed to cure (1801).

Automobile bodies for sports cars have been molded using a plaster male mold and a reinforced polyester female mold. Curing time is speeded by the use of infrared heating (1772). No-pressure molding is suitable for low-volume sport car production where the higher operational and raw material costs are offset by the lower tooling cost, as compared to costs for production of the same parts from steel (1818).

Oil transport tanks have been molded using only a wooden master male mold. The tanks are made in partially cured halves, which are then joined together, and the whole assembly is cured by blowing steam into the tank (1773).

The no-pressure methods have certain disadvantages which limit their applications (1855, 1861). The chief disadvantage is the time required to lay-up and mold each part. This is the primary factor which prevents their effective use in large-scale production. Although tooling costs are low, the higher labor costs involved in no-pressure molding may cause over-all costs to be excessive. Another important disadvantage is the difficulty in obtaining a high resin-to-glass ratio, which means lower mechanical strength.

Positive-Pressure Molding With Matched Metal Dies

Positive-pressure molding with matched metal dies is used especially for the production of reinforced polyester items for the consumer field.

[4]Dow Chemical Co. trade name.

The dies used are generally of steel and therefore expensive. The presses used are hydraulically operated.

The glass fiber reinforcement, usually in the form of mat or preforms, is placed in the dies, a weighed amount of resin is introduced, and the dies are closed. The closure is in three stages: (1) a fast approach at a speed of about 300 feet per minute; (2) as the dies approach each other, a slow down to about 30 feet per minute to let entrapped air escape from the mold; and (3) approximately 1 inch before final closure of the die, a slow down to under 5 inches per minute to permit the resin to saturate the reinforcement. At stage (3), the mold also pinch-trims the part. After the dies are closed a predetermined pressure is built up (usually from 100 to 200 pounds per square inch), and the part is cured. The die is then rapidly opened and the part removed (1767).

Advantages. The advantages of positive-pressure molding with matched metal dies are:

(1) Vaporization of the styrene is reduced, which in turn reduces the amount of blistered and pitted areas. Furthermore, because the styrene cannot escape, it is forced to polymerize and copolymerize with the polyester, creating a larger molecule and increasing the strength of the part.

(2) With the proper resin amount and distribution the entrapped air is forced out by the closing cycle of the press, eliminating surface pinholes and bubbles.

(3) Filled resins are more easily hardened by this method, because the high pressure forces viscous materials to spread more easily.

(4) Higher pressures transfer heat more rapidly because of better contact. This reduces curing time and speeds production.

(5) Surface shrinkage is reduced, so that the surface fiber pattern so evident on parts molded by other methods is minimized. Metal die surfaces are accurately reproduced, making any type of finish desired possible.

(6) The dies are easily cleaned, and their highly polished surfaces need only infrequent application of a parting agent, if at all (1731).

Disadvantages. Disadvantages of positive-pressure molding with matched metal dies are:

(1) The cost is high, because construction of the dies is expensive, and corrections in them are difficult and expensive to make. This molding operation can therefore only be used on parts in large-volume production and not for experimental operation. It is estimated that for one part 500 moldings must be made to make this process economical (1862).

(2) No undercuts can be molded because moving parts in the dies have not been found practical.

(3) Presses to handle these dies must of necessity be heavy and strong, and thus are expensive (1731).

Glass Reinforcement. Glass mat or preforms used with matched metal dies should be strongly bonded. Further, the thickness and fiber distribution should be very even, with no thick or thin sections. Uneven fiber distribution can cause crushing of fibers, as well as warping of the molded part due to variation in resin shrinkage (1731).

Glass mat reinforcement is recommended for forming simple shapes, such as shallow draw parts. Flat mat can be readily tailored with little waste to conform with the part contour and at less cost than preforming. Preform molding, on the other hand, is recommended for making complex, deep-draw parts. Material waste and labor costs are considerably lower than those inherent in tailoring mats to suit intricate shapes. In addition, the preformed part has a more uniform surface finish and appearance (1844).

Preimpregnated glass fiber materials are widely used in matched metal die molding, as well as other molding processes. These materials, which are commonly called prepreg, are a combination of resin and glass cloth or mat purchased in catalyzed, ready-to-use sheet rolls. Prepreg can be laid-up directly on the mold or made into preforms. Polyester resins, including both styrene and diallyl phthalate copolymers, are used to a great extent in prepreg; the ones containing no styrene are the most stable and widely accepted (1907).

Prepreg is characterized by the following properties (1846):

(1) It is relatively dry or has a slight tack so that it does not readily adhere to the hand but does adhere to itself.

(2) It is stable in that it can be stored for practical periods (over 3 to 6 months) at room temperature (approximately $70°$ F.).

(3) The resin will flow and cure under heat and minimum pressure to produce a good laminate.

High-grade prepreg is thoroughly predried just before impregnation, which improves wetting of the fibers and is generally reflected in better properties (1907). Since resin distribution and resin content can be closely controlled, the danger of resin-rich or resin-starved areas is eliminated and quality control of the products is made easier. With prepreg, irregular shapes, build-ups, and varying thicknesses can be readily attained because the material can be cut with accuracy, with nonraveling edges, and placed where desired (1846, 1907).

Prepreg material impregnated with a partially cured resin could probably be fed continuously into heated stamping and drawing presses like those used for sheet metal. Such mechanization of fabrication processes would place reinforced polyesters on a more even footing for competition with sheet steel.

Prepreg costs more than other molding materials, although this disadvantage may be offset by labor and other savings (1907). Another disadvantage is the difficulty in removing air entrapped in the glass cloth during prepreg preparation. The resin in prepreg does not become sufficiently liquid upon heating in the mold nor does it move enough to allow air to escape. Vents are therefore often necessary on molds to prevent air locks (1846, 1906). In addition, it is difficult to use pinch-off dies with prepreg (1846).

Preimpregnated, ready-to-mold reinforced sheet produced by bonding together individual thin plies of unidirectional glass fiber filaments encased in resin (epoxy or polyester) has been developed (3221). This material permits controlled alinement of the reinforcing filaments, making possible controlled directional strength.

Other Types of Dies. A less expensive type of matched metal dies is useful when the number of items needed is not large, but surface finish and part tolerances (in dimensions) are important. Cheaper metals, such as aluminum or Kirksite, may be used, and presses are not essential but may be used. The lay-up is done by hand or by preforming. The resin is applied, the molds are closed and heated, and the parts are removed after cure. Pressures on the part in molding with nonsteel dies are usually under 100 pounds per square inch. For example, helicopter rotor blades have been molded with cast Kirksite matched dies in a clamped set-up at a pressure of 50 to 75 pounds per square inch (1898). Ammunition boxes have also been made by a similar process using aluminum molds heated to 275° F.; the part is cured at a pressure of 80 pounds per square inch for 4 to 10 minutes (1879).

Other processes that use metal molds and that might be applicable to polyesters are described in references (457, 459, 464).

Mold Release Agents

Polyester resins have a tendency to stick to surfaces unless they are perfectly smooth. Even then certain shapes are difficult to separate from the molds. Application of a mold release or parting agent to molds is therefore generally required in polyester molding.

Parting agents should be inexpensive, easily handled, heat stable over the molding temperature range, resistant to oxidation, aging, and decomposition, and inert to both the mold material and resins. They should wet and adhere to the mold surface, and should decrease the friction between the mold and molded part (1856).

If the mold surfaces are porous, as in the case of plaster, wood, and some metal molds, a sealer must be applied before the parting agent. Furane, phenolic, and urea resins, waxes, and modified styrene have been used (1856, 1857). Lacquers, shellac, and varnish also have been used, but are not dependable because they are likely to be vulnerable to the solvent action of the resin or the heat of cure.

Classes. Mold release agents may be divided into four general classes: films, film-forming solutions or emulsions, waxes, and lubricants. Films commonly used are cellophane, vinyl films in the form of polyvinyl alcohol or polyvinyl chloride-acetate combinations, and glassine paper. These are useful only if no complex shapes are involved, since they wrinkle if they are applied over a multicurved surface (1856). Film formers used include alginates, cellulose derivatives such as methyl cellulose and cellulose acetate, and polyvinyl alcohol solutions. Such waxes as carnauba and candelilla may be used. Lubricants in common usage are sulfate esters, graphite, lecithin, alkyl phosphates, petroleum jelly, and silicones.

Oleic acid has been incorporated into polyesters, and is said to migrate to the surface, effecting mold release without affecting the cure of the resin (1856). Saran latex and some vinyl lacquers have been tried, but did not provide good mold release (1893).

When some resins are molded, two-component systems, for example, polyvinyl alcohol and cellophane, are necessary (1857).

Recommendations. One fabricator gives the following recommendations for different types of molds (1857):

(1) On polished metal matched dies used in press molding, a lubricant type agent should be applied infrequently.

(2) On a sprayed-metal mold used in bag molding, a lubricating agent is first applied, followed by a sprayed film coat. The parting system must be renewed after each molding operation.

(3) Plaster master patterns should be sealed and sanded, and a heavy coat of wax applied for parting. The coating must be renewed after each molding operation.

(4) Aluminum molds for bag molding require the application of a lubricant type of release agent after each molding.

(5) Gel-coated polyester molds and tool plastic (cast phenolics and others) molds require the combination of a lubricant and a sprayed film coating, which is renewed after each molding.

For permanent application to a separate surface, where high production is involved, a thin sprayed plastic coating of "Teflon,"[5] baked at 750° F. for a fused surface, is recommended (1936). The film formed has exceptional wear resistance, is insoluble in almost all solvents, and no ordinary resin will stick to it. Another parting agent is "Pan Glaze,"[6] a

[5] Du Pont trade name.
[6] Dow Corning trade name.

silicone varnish that is sprayed on the mold surface and baked. The film formed is not so tough or so thick as that of Teflon but is satisfactory for ordinary purposes (1936).

A test has been described for evaluating mold release agents in which a measurement of the force necessary to remove a part from a mold is used as a criterion (1909).

Variables in Molding

The effects of humidity during fabrication on the flexural strength and other physical properties of glass fabric-polyester laminates were evaluated by J. E. Wier et al. (1903, 1904). These effects were pronounced at molding temperatures above 160° F. The finish on the glass fabric was 114 finish, however; newer types of sizes and finishes have greatly increased the moisture resistance of reinforced plastics.

The laminating pressure has little effect on the physical properties of laminates made in positive-pressure dies. An increase in pressure may aid in void removal, especially in open mold operation. Care should be taken not to force an excess of the resin out of the laminate. An increase in pressure decreases the cure time (1902).

Cure times are variable, and depend on the catalyst, filler, and resin used and the molding pressure and temperature. Plant operational cure times are usually established by trial and error.

An attempt has been made to standardize the terminology used for defects in molded parts. This work is summarized in references (1833, 1889).

PREFORMING

Three major types of preforming are used in the plastics industry today; they may be called "pellet," "pulp," and "dry" preforming.

Pellet preforming is used mostly with molding powders, but polyester molding compounds might be used. The molding powders are weighed and shaped into solid rectangular, cylindrical, or oval pellets. The pellet preforms are preheated by high-frequency, infrared, or other methods, and molded by compression or transfer molding techniques (1747, 1754, 1826, 1839, 1927).

Pulp or "slush" preforming has been used extensively for paper reinforced thermosetting resins (1917). In this method a slurry is made of the resin and the reinforcing material; the viscosity of the slurry is controlled by varying the concentration of the two ingredients. One or more preform screens are suspended on one end of a hollow dipping arm; the other end of the arm has a trap and return for the excess resin and a vacuum outlet. The screen is dipped into the slurry, and the vacuum pulls the resin-fiber mixture against the screen. The thickness of the preform can be controlled by the amount of the vacuum, the viscosity of the slurry and the concentration of resin in it, the type of filler, and the time of immersion (1924). Polyester and allyl resins have been suggested for preforming by this method (1925), but the bulk of the preforming for polyester molding is done by the dry process.

Dry or "loose fiber flock" preforming is a technique used for many years in the felt hat industry. The process consists basically of depositing loose fibers on a screen by means of suction. The fibers are built up to a predetermined thickness or weight, held together by a binder. After the binder is cured, the preform unit is removed from the screen and molded, usually in a positive-pressure molding operation (1911).

Preforming for Polyester Molding

Three glass fiber preforming processes are used in polyester resin molding: the tailored mat, open-air, and closed-chamber processes.

Tailored Mat Preforming. Tailored mat or hand-made preforms are made by wrapping a frame with mat and stapling the mat in place. The mat may be tailored (or trimmed) either before or after stapling. This process is useful for products in which frames or staples are allowed (1919). It is slow, however, and uses much glass.

Open-Air Preforming. Open-air preforming is accomplished by spraying cut glass fibers on a rotating screen while applying a binder. The glass fibers are cut by feeding rovings into a cutter, and are air-blown onto the screen. This operation requires good coordination on the part of the operator. It is particularly adaptable to building up fibers in a part with square corners, or where the wall thickness is to vary, or where inserts are to be used. This process is more variable than machine-controlled preforming, although weight variations on the preform may be held within 10% (1919).

Closed-Chamber Preforming. Closed-chamber preforming is done on a machine basically similar to those used in the felt hat industry. This machine consists of the following parts: (1) a cutter that chops the glass fibers into predetermined lengths; (2) a suction chamber to draw the fibers out onto the preform screen; (3) a turntable, which is usually tilted for more even fiber distribution and which has a preform screen on top; and (4) a system for applying a powdered or a liquid binder to the preform (1920).

In operation this machine draws air in from the top; the air picks up the loose fibers fed into the air stream by the cutter, and deposits them on the screen. The binder is applied, the screen and preform are removed to an oven·to cure the binder, and the screen is then removed from the preform. The preform is placed in a positive-pressure mold, the resin applied, and the part molded (1569).

A basically similar machine that is entirely automatic in operation was developed recently. This machine uses recirculated heated air. It has cycle timers that (1) delay the cycle after the removal of each preform until the chamber comes to the required temperature, (2) start the flow and control the amount of glass fibers, (3) delay the flow of binder until a layer of fiber has been applied to the screen, (4) control the amount of binder applied, and (5) provide time for curing the binder (1922).

Advantages of loose fiber preforming over other methods of lay-up are: (1) lower material costs, since this method uses the glass fibers in a basic form; (2) elimination of tailoring; (3) mechanical control for high-speed production; (4) possibility of planning and controlling variations in wall thicknesses; (5) easy loading of molds; (6) less scrap loss; and (7) possibility of reclaiming rejected preforms (1920).

Preforming Variables

Variables associated with preforming and molding with preforms are the type, amount and distribution, and cure of the binder; the texture and amount and distribution of the fibers in the preform; the type of resin and the type and amount of catalyst and pigmentation used in it; and the press used (1915).

Binder. Both liquid and powdered binders are used in preforming. Liquid binders are more easily distributed on the preform than the powdered variety (1921). Binders in common usage are water emulsions of liquid polyesters (1923), polystyrene emulsions, which may be used in conjunction with a urea-formaldehyde binder (1920), and polyester powders (1920, 1922). Other binders not so commonly used are phenol-formaldehyde, urea-formaldehyde, and starch binders; the first gives a dark color to the molding; the second has poor water resistance; and the third has a tendency to produce lumpy preforms (1920).

Variations in the amount of binder may cause a difference in fiber emphasis great enough to change the color of the molding. Variations in binder distribution may cause areas of high and low fiber emphasis leading to moldings of nonuniform appearance (1915). Insufficient binder may also cause fiber washing, resulting in moldings of uneven appearance and strength. Automatic control over the amount of binder and proper selection of the type of binder may be sufficient to control these variables (1915).

Cure of the binder is controlled by oven cycle. One advantage of the automatic preforming machine is that the binder is cured in the preforming operation, eliminating one handling operation and reducing the number of screens necessary for production (1922).

An increase in flexural strength of 100% was obtained in test polyester-glass laminates made from glass fibers treated with a binder as they were freshly formed and in a nascent state of reactivity (1926). The increase in strength was attributed to improved adhesion between the glass fibers and the adjacent plastic. Epoxy resin binders were used in these experiments.

Fibers. Accurate control over the fibers is a must for production preforming. Important variables to be controlled are the texture, length, weight, and distribution of the fibers.

Texture. The texture of the fibers must be uniform, to avoid wrinkles in the molded part (1915). If the fibers are too soft, it is difficult to collect them properly on the screen. This variable may be controlled, if necessary, by installing a beater after the fiber chopper to condition the fibers before their collection. If the texture of the fibers is too fluffy, they will "mat" on the screen, cutting down the air flow.

Length and Weight. The length of the fibers is controlled by regulating the speed of the chopper and feed (1921). An automatic variable-feed chopper, which can chop various lengths of glass, has been built for use with the automatic preform machine. For example, ½-inch glass fibers can be chopped first for a surface layer; next, 2-inch glass fibers for the body of the preform; and third, another layer of ½-inch glass fibers for the second surface. The 2-inch fibers give strength to the part, and the ½-inch fibers give better resin retention and thus help to give a smooth surface to the molded part (1922).

The weight of the fibers for each preform is controlled either by weighing the amount of fibers before chopping, or more commonly, by controlling the time of the chopping cycle.

Distribution. Even and consistent distribution of the fibers on the preform is most essential to production of parts by this method. Uneven distribution will result in variation in the wall thickness and strength (1920). Parallel orientation of the fibers on the screen may cause the fibers to "wash" or separate, resulting in uneven distribution of the filler in the molded part.

Distribution of the fibers is regulated by rotating and tilting the turntable and by controlling the amount of air flow (both the total amount and the amount passing through each part of the screen) by variations in the size and number of perforations in the screen, or by baffles. Dirty air and screens will unevenly reduce the flow of air through the screen, causing uneven distribution of fibers. Dirty air will also produce dirty preforms, and consequently a nonacceptable molded product. All air used in preforming should be filtered (1915, 1921).

Uncontrolled bulkiness of the preform will result in uneven resin penetration or wrinkled moldings. Bulk is reduced by increasing the air flow during preforming and curing of the binder, or by compression of the preform before and after curing of the binder (1921).

Resin. Variations in the cure time, catalyst concentration, and pigmentation of the resin can cause variations in the strength properties and appearance of the molded part. Since a change in any one of these usually necessitates a change in the other two, these three factors must be carefully adjusted and kept in balance by laboratory control (1915).

Press. The closing speed of the press is important. If too fast, the preform may tear or wash, the resin may be unevenly distributed, and air may be entrapped in the molding. If the closing speed is too slow, the resin may gel before the dies are closed, resulting in entrapped air, surface pinholes and other defects, and uneven distribution of the resin. The cycle must be carefully adjusted before the beginning of production, and then automatically controlled.

Fluctuation in shop temperature causes changes in the viscosity of the oil used in hydraulic presses, which in turn influences the closing speed of the press. This variable is controlled by warming the oil to a constant temperature (1915).

CASTING

Another method of shaping polyesters is casting. This operation is used particularly in the electrical industry for "potting" electrical parts such as transformers. One advantage of polyesters for this application is the contribution of these resins to the physical strength of the product. The heavy cases required with other potting media may be made lighter, or entirely eliminated.

Casting consists of pouring the resin into a mold and allowing it to harden without much external pressure. The resin should be poured down the side of the mold to the bottom, to avoid entrapping air (1929). The casting temperature is around $50°$ C. (20 to 30 minutes) followed by a postcure at $100°$ C. for at least one-half hour (1770).

Resins which have low shrinkage and a low exotherm during cure are recommended for casting in order to obtain crack-free and strain-free castings. Fillers may be incorporated in the resins, usually as short fibers or powders, to enhance the appearance or increase the strength of the part (368). An even more important function of mineral fillers is to absorb part of the heat of reaction and thus reduce the tendency for cracking. Shrinkage is also reduced (1770).

Castings produced by swelling the cast resin with a polymerizable monomer, and subsequently polymerizing the monomer, are claimed to be strain free and useful for optical glasses (495, 497).

To speed up casting operations it has been suggested that the resin be polymerized in the mold only to the gel state. As soon as the part can be removed without falling apart, it is taken from the mold and subsequently heated to achieve the desired degree of cure (492). This method is also claimed to reduce the internal strains in cast objects (496). The use of flexible molds or mold sections will help prevent cracking of the resin when it solidifies.

Potting of electrical equipment may be divided into two types: (1) the deep impregnation and embedment of parts, such as capacitors and resistors, and (2) the outer protection of coils or assemblies, which is called encapsulation (1936).

According to G. Firth, an ideal resin for impregnating of electrical equipment would have the following properties (1936):

Mixed resin

Low viscosity (below 1000 centipoises)[7]
Long pot life (more than 4 hours)[7]
Curing temperatures below 200°F.
Short cure time (2 hours or less)
Nontoxic
Good storage life
100% solids—no solvents or unreactive materials
Volume shrinkage in cure below 2%
Good wetting of surfaces and tolerance for presence of moisture
Nonhygroscopic
Adherence to material surfaces after cure

Polymerized resin

High heat distortion (above 80°C.)
Reasonably low coefficient of thermal expansion
Resistance to solvent action and absorption of common fluids
    such as alcohol, fuels, lubricants, and water
Tough enough to withstand mechanical abuse
Good power factor and dielectric strength over the ambient
    temperature range
High arc resistance

No commercially available resin meets all of these qualifications, but some can be formulated to be close.

One of the most common methods of potting is the vacuum impregnation technique. The electrical device, in a mold or permanent container such as a can or molded case, is freed from moisture by baking in an oven and then placed in a vacuum chamber to cool with the vacuum on. Dry air or gas is admitted and the resin poured into the mold. The chamber is then closed and a vacuum drawn. After all bubbling has ceased, air is admitted and the molds are placed in an oven for cure (1936).

A newer and faster method of potting uses a centrifugal spinner in which the resin-loaded devices are spun to obtain more thorough penetration (1936).

---

[7]Higher viscosity and shorter pot life are recommended for encapsulation.

POSTFORMING

Postforming, as the name implies, is a shaping of thermosetting resins after partial curing. This process is applicable to polyesters to a slight degree, but is more important for the other thermosetting resins. It is particularly suitable for resins that rapidly become flexible above 100° C. without giving off volatile matter (1942), or for the resins that are slow in curing to an absolutely rigid structure (1830).

The glass reinforcement often complicates postforming of glass fiber filled polyesters. Once the glass becomes rigidly held by the resin, the strands are no longer free to slip past one another. Thus, the degree of postforming is limited to the amount the glass will stretch, which is about 3% (remarks by A. Smith, *Reinforced Plastics Division*, *Society of the Plastics Industry Conference*, *7th Annual*, 1952, Section 24, p. 14). Even so, combinations of glass fiber and certain polyester resins can be post-formed to a certain extent (remarks by H. M. Day and R. Brinkema, same source, Section 24, p. 14). Postforming may well prove a good field of entry for reinforcing fibers of treated cotton or other materials of relatively high elasticity.

HONEYCOMBS AND FOAMED RESINS

Cellular and expanded plastics are useful for insulation purposes, buoyancy, and various structural uses (1970). Their advantages include low density, high strength, high stiffness, insulating properties and, in some cases, ease of fabrication (1953). Three types of structures are used: foams, which have unit cells; sponge, in which all cells interconnect; and honeycomb, in which the cells run the length of the structure. The sponge structure is very seldom made from polyester resins. Honeycomb and foamed plastics are used extensively as core for sandwich construction, which consists of thin skins or facings separated by a relatively thick low-density core material.

Foams

Foams have been made from almost every plastic, including polyesters, but the polyesters and other thermosetting resins have not received as much attention as the thermoplastics (1951). The advent of di-isocyanate-modified polyesters, which can be foamed-in-place, promises to change this situation. A full discussion of di-isocyanate-polyester foams can be found on page 228. For further reviews of foamed plastics, see references (1950, 1960).

The methods used to make plastic foams are numerous. Each method, however, generally involves the release of a gaseous blowing agent at an opportune time during the process of curing, usually as the plastic is about to harden. The foaming agent may be a gas whipped into a harden-ing viscous plastic mass, the gas released from a plastic as a vacuum is applied, by-product gas evolved from the plastic during polymerization, or an agent added to the mix that releases a gas (1957). When water is added to di-isocyanate-polyesters, carbon dioxide is released, which causes foaming (1954). A combination of sodium bicarbonate and an acid has been used as a blowing agent for styrene cross-linked polyesters (1969). Vinyl acetate vapors have also been used as blowing agents (1969).

Honeycomb

Early methods for making plastic honeycomb used cellophane tubes filled with sand and placed alternately over and under a reinforcing glass web. Resin was applied to the web, outer layers were built up on top and bottom, and the set-up was cured under pressure. After the cure, the tubes were removed, resulting in a cellular structure (1972, 1973).

Two general methods are used for making glass cloth and other types of honeycomb today (1966). In one method resin-impregnated sheets are formed and cured in a continuous corrugating machine. The corrugated sheets are then cut to length, indexed, and assembled into a square-shaped log. The log is sliced lengthwise across the honeycomb structure on a bandsaw to give a sheet of desired thickness.

In the second method, indexed sheets of resin-impregnated material are strip-glued in a flat assembly and pressed. The pack is then cut into narrow strips which are expanded to form the honeycomb core. After the impregnating resin is cured, the core will hold its expanded shape.

Glass-polyester honeycomb, because of its high transparency to radar rays, is used in sandwich-type housings for radar equipment, or radomes. The radomes are usually made in female molds by vacuum bag molding techniques. The outer plies of glass-polyester laminates are laid up first, resin is applied, and bubbles are smoothed out. The honeycomb core is dipped in resin, the resin allowed to drain, and the core carefully placed in the mold. The inner-skin plies are placed in next, resin is ap-plied, and the set-up is cured (498, 1956, 1958). This entire process re-quires skill, because the dimensions of radomes are very critical.

Honeycomb radomes have also been made on a male plastic mold, using a technique similar to that used with the female mold (1852). [Solid-wall types of radomes are made by forming a thin shell of polyester-glass laminate with female or male molds and the rubber bag technique (1852).]

Because radome dimensions are critical, it was originally thought that damaged structures could not be repaired. These items are expensive to replace, however, and a method has been worked out that permits satis-factory repair (1967).

A method that eliminates the difficulty of forming honeycomb structures with compound curves has also been developed. Bundles of honeycomb cylinders which can be moved independently and made to conform to compound curved surfaces are used. If both surfaces of a part have compound curves, molds are used and the structure is joined in the middle (1959).

Due to the extremely light weight of honeycomb in relation to its strength and insulation values, its use in sandwich building panels would represent considerable savings in labor. On the basis of today's costs primarily, and labor practices secondarily, however, the time has not yet arrived when honeycomb sandwich construction is to take its place as a major factor in the building industry. When it does, resin-impregnated paper honeycomb will probably prove to be the choice material from a cost standpoint (1974).

The labor cost involved in producing foams is inherently lower than for honeycomb, and the insulation values are better because of the smaller cell size. It seems plausible, therefore, to expect that sandwich materials with foamed-in-place polyester-di-isocyanate cores will find major uses in building.

VI. FINISHING

Most fabricated polyester products require some finishing operation to give them a surface with customer appeal. In general, the machining and surface finishing techniques used for polyesters are similar to those used for most thermosetting plastics (2003). The presence of glass reinforcing material may present difficulties, however, such as excessive wear on tools or an undesirable surface appearance. This chapter is therefore mainly concerned with recommendations for finishing reinforced polyester products.

MACHINING

Usually it is not necessary to employ extensive machining on polyester molded parts other than flash removal. Surfaces may need to be sanded or abraded for smoothness, especially if a surface coating is to be applied. If parts are to be joined, conventional polyester resins are satisfactory as adhesives (2013), and these may be reinforced for strength with glass fiber in some form if necessary. Epoxy resins are likewise used as adhesives for polyesters. Mechanical fasteners, such as bolts, rivets, and screws, may also be used for joining.

Glass reinforced polyesters may be machined by standard equipment. One of the difficulties involved is the hard wear on the tools used, because of the abrasiveness of the glass. For this reason, carbide abrasive wheels have been recommended for major cutting, trimming, and turning operations in place of saws (1645, 2007, 2010, 2011), and carbide-tipped drills for drilling operations (2006, 2010, 2011). In some applications an increase in tool speed has been unexpectedly beneficial to tool life, possibly because at the increased speed the reinforcement breaks ahead of the leading edge of the tool.

Because a skin irritation may result from the dust produced in machining operations, dust removal is also a problem. All dry machining operations should have a vacuum dust removal system.

Recommendations

Recommendations for machining operations and speeds for glass reinforced polyesters are given in the following paragraphs (1988, 2003, 2005, 2006, 2010, 2011). The speeds given are not hard-and-fast rules, and machining trials should be made to determine optimum speeds for a particular plastic.

Drilling and Tapping. For drilling holes up to $\frac{3}{16}$ inch in diameter high-speed steel drills may be used. The speeds generally used are 50 to 150 feet per minute, depending on the size of the drill, the depth of the hole, and the capacity of the machine. Carbide-tipped drills should be used for drilling holes larger than $\frac{3}{16}$ inch in diameter or for long-run production. These drills are usually operated at a surface speed of 250 to 350 feet per minute.

Drilling parallel to laminations must be done carefully to prevent splitting. Faster drilling perpendicular to laminations is possible if the material is backed with a tightly clamped support of wood or metal. The use of drilling jigs eliminates the need for backing and produces a more accurate hole.

For tapping and threading, a high-speed nitrided and chromium-plated tap is best. Ground taps are desirable. Holes to be tapped should be drilled larger than is customary for metal in order to leave only about 75% of a full thread. This will prevent the top of the thread from breaking or peeling off and give a cleaner job.

Drill and tap wear is rapid at first but becomes stabilized after the first few pieces. Wet operation will greatly prolong tool life and eliminate dust.

In parts with a high percentage of filler, holes are usually molded rather than drilled or tapped. Threaded metal inserts may be molded into the part.

Punching. Holes and blanks can be made in sheet laminates with dies similar to those used for punching metal.

The recommended minimum distance between the holes and the edge of the sheet is three times the thickness of the sheet. Punched holes should not be smaller in diameter than the thickness of the sheet.

Sawing. Reinforced polyesters can be sawed with all types of hand metal-cutting saws. Power sawing of these plastics is limited to band-saws, carbide circular saws, and abrasive wheels. Abrasive wheel cutting gives the cleanest cut and the cost of blade maintenance is appreciably lower than for other types of saws. The wheels are run at 3,500 to 6,000 revolutions per minute. Wet cutting permits greater speeds and requires less power than dry cutting, and the dust problem is eliminated.

Smooth, accurate edges and fast cutting can be obtained with extremely high blade speeds (5,000 to 10,000 feet per minute) with certain types of bandsaws, but extra low blade speeds (300 to 400 feet per minute) are recommended for longer blade life with standard machines.

Grinding and Sanding. With the proper wheel (glass or cotton fiber reinforced silicon carbide resinoid wheels are recommended) grinding of reinforced polyesters can be done with light cuts and feeds but the glass fibers tend to heat up. Efficiency may be considerably improved if the liquid coolant is refrigerated.

Sanding works very well for both flash removal and surface and edge finishing. Disk sanders are suitable for preparing a surface for coating, which involves removal of the mold lubricant and the top surface of the plastic. This operation can be performed either wet or dry. For heavier sanding jobs, such as removal of wrinkles and surface blemishes, removal of flash, or sanding of rough edges, the endless belt type of sander is usually recommended. (Disk sanders are useful for removal of blemishes from large surface areas, such as the top of an automobile body.) Belt sanding is preferably done dry, with suction to remove the dust rather than a liquid coolant.

Belt sanders are operated at speeds of 2,000 to 5,000 feet per minute; for cold-molded articles the speed is usually 3,000 to 4,000 feet per minute. Disk sanders are run at 1,750 to 2,000 revolutions per minute for cold-molded articles.

Turning and Milling. High speeds, similar to those recommended for brass, and carbide-tipped tools are most satisfactory for working reinforced polyesters. The tools should be kept sharp in order to avoid inaccuracies and delamination where the cutting edge rises over the laminations.

Shearing. Thin sheet laminates can be cut by hand with sheet metal shears, or they can be cut with foot-power square shears such as are used for thin sheet metal.

Routing. Properly set up for edging operations, routing will give clean and accurate surfaces in reinforced polyesters. It has to be done dry, however, and produces a great amount of dust which must be removed by a vacuum system. Carbide bit construction is essential.

SURFACE COATINGS AND TREATMENTS

In the early years of the plastic industry, most of the objects made were small. Therefore, the cost of the plastic was relatively slight in relation to the cost of fabrication, and the industry developed a habit of depending only on plastic selection to achieve the desired surface properties. (This habit still persists to a surprising degree today.)

As the size of fabricated plastic parts and objects increased, and as they became more specialized, it became necessary to develop various coating and surface treatments for plastics. Designers seized upon the possibility of using the plastic that is most desirable mechanically for each application, and coating it to give it the desired surface characteristics. Inclusion of pigments opened the way to decorative applications as well.

The most highly developed surface treatments can be compared with electroplating in the metal industry—they provide a body of one plastic with a surface of another, adhered so firmly that it cannot be removed by any amount of mechanical violence, short of destroying the entire object. The first of these integral coatings were the Logoquant[1] coatings for making polystyrene resistant to oil and gasoline. These coatings are described in patents issued to the Nash-Kelvinator Corp. (515, 516, 519, 522) and are essentially cellulose ester coatings integrally bonded to polystyrene.

Usually finishing coats are applied by spraying, brushing, silk-screening, or printing. One development utilizes an electrostatic field for spraying. In this operation the parts to be coated are passed through an electric field, and a difference in charges attracts the paint to the part. One advantage claimed for this process is that the entire piece may be coated by spraying from one side only. This process is also useful for removing excess paint, or "de-tearing" (2027).

Paints and Other Coatings

Polyesters are difficult to finish using conventional paints or coatings. One manufacturer had to resort to nine operations to finish a part of a machine which would duplicate the finish on the rest of the machine. These operations were: (1) cleaning the part with naphtha or xylene; (2) drying to evaporate the solvent; (3) filling the surface with a light wood filler, working it into all pinholes, and removing all excess filler; (4) drying for 2 hours; (5) applying a primer coat; (6) baking for 45 minutes at 150° to 160°F.; (7) sanding with 220 grit abrasive paper; (8) applying two cross-sprayed coats of enamel; and (9) baking for 20 hours at 150° to 160°F. (2036).

In most applications where a polyester is to be finished, a high-quality coating is required. In many instances it is required to pass an exposure test of 1,000 hours at 100°F. and 100% relative humidity; in some cases it must withstand salt spray at 100° or 110°F.; and frequently it must also pass grease and water-soak tests. Good hardness and resistance to shock and embrittlement are usually required. If the coating is applied to improve the decorative appearance or sales appeal of the part, or to match adjoining metal parts, it is obvious that the quality must be high.

For polyester parts that are to be surface coated, it is important to select a mold release agent that can be removed entirely before the coating is applied or that is compatible with the coating. Otherwise, the mold release agent will weaken the bond between the part and the coating and cause the coating to peel and chip off. In some cases the coating may not even wet the plastic parts at all (comments by S. A. Moore,

[1] Trade name of Logo, Inc.

Reinforced Plastics Division, Society of Plastics Industry Conference, 6th Annual, 1951, Section 14, p. 12).

One of the main difficulties in finishing polyester moldings is that pinholes are often present in the surface of the part. These must be eliminated before applying any baked-on finishes, as entrapped air or solvents in the pinholes blow out (blowholes) during baking, thus spoiling the finish.

Although larger surface imperfections and irregularities cannot be overcome to any degree without filling and sanding, an obvious method of overcoming the problem of blowholes is to use an air-drying coating. A coating material was recently announced that can be used as either an air-drying finish or a baked-on finish (2016). The baking, which is done at low temperature, principally gives the advantages of fast through-dry and slightly increased hardness. This particular coating is used as an air-drying finish in numerous applications where the longer time of through-drying before handling is not objectionable.

Good results in filling pinholes and obtaining a uniform surface for subsequent coating have been obtained by using polyester surfacers. These are resins which have enough stickiness to be sprayable, yet enough flow to enter pinholes easily and fill them completely. Since they are 100% converted to a solid on drying (about 10 minutes at 300°F.; 20 minutes at 180°F.), the pinholes are thus eliminated.

The production of a uniform, smooth surface on reinforced polyester automobile bodies is particularly important, in order to give them the type of finish to which the public has become accustomed. In the manufacture of plastic bodies for sports cars, polyester surfacers have been used as primer coatings under nitrocellulose lacquer.

When polyester surfacers are to be used, the vinyl silane type of finish should be used on the glass to minimize moisture adsorption, so that no blisters will be formed between the primer and the surfacer. This is particularly important in matched die moldings, in which very small and numerous pinholes are formed. Bag-molded parts are much less touchy in this respect.

Wrinkle finish is very sensitive to pinholes. When the outside finish is set, any pinhole is likely to blister, particularly if it reaches a fiber bundle which has retained moisture.

National Cash Register Co. uses spray coats of a low viscosity vinyl plastisol as a primer, to close pinholes, on reinforced plastics. The nozzles are controlled so that globules are sprayed; heating causes the globules to merge into a uniform coating (Discussion, *Reinforced Plastics Division, Society of Plastics Industry Conference, 9th Annual,* 1954, Section 5).

Initial coatings on plastic parts can be formed in the molding operation by the use of gel coats. These are essentially pigmented polyester resin mixtures which can be applied by simple brush or spray technique before molding or laminating operations. The pigmented layer then coreacts with the molding resin during the curing cycle and becomes an integral part of the molded product. By this process continuous colored surfaces are produced without any subsequent finishing operations. Reinforced products can be obtained with porcelain-like surfaces which have excellent weathering properties (2120).

Post-mold gel coating, in which filled and pigmented resin is applied directly to the molded part instead of to the mold surface, can also be used. This process may be applied on conveyorized paint lines and thus offers the advantage of not extending molding press cycle times and slowing up molding production (2035).

Coloring Plastics

One system for dyeing or coloring the surfaces of plastic parts which may be applicable to polyester resins is given in reference (512). In this system the surface of the plastic part is first made hydrophilic by treatment with sulfuric acid or similar compounds, and then a basic dye is applied from an aqueous solution. Another method, useful for diallyl phthalate resins (and similar resins), uses a dye dissolved in a glycol or a glycol-water mixture to color the part (513, 525).

The Polyfax process for the reproduction of wood grains, leather, and similar patterns on flat or irregular surfaces may be applicable to polyester resins. A polyester resin is used as a coating in this process (2030).

A review of coloring methods for phenolic plastics is given in reference (2041).

Decorative printing of polyester sheet laminates requires special inks that do not dissolve in the resin used. Commercial inks for this purpose usually have a dextrin base in water solution.

Metalizing

A fairly recent commercial application of coatings is that of metalized plastics. This process has not been applied extensively to polyesters, although the technical difficulties involved are being overcome. For further review of this subject see references (2031, 2032, 2033, 2037). "Mylar"[2] polyester (polyethylene terephthalate) film is available with an aluminized mirror-like surface.

[2] Du Pont trade name.

The clear finishes used in conjunction with metalizing hold the key to success for this process. If metal were vacuum-deposited directly on a plastic surface and left there without after-coating, it would normally not be smooth, not adhere well, and would soon lose its luster and form blemishes. Therefore, a base coating is applied to the plastic before metalizing, to provide a smooth, fresh surface, free from fingerprints or adsorbed matter. After metalizing, a top coating is applied to seal the metal surface and to protect it from oxidation, moisture, and marring.

The specifications for both the base and top coatings are exacting. The base coat must have exceptional flow-out and must adhere to the base plastic as well as to the metal. It must be free from any ingredient which in itself, or on aging, could attack the metal or which could cause blistering in the very high vacuum employed in metalizing. The top coating must also adhere to the metal, and its solvent system must be a nonsolvent for the base coat, so as not to dissolve it in the metal coating. Further, the top coating must provide an excellent moisture seal and good mar resistance. The formulation of such coatings, which is a recent development, has made possible the adaptation of metalizing as a finishing process for plastics (2016).

In many cases, effects equivalent to metalizing can be attained at lower cost by using finishes for polyesters in which metallic powders of the bronze or aluminum type are incorporated (2016). These finishes give highly attractive effects that increase sales appeal. A clear finish is applied over the metallic coating, thereby giving an appearance of depth and richness. The clear finish is usually applied immediately after the application of the metallic coating, so that only one handling of the part and one air-drying or baking cycle are needed. The finishes may be baked in 7 to 30 minutes at 250° to 300°F., after air-drying for 10 to 15 minutes.

As-Molded Surfaces

Reinforced plastic parts can be produced with "as-molded" surface finishes that do not require further finishing unless desired. One of these is the "pronounced fiber" system in which the characteristically raised fiber pattern is accentuated to produce a contrasting pattern against the resin background (2035). Colored fibers can be used with different colored resins to obtain this effect (2025). A "suppressed fiber" system, in which fine surfacing fibers or mats are applied to preformed or mat parts before molding (2035), can also be used. This system produces a very fine filament-resin surface that is fairly smooth.

VII. COMMERCIAL RESINS

In this chapter specific resins offered by various manufacturers and suppliers are described. The lists of resins given should by no means be taken as complete, since new products are constantly appearing. In addition, space limitations do not permit listing of the entire selection of resins offered by many large manufacturers. The lists do, however, include representatives of important types of polyester resins on the market as of June 1, 1954.

In general, the data on physical properties given in this chapter are taken from manufacturers' technical literature. The data are also from tests conducted at room temperature, unless otherwise indicated.

GENERAL-PURPOSE RESINS

General-purpose (rigid) resins can be used for most types of molding and laminating. Table No. 13 shows, however, that these resins have a wide range of properties, and a particular resin may have properties that make it especially suitable for certain applications. For example, high-viscosity resins are useful in vertical lay-ups, where low-viscosity resins would run off. Low-viscosity resins are needed when rapid penetration is desirable. Some general-purpose resins are fast curing and have good "hot strength," which are properties of value in matched metal die molding. Other resins meet the qualifications of a good casting resin (p. 145). Resins containing diallyl phthalate (DAP) may be preferred for some applications because they do not contain odorous volatile constituents. DAP resins also generally have a longer pot life than resins containing styrene, which is an advantage in laying-up large parts such as radomes.

Table No. 14 lists a number of rigid general-purpose resins and their manufacturers, as well as some special properties of these resins.

Table No. 13.—*Properties of unfilled, cast rigid and flexible polyester resins**

NOTE: This table is based on maximum and minimum values submitted by a number of manufacturers and should not be used as a guide in choosing a resin for a specific use. Manufacturers should be consulted for the properties of particular resins.

Property	Cast rigid polyester resins	Cast flexible polyester resins
Specific gravity	1.10–1.46	1.12–1.20
Refractive index, n_D	1.53–1.57	1.537–1.55

MECHANICAL PROPERTIES

Tensile strength, psi	6,000–10,000	800–1,800
Elongation, %	5	50–310
Modulus of elasticity in tension, 10^5 psi	3.0–6.4	......
Compressive strength, psi	13,000–27,000	......
Flexural strength, psi	8,500–17,000	......
Impact strength (Izod), ft.-lb. per in. notch	0.2–0.4	> 7.0
Hardness	M70–M115 (Rockwell)	89–94 (Shore)

THERMAL PROPERTIES

Thermal conductivity, 10^{-4} cal. per sec. per sq. cm. per $1°C.$ per cm.	4	......
Coefficient of thermal expansion, 10^{-5} per $°C.$	8–10	......
Heat distortion temperature, $°F.$	140–400	......

ELECTRICAL PROPERTIES

Dielectric strength, ⅛ in. thickness, volts per mil		
Short-time	380–500	250–400
Step-by-step	280–420	170
Dielectric constant		
60 cycles	3.0–4.36	4.4–7.2
1 kilocycle	2.8–5.2	4.5–5.1
1 megacycle	2.8–4.1	4.1–5.2
Dissipation factor		
60 cycles	0.003–0.028	0.026–0.26
1 kilocycle	0.005–0.025	0.016–0.019
1 megacycle	0.006–0.026	0.023–0.052
Arc resistance, sec.	125	135

*Source: *Modern Plastics Encyclopedia*, plastics properties chart.

Table No. 13.—*Properties of unfilled, cast rigid and flexible polyester resins** (Cont'd)

Property	Cast rigid polyester resins	Cast flexible polyester resins

CHEMICAL AND SOLVENT RESISTANCE

Effect of weak acids	Nil	Nil
Effect of strong acids	None to considerable	None to considerable
Effect of weak alkalies	None to slight	None to slight
Effect of strong alkalies	Attacked	Attacked
Effect of organic solvents	Attacked by ketones and chlorinated solvents	Attacked by ketones and chlorinated solvents

MISCELLANEOUS

Water absorption, 24 hr., 1/8 in. thickness, %	0.15–0.60	0.50–2.5
Burning rate (ASTM Method D635)	1.1 to self-extinguishing	......
Effect on metal inserts	Nil	Nil
Machining qualities	Good	Fair
Clarity	Transparent to opaque	Transparent to opaque
Color possibilities	Unlimited	Unlimited

Table No. 14.—*Rigid general-purpose polyester resins and their manufacturers*

Manufacturer's designation	Manufacturer	Remarks
AR-403	General Electric Co.	Medium viscosity; can be used for matched metal die molding and casting
Aropol 7110	Archer-Daniels-Midland Co.	Medium viscosity; light color; exceptional chemical resistance
Atlac 382	Atlas Powder Co.	Powder; dissolves in styrene to give resin of high viscosity, high heat resistance, low shrinkage
BRS-264	Bakelite Co.	Medium viscosity; high degree of toughness; recommended for casting
BRS-265	Bakelite Co.	Medium viscosity; high degree of toughness; recommended for casting

Table No. 14.—*Rigid general-purpose polyester resins and their manufacturers* (Cont'd)

Manufacturer's designation	Manufacturer	Remarks
Duolite 364	Chemical Process Co.	Low viscosity; high heat resistance
Glidpol 1001	Glidden Co.	Low viscosity; can be used for casting
Glidpol 1001-HV	Glidden Co.	High viscosity variation of Glidpol 1001
Glidpol 1011	Glidden Co.	Low reactivity; recommended for molding where warpage is possible
Glidpol 1012	Glidden Co.	High reactivity; good "hot" strength
Glykon R-100	General Tire & Rubber Co., Chemical Division	Low viscosity; high hardness; can be used for matched metal die molding and casting
Glykon R-100MV	General Tire & Rubber Co., Chemical Division	Similar to Glykon R-100 except for higher viscosity
IC-312	Interchemical Corp.	Medium viscosity; can be used for matched metal die molding and potting; excellent outdoor weathering characteristics.
IC-420HV	Interchemical Corp.	High-viscosity variation of IC-312
Laminac 4116	American Cyanamid Co.	Low viscosity; low shrinkage; low heat distortion point; low exotherm; very adaptable to casting and potting
Laminac 4119	American Cyanamid Co.	Medium viscosity; high heat resistance; good resistance to abrasion and staining
Laminac 4120	American Cyanamid Co.	High viscosity; high heat resistance; good resistance to abrasion and staining
Laminac 4123	American Cyanamid Co.	Medium viscosity; provides good surface finish in compression molding
Laminac 4128	American Cyanamid Co.	Low viscosity; high heat resistance; superior resistance to abrasion and staining
MR-28C	Celanese Corp., Marco Products Department	Low viscosity; cures tack-free in air; can be used for casting and coating

Table No. 14.—*Rigid general-purpose polyester resins and their manufacturers* (Cont'd)

Manufacturer's designation	Manufacturer	Remarks
MR-28H	Celanese Corp., Marco Products Department	High-viscosity variation of MR-28C
MR-28R	Celanese Corp., Marco Products Department	Medium-viscosity variation of MR-28C
MR-28V	Celanese Corp., Marco Products Department	Very low viscosity variation of MR-28C
Narmco Formula 3117	Narmco Resins & Coating Co.	Low-viscosity, mineral-filled resin
Paraplex P-43	Rohm & Haas Co.	Low viscosity; can be used for matched metal die molding and casting
Paraplex P-43HV	Rohm & Haas Co.	High-viscosity variation of Paraplex P-43
Plaskon 911	Allied Chemical & Dye Corp., Barrett Division	DAP* resin; high viscosity; high heat distortion point; suited for hand lay-up
Plaskon 920	Allied Chemical & Dye Corp., Barrett Division	DAP resin; low viscosity; high heat distortion point; primarily used as mat or preform binder in emulsified form
Plaskon 941	Allied Chemical & Dye Corp., Barrett Division	Low viscosity; cures tack-free in air; good heat stability; can be used for matched metal die molding
Plaskon 942	Allied Chemical & Dye Corp., Barrett Division	Similar to Plaskon 941 except for medium viscosity, which makes it preferred for matched metal die molding
Polylite 8000	Reichhold Chemicals, Inc.	Low viscosity; medium reactivity; can be used for matched metal die molding
Polylite 8001	Reichhold Chemicals, Inc.	Low viscosity; low reactivity; can be used for casting
Polylite 8002	Reichhold Chemicals, Inc.	Low viscosity; good "hot strength"; outstanding for deep-draw matched metal die molding or rubber plug molding
Polylite 8006	Reichhold Chemicals, Inc.	Identical to Polylite 8000 except for medium viscosity

*Diallyl phthalate.

Table No. 14.—*Rigid general-purpose polyester resins and their manufacturers* (Cont'd)

Manufacturer's designation	Manufacturer	Remarks
Polylite 8007	Reichhold Chemicals, Inc.	Identical to Polylite 8001 except for lower viscosity
Polylite 8008	Reichhold Chemicals, Inc.	Identical to Polylite 8001 except for medium viscosity
Polylite 8009	Reichhold Chemicals, Inc.	Medium viscosity; good "hot strength;" recommended for all forms of matched metal die molding
Selectron 5003	Pittsburgh Plate Glass Co.	Low viscosity; can be used for casting
Stypol 405	H. H. Robertson Co.	Low viscosity; excellent wetting; high degree of translucency; for general-purpose laminating
Stypol 407	H. H. Robertson Co.	Medium viscosity; excellent wetting; high degree of translucency; for general-purpose laminating
Stypol 705	H. H. Robertson Co.	Low viscosity; excellent wetting; for general-purpose laminating
Synvar V-30	Synvar Corp.	Low viscosity; for laminating and casting
Synvar V-301	Synvar Corp.	Low viscosity; for laminating and casting
Synvar V-32	Synvar Corp.	Low viscosity; gives water-clear castings
Synvar V-322	Synvar Corp.	Low viscosity; gives water-clear castings
Synvar V-35	Synvar Corp.	High viscosity
Vibrin 114	U. S. Rubber Co., Naugatuck Chemical Division	Low viscosity; air curing; good high temperature strength; can be used for matched metal die molding and potting
Vibrin 117	U. S. Rubber Co., Naugatuck Chemical Division	Low viscosity; medium heat distortion temperature; excellent transparency in laminates

FLEXIBLE RESINS

Certain polyester resins cure to a flexible, tough solid rather than a rigid solid. These flexible resins are usually obtained by reducing the ratio of unsaturated acid groups to saturated acid groups, as by the use of a long-chain saturated acid such as adipic acid in the resin formulation. The following flexible resins can be used alone or blended with rigid resins for applications requiring increased impact or shock resistance.

Manufacturer's designation	Manufacturer
AR-501	General Electric Co.
Aropol 7300	Archer-Daniels-Midland Co.
Atlac FLX (in development)	Atlas Powder Co.
BRS-136	Bakelite Co.
Duolite 211	Chemical Process Co.
Glidpol 2002	Glidden Co.
Glykon F-600	General Tire & Rubber Co., Chemical Division
IC-401	Interchemical Corp.
Laminac 4134	American Cyanamid Co.
MR-30C	Celanese Corp., Marco Products Department
MR-30V	Celanese Corp., Marco Products Department
Paraplex P-13	Rohm & Haas Co.
Plaskon 9600	Allied Chemical & Dye Corp., Barrett Division
Polylite 8150	Reichhold Chemicals, Inc.
Selectron 5096	Pittsburgh Plate Glass Co.
Stypol 12	H. H. Robertson Co.
Synvar V-2	Synvar Corp.
Vibrin 121	U. S. Rubber Co., Naugatuck Chemical Division

The range of properties of commercial unfilled, cured flexible polyester resins is given in table No. 13.

SEMIRIGID (RESILIENT) RESINS

Semirigid or resilient resins combine high flexural strength with a comparatively low flexural modulus. They are tougher and less brittle than the rigid general-purpose resins and usually have a lower heat distortion point. The following resins have the properties of semirigid resins:

Manufacturer's designation	Manufacturer
BRS-262	Bakelite Co.
Glidpol 2001	Glidden Co.
IC-433	Interchemical Corp.
IC-585	Interchemical Corp.
Laminac 4160	American Cyanamid Co.
Plaskon 9500	Allied Chemical & Dye Corp., Barrett Division
Selectron 5083	Pittsburgh Plate Glass Co.

Table No. 15 lists the properties of BRS-262 (2054), Plaskon 9500 (2044), and Selectron 5083 (2083).

LIGHT-STABLE RESINS

The aging properties of general-purpose polyester resins are unsatisfactory for some applications requiring exposure to sunlight, such as structural panels and skylights. The resins in the following list are offered to fill this need. They have improved light stability (probably

Table No. 15.— *Properties of three semirigid cured polyester resins*

Property	BRS-262 (Bakelite)	Plaskon 9500 (Allied Chemical & Dye)	Selectron 5083 (Pittsburgh Plate Glass)
Specific gravity	1.246	1.22	1.22
Heat distortion point, °F.	136	140	160
Tensile strength, psi	......	7,000	10,000
Flexural strength, psi	18,750	16,000	17,000
Modulus of elasticity in flexure, 10^6 psi	0.47	0.4	0.5
Compressive strength, psi	15,900	30,700	23,000
Impact strength (Izod), ft.-lb. or ft.-lb. per in. notch	2.70 (unnotched)	......	0.25 (notched)
Hardness:			
Rockwell M	98	......	105–110
Barcol	44	31	40–45
Water absorption, 24-hr. immersion, %	0.26	0.23	0.21
Viscosity of resin as supplied, cps.	450–650	800	525–725

through the addition of a stabilizing agent) but otherwise have properties similar to those of the standard resins.

Manufacturer's designation	Manufacturer
Aropol 7110LS	Archer-Daniels-Midland Co.
BRS-193	Bakelite Co.
Duolite 022	Chemical Process Co.
Duolite 023LS2	Chemical Process Co.
Glidpol 1001-LS	Glidden Co.
IC-312-2	Interchemical Corp.
Laminac 4123LS-1	American Cyanamid Co.
MR-28RL	Celanese Corp., Marco Products Department
Paraplex P-431	Rohm & Haas Co.
Plaskon 9404	Allied Chemical & Dye Corp., Barrett Division
Polylite 8010	Reichhold Chemicals, Inc.
Selectron 5051	Pittsburgh Plate Glass Co.
Selectron 5051A	Pittsburgh Plate Glass Co.
Stypol 4055	H. H. Robertson Co.
Vibrin 152LS	U. S. Rubber Co., Naugatuck Chemical Division

EXTENDED POT-LIFE RESINS

Resins with an extended pot (or tank) life are useful when fabricating conditions require that the catalyzed resins remain liquid over periods of time during which most conventional resins gel. (For example, in molding large or complex parts a resin with a long flow period is desirable in order to fill all parts of the mold before the resin gels.) These resins usually contain an inhibitor system which extends the liquid flow period before gelation but not the other curing characteristics. The fully cured resins exhibit the same properties as the general-purpose resins.

Marco MR-28CS (Celanese Corp.), which is identical in properties to MR-28C when cured, Selectron 5003L (Pittsburgh Plate Glass Co.), which is identical to Selectron 5003 when cured, Glidpol 1001-A, which is identical to Glidpol 1001 when cured, and Laminac 4108 (American Cyanamid Co.) are examples of this type of resins. Table No. 16 compares the gel times of MR-28C and MR-28CS (2058). Table No. 17 compares the tank lives and gel times of Selectron 5003 and 5003L (2083).

Table No. 16. — *Gel time of Marco MR-28C and MR-28CS resins* *

Marco MC-1 catalyst	Marco Accelerator E	Gel (bulk) time	
		MR-28C	MR-28CS**
%	%	Min.	Min.
2	2	45–55	109
2	3	35–40	76
2	4	30–35	59
2	5	25–30	35

*Source: Celanese Corp. of America, Marco Products Department, Customer Service Bulletin No. M1.

**Specially modified for long catalyzed working life.

Table No. 17. — *Tank life and gel time of Selectron 5003 and Selectron 5003L* *

Resin	Catalyst	Tank life at 77°F., minimum	Gel time (SPI procedure)
Selectron 5003	1% benzoyl peroxide	12 hr.	4.5–6.0 min.
Selectron 5003	0.5% tert.-butyl hydroperoxide	30 min.	......
Selectron 5003L**	1% benzoyl peroxide	7 days	5.7–7.3 min.
Selectron 5003L**	0.5% tert.-butyl hydroperoxide	10 days	......

*Source: Pittsburgh Plate Glass Co. booklet on Selectron polyester reinforcing resins (5000 series).

**Specially modified to give a long tank life.

NONAIR-INHIBITED RESINS

Conventional resins do not develop the hardness in contact with air that they do when protected by a cover sheet or die. In some applications, such as boat coverings or tanks, however, it is impossible to exclude air from all resin surfaces. Resins have therefore been developed that will cure to a tack-free condition on exposure to air. The resins listed below have this property and are also specifically designed for low- or room-temperature curing. The gel times of these resins are controlled by the percentage of catalyst used. Their properties, when cured, are in the range of general-purpose resins.

Manufacturer's designation	Manufacturer
Glidpol 1002	Glidden Co.
IC-625	Interchemical Corp.
IC-670	Interchemical Corp.
Laminac 4110	American Cyanamid Co.
MR-28C	Celanese Corp., Marco Products Department
Polylite 8027	Reichhold Chemicals, Inc.
Selectron 5119	Pittsburgh Plate Glass Co.

FLAME-RESISTANT RESINS

General-purpose polyester resins may be rendered flame-resistant by the use of fireproofing fillers such as antimony trioxide. The commercial flame-resistant resins, however, are usually prepared by using an ingredient in the synthesis of the resin which will make the product flame-resistant. The ingredients most commonly used are tetrachlorophthalic anhydride and hexachloroendomethylene tetrahydrophthalic acid[1] (HET[2] acid). They are substituted for phthalic anhydride in general-purpose formulations. Resins containing HET acid ("Hetron"[2] resins) have especially good flame resistance. Some resins designated as flame-resistant and self-extinguishing require the addition of at least 5% of antimony trioxide to develop these properties to the maximum.

The following commercial resins are flame-resistant or self-extinguishing:

Manufacturer's designation	Manufacturer
Aropol 7200	Archer-Daniels-Midland Co.
Atlac FP (in development)	Atlas Powder Co.
BRS-203	Bakelite Co.
Cordo H57C-FR	Cordo Molding Products, Inc.
Duolite 371LS1 (also light-stable)	Chemical Process Co.
Glidpol 1010	Glidden Co.
Hetron 23	Hooker Electrochemical Co.
Hetron 92	Hooker Electrochemical Co.
Hetron X-31 (semirigid, low viscosity)	Hooker Electrochemical Co.
Hetron X-32 (semirigid, low viscosity)	Hooker Electrochemical Co.
Hetron X-32A (semirigid, low viscosity)	Hooker Electrochemical Co.
IC-594FR	Interchemical Corp.
IC-636FR	Interchemical Corp.

[1] Also called chlorendic acid.
[2] Trade names of Hooker Electrochemical Co.

Manufacturer's designation (Cont'd)	Manufacturer (Cont'd)
IC-670FR (cures tack-free in presence of air)	Interchemical Corp.
Laminac 4146	American Cyanamid Co.
MR-32	Celanese Corp., Marco Products Department
MR-33C	Celanese Corp., Marco Products Department
Polylite 8061	Reichhold Chemicals, Inc.
Selectron 5041	Pittsburgh Plate Glass Co.
Selectron 5000, 514-68	Pittsburgh Plate Glass Co.
Synvar V-33	Synvar Corp.
Vibrin 142	U. S. Rubber Co., Naugatuck Chemical Division
Vibrin 144	U. S. Rubber Co., Naugatuck Chemical Division

HIGH HEAT DISTORTION POINT RESINS

One of the difficulties in the use of polyester resins for some applications is their low heat distortion point. Some manufacturers offer high heat distortion point resins, which retain their initial strength at higher temperatures than most general-purpose resins. The following resins are designated as having a high heat distortion point by their manufacturer or have a heat distortion point of at least 110° C.

Manufacturer's designation	Manufacturer
BRS-141	Bakelite Co.
BRS-142	Bakelite Co.
BRS-147	Bakelite Co.
BRS-193	Bakelite Co.
Duolite 354	Chemical Process Co.
Glidpol 1005	Glidden Co.
Hetron 23	Hooker Electrochemical Co.
Hetron 92	Hooker Electrochemical Co.
Hetron X-31 (semirigid, low viscosity)	Hooker Electrochemical Co.
Hetron X-32 (semirigid, low viscosity)	Hooker Electrochemical Co.
Hetron X-32A (semirigid, low viscosity)	Hooker Electrochemical Co.
IC-382 HHDT	Interchemical Corp.
Laminac 4111 (designed primarily for resistance to hot aqueous solutions)	American Cyanamid Co.
Laminac 4119	American Cyanamid Co.
Laminac 4128	American Cyanamid Co.
Laminac 4146	American Cyanamid Co.
Laminac PDL 7-719	American Cyanamid Co.
MR-32	Celanese Corp., Marco Products Department
MR-33C	Celanese Corp., Marco Products Department
Paraplex P-47	Rohm & Haas Co.

Manufacturer's designation (Cont'd)	*Manufacturer* (Cont'd)
Paraplex P-49	Rohm & Haas Co.
Plaskon 911	Allied Chemical & Dye Corp., Barrett Division
Plaskon 920	Allied Chemical & Dye Corp., Barrett Division
Polylite 8009	Reichhold Chemicals, Inc.
Polylite 8061	Reichhold Chemicals, Inc.
Selectron 5016	Pittsburgh Plate Glass Co.
Selectron 5117	Pittsburgh Plate Glass Co.
Selectron 5118	Pittsburgh Plate Glass Co.
Stypol 407	H. H. Robertson Co.
Vibrin 115A	U. S. Rubber Co., Naugatuck Chemical Division

Even the commercial resins designated as high heat distortion point resins are not sufficiently high in this respect to compete with metals. Recently, however, resins have been developed that exhibit good properties when aged at 300° F. and which retain much of their strength at 500° F. Triallyl cyanurate, instead of styrene or diallyl phthalate, is used as the cross-linking agent in some of these resins.

The following are newer heat-resistant resins that retain strength properties at very high temperatures:

Manufacturer's designation	*Manufacturer*
AR-493	General Electric Co.
Laminac PDL 7-669	American Cyanamid Co.
Laminac PDL 7-679 (solid, for dry impregnation)	American Cyanamid Co.
Laminac PDL 7-680 (self-extinguishing)	American Cyanamid Co.
Selectron 5000, 468-53	Pittsburgh Plate Glass Co.
Stypol 16B	H. H. Robertson Co.
Stypol 25	H. H. Robertson Co.
Vibrin X-1047	U. S. Rubber Co., Naugatuck Chemical Division

The compositions of AR-493 and the Stypol resins have not been revealed, but all of the other resins listed contain triallyl cyanurate. General Electric AR-493, Stypol 16B, and Stypol 25 have heat and chemical resistance far superior to conventional polyester resins, however. Test results indicate that the maximum operating temperature for glass cloth laminates prepared with AR-493 resin may be as high as 150° C. (302° F.) and intermittent temperatures as high as 250° C. (482° F.) may be tolerated (2069). Stypol 25 has excellent strength retention at high temperatures (350° F.) after continuous exposure at these temperatures. Stypol

Table No. 18.—*Flexural properties of laminates made with polyester resins containing triallyl cyanurate*[*]

Property and test condition	Laminac PDL 7-669 (American Cyanamid)	Selectron 5000, 468-53 (Pittsburgh Plate Glass)	Vibrin X-1047 (Naugatuck Chemical)
Flexural strength, psi			
Initial, at room temperature	31,500	38,000	40,000
At 500° F.:			
After ½ hr. at test temperature	25,700	......	24,000
After 1 hr. at test temperature	......	29,000	......
After 3 hr. at test temperature	27,200	......	......
After 24 hr. at test temperature	32,800	33,600	30,000
After 72 hr. at test temperature	......	23,000	22,000
Modulus of elasticity in flexure, 10^6 psi			
Initial, at room temperature	2.4	2.27	2.9
At 500° F.:			
After ½ hr. at test temperature	2.4	......	2.0
After 3 hr. at test temperature	2.15	......	......
After 24 hr. at test temperature	2.48	2.48	2.2
After 72 hr. at test temperature	......	2.60	2.0

[*]The laminates were made with 11 or 12 plies of 118-114 glass cloth and were not postcured. Postcuring is recommended for all three of these resins to obtain optimum elevated-temperature properties.

16B was developed especially for short term high-temperature (300° – 550° F.) applications.

Table No. 18 gives the flexural properties of laminates made with Laminac PDL 7-669 (2046), Selectron 5000, 468-53 (2084), and Vibrin X-1047 (2101).

LOW-EXOTHERM RESINS

Some polyester resins are characterized by a low exotherm, which means that less heat is generated during cure of these resins than during cure of general-purpose resins. This property is valuable when strain-free castings or moldings are desired, as in applications requiring thick sections. The heat distortion points of these resins are generally lower than those of general-purpose resins. The following are examples of low-exotherm resins:

Manufacturer's designation	*Manufacturer*
Glidpol 1010	Glidden Co.
Laminac 4116	American Cyanamid Co.
MR-31C	Celanese Corp., Marco Products Department
MR-31L	Celanese Corp., Marco Products Department
Plaskon 951	Allied Chemical & Dye Corp., Barrett Division
Polylite 8001	Reichhold Chemicals, Inc.
Polylite 8004	Reichhold Chemicals, Inc.
Selectron 5081	Pittsburgh Plate Glass Co.
Selectron 5107	Pittsburgh Plate Glass Co.

The properties of Polylite 8001 (2092) and Selectron 5081 (2083) are summarized in table No. 19.

Table No. 19. —*Properties of two polyester resins with a low exotherm*

Property	Polylite 8001 (Reichhold Chemicals)	Selectron 5081 (Pittsburgh Plate Glass)
Liquid resin as supplied:		
Viscosity, cps.	800–1000	325–450
Peak exotherm, °F.	300–350	300–330
Cured, unfilled resins:		
Specific gravity	1.22	1.22
Shrinkage during cure, %	6.5	......
Heat distortion point, °F.	155	130
Tensile strength, psi	6,865	6,000
Flexural strength, psi	11,790	13,000
Modulus of elasticity in flexure, 10^6 psi	......	0.54
Compressive strength, psi	20,715	22,000
Impact strength (Izod), ft.-lb.	......	0.18 (unnotched)
Hardness:		
Rockwell M	109	108–113
Barcol	44	43–48
Water absorption, 24 hr. immersion, %	......	0.20

CASTING RESINS

Resins which combine several of the following properties serve best for casting applications:

(1) Low shrinkage during cure.
(2) Good resistance to cracking and crazing.
(3) Low exotherm if strain-free castings are desired.
(4) Clearness and minimum color.
(5) Toughness (increased by blending with flexible resins).

The resins in the following list are recommended for casting applications by their manufacturers and suppliers:

Manufacturer's designation	Manufacturer
Alkydol S-452	Alkydol Laboratories, Inc.
AR-401	General Electric Co.
AR-403	General Electric Co.
Bio-Plastic (embedding)	Ward's Natural Science Establishment
BRS-262	Bakelite Co.
BRS-264	Bakelite Co.
BRS-265	Bakelite Co.
Castolite (embedding)	Castolite Co.
Chemiglas (embedding)	Technicraft Co.
Cordo H57C	Cordo Molding Products, Inc.
Formula 3117	Narmco Resins & Coatings Co.
Glidpol 1001	Glidden Co.
Glidpol 1002 (nonair-inhibited)	Glidden Co.
Glidpol 1010 (flame-retardant; low exotherm)	Glidden Co.
Glykon F-600 (flexible)	General Tire & Rubber Co., Chemical Division
Glykon R-100	General Tire & Rubber Co., Chemical Division
Homalite 100[3]	Homalite Corp.
Homalite 101[3]	Homalite Corp.
IC-312 (water-white)	Interchemical Corp.
IC-401 (flexible)	Interchemical Corp.
IC-433 (semirigid)	Interchemical Corp.
IC-457	Interchemical Corp.
IC-514 (water-white)	Interchemical Corp.
IC-548	Interchemical Corp.
IC-585	Interchemical Corp.
Laminac 4116 (low exotherm)	American Cyanamid Co.
MR-28C	Celanese Corp., Marco Products Department
MR-30V (flexible)	Celanese Corp., Marco Products Department
MR-31C (low exotherm)	Celanese Corp., Marco Products Department

[3]Available in cast sheets.

Manufacturer's designation (Cont'd.)	*Manufacturer* (Cont'd.)
MR-31V (low exotherm)	Celanese Corp., Marco Products Department
Paraplex P-43	Rohm & Haas Co.
Paraplex P-13 (flexible)	Rohm & Haas Co.
Plaskon 951 (low exotherm)	Allied Chemical & Dye Corp., Barrett Division
Polylite 8001 (low exotherm)	Reichhold Chemicals, Inc.
Polylite 8004 (low exotherm)	Reichhold Chemicals, Inc.
Selectron 5003	Pittsburgh Plate Glass Co.
Selectron 5081 (low exotherm)	Pittsburgh Plate Glass Co.
Selectron 5096 (flexible)	Pittsburgh Plate Glass Co.
Selectron 5107 (very low exotherm)	Pittsburgh Plate Glass Co.
Stypol 102E	H. H. Robertson Co.
Stypol 107E	H. H. Robertson Co.
Synvar V-2 (flexible)	Synvar Corp.
Synvar V-30	Synvar Corp.
Synvar V-32 (water-clear)	Synvar Corp.
Synvar V-50 (styrene-free, for use at elevated temperatures)	Synvar Corp.
Vibrin 108 (minimum color)	U. S. Rubber Co., Naugatuck Chemical Division
Vibrin 114	U. S. Rubber Co., Naugatuck Chemical Division
Vibrin 121 (flexible)	U. S. Rubber Co., Naugatuck Chemical Division

Table No. 20 gives the properties of the following resins: Laminac 4116, which has excellent electrical properties and is recommended for casting because of its low shrinkage (2046); Polylite 8004, which has a low exotherm and is recommended for casting, potting, and tooling applications (2092): and Paraplex P-43, which is a general-purpose resin with a very light color (1506).

RESINS FOR ELECTRICAL APPLICATIONS

The polyester resins in general have very good electrical properties at room temperature (table No. 13) and are widely used in electrical equipment. In certain applications, however, it is desirable to have a resin exhibiting no drop-off in electrical properties at elevated temperatures or electrical properties superior to those of conventional resins. Other resins are made especially for use as insulating varnishes or coatings. Resins for potting should have the properties of good casting resins (p. 145), as well as good electrical properties. The following resins are either of electrical grade or recommended for specific types of electrical applications by their manufacturers:

Table No. 20.—*Properties of three cured polyester resins recommended for casting*

Property	Laminac 4116 (American Cyanamid)	Paraplex P-43 (Rohm & Haas Co.)	Polylite 8004 (Reichhold Chemicals)
Shrinkage during cure, %	6.5	7.0	6.5
Tensile strength, psi	6,800	9,000	9,000
Flexural strength, psi	12,800	17,500	9,400
Modulus of elasticity in flexure, 10^6 psi	0.61	0.53	......
Compressive strength, psi	......	21,300	20,000
Hardness			
Rockwell M	107	110–120	111
Barcol	42	45–50	45–50
Water absorption, 24-hr. immersion, %	0.24	0.3	0.11
Viscosity of resin as supplied, cps.	330	2000–2400	1760–2270

Manufacturer's designation	*Manufacturer*
Alkydol S-452 (casting of electronic equipment)	Alkydol Laboratories, Inc.
AR-401	General Electric Co.
AR-403	General Electric Co.
BRS-147	Bakelite Co.
Glidpol 1001 (potting)	Glidden Co.
Glidpol 1002 (potting and impregnating)	Glidden Co.
Glykon F-600 (flexible; potting)	General Tire & Rubber Co., Chemical Division
IC-237 (impregnation of copper electrical devices)	Interchemical Corp.
IC-312 (potting)	Interchemical Corp.
IC-401 (potting)	Interchemical Corp.
IC-433 (potting)	Interchemical Corp.
IC-457 (potting)	Interchemical Corp.
IC-514 (potting)	Interchemical Corp.
IC-548	Interchemical Corp.
IC 585	Interchemical Corp.
Laminac 4116 (potting)	American Cyanamid Co.
Laminac PDL 7-719	American Cyanamid Co.
MR-28C (potting)	Celanese Corp., Marco Products Department
MR-28CS (impregnating of electrical components)	Celanese Corp., Marco Products Department
MR-32 (flame resistant, used as base for electrical molding putties)	Celanese Corp., Marco Products Department
MR-33C (flame resistant)	Celanese Corp., Marco Products Department
Plaskon 951 (potting)	Allied Chemical & Dye Corp., Barrett Division
Polylite 8004 (potting)	Reichhold Chemicals, Inc.
Selectron 5209 (potting)	Pittsburgh Plate Glass Co.
Stypol 102E (flexible, impregnation of electrical windings, pottings)	H. H. Robertson Co.
Stypol 107E (impregnation of electrical windings, pottings)	H. H. Robertson Co.
Vibrin 109	U. S. Rubber Co., Naugatuck Chemical Division
Vibrin 114 (potting)	U. S. Rubber Co., Naugatuck Chemical Division

Filled materials based on Stypol 102E and 107E are available for casting and potting applications (Stypol 302E, 502E, 207E, 507E). Filled materials based on Stypol 102E are also available for dip-coating applications (Stypol 602E, 602EP).

The properties of BRS-147, which is recommended for high-frequency electrical applications (2054); Laminac PDL 7-719, which has uniform dielectric properties over a wide temperature range (2107); Selectron

Table No. 21.—*Properties of some cured, unfilled polyester resins recommended for different types of electrical applications*

Property	BRS-147 (Bakelite)	Laminac PDL 7-719 (American Cyanamid)	Selectron 5209 (Pittsburgh Plate Glass)	Stypol 107E (H. H. Robertson)
Heat distortion point, °C.	118	126	......	53
Tensile strength, psi	......	6,300	1,180	7,000
Flexural strength, psi	13,000	10,350	......	11,300
Modulus of elasticity in flexure, 10^6 psi	0.50	0.53	......	0.36
Compressive strength, psi	36,000	......	1,040	......
Impact strength (Izod), ft.-lb. or ft.-lb. per in. notch	2.51 (unnotched)	......	9.8 (notched)	0.7 (notched)
Dielectric constant, 1 megacycle	2.95	2.88	4.84	3.35
Dielectric strength, short-time, volts per mil	......	420	325	255
Power factor, 1 megacycle	0.0105	0.0091	0.0187	0.024
Loss factor	0.030	......	0.0905	......

5209, which was especially developed for potting (2084); and Stypol 107E, an insulating varnish (2093); are given in table No. 21.

RESINS FOR MATCHED METAL DIE MOLDING

Two properties are of importance in resins for matched metal die molding: a fast cure rate and good "hot strength" (that is, the cured resin

Table No. 22.—*Properties of three cured polyester resins recommended for matched metal molding*

Property	AR-401 (General Electric)	Paraplex P-49 (Rohm & Haas)	Plaskon 942 (Allied Chemical & Dye)
Specific gravity	1.29 ± 0.02	......	1.23
Heat distortion point, °C.	68.5–70.0	110	90
Flexural strength, psi	18,600	15,000	12,300
Modulus of elasticity in flexure, 10^6 psi	0.58	0.46	0.63
Compressive strength, psi	27,350	......	25,800
Impact strength, ft.-lb.	0.246 (Izod notched)	3.2 (Charpy unnotched)	......
Barcol hardness	46 ± 2	42	50
Water absorption, 24-hr. immersion, %	......	0.5	0.22
Viscosity of resin as supplied, cps.	3000–4000	2000–2400	2200

will hold together when taken from the mold). The following are examples of resins recommended for this type of molding by their manufacturers:

Manufacturer's designation	*Manufacturer*
AR-401	General Electric Co.
AR-403	General Electric Co.
AR-493	General Electric Co.
Aropol 7100	Archer-Daniels-Midland Co.
Glidpol 1012	Glidden Co.
Glykon R-100	General Tire & Rubber Co., Chemical Division
IC-312	Interchemical Corp.
IC-457	Interchemical Corp.
IC-514	Interchemical Corp.
IC-548	Interchemical Corp.
Laminac 4108	American Cyanamid Co.
Laminac 4123	American Cyanamid Co.
Laminac 4128	American Cyanamid Co.
Paraplex P-47	Rohm & Haas Co.
Paraplex P-49	Rohm & Haas Co.
Plaskon 941	Allied Chemical & Dye Corp., Barrett Division

Manufacturer's designation (Cont'd)   *Manufacturer* (Cont'd)

Plaskon 942	Allied Chemical & Dye Corp., Barrett Division
Polylite 8000	Reichhold Chemicals, Inc.
Polylite 8002	Reichhold Chemicals, Inc.
Polylite 8009	Reichhold Chemicals, Inc.
Selectron 5117	Pittsburgh Plate Glass Co.
Selectron 5118	Pittsburgh Plate Glass Co.
Vibrin 114	U. S. Rubber Co., Naugatuck Chemical Division
Vibrin 115A	U. S. Rubber Co., Naugatuck Chemical Division

Table No. 22 gives the properties of AR-401 (2069), Paraplex P-49 (2094), and Plaskon 942 (2044). Paraplex P-49 cures to a rigid solid; Paraplex P-47 cures to a tough solid and is designed for applications requiring some flexibility.

THIXOTROPIC RESINS

Celanese Corp., Marco Products Department, makes a thixotropic rigid resin, Marcothix #1, especially for use in hand lay-up. It is claimed that this resin will not even drain from smooth vertical surfaces (2058). Marcothix #2 is a thixotropic flexible resin designed primarily for modification of Marcothix #1. Marcothix #3 is a semirigid resin with thixotropic characteristics like those of Marcothix #1.

Some resins may be made thixotropic by addition of a filler (pp. 93, 173). For example, Laminac 4110 or Laminac 4111 (American Cyanamid Co.), which are low-viscosity resins, can be used in hand lay-up without danger of run-off if they are compounded with a thixotropic filler such as Cab-o-sil (Godfrey L. Cabot, Inc.).

COATING RESINS

Polyester resins are used for certain types of coating and surfacing applications. Open-assembly surfacing applications require a resin that cures at room temperature in contact with air. (Even some of the nonair-inhibited polyesters will not dry to a tack-free surface in film form. The resins used for thin surface coatings are generally modified polyesters whose compositions are commercial secrets.) Other coating applications include gel coats, or pigmented surfacing resins applied to molds before molding, impregnating resins for porous materials such as wood, metal, and brick, and baking finishes. Some resins recommended for various coating purposes are:

Manufacturer's designation   *Manufacturer*

Alkydol S-1700 (baked-on finish)	Alkydol Laboratories, Inc.
Amberlac 292 (baked-on finish)	Rohm & Haas Co.
Cordo H57C (gel coating)	Cordo Molding Products, Inc.

Manufacturer's designation (Cont'd)	*Manufacturer* (Cont'd)
Duolite 64C (protective coating for wood, etc.)	Chemical Process Co.
Gel-Kote (gel coating)	Glidden Co.
Glidpol 1002 (cures tack-free in presence of air)	Glidden Co.
Glidpol 4001 (cures tack-free in presence of air)	Glidden Co.
IC-237 (impregnating of metals, including copper and copper alloys)	Interchemical Corp.
IC-336HV (high viscosity, excellent wear and stain resistance)	Interchemical Corp.
IC-988 (impregnating of metals, except copper)	Interchemical Corp.
Laminac 4110 (cures tack-free in presence of air; gel coating)	American Cyanamid Co.
Laminac 4111 (for chemical resistant applications)	American Cyanamid Co.
Laminac 4116 (gel coating)	American Cyanamid Co.
Marcothix #1 (protective coating for concrete or cement block)	Celanese Corp., Marco Products Department
MR-28C (spray coating and impregnating)	Celanese Corp., Marco Products Department
MR-28VS (impregnating of porous surfaces)	Celanese Corp., Marco Products Department
MR-28V (impregnating of porous surfaces)	Celanese Corp., Marco Products Department
Plaskon 9500 (gel coating)	Allied Chemical & Dye Corp., Barrett Division
Synvar V-30 (baked-on finish)	Synvar Corp.
Synvar V-32 (baked-on finish)	Synvar Corp.
Synvar V-35 (baked-on finish)	Synvar Corp.
Vibrin 108 (protective coating)[4]	U. S. Rubber Co., Naugatuck Chemical Division
Vibrin Shellcoat X-1626 (for automobile bodies)	U. S. Rubber Co., Naugatuck Chemical Division

PREIMPREGNATING RESINS AND PREFORM BINDERS

Certain resins are recommended for preimpregnating of glass filler when the material is to be stored and later used in molding or laminating. Some of these resins may be supplied as a powder, which is dissolved in a solvent before use.

Other resins are recommended for use as mat or preform binders. These resins are generally used in emulsion form.

Examples of preimpregnating resins and binders are:

[4]Applied by special film transfer method. Vibrin 109, 112, 132, and 142 may also be used in this method.

Manufacturer's designation	*Manufacturer*
AR-499 (for preimpregnating)	General Electric Co.
Atlac 382 (powder; for preimpregnating)	Atlas Powder Co.
Atlac 370E-32Z (low-solubility powdered binder)	Atlas Powder Co.
Atlac LV (used as emulsion binder)	Atlas Powder Co.
Glidpol 1002 (preform binder)	Glidden Co.
Glidpol 1007 (preform binder)	Glidden Co.
IC-524 (emulsion binder)	Interchemical Corp.
IC-553 (nonvolatile emulsion binder)	Interchemical Corp.
IC-625 (used as emulsion binder)	Interchemical Corp.
IC-638 (very high viscosity DAP[5] resin for preimpregnating)	Interchemical Corp.
Laminac 4128 (used as emulsion binder)	American Cyanamid Co.
Laminac 4171 (powder; for preimpregnating)	American Cyanamid Co.
MR-33H (for preimpregnating)	Celanese Corp., Marco Products Department
Plaskon 920 (DAP resin; used as emulsion binder)	Allied Chemical & Dye Corp., Barrett Division
Paraplex Binder P-800 (emulsion)	Rohm & Haas Co.
Selectron 5930 (preform binder)	Pittsburgh Plate Glass Co.
Vibrin X-1055 (for preimpregnating)	U. S. Rubber Co., Naugatuck Chemical Division

PREFILLED MATERIALS

Certain polyester manufacturers offer prefilled resins. The fillers may be inert mineral fillers, such as silicates and carbonates, or reinforcing fillers, such as glass fibers. Interchemical Corp. offers a wide range of mineral-filled resins for molding, casting, potting, and hand lay-up (2074). Formula 3118, which is a puttylike polyester molding compound produced by Narmco Resins & Coatings Co., also contains inert mineral filler (2082).

The glass fiber filled resins are precatalyzed, ready for immediate use in molding. They are widely used for compression molding at low pressures. Examples of this type of product are:

Manufacturer's designation	*Manufacturer*
AICO 100	American Insulator Corp.
Cordopreg Molding Fiber	Cordo Molding Products, Inc.
Glaskyd 1901 (supplied in rope form)	Glaskyd, Inc.
Glaskyd 1902	Glaskyd, Inc.
Glastic	Glastic Corp.
Fiberfil Styrene G	Fiberfil Corp.
Plaskon 446	Allied Chemical & Dye Corp., Barrett Division

[5]Diallyl phthalate.

Table No. 23.— *Properties of some glass reinforced polyester molding compounds**

Property	Fiberfil Styrene G (Fiberfil Corp.)	Glaskyd 1901 (Glaskyd, Inc.)	Pre-imp (Flexfirm Products)	Thermaflow 100T (rigid) (Thermaflow Chemical)
Specific gravity	1.33	2.15	1.94	1.8
Heat distortion point, °F.	218–222	Above 200	390–410	300
Mold shrinkage, in. per in.	0.001–0.003	0.003	0.001–0.002	0.0005–0.0015
Tensile strength, psi	10,000–12,000	......	12,000–15,000	......
Flexural strength, psi	16,000–18,000	15,000–20,000	14,000–25,000	20,000–25,000
Compressive strength, psi	......	......	35,000–40,000	26,000
Impact strength (Izod), ft.-lb. per in. notch	1.5–2.5	4–5	10–12	12–24
Water absorption, 24-hr. immersion, %	0.10	0.28	0.06–0.09	0.18

*Strength values increase with increase in thickness of section.

Manufacturer's designation (Cont'd)	Manufacturer (Cont'd)
Pre-imp	Flexfirm Products
Thermaflow	Thermaflow Chemical Co.

Some of these compounds may be obtained with special properties, depending on the type of resin used. For example, Thermaflow is available as rigid, semi-rigid, high arc resistance, and flame-resistant types. AICO and Cordopreg are also available as fire-resistant types, as well as standard types. The properties of Fiberfil Styrene G (2065), Glaskyd 1901 (2071), Pre-imp (2067), and Thermaflow 100T (2100) are given in table No. 23.

Precatalyzed resin-impregnated glass cloth materials (prepreg) are available for laminating. These materials are easily handled and provide better control of the resin-to-glass ratio in laminates. The following are examples of preimpregnated glass cloth products:

Manufacturer's designation	Manufacturer
Cordopreg	Cordo Molding Products, Inc.
Dryply	Flexfirm Products
Sunform	Sun Chemical Corp., Electro-Technical Products Division

VIII. TAILOR-MAKING POLYESTERS

In the utilization of plastics by various manufacturers, it is a rare occurrence when requirements of even two of the manufacturers are identical. For example, in the polyester field one manufacturer may require tremendous strength in his product, another flexibility, and still another decorative beauty. Most of the polyesters supplied by the major commercial firms, however, are designed for general-purpose use. To meet a specific requirement, it may be necessary to tailor-make a polyester resin. It may also be necessary to compromise on certain properties in order to obtain a special property.

The main factors with which we can work in tailor-making polyesters are:

(1) The acid components.
(2) The glycol components.
(3) The cross-linking agent.
(4) The molecular weight of the polyester.
(5) The catalyst and inhibitor systems.
(6) The filler materials.

The changes which take place in polyester resins when modifications are made in these factors are discussed in this chapter.

GENERAL CONSIDERATIONS

Before the effects of specific components in unsaturated polyesters are described, some general relationships between properties and chemical composition and structure will be summarized. These will serve as guides for selecting reactants which will contribute desired properties to polyester resins.

Mechanical Strength

In general, the higher the molecular weight of the condensed portion of the polyester resin, the greater the ultimate hardness and strength properties of the cured resin. Flexural strength (bending strength) in particular increases with an increase in molecular weight.

Thermosetting resins which cure to a rigid solid are obtained by cross-linking unsaturated polyester resins with other unsaturated substances. The more unsaturation present in the polyester, the more cross-linking that can occur, and the more rigid is the cured resin. High-molecular-weight unsaturated resins, of course, provide more double bonds for cross-linking and thus a more rigid structure when cured than do low-molecular-weight resins. Abrasion resistance also increases with an increase in the amount of cross-linking.

Flexural strength increases with an increase in the polarity as well as in the molecular weight of the resin (1991, 2159). The introduction of excess hydroxyl or carboxyl groups or an increase in the number of ester or ether linkages will increase the polarity of polyester resins.

Tensile strength depends on a high degree of linear growth of the polyester molecule in the condensation reaction (642). When glycols and dicarboxylic acids containing no nonaromatic unsaturation are used, strictly linear polyesters of high tensile strength are obtained. When the reactants contain substantial amounts of unsaturation, however, it is not always possible to achieve a high degree of linear growth because of cross-linking at the double bonds. To secure maximum tensile strength in the cured polyester, the condensation reaction must be carried out under conditions which will prevent cross-linking and insure the maximum degree of esterification before the reaction is interrupted.

The degree of order in the molecular chain of the polyester also plays an important part in obtaining high tensile strength. Regular spacing of polar groups gives higher tensile strength than random spacing. Therefore, the total number of glycols and acids used in a single polyester should be limited as far as possible if an increase in strength characteristics is desired (643).

Although inherent strength in the resin is desirable, the strength properties of reinforced plastics are largely contributed by the reinforcing filler, i.e., glass fiber. Other properties, such as thermal stability, chemical resistance, and electrical insulation ability, may be of greater importance in the unsaturated polyesters used in reinforced plastics. When polyesters are used without reinforcement, as in casting, potting, or coating, good strength properties are usually required. A certain amount of flexibility is also necessary to help prevent crazing, cracking, and brittleness in the unsupported structure.

Flexibility

Flexibility in polyesters is due mainly to long saturated molecular chains (1991, 2159). It is obtained by reducing the amount of unsaturation, which in turn reduces the chances for cross-linking and prevents branched chain growth.

A high ratio of saturated dibasic acid to unsaturated dibasic acid in the resin formulation imparts softness and flexibility to the cured resin (632). Aliphatic saturated acids have greater effects in these respects than aromatic saturated acids. The flexibility and softness of the resin also increases with increase in the chain length of the saturated acid or with increase in the molar ratio of saturated acid to unsaturated acid. Increased flexibility may require a compromise in regard to the curing rate of the resin, which decreases with increase in the amount of saturated acid since there are fewer chances for cross-linking.

The higher saturated glycols also impart increasing flexibility with increasing length of hydrocarbon chain between the hydroxyl groups. However, it is easier to control the degree of flexibility obtained when long-chain acids are used, and the final resins generally have better strength properties.

The brittle point of cured resins occurs at higher temperatures as the concentration of groups having polar activity, e.g., ester, aromatic, and hydroxyl groups, increases in polyesters. Compounds with long methylene chains tend to form polyesters having low brittle points. Polyesters containing no aromatic groups and fewer than one ester group per five atoms in the linear chains will produce cured polymers which have brittle points below $-40\,^\circ$C. (643).

Crystallinity

Liquid resins are generally preferred in the low-pressure laminating and molding processes in which unsaturated polyesters are used. They give good impregnation of glass reinforcing material and will flow into all parts of a mold cavity. Limited crystallinity at room temperature, however, may be desirable to improve ease of handling in shipping. This property is also of value in the resins used in preimpregnated glass cloth or mat (prepreg) which is to be stored for later use. Application of heat will melt the resin crystals.

Crystallinity can be controlled by the choice of reactants in preparing the polyester. Resins formed by the reaction of a polymethylene glycol, such as ethylene glycol, with a polymethylene dicarboxylic acid, such as adipic acid, are very crystalline. On the other hand, noncrystalline resins are usually formed by the reaction of glycols with dicarboxylic acids where either contains frequently occurring or large side chains, large amounts of nonaromatic unsaturation, aromatic groups, or hetero atoms. However, if the other member of the reaction mixture is a polymethylene glycol or polymethylene dicarboxylic acid, the crystallizing tendency increases as the length of the polymethylene chain increases (3, 414, 643).

Propylene glycol, which may be considered an alkyl-substituted polymethylene glycol, reduces the crystallizing tendency of polyesters because it introduces methyl groups unsymmetrically into the polyester chain. (The reduction in crystallizing tendency is less if side chain constituents are introduced symmetrically, as with neopentyl glycol.) Unsaturation may be introduced by the use of unsaturated acids such as fumaric acid or maleic anhydride. Phthalic anhydride provides aromatic groups and thus reduces crystallinity. The most readily available reactants containing hetero atoms are diethylene and dipropylene glycols, which contain oxygen bridges.

The greater the number of acids and glycols used in the resin, the lesser is the tendency to crystallize.

Thermal Stability

The thermal stability of polyesters may be improved by elimination of weak spots in the polyester molecular chain and by using catalysts which do not leave unstable decomposition products. Cross-linking, crystallinity, and aromatic groups also contribute to heat resistance (2173). Other beneficial changes in chemical structure are incorporation of fluorine, chlorine, or inorganic nuclei such as boric acid in the molecule.

The introduction of structures which have poor thermal stability should be avoided, since these structures will in turn reduce the stability of the final resin. Oxygen ether linkages in glycols, for example, result in resins of low heat resistance. Heat resistance also decreases with increase in the length of the glycol chain. Unreacted carboxyl groups in polyesters provide a weak point for thermal degradation; polyesters without these groups but otherwise similar are more stable. Other weak points are alkyl branching on alpha carbon atoms; nitrile, acetoxy, chloro, or hydroxyl groups on alternate carbon atoms of hydrocarbon chains; and terminal hydroxyl groups.

The presence of a methylene group ($-CH_2-$) two carbon atoms removed from either oxygen of a carboxyl group is a key weak point for thermal degradation (1311). Replacing a hydrogen of this beta-methylene group with a methyl group (CH_3-) considerably increases thermal stability. Accordingly, it would seem that glycols whose beta carbon atom is methylated, as in neopentyl glycol (2,2-dimethyl propanediol-1,3), should give good heat resistance.

In the glass reinforced polyesters, the use of vinyl trichlorosilane finish on the reinforcement results in a better bond between the glass and the resin, thus increasing the thermal stability of the reinforced plastic.

Melting Point

High-melting polyesters generally contain aromatic nuclei introduced through the use of an aromatic acid. An aromatic glycol such as *trans*-quinitol may also be used (4). It is virtually impossible to obtain polyesters of relatively high melting point (above 180°-200°C.) from ordinary aliphatic dicarboxylic acids and glycols.

An odd number of atoms in the hydrocarbon chain will give low melting points (1169).

Flame Resistance

Introduction of suitable chlorine compounds into polyester molecules results in lowering of flammability. The chlorine in these compounds must be stably bound, in order to retain flame-proofing effectiveness at relatively high temperatures. Chlorinated paraffins are sometimes added to polyesters in an attempt to reduce flammability, but the chlorine in these compounds is very loosely held (2108). More effective agents are chlorinated aromatic dicarboxylic acids, such as tetrachlorophthalic acid, which also provide aromatic nuclei for added heat resistance. Polyesters of very high flame resistance are produced with hexachloroendomethylene tetrahydrophthalic acid, which contains over 50% of stable chlorine.

Addition of antimony oxide to chlorine-containing polyesters further improves flame resistance.

Bromine and fluorine compounds in which the halogen is stably bound can also be used to impart flame resistance. Fluorine might give even higher resistance than chlorine because of the high thermal stability obtained by incorporation of fluorine in polyester molecules. For example, a polyester from difluorotetrachloroendomethylene tetrahydrophthalic acid, maleic anhydride, and ethylene glycol had a weight loss of only 6.7% after exposure to 200°C. for 30 days. Corresponding polyesters from phthalic anhydride and from hexachloroendomethylene tetrahydrophthalic anhydride had weight losses of 25.6% and 14.4%, respectively (2203).

Certain phosphonate compounds, such as diallyl isobutenyl phosphonate and diallyl phenyl phosphonate, increase flame resistance when used as cross-linking agents (700, 701).

High hydrocarbon content should be avoided when low flammability is desired in polyesters (2173).

Electrical Properties

The electrical insulating properties of polyesters improve with a decrease in polarity and an increase in hydrocarbon content. Since mechanical strength improves with an increase in the number of polar groups in the resin, there must often be a compromise between strength and electrical properties (2173).

For low electrical conductivity, the number of unreacted hydroxyl and carboxyl groups should be kept as low as possible. One method of achieving this is to use the methyl esters of dicarboxylic acids and prepare polyesters by an ester-exchange reaction. Resins of very low acid number are obtained because the residual carboxyl groups remain esterified with the methyl group.

For optimum electrical properties, it is also preferable to use glycols which do not have any oxygen bridges, since ether linkages increase the polarity of the resin.

Chemical Resistance

Cross-linking and crystallinity are the building elements for chemically resistant polyesters (2173). Fluorine also improves chemical resistance (2159).

Resins of high hydrocarbon content should not be used for applications requiring chemical resistance. Ester and amide linkages are not stable in strong alkali (2173). However, polyesters containing a large number of ester groups in their linear chains are claimed to have good resistance to liquid hydrocarbons (643).

Addition of compounds containing olefinic unsaturation and having a functionality greater than two is claimed to increase the resistance of polyesters to hydrolysis (3). Aconitic acid is especially suitable for this purpose.

Viscosity

The viscosity of a polyester in the liquid state can be controlled by the type of reactants used in its preparation. The more nearly equal the molecular proportions of dicarboxylic acids and dihydroxy alcohols used, the greater is the average number of acid and alcohol residues in the molecular chain of the polyester, and the greater the viscosity (420). Modification with monohydroxy alcohols and monocarboxylic acids helps terminate linear chain growth, thus reducing the average number of acid and glycol residues and lowering the viscosity (610).

The addition of alcohols with more than two hydroxyl groups or acids with more than two carboxylic groups to the resin formulation will increase viscosity, since additional cross-linking can occur through the excess hydroxyl or carboxyl groups. The danger in using these reactants is that excessive viscosity will be obtained through cross-linking before maximum esterification and linear growth can occur (420).

Water Sensitivity

Low water absorption is related to high hydrocarbon content and crystallinity (2173). Structural features to be avoided if water sensitivity is undesirable include excess hydroxyl groups, amide linkages, and ether linkages.

Ether linkages are sometimes introduced in polyester resins to obtain water solubility (731). Glycols which contain oxygen bridges, such as diethylene glycol, are used in this case. However, the water sensitivity of the ether linkages makes other methods of obtaining soluble resins more advantageous (see p. 167).

Clarity and Light Stability

To obtain clear, colorless resins, the first step is to use raw materials which are free from color-forming impurities (see p. 233) or which do not give rise to color bodies during preparation of the resins. It is best to use glycols which do not contain oxygen bridges, since the presence of oxygen bridges may lead to the formation of color bodies. Metallic ions (e.g., cobalt ions from cobalt salts used as accelerators) also act as color formers.

Clear, colorless resins for use in transparent laminates may be prepared by using compounds with a high index of refraction, close to that of glass. High-boiling allyl compounds, such as allyl diglycolate and diallyl phenyl phosphonate, are particularly suitable since they can be used as cross-linking agents. These compounds also reduce the rate of cure, and in some instances a compromise must be made between this property and the degree of transparency desired.

Even if care is taken in choosing high-purity raw materials and formulating resins, conventional polyesters are not stable on prolonged exposure to light. They strongly absorb ultraviolet light (sunlight contains 3 to 5% of ultraviolet radiation) which initiates chemical changes causing yellowing or darkening. The aromatic nuclei of the phthalic esters and styrene groups in cured polyesters are largely responsible for the ultraviolet absorption properties of these products (3227).

In translucent glass fiber-polyester panels used as decorative and structural materials, light stability is necessary. To provide this property, resin manufacturers incorporate in the resin materials which have a high absorption capacity for ultraviolet light but which dissipate the absorbed energy in a manner that neither physically damages the polyester nor produces color. Dean and Manasia investigated a number of such stabilizers (3227). They found that ortho-hydroxy-benzophenone derivatives were very effective in stabilizing polyesters. Phenyl salicylate was also a good stabilizer but somewhat less active.

Air-Drying Properties

The preparation of polyester resins substantially insensitive to inhibition by atmospheric oxygen has been an objective of commercial research for several years. The successful development of such resins would facilitate continuous production of curved shapes, by eliminating requirements for surface protection by films or inert gas, and would open the field to new lacquer-type products. Ordinary polyesters are air-inhibited in thin films even when so-called driers such as cobalt naphthenate are present.

Several commercial firms have recently introduced resins with markedly improved resistance to air inhibition (see p. 139). The approaches used in these developments may include:

(1) Placing protective end groups on unsaturated polyester chains. Monocarboxylic acids or monohydroxy alcohols may be used for this purpose, depending on whether the polyester contains an excess of hydroxyl or carboxyl groups (see p. 170).

(2) Using mercaptans as accelerators (see p.63).

(3) Mixing with the resin a substance which becomes less compatible with the resin as it polymerizes and therefore synerizes out to the resin surface and forms an air-excluding film.

(4) Using certain chemical types of polyester resins which are less susceptible to air inhibition than others. Pentadiene polyesters with certain accelerator-catalyst systems (see p. 164) offer some advantages. Isophthalic acid also decreases air inhibition.

Commercial nonair-inhibited resins will dry to a nontacky surface under most conditions, but not usually in thin film form. Those resins recommended for film coatings are generally modified polyesters whose compositions are commercial secrets.

VARIATION IN INGREDIENTS

Unsaturated Acids

The most important unsaturated dicarboxylic acids used in commercial polyester resins are maleic acid (anhydride) and fumaric acid, which have alpha,beta unsaturation. When maleic acid is used, a certain amount of isomer conversion to fumaric acid occurs during the esterification reaction. However, resins prepared from each of the acids do exhibit some differences.

Maleic acid polyesters are more quickly prepared and are less crystalline than fumaric acid polyesters. The latter difference is especially apparent in polyesters prepared from glycols which possess a symmetrical structure and which are free from oxygen bridges (219, 2181). Such glycols include ethylene glycol, trimethylene glycol, and neopentyl glycol. If ethylene glycol is used, for example, the fumaric acid polyesters tend to crystallize from styrene solution on standing, but the maleic acid polyesters are more stable in this respect.

The pastelike consistency of fumaric acid polyesters in styrene is sometimes a useful property when a thixotropic resin is necessary, as in vertical lay-ups. The fumaric polyesters can also be converted to a free-flowing granular form which is easier to handle in shipping than a liquid resin (219).

When nonsymmetrical glycols such as propylene glycol are used in fumaric acid polyesters, there is a slight increase in the solubility of the ester in styrene and in the softness of the cured resin. Fumaric acid-propylene glycol polyesters have a slightly higher heat distortion point than their maleic acid counterparts.

One of the principal reasons for using fumaric acid instead of maleic acid in the preparation of polyesters is the corrosiveness of the maleic acid vapors. Glass-lined equipment or a diluent (usually xylene) for the corrosive vapors should be used in the preparation of maleic acid polyesters. An antioxidant should also be used to prevent premature gelation. These precautions are not necessary in the preparation of fumaric acid polyesters.

Other alpha,beta-unsaturated dibasic acids, such as muconic, dihydromuconic, citraconic, mesaconic, and itaconic acids, are sometimes used in polyesters. With increase in the chain length of the acid used, a corresponding increase in flexibility and softness is obtained. No advantages in strength or other properties are obtained, however, over the fumaric and maleic acid polyesters. Price restrictions also limit the commercial use of these acids.

Polycarboxylic acids having a functionality greater than two, for example, aconitic acid, may be added to reaction mixtures in order to obtain polyesters with increased viscosity in the liquid state and increased resistance to hydrolysis (3).

Adducts of maleic anhydride with certain conjugated dienes can be reacted with glycols to form polyesters. Two compounds of this type are of special interest: endomethylene tetrahydrophthalic acid ("Carbic Anhydride"[1]) from cyclopentadiene and hexachloroendomethylene tetrahydrophthalic acid (HET[2] acid) from hexachlorocyclopentadiene. The first is used in polyesters to improve air-drying properties, generally in conjunction with a cobalt drier to reduce stickiness (271). (The resins obtained, however, are not air-drying in thin films.) The second contains over 50%

[1]Trade name of Carbide & Carbon Chemicals Co.
[2]Trade name of Hooker Electrochemical Co.

by weight of stable chlorine and imparts unusually high flame resistance to polyesters.

Tetrahydrophthalic acid is the adduct of maleic anhydride with butadiene. It forms resins with properties similar to those from endomethylene tetrahydrophthalic acid (612).

All three adducts contain double bonds, but these bonds do not have sufficient reactivity to enter into addition reactions with styrene under the usual conditions for cross-linking polyesters. In order to form thermoset resins, it is necessary to incorporate active unsaturation. Such unsaturation can be provided by maleic anhydride or fumaric acid, usually in the ratio of 2 moles of active unsaturated compound to 1 mole of adduct.

Saturated Acids

In commercial unsaturated polyesters, phthalic anhydride is the saturated acid used in largest volume. It is used primarily in rigid resin formulations, where its principal functions are to increase the compatibility of the resin with styrene and to reduce brittleness. It is sometimes added to resin formulations in order to obtain some flexibility without too much sacrifice in ultimate flexural strength. The aromatic groups introduced by phthalic anhydride may also serve to reduce crystallizing tendencies.

The molar ratio of phthalic anhydride to unsaturated acid usually ranges from $1:2$ to $1:6$. The latter ratio gives very rigid resins with very high heat distortion points. An increase in the molar ratio of phthalic anhydride to unsaturated acid results in an increase in the softness and flexibility of the cured resin. However, this is not generally used as a means for preparing commercial flexible polyester resins, since there is a corresponding decrease in tensile strength. When the molar ratio (saturated: unsaturated) is between $2:1$ and $4:1$ the cured resin is very "cheesy" and shatters rather than bends upon impact.

Other saturated aromatic acids used in unsaturated polyesters are, for the most part, chlorinated dicarboxylic acids used in preparing flame-resistant resins. The most common of these acids is tetrachlorophthalic anhydride. Dicarboxylic acids containing chlorinated aromatic nuclei, however, should not be used for the preparation of polyesters for high-temperature applications, since they are more easily decarboxylated than their analogues containing no chlorine (2194).

Increased strength, higher melting points, and other advantages might be obtained by substitution of isophthalic or terephthalic acids for phthalic anhydride.

Isophthalic acid produces polyesters with substantially higher softening points than those of phthalic anhydride polyesters (3225). Cured isophthalic resins have higher heat distortion temperatures, and better flexural and impact strength properties than similar resins prepared from phthalic anhydride. The viscosity of isophthalic unsaturated polyesters is considerably greater than that of phthalic anhydride polyesters of corresponding acid number. If a phthalic anhydride-maleic anhydride polyester which has a 1:1 molar ratio of saturated to unsaturated acid is cooked to an acid number of 18 and dissolved in 30% of styrene, the solution has a viscosity of 2700 centipoises. An isophthalic acid-maleic anhydride polyester with the same molar ratio and cooked to an acid number of 16 gives a viscosity of 27000 centipoises in 30% of styrene.

Terephthalic acid at present is used largely in the preparation of linear saturated polyesters for high-strength films and fibers (see p. 199). Although no data are available, it is possible that the substitution of this acid for phthalic anhydride in unsaturated polyesters would cause even further increases in certain strength values for cured resins, particularly in tensile strength.

Not much advantage is gained by using an aliphatic dicarboxylic acid as the saturated component of polyesters until the chain of the acid becomes long enough to contribute a certain amount of flexibility and still retain tensile strength. Straight-chain saturated (polymethylene) acids increase the crystallizing tendencies of polyesters, especially if used with polymethylene glycols.

Commercial flexible resins are generally prepared by using a fairly high molar ratio of saturated acid to unsaturated acid. Adipic acid is the saturated acid commonly used for this purpose, although other long-chain aliphatic acids such as sebacic and pimelic acids may also be used.

Adipic acid may be used in molar ratios of saturated to unsaturated acid ranging from 2:1 to 8:1. A molar ratio of 8:1 usually gives a resin which approaches the point of being "cheesy" and loses much of its tensile strength. A molar ratio of 2:1 yields a resin which is very stiff but which still has a certain degree of toughness and impact resistance. Intermediate degrees of flexibility are obtainable by using molar ratios between these two extremes. The usual ratio of adipic acid to unsaturated acid in commercial flexible resins is 6:1.

Glycols

The glycol component, as well as the acid component, has important effects on the properties of a polyester resin. Properties which are particularly affected by the choice of glycol include flexibility, crystallinity, and water sensitivity.

As the chain length of the glycol increases, the flexibility of the polyester increases. The resultant resins, however, do not have the general overall strength characteristics of the flexible resins made by increasing the chain length of the saturated acid component, unless the chain length of the glycol is very long. Price considerations in this case dictate preparation of commercial flexible resins from saturated acids.

Polymethylene glycols and other glycols of symmetrical structure increase the crystallizing tendency of polyesters. Ethylene glycol is the most readily available glycol of symmetrical structure. Polyesters prepared essentially from ethylene glycol and unsaturated dicarboxylic acids, especially fumaric acid, tend to become hazy or to crystallize upon standing (684). With polymethylene acids such as adipic acid, ethylene glycol produces very crystalline polyesters.

Higher polymethylene glycols, such as trimethylene, tetramethylene, and decamethylene glycols, increase the crystallizing tendency in proportion to the increase in chain length of the glycol. Glycols in which methyl groups are attached symmetrically to the glycol chain will also produce crystalline polyesters. Neopentyl glycol (2,2-dimethyl propanediol-1,3), for example, contains two symmetrical methyl groups and produces crystalline polyesters with fumaric acid (1297).

The most available glycols for reducing crystallinity are propylene glycol, which contains an unsymmetrical methyl group, and diethylene and and dipropylene glycols, which contain an odd oxygen atom. Propylene glycol produces viscous gums with most dicarboxylic acids. Even with polymethylene dicarboxylic acids (between succinic and sebacic) it yields noncrystalline polyesters (3, 414, 643).

The oxygen bridges in diethylene and dipropylene glycols will increase the water sensitivity of the cured resins. This is also true of the tri- and tetra- ethylene and propylene glycols which are occasionally used in commercial polyesters.

Propylene glycol will give water solubility without the introduction of an undesirable oxygen bridge (271). Propylene glycol polyesters also generally dissolve more easily in styrene than polyesters from other glycols, e.g., diethylene or ethylene glycols.

The introduction of propylene glycol into ethylene glycol polyesters (1:1 molar ratio of ethylene to propylene glycol) increases the stability of these polyesters in the liquid state and their miscibility with styrene (684). The propylene glycol-ethylene glycol polyesters also have high compressive strength as compared to the low strength of polyesters prepared from propylene glycol alone.

Substitution of polyhydroxy alcohols containing more than two hydroxyl groups for commercially used glycols permits more cross-linking through the additional hydroxyl groups. Resins with a highly branched structure and a great rigidity can be produced in this manner. However, the polyhydroxy alcohols react very readily with unsaturated acids, and it is not easy to control the reaction and prevent premature gelation. Polyhydroxy alcohols such as glycerol and pentaerythritol are used in resins which are to be cross-linked by isocyanates to provide the excess hydroxyl groups required for this reaction.

Resins which are water soluble but not water sensitive can be prepared from maleic anhydride and certain polyhydroxy alcohols (731). The alcohols should contain 2–6 hydroxyl groups but no oxygen except in the hydroxyl groups and have an OH/C ratio of 0.6 to 1.0. Pentaerythritol is listed as a suitable alcohol for this purpose.

One type of glycol which has not been thoroughly investigated is unsaturated glycols, probably because these compounds have not been commercially available until recently. Several unsaturated glycols are now on the market, including 2,5-dimethyl 3-hexyne-2,5-diol, 3,6-dimethyl 4-octyne-3,6-diol, and 2-butene-1,4-diol (1371, 1373, 1377).

It would seem that resins prepared from unsaturated glycols should have certain advantages if the glycols could be obtained relatively cheaply. An additional point for cross-linking in the glycol part of the polyester molecule would provide for a more highly branched structure, and, consequently, a more rigid structure. It remains to be seen, however, whether such a structure would have sufficient tensile strength to be usable.

Cross-Linking Agents

Styrene is commonly used for cross-linking polyesters. The most important properties of resins which are affected by varying the amount of styrene are hardness and strength. If the theoretical amount of styrene for a 1:1 reaction with the resin unsaturation (around 15 to 20%) is used, the the resultant polymer is fairly brittle and hard and has little strength value for commercial application. Optimum strength is obtained by increasing the amount of styrene to about 30%, as is common with most commercial resins. (See table No. 13, p. 132, for the range of strength properties of commercial rigid and flexible polyester resins.) Increasing the styrene amount to 40%, 50%, or 60% results in a decline in the strength properties of the resin.

Diallyl phthalate is also important commercially as a cross-linking agent. It is used to obtain resins for applications where a slower cure may be tolerated and somewhat greater flexibility is necessary, as in reinforced pipe manufacture. The polymerization of resins cross-linked with diallyl phthalate can be interrupted in the gel state, which is an advantage for use in preimpregnated cloth and mat. Diallyl phthalate has a very low vapor pressure and thus is less likely to evaporate in wet lay-up processes.

Triallyl cyanurate is used as a cross-linking agent when high-temperature stability is required. It forms extremely stable cross-linkages which impart not only heat resistance but also chemical resistance. Glass cloth laminates prepared from polyester resins cross-linked with triallyl cyanurate exhibit good properties when aged at 300° F. and retain much of their strength at 500° F. (see table No. 18, p. 143).

Diallyl bicyclo(2,2,1)-hept-5-ene-2,3-dicarboxylate also forms polyesters with high strength retention at 500° F., according to Cummings and Botwick (3226). Mixtures of this monomer with triallyl cyanurate give polyester-glass cloth laminates which heat age better than laminates prepared with either monomer alone. This synergism is related to a reduction of laminate crazing and a corresponding decrease in surface exposed to oxidative attack.

A tremendous variety of cross-linking agents may be used for polyester resins, including any material which has vinyl unsaturation and which can be polymerized. Materials which have been specifically mentioned for this purpose are divinylbenzene, vinyltoluene, a great number of acrylate and methacrylate monomers, and many allyl compounds. Aside from special properties contributed by certain of these agents (pp. 30-32), their main effects are on the cure time, either lengthening or shortening it, and on the softness and flexibility of the resin. For example, divinylbenzene gives additional rigidity to polyester resins but the cure cycle of the resins is very difficult to control. In the preparation of the resins, premature gelation may occur unless conditions are closely controlled. Vinyltoluene produces no great changes in polyester resins as compared with resins cross-linked with styrene. Any of the materials mentioned for use as cross-linking agents may, of course, be used to produce resins of varying softness by varying the amount of cross-linking agent used.

MOLECULAR WEIGHT CHANGES

An increase in the molecular weight of a polyester resin results in an increase in the hardness, softening point, and flexural and tensile strength values of the cured resin. To increase the (average) molecular weight of a resin, low-molecular-weight chain segments must be eliminated. This is accomplished in unsaturated polyesters by controlling the polycondensation conditions so that maximum esterification is obtained and addition polymerization through double bonds is prevented. Inhibitors of addition polymerization, such as hydroquinone, are therefore usually added during the polycondensation reaction. Cooking for a longer time at a lower temperature will increase the formation of high-molecular-weight chain segments.

The greater the amount of unsaturation present, the more closely the cooking time and temperature have to be controlled in order to prevent gelation through double-bond polymerization. One method for reducing this danger is to esterify the saturated acid with the glycol until an acid number of about 50 is reached and at this point to add the unsaturated acid and continue the polymerization. By this means, the unsaturated acid is not allowed to react at the esterification temperature and double-bond polymerization is prevented. The resultant resin has a higher molecular weight, as indicated by viscosity, and somewhat better strength characteristics when cured than a resin prepared by adding all reactants simultaneously.

In another method used for varying the molecular weight of commercial polyester resins, a resin batch with a low acid number of about 20 is prepared and blended with other resin batches with an acid number of about 50. A resin with a large proportion of highly polymerized molecules is obtained in less time by this method than by straight polymerization. Flexible resins, that is resins containing adipic acid, may be safely condensed to a low acid number because of the smaller proportion of unsaturated acid they contain.

A third method for controlling molecular weight in polyester resins is the use of either monocarboxylic acids or monohydroxy alcohols to provide chain-terminating groups. In this procedure if an excess of glycol is used in the reaction, the end of each chain should contain a glycol group after a certain point in the reaction has been reached. Sufficient monocarboxylic acid, such as acetic acid, is then added to react with the glycol groups and thus end the chain growth and the polymerization reaction. Monohydroxy alcohols have similar effects when excess dicarboxylic acid is used and the chain ends contain carboxyl groups.

Commercial polyester resins are usually based on a molecular weight which is a compromise between desired strength factors and an economical time of preparation. Final viscosity adjustments on all commercial resins are made with styrene.

CATALYST AND INHIBITOR SYSTEMS

The catalysts used with polyester resins largely determine the cure cycle of the resin (see chapter on catalysis and inhibition, p. 46), which may in turn influence the physical properties of the final products. The catalyst benzoyl peroxide, for example, effects the rapid cure of polyesters at elevated temperatures; methylethyl ketone peroxide is commonly used for slower room-temperature cures. Table No. 24 gives a comparison of the electrical properties of a typical glass reinforced polyester laminate cured by heat and at room temperature.

In general, moldings produced by low-temperature cures are more strain-free than those produced by high-temperature cures. Mohaupt and Freas, however, found that glass cloth polyester laminates cured with benzoyl

Table No. 24.—*Electrical properties* of a typical glass reinforced polyester laminate cured by heat and room temperature***

Electrical property	Heat cure (25 psi, 110°–120°C.)	Room-temperature cure (contact pressure)
Dielectric strength, volts per mil		
Short-time	278	422
Step-by-step	244	350
Power factor at 25°C., 1 megacycle		
Dry	0.0173	0.0148
3 days wet	0.061	0.0574
Dielectric constant at 25°C.		
Dry	4.20	4.13
3 days wet	4.86	4.60
Arc resistance at 25°C., sec.	154	135

*Average.

**Source: General Electric Co. booklet on "Polyester Resins for Matched Die Molding, Wet Lay-Up, and Laminating."

peroxide at high temperatures had slightly higher hardness and static strength than laminates formulated with the same resin-catalyst system but with promoters added in order to effect cure at room temperature (3169). High-temperature cures are also faster and therefore more economical than low-temperature cures.

Resin manufacturers must compromise between the most desirable properties for their products and the most economical molding cycles. In most cases this can be determined only by actual plant tests with various catalyst systems and operating conditions. Valuable information can also be obtained from catalyst manufacturers on the effects of their products.

The effect of the catalyst system on the light stability and other aging properties of polyester resins is important, especially if a clear, colorless resin is desired. Cumene hydroperoxide is claimed to cause less yellowing or darkening of cured resins after aging than other common catalysts. Dean and Manasia found that cast polyester panels cured with benzoyl peroxide paste (50% benzoyl peroxide in tricresyl phosphate) had poorer light stability than panels cured with solid benzoyl peroxide (3227). This was attributed to an adverse action of the tricresyl phosphate. In the same series of tests, addition of small amounts of cobalt naphthenate with benzoyl peroxide, methylethyl ketone peroxide, or cumene hydroperoxide did not affect the light stability of cured panels. When the cobalt naphthenate content became appreciable, however, there was noticeable deterioration. (Cobalt and other metallic ions, even in minute amounts, act as catalysts for the development of color.)

The R_1R_2CHO— radicals formed in decomposition of hydroperoxide catalysts are said to serve as centers of thermal degradation (2163).

Certain accelerators used with peroxide catalysts, such as cobalt naphthenate and mercaptans, will improve the air-drying properties of polyester resins (see pp. 63, 163, 164).

Inhibitors play an important part in the determination of resin properties. The peak exotherm (highest temperature reached by the resin during curing) and the cure time of polyester resins are mainly determined by the inhibitor they contain. To some extent the inhibitor may also affect the strength and flexibility of the cured resin, if the amount of inhibitor is so great as to prevent the full cure of the resin under ordinary conditions.

The amount of heat (or exotherm) liberated during curing is constant for a particular type of polyester. The rate at which this heat is liberated, however, can be greatly changed by variations in either the concentration or type of inhibitor. For all practical purposes, resins can be fashioned which meet almost any curing conditions simply by varying the amount of inhibitor. Resins which will gel in 2 minutes or in 25 to 30 minutes at 180°F. may be prepared by using the same resin base and catalyst system and varying the amount of inhibitor. In like manner, peak exotherms for these resins can be varied from approximately 450°F. down to 190°F.

Inhibitor formulations used in commercial polyester resins are closely guarded secrets. In order to avoid violating commercial confidences, the comments made here will be restricted to published information regarding inhibitors. The various types of inhibitors have been discussed fully in the chapter on catalysis and inhibition (p. 52). We shall therefore also limit this discussion to remarks on the effects of specific inhibitors on resin properties.

Hydroquinone, a widely used inhibitor, is generally used in concentrations of 0.005% to about 0.01%, based on the total weight of the resin. Greater amounts of hydroquinone cause the exotherm curve to be drawn out and the peak exotherm to be lower. Increasing the amount of hydroquinone may also cause yellowing and other undesirable aging characteristics such as poor surface and decreased weather resistance.

Excellent inhibition is obtained with quaternary ammonium salts, such as trimethyl benzyl ammonium chloride, and most important, side effects, such as gelation caused by metal contaminants, are eliminated. Inhibitors of this type are covered by a patent issued to the Pittsburgh Plate Glass Co. (333).

Quinone is ordinarily used when the resin is to be sold and used immediately; this inhibitor, in the concentrations in which it is generally used, may not prevent gelation during long-term aging. A common practice when quinone is used in resins that are to be stored for any length of time or shipped great distances is to add some hydroquinone. Increasing the amount of quinone greatly increases yellowness in polyester resins.

Para-tertiary-butyl catechol may be used in resins to be stored at room temperature, but high-temperature stability is not practical with this inhibitor.

FILLERS

Fillers have been discussed previously (p. 73), but it may be advisable to mention again some of the variations which are possible by the use of fillers.

Structural fillers, such as glass fiber, are used mainly to prepare panels and other materials having high flexural and tensile strengths. The strength characteristics of the final materials are due almost entirely to the glass. The resin serves as a supporting medium for the glass fiber to allow it to attain as much of its ultimate strength as possible.

The usual reasons for modification of polyesters with bulk fillers are to increase water resistance, relieve strains, lower price, or provide opaqueness. Another change possible with bulk fillers is adjustment of viscosity. The most important application of fillers, particularly clays, for this purpose is in thixotropic resins. The thixotropic resins are the so-called stay-put materials and flow only when pressure is applied.

EQUIPMENT FOR TAILOR-MAKING POLYESTERS

When polyesters are prepared on a laboratory scale with the aim of working out process variables, it is important to work under such conditions that the results can be projected immediately to a large-scale plant. If the ultimate resin is to be prepared in glass-lined containers, the laboratory preparation obviously should be in glass containers. Likewise, if stainless steel equipment is to be used in the plant preparation of these resins, it is advisable to use stainless steel laboratory equipment. Even in laboratory preparation of polyesters the inert gas flow and the mixing action in the reactor must be carefully controlled, since these two factors materially affect the rate of polymerization.

Miniature stainless steel polymerization vessels are available commercially.[3] These vessels have automatic programming equipment and thus a precise duplication of large-scale results is possible.

[3]Castor Engineering Co., Carnegie, Pa.

IX. FINAL PRODUCTS

The end results of the knowledge gained by researchers and fabricators, as found in the application and use of polyester and reinforced polyester products, are discussed in this chapter. Only a brief mention of most of the numerous consumer items appears, but the important classes of products are covered with attention to their properties.

Shortages of materials during World War II promoted the acceptance and use of polyesters, and military purposes are still among the most important ones utilizing these materials. Industrial and consumer uses are rapidly coming to the forefront, however, and expansion of the polyester industry is definitely in that direction.

A section on the general properties of polyester resins and reinforced polyesters is included in order to illustrate the advantages and disadvantages involved in their use in fabricated products. A short discussion of the future of the polyester field is also included.

PROPERTIES OF POLYESTER RESINS

Cured, Unfilled Polyester Resins

Cured polyester resins vary from soft and flexible to hard and rigid. Their electrical properties are excellent, they are dimensionally stable, and they can be obtained in many colors.

The range of properties of unfilled, cured rigid and flexible resins is shown in table No. 13 in the chapter on commercial resins (p. 132). The general types of polyester resins available are also discussed in that chapter.

Reinforced Polyesters

Addition of reinforcing material, such as glass fibers, to polyester resins gives them greater strength, dimensional stability, and over-all versatility for a wider range of product uses.

It is impossible, however, to list specific properties for reinforced polyesters, as one can do for a metal. The properties vary with the type of resin (p. 131) and the amount and type of filler and reinforcement (p.

174

73). Fabrication variables also affect the properties of finished materials (p. 97).

Even if reliable property data were available, the absence of practical experience with many products and the absence of good nondestructive test methods would prevent engineers from designing to the highest property values. The Standards of the American Society for Testing Materials and other test methods set up for quality control and comparison of resins are not intended as a basis for engineering design data. Load-deformation curves indicate that parts may fail at strength levels far below the ultimate determined by these tests (1926). Some designers recognize this fact and design at 20% of ultimate strength.

At present, experience and experimentation are the most reliable guides in choosing a reinforced polyester for a product and in designing the product.[1] Some general property indications, however, can be given for reinforced polyesters. Their outstanding properties are:

(1) A high strength-to-weight ratio. This may result in a saving of over 50% in weight when reinforced polyesters are substituted for steel, and over 30% when substituted for aluminum.

(2) Resiliency. The impact resistance of reinforced polyesters compares favorably with that of aluminum and steel.

(3) Excellent electrical properties. Reinforced polyesters have a low power factor, good arc resistance, and high dielectric strength.

(4) Good resistance, in general, to attack by water, salts, weak acids and alkalies, and organic solvents. Actual plant tests are advised, however, for specific applications.

(5) Moldability. It is possible to mold any shape, and once the reinforced polyester has set, it is dimensionally stable. Color and metal parts can be molded in directly.

(6) Low heat transmission.

(7) Good light transmission.

Some properties of reinforced polyesters, however, are disadvantages in many applications. These include the following:

(1) Rapid loss of strength with temperature increase. Many commonly used resins begin to lose their strength above 180° F. Resin manufac-

---

[1]Since this text was written, one book has been published and another is near publication which will aid designers of reinforced plastic products. "Fiberglas Reinforced Plastics," prepared by Owens-Corning Fiberglas Corp. (Reinhold, New York, 1954, 250 pp.), contains a chapter on design considerations, as well as useful property tables. In the revised ANC-17 *Bulletin on Plastics for Aircraft*, which is being prepared by the U. S. Forest Products Laboratory in cooperation with the Air Force, Civil Aeronautics Authority, and Navy Bureau of Aeronautics, data on the properties of glass reinforced plastic laminates will be compiled and summarized (expected publication date: June 1956).

turers should be consulted for the heat distortion point of each resin, however, since high heat resistance resins are available for special purposes. The loss of strength with temperature increase should be watched particularly when continuous pressure is present, as in pipes.

(2) Poor abrasion resistance. Surface hardness comparable to steel and aluminum has not yet been obtained.

Table No. 25.— *Properties of glass reinforced polyester laminates**

Property	Polyester laminate with—	
	Glass fabric base	Glass mat base
MECHANICAL PROPERTIES		
Specific gravity	1.5–2.1	1.5–1.8
Tensile strength, psi	40,000–50,000	15,000–24,000
Modulus of elasticity in tension, 10^5 psi	10–28	10–19
Compressive strength, psi	30,000–60,000	30,000–50,000
Flexural strength, psi	50,000–63,000	20,000–35,000
Impact strength (Izod), ft.-lb. per in. notch	19–35	11–25
Bond strength, lb.	......	700–1,100
Hardness (Rockwell M)	100–110	90–100
ELECTRICAL PROPERTIES		
Dielectric strength, short-time, $\frac{1}{8}$ in. thickness, volts per mil	200–600	250–500
Dielectric constant		
60 cycles	......	4.3–4.8
1 megacycle	......	4.0–4.7
Dissipation factor		
60 cycles	......	0.01–0.02
1 megacycle	......	0.01–0.04
Arc resistance, sec.	80–120	80–180
CHEMICAL AND SOLVENT RESISTANCE		
Effect of weak acids	None	None
Effect of strong acids	Some attack	Some attack
Effect of weak alkalies	Slight	Slight
Effect of strong alkalies	Attacked	Attacked
Effect of organic solvents	Generally nil	Generally nil
MISCELLANEOUS		
Water absorption, 24 hr., $\frac{1}{8}$ in. thickness, %	0.3–0.9	0.3–1.0
Burning rate	Slow to nil	Slow to nil
Effect of sunlight	Approximately nil	Approximately nil
Machining qualities	Fair	Good

*Source: *Modern Plastics Encyclopedia.*

(3) Tendency to creep and flow under continuous loading.

(4) Poor fatigue strength under repeated loads.

(5) Difficulty in obtaining a smooth surface finish. (See chapter on finishing, p. 126, for some approaches to this problem.)

(6) Low modulus of elasticity in bending. The stiffness of a glass fabric reinforced polyester laminate is much less than that of common metals, such as magnesium, aluminum, titanium, and steel (2411). The development of a higher modulus glass fiber is under investigation, since only minor improvements can be expected through resin or resin-glass bond modifications (3234). Additional stiffness may often be obtained by the use of sandwich construction. Recently developed prestressing techniques for reinforced plastics also give some increase in average-stiffness (3229).

Table No. 25 lists the range of mechanical, electrical, and other properties of glass reinforced polyester laminates. It is based upon maximum and minimum values submitted by a number of manufacturers.

Chemical resistance ratings for reinforced polyesters reflect a wide difference of opinion. Table No. 25, based on manufacturers' information, gives these products a generally high rating, which, however, appears optimistic. Table No. 26 gives a more cautious rating (p. 184). Seymour and Steiner, basing their rating on laboratory test data and practical experience, state that properly designed and fabricated polyester structures are possibly satisfactory for continuous exposure to water, salts, and nonoxidizing acids at temperatures up to 100° F. (possibly up to 140° F. for specific applications) (2279).

TRANSPORTATION

Aircraft

The aircraft industry was one of the first to find practical and successful applications of reinforced polyesters. The shortage of metals and certain plastics in World War II was an effective stimulus to the use of reinforced polyesters as a replacement for other materials. The physical properties of the reinforced polyesters, however, and their adaptability to the making of specific parts soon made them in demand in their own right.

The uses of reinforced polyesters in aircraft up to the present time can be classified as follows: (1) applications based on their superior dielectric properties; (2) nonstructural highly stressed parts; (3) ballistics applications; (4) parts of complex contours that are difficult to fabricate (2413, 2414).

The superior dielectric properties of reinforced polyesters made them a natural choice for radomes and other antenna housing structures. In the slower propeller-driven aircraft of World War II, the reinforced polyester housings stood up well in use and their service life was usually as long as that of the aircraft itself. When damaged by combat operations, they could be repaired by ground crews if the damage wasn't too extensive, but in any case they could be replaced with a minimum of effort.

Today's jet aircraft which operate at near sonic or sonic speed present special problems. For example, at these extreme speeds erosion of the polyester laminates, caused by the impact of rain particles, increases and could result in failure of the radar or radio apparatus. At present, in order to overcome this drawback, the Air Force uses thin air-drying neoprene coatings over the radomes (2409). An elastic coating with higher temperature resistance and high tensile strength would be desirable.

Because higher temperatures are encountered at the high speed of jet aircraft and guided missiles, glass fiber reinforced laminates which have greater strength retention at temperatures near 500° F. are required. This property is attained by the addition of triallyl cyanurate to the polyester resin (pp. 31, 142).

The high strength-to-weight ratio of the reinforced polyesters is the reason for their use in such parts as hatches, doors, fairings, bulkheads, and wing tips, where rigidity and ruggedness with a minimum weight are important. They have replaced relatively corrosion susceptible alloys of magnesium and aluminum. Fabrication time is also cut down because the parts can be made in one operation with simple molds.

In ballistics applications one of the most notable items made from polyester laminates is the liner between the metal shell and the natural rubber innerlayer (which swells in the presence of gasoline) in the self-sealing gas tanks of military aircraft. (This was the first application of reinforced polyesters in World War II.) Before the liner was used, a bullet penetrating the metal shell would cause it to splay or "flower." This would keep the inner rubber layer away from the hole, so that it could not perform its self-sealing function. The polyester tank-liner prevents this by acting as a shield between the jagged metal and the rubber sealer and thus contributes greatly to the dependability of self-sealing tanks (1297).

Special polyester-glass laminates with low resin content may serve as flak and fragmentation armor for combat aircraft (2391). The performance of the armor depends on a property that is undesirable in most applications of polyester laminates—the ability to delaminate. If properly used, however, delamination is extremely effective in absorbing the impact energy of projectiles.

Polyester laminates are used for air and heater ducts in aircraft because they lend themselves easily to the manufacture of complex contours which are difficult to fabricate from metal (2414). The plastic parts can be made more cheaply than metallic parts, even though the cost of raw materials is higher, because costly hand assembly is eliminated. The low heat transmission of the reinforced polyesters also makes them valuable for this use.

The use of sandwich construction in aircraft offers one solution to the low modulus of elasticity of reinforced polyesters. By using two high-strength laminates as outer faces, separated by a thick, lightweight core, much greater rigidity is obtained than with ordinary laminate construction. Sandwich construction with reinforced polyester facings is used for radomes, airfoil surfaces, and helicopter rotor blades (1898). Polyester-isocyanate foams (p. 228), which can be foamed-in-place, are used as core materials for sandwich structures of complex contour.

Polyester usage in aircraft is not completely limited to reinforcing structures. Rigid, cast polyester sheets laminated with a soft polyvinyl innerlayer provide a nonshatterable, transparent material for aircraft canopies, enclosures, and windows (2407, 2451).

Many of the applications of reinforced polyesters on commercial aircraft are identical to those on military aircraft. In general, however, commercial emphasis is placed on nonstructural functions. In one commercial plane, polyester resin laminates are used as cargo compartment liners, battery containers, wing trailing edge strips, power distribution boxes, oil drip pans, and antenna masks (2408). The use of sandwich construction (polyester-impregnated glass cloth skins, cellular cellulose acetate core) helped provide the weight reduction required to compensate for the greater passenger load carried on tourist-class transatlantic planes (2340).

In agriculture, airplanes are widely used for crop dusting, spraying, seeding, and fertilizing. The Personal Aircraft Research Center of Texas A & M College has conducted research on corrosion of aircraft structural materials by agricultural chemicals. Of the 512 materials tested, only two—glass fiber reinforced polyesters and stainless steel—withstood all the chemicals tested (2223).

Boats

Reinforced polyesters have several properties that have attracted the manufacturers of boats. They are resistant to attack by salt water, sunlight, worms, termites, barnacles, and rot. They can be molded easily into any shape the hull designer wants. The light weight of the hulls is also an advantage (2404). Generally, the first cost of plastic boats seems to be higher than that of wooden boats (2394), but the lower maintenance and repair costs, as well as the longer service life, must also be considered. Many small boats made from reinforced polyesters are used by civilians and by the Armed Forces.

The Navy has successfully made a number of reinforced plastic harbor craft, such as wherries and whaleboats. These boats are seamless and thus require no calking; are nonsinkable due to the incorporation of foamed plastics during manufacture; are stronger than the wooden boats they replace; are not attacked by sea water; and require very little upkeep (2385, 2393). Because of the success with the smaller boats, the Navy has also experimented with 36-foot landing craft (LCVP) and 57-foot minesweepers (1864, 2394).

The Coast Guard has also had a program for procuring, testing, and evaluating laminated plastic boats. Included were such boats as landing craft, surf boats, sailboats, dinghies, and even a 40-foot utility boat (1827).

Boats manufactured from reinforced polyesters for civilian use range from small rowboats to a 42-foot sailing ketch (2290, 2331, 2389, 2401). To aid the owner of a leaky or damaged wooden boat, kits are on the market which will permit him to cover his craft with a polyester-glass fiber covering, thus adding years to its use (1801). The racing enthusiast can protect his speedboat hull from many minor repairs if he coats it both inside and out with polyester resin and glass cloth (2315, 2326).

The use of reinforced polyesters has been most successful with small boats. Experience with larger boats which cannot be molded in one piece, so far as known, has been unsatisfactory or spotty, largely due to the difficulties of joining, the need for special design to compensate for a lower modulus, and the lack of nondestructive methods for testing the laminates.

Sandwich construction may offer the increased strength and rigidity required in large reinforced plastic boats, just as it does in aircraft. A 50-foot self-propelled barge has been built using sandwich construction with glass reinforced polyester facings and a phenolic impregnated cotton duck honeycomb core (2402). This type of construction is also favored in present design plans for the 57-foot minesweepers of the Navy (2394). By varying the thickness of the honeycomb used, it is predicted that boats up to 100 feet long could be constructed (2402).

Reinforced polyesters have a potential future in certain types of installations on large ships, such as storage tanks and piping systems. These materials are noncritical in supply, completely nonmagnetic (a requirement in minesweepers), and not attacked by saltwater. In addition they offer weight savings of about 40% over metal tanks and about 20% over metal piping (2394).

In one installation by the Navy, reinforced polyester pipes were more durable than metallic pipes, once the problem of pinholes was controlled (1790). Metal pipes installed close to the forward guns in a combat vessel failed from a combination of corrosion and shock, but plastic pipes nearby remained intact.

Rigid glass reinforced plastic construction or semirigid rubber construction is required for the small "ready" tanks (20 to 250 gallon capacity) used for storage of fresh water and diesel oil on present-day minesweepers. The use of larger reinforced plastic tanks which are built right into the hull awaits the results of service tests on the tanks now installed (2394).

There are some reservations concerning the use of reinforced polyester piping and tanks on ships. In order to use plastic pipes extensively below decks, they must have improved fire resistance (2385, 2393). The new resins containing HET[2] acid (p. 140) may be an answer. Porosity, which permits leakage of the liquids they contain or carry, is another problem to be solved before shipboard use of plastic tanks and pipes receives wider acceptance (2394).

Automobiles

Adoption of reinforced polyesters as a material for volume production of automobile bodies was brought a step closer by the announcement at the end of 1953 of assembly-line production of Chevrolet's Corvette sports car (2344). The Corvette has a reinforced polyester body made up of 41 parts. Chevrolet was the first major U. S. car manufacturer to set up a production line to turn out automobiles with plastic bodies. Previously, most reinforced plastic car bodies produced in the United States were handled on an experimental or prototype basis, or produced by independent body firms for custom installation on a modified chassis (2337).

The advantages of reinforced polyester automobile bodies include weight saving without sacrifice in strength, resistance to weathering, greater resistance to shock than steel bodies, and ease of repair and maintenance. Surface finishing presents a major problem, however. Glass fiber show-through is often considered attractive in building panels and other products. But in automobiles the public demands a smooth, mirrorlike finish. Finishes used on reinforced plastic bodies are discussed in the chapter on finishing (p. 126).

Cost of the tooling for the Corvette plastic bodies is reported to be $500,000 as compared to an estimated $4,500,000 if steel bodies were used. Chevrolet engineers calculate that polyester bodies are less expensive than steel in runs of 15,000 cars or less. (Present planning calls for a production rate of 30 Corvettes a day in 1954). If this proves true, plastic would prove the choice over steel for such low-volume items as truck cabs, ambulances, and airport limousines, as well as sports car bodies.

[2]Trade name of Hooker Electrochemical Co.

For long production runs, the higher initial tooling costs required for steel bodies can be justified by the faster rate at which these bodies can be produced, as well as the lower material cost. Steel might even reclaim the low-volume items now being groomed for plastics if the development of cheap reinforced plastic dies and tools for forming sheet steel continues (p. 185).

Glass fiber reinforced polyesters will probably completely replace steel, however, for prototypes or testing models of automobiles (1707). Operating models are produced faster and at lower cost from the reinforced polyesters.

Polyester resins are also used in truck trailer production. Some new trailers have a skylight roof of reinforced polyester; others have reinforced polyester sides, interior lines, and doors (2341). The light weight of the reinforced polyester trailers permits pay-loads to be increased.

Miscellaneous

The use of reinforced plastics for transportation equipment has not been entirely limited to the aircraft, boat, and automobile fields. When used for tie plates for railroad tracks, they have proved stronger and tougher than the steel plates they replaced (2332). Glass fiber-polyester mats are also used for parts of railroad coach seats (2323).

Sleds molded of reinforced polyesters are used by the Army for transporting supplies and ammunition and evacuating wounded on snow and ice. They are strong enough to withstand usage on rough terrain and have a permanent white surface for camouflage purposes (2397).

ELECTRICAL APPLICATIONS

From the standpoint of the electrical industry, polyesters have two outstanding properties: They dry without losing any volatiles, and they increase the mechanical strength of the material or parts to which they are applied.

Before the advent of polyesters it was the practice to apply insulating varnishes from which a solvent was evaporated. This left the insulation more or less porous, which led to imperfect electrical resistance. No such weakness is present when polyesters are used; they can be applied in a low-viscosity condition, and they harden throughout, without any porosity.

The strength of polyesters permits reduction of the amount of iron or steel in the composite mechanisms to which they are applied. When they were introduced for electrical use, the industry, for the first time, had insulation that contributed significantly to strength. The savings in weight, space, and cost were immediately apparent. Therefore, the electrical industry was among the first to enter the field of manufacture of polyesters.

In order to control composition and properties, the major electrical firms manufacture their own polyesters. Relationships between composition and electrical properties of polyesters are discussed in the chapter on tailor-making polyesters (p. 160).

The polyester resins and reinforced polyesters now have wide-spread use in electrical applications. Their use for radomes led the way for such items as insulators on television aerials (2432), potting compounds (2403, 2430), binding materials for asbestos tape used as a coil insulator in electric motor construction (838, 839, 2433), switch gear parts (2422), dielectric plates for the determination of x-ray intensity (2428), insulation for cables (830), parts of transistors (2454), and many other electrical products (2458).

Resin impregnated tapes which can be applied in a single operation with no mixing, brushing, or spraying provide a convenient form of insulation (3238). These tapes may be wrapped upon coils, wires, or other parts and then fused in place. Such tapes are, or can be, available with a variety of backings and impregnating resins. For example, glass cloth, glass mat, glass filaments, polyester mat, or polyester cloth may be used as backing. A polyester or other type of cross-linking resin may be used to impregnate the tape.

The development of polyester film ("Mylar"[3] film produced by E. I. du Pont de Nemours & Co., Inc.) enables the bulk of insulation in electrical equipment to be reduced and makes possible the use of higher working temperatures. The properties and applications of polyester film are discussed more fully on page 220.

INDUSTRIAL USES

The combination of light weight and high strength is a big selling point for the use of reinforced polyesters for many industrial purposes. Among the most important uses are pipe, tanks, and other plant equipment, and dies, molds, and other tooling.

Pipe, Tanks, and Other Equipment

Pipe, tanks, fume hoods, ducts, and other equipment made of reinforced polyesters have been used satisfactorily for certain applications in the chemical, paper, metal finishing, and related industries. When the problems of leakage and resin degradation under severe process conditions are solved, reinforced polyesters should take an important place as a chemical engineering material. [It is estimated that the reinforced plastic pipe industry alone could consume 10 million pounds of reinforced plastics a year (1800).]

[3]DuPont trade name.

Table No. 26.—Limitations of polyester and other plastic materials used for industrial process equipment*

| Plastic | Chemical resistance | | | | | Temperature limitation °F. | Structural strength | Ease of fabrication | |
	General	Reducing conditions—acid	Oxidizing conditions—acid	Alkaline	Solvents			Field	Manufacturer
Polyester	Fair	Fair	Good	Poor (non-siliceous filler)	Fair	250 (reinforced)**	Excellent (glass fiber reinforced)	Excellent	Excellent
Acrylic	Poor	Fair	Poor	Fair	Poor	180	Fair	......	Fair
Cellulose ester	Poor	Poor	Poor	Poor	Poor	180	Poor	......	Poor
Epoxy	Fair	Fair	Poor	Good	Excellent	250 (reinforced)	Excellent (glass fiber reinforced)	Excellent	Fair
Fluorocarbon	Excellent	Excellent	Excellent	Excellent	Excellent	500	Good	......	Poor
Furan	Good (filled)	Good (filled)	Poor	Good (carbon filled)	Good	250 (filled)	Good (filled)	Good	Excellent
Nylon	Poor	Poor	Poor	Poor	......	250 (reinforced)	Good	......	......
Phenolic	Good (filled)	Good (filled)	Poor	Poor (carbon filled)	Good	250 (filled)**	Excellent (glass fiber reinforced). Good (filled)	Poor	Excellent
Polyethylene	Good	Good	Fair	Good	Good	180	Fair	......	Good
Polyvinyl alcohol	Poor	......	......	......	Excellent	180	Poor	......	Poor
Saran	Good	Good	Good	Fair	Good	180	Fair	......	Good
Styrene	Fair	Fair	Fair	Fair	Fair	180	Fair	Good	Good
Vinyl	Good	Good	Good	Good	Good	180	Poor	......	Good

*Source: S. W. Shepard, "Chemical Resistant Applications of Plastics," Reinforced Plastics Division, Society of the Plastics Industry Conference, 9th Annual, 1954, Section 19.

**Newly developed polyester and phenolic plastics will withstand temperatures up to 500° F.

The light weight and outstanding strength of reinforced polyester pipe make it economical in many applications where these special properties are needed. It is unaffected by many of the acids, alkalies, and organic solvents in common use in the chemical and allied industries (1809, 2389, 2504, 2519). Pipe designed primarily for use in the petroleum industry, with high resistance to the severe corrosion encountered in oil fields, is available (2468). Glass fiber reinforced polyester tubing made of "Hetron"[4] resin is used in Hooker Electrochemical Co.'s brine wells at the brine level. The plastic tubing has a lower rate of corrosion here than steel and is easier to withdraw and replace if damaged.

Tanks made of reinforced polyesters have been used for storage of oil, water, and chemicals (1800, 2301, 2487). One manufacturer has replaced lead- and brick-lined tanks used in the manufacture of alum with glass fiber reinforced polyester tanks (2504). The advantages gained are lower cost, lighter weight, longer life, and no product contamination.

Tanks mounted on trucks have been used for transportation of fuel across the Arabian desert (1773, 2517), as well as transportation of chemicals (2489). A one-piece molded tank for milk transportation is also available (2493). This tank has sandwich walls made of reinforced polyester skins and balsa wood core.

S. W. Shepard has listed polyesters and other plastics used for industrial process equipment according to their limitations in chemical resistance, temperature range, structural properties, and versatility in fabrication (2552). These ratings are given in table No. 26.

Caution in accepting claims for the chemical resistance of polyester plastics is advised by Seymour and Steiner (2279). They urge that before plastics producers and fabricators recommend their products for handling of corrosive chemicals, they at least become acquainted with the chemicals and chemical reactions potentially involved and make screening tests to assure satisfactory performance.

Dies, Molds, Tools, and Jigs

The increasing use of reinforced polyesters for the molds or dies in which more reinforced polyesters are formed has put these materials in the unique position of creating their own brothers (1711, 1725, 1772). The use of polyester laminates for dies for forming sheet metal is another notable development (1710, 1725, 1726). The reinforced polyester molds and dies not only have long life, but are easier to duplicate and repair and often are cheaper (particularly in low-volume production) than metal molds and dies. However, only materials that can be molded by low- or no-pressure techniques can be molded in these molds and dies.

[4]Hooker Electrochemical Co. trade name.

The value of reinforced polyesters as the project tools (special tools for definite fabricating operations) of industry has been known for some years, and many tools, such as drill jigs, checking and assembly fixtures, and spotweld fixtures, have been made from them (1721, 1725, 1726, 2555). The inherent accuracy, low bulk, and light weight of these tools, combined with the simplicity of their manufacture, make them adaptable to many manufacturing lines, including aircraft, automobiles, boats, furniture, and sheet metal products.

Miscellaneous Uses

Other industrial uses for polyesters, particularly reinforced polyesters, include housings for various machines, such as power scythes and air compressors (2482, 2533); driers and boxes for foundry cores (2485, 2531); and safety helmets for welders and other workers (2518, 2527).

Trays and tote boxes made of reinforced plastics are light, strong, and chemical resistant (2404). They are manufactured for numerous materials-handling purposes in the chemical, pharmaceutical, and food-handling industries.

Because the material is transparent, drawings made on a glass fiber-polyester drafting medium are much easier to reproduce than drawings made on opaque metal drafting sheets. The contact-printing process, which is simple and economical, can be used to reproduce drawings on the laminate on any other sensitized surface—glass cloth, metal, wood, etc. (2497).

COATINGS, ADHESIVES, PLASTICIZERS, LUBRICANTS

Polyester-vinyl monomer resins provide the closest approach at present to the long-sought solventless varnish (2568). They require no solvent for application, and no by-products are produced during the curing process. The need for solvent recovery systems is therefore eliminated, and the dangers of toxicity and fire hazard are reduced. The advantages of solventless varnishes as insulating coatings for wires and other electrical equipment were pointed out in the section on electrical applications (p. 182).

Protective features, such as dimensional stability and chemical, moisture, and weathering resistance, can be imparted to wood, metal, cloth, stone, plastic, and other surfaces by the use of polyester resin coatings. Decorative features can also be obtained; for example, baked-on finishes have an attractive enamel-like appearance. The polyesters used for thin surface coatings are generally modified polyesters which will dry to a tack-free surface in the presence of air (see p. 139).

Polyester resins have been used as sealing agents for porous metal parts and equipment (880, 2564, 2573); coatings for the inside of food and beverage cans (855); coatings for cinder, concrete, and cement building blocks (2564, 2595); and even moisture-proof coatings for diaper material (874).

Some special polyester coatings for reinforced plastics are described in the chapter on finishing (p. 128). Other coating applications of polyesters are discussed in the chapter on isocyanate-modified polyesters (p. 231).

Although the application of polyester resins as adhesives is rather limited at present, they have shown promise. Reinforcement of conventional polyester resins with glass fibers provides them with additional strength for use as adhesives for reinforced plastics parts (2013). Polyesters are also used as binders in abrasives (861, 883); adhesives in calking tape (870); and mastics for holding laminated windows in place (884). Adhesives for optical equipment based on copolymers of maleic or fumaric acid polyesters with styrene have been patented by E. L. Kropa (867).

The patent literature contains many examples of the use of polyesters as plasticizers, particularly for polyvinyl resins (879, 882, 903). As plasticizers, the polyesters show the advantages of extremely low volatility and migratability, high resistance to water and solvents, excellent stability under ultraviolet light and at elevated temperatures, and improvement in some processing characteristics (2568).

Polyesters have been added to lubricating oils and motor fuels for a variety of purposes, such as pour-point depressants and viscosity-index improvers, stabilizers, and antirusting compounds (862, 872, 877, 886).

BUILDING INDUSTRY

The largest volume application of polyesters to date has been in glass fiber reinforced panels for architectural uses. Sales of these panels topped 16,000,000 square feet in 1953, and this total is expected to triple by 1957 (2594).

The translucent reinforced polyester sheets have largely been used as a replacement for glass in skylights, greenhouses, windows of industrial buildings, and similar uses. Bond failure between the resin and the glass fiber, especially when wet, and flammability have been the major stumbling blocks to more extensive service as a structural material. The bond failure problem has been met, however, by new sizes and finishing agents which reduce strength losses on wetting from as much as 50% to almost negligible values (p. 86). The development of self-extinguishing resins (p. 140) provides an answer to the problem of flammability. The use of stabilizers in the resins (p. 162) has improved color stability to a marked degree.

As far as strength is concerned, reinforced polyester panels have been developed which not only are capable of carrying their own weight but also can withstand loads in excess of 30 pounds per square inch. This has been demonstrated by the Ford Geodesic Dome, which was created as a part of the Ford Motor Co.'s Fiftieth Anniversary Celebration. The dome, which stands 40 feet high, has a base diameter of 93 feet and covers the inner court of the rotunda in the exhibition hall at Dearborn, Mich. It consists of an aluminum framework covered with a shell of reinforced plastic panels. The reinforced plastic dome weighs only 17,000 pounds; a dome made of conventional materials would weigh 18 times as much (2607).

From specifications submitted by manufacturers, the editors of *Modern Plastics* determined the following average strength properties for reinforced plastic building panels on the market (2608):

Tensile strength	11,000 psi
Flexural strength	17,000 psi
Load-bearing strength	Greater than 100 psi on a 4-foot span.
Impact strength	10–15 foot-pounds per inch of width (Izod) unnotched
Modulus of elasticity	1.4×10^6 psi

The translucent reinforced polyesters are available as flat or corrugated sheeting. They make attractive and weatherproof building materials for porch roofs (2601), wall panels for screening off an unsightly view (2624), glazing in corrugated metal buildings (2598), and plastic panels to be placed over windows in areas where damage from hurricanes might be expected (2626). The corrugated sheeting also makes very handsome door and window awnings (1546, 2604). Combining light weight with strength, the awnings permit light to enter the structures on which they are placed and yet have all the advantages claimed for awnings made of conventional materials, such as aluminum, canvas, and wooden lattices. They are, in addition, completely weather-resistant, will not rot, require no painting, and can be left up all year around in all climates.

The use of reinforced polyester plastics in greenhouse glazing has been tested by the Santa Barbara Botanic Gardens in California (2627). As a result of a 4-year evaluation, the translucent panels were found to be capable of transmitting a good balance of light from infrared through ultraviolet; they give even illumination; no leaf burn is induced on plants normally requiring shade; and damage from rain splatter, hail, and similar hazards has been eliminated. These panels exhibited no deterioration during the 4-year test.

An interesting note to record at this time is the comparison of these translucent panels with glass. Depending upon the color and thickness of the panel, reinforced polyester panels will transmit up to 90% of the amount of light that glass transmits. Heat transfer is another story. The reinforced polyesters conduct only 40% as much heat as glass by direct conduction and 20% as much by radiation (2629). This low heat transmission would be a boon to those living in desert or tropical regions.

The light weight of reinforced polyester sheeting, which permits it to be transported cheaply by air, is a big factor favoring its use in barracks, shelters, and other military buildings. For example, the Quartermaster Corps anticipates a saving in weight of 500 pounds by the use of a reinforced plastic frame for a 16- by 16-foot shelter tent previously made of wood (2660). An answer to the problem of aircraft maintenance in the Arctic has been provided by the development of an alert shelter for jet aircraft made from magnesium arches and many polyester-glass fiber panels. This structure is 64 feet long and 24 feet high (2605).

The use of reinforced polyesters for wall tiles, work-counter tops, and walls proves that they can be decorative and useful at the same time (908, 2596, 2600, 2603, 2634).

In addition to flat and corrugated sheeting, many other fields in the building industry are open to development by reinforced polyesters. These include such building materials and shapes as flashing and counterflashing for waterproofing of intersections between roofs and walls, base courses, copings, cornices, roof vents, termite shields, gravel stops, gutters, downspouts, and anchors, ties, hangers, and miscellaneous inserts used in concrete and brick work (3232). Forms made of reinforced polyesters are strong, lightweight, and practically indestructible (2625).

The advantage of the light weight of reinforced polyesters will be readily apparent to the home repairman. For example, if he wishes to install a reinforced plastic shower stall base he won't have to worry about reinforcing the floor, because the base weighs only 20 pounds (2635). A steel base would tip the scales at 80 pounds and could chip and rust. The use of terrazzo with a weight of 300 to 400 pounds would require a major reinforcing job.

Structural members are a more remote but not unlikely application of reinforced plastics. One architect has predicted that it would not take much improvement in technique and material to produce a strong, lightweight, easily workable reinforced plastic joist and/or stud (3232). Lightweight plastic sections and wall panels could be applied to these structural shapes.

E. A. Byars made an experimental investigation of the structural use of plastic reinforced with parallel glass fibers and concluded that the material warrants serious consideration where maximum strength and minimum weight are desirable (3223). A deck truss, similar to a bar joist, was tested for deflections, loads, and strains as measured by strain gages. It proved superior to 1020 steel and 24ST aluminum on a strength-to-weight ratio basis, although deflections were two to five times greater. It was somewhat brittle and sensitive to stress concentrations.

MILITARY USES

Military uses of polyester plastics overlap many civilian uses, notably in the transportation field. There are some specialized uses of reinforced polyesters, however, that are essentially military.

One of these is the much publicized body armor that was developed during World War II. At present the armor is made by the use of small curved plates which overlap each other and which are sewn to a nylon backing garment. As the ratio of glass cloth to resin is very high (35% resin to 65% glass), the impact of a projectile causes the plate to delaminate, thus absorbing the force of the projectile and preventing penetration (2643, 2645, 2827). The same general construction was used for body armor for the combat infantrymen in the Korean War with a great degree of success. Pants of the same material have been tested. (Even body armor cannot be considered as a use strictly limited to the armed forces because of the possibilities of its adaptation for hunters, policemen, and guards.)

The properties that the reinforced polyesters offer, such as durability, light weight, weathering resistance, and resistance to attack by fungi, have been a great inducement for the Quartermaster Corps of the Army to explore their potentialities. Packboards, ski-pole rings, ski poles, Arctic sleds, tropical helmets, snowshoes, table tops, skis, bread boxes, and trunk lockers are some of the items that have been made (2653).

The Corps of Engineers with specialized problems of their own also have found advantages in polyester plastics. They have tested items such as landing mats, boats, prefabricated buildings, pipe, and storage tanks (2649). To further the application of reinforced plastics for military purposes, a cooperative effort was initiated in 1951 between the Engineering and Development Laboratories, Ft. Belvoir, Va., and the Society of the Plastics Industry, Inc. (1862).

Because of their superior impact resistance, as well as their resistance to weathering, reinforced plastics merit serious consideration for many military container applications. For example, full-scale tests of reinforced plastic ammunition cases led the Navy Bureau of Ordnance to conclude that they are acceptable alternates (not just "substitutes") for steel and aluminum cases (2648).

Reinforced polyesters are used for many other items by the Armed Forces. In some cases they have been treated as substitute materials. As their properties become more widely known throughout the various military departments, however, they are being accepted as a material which can stand on its own rather than be just a stopgap or a substitute for essential metals. The finding of new uses depends largely on the development of specific design data and field experience.

SCIENTIFIC USES

The uses of polyester resins in the scientific field have kept pace with the atomic age. They are used as a coating for concrete blocks in a radiation shield at the Brookhaven National Laboratory (2668), and, combined with glass fibers, in parts for the vacuum chamber of a synchroton (combination of a cyclotron and betatron) in California (2664).

A "wounded" mannequin that "bleeds" as well as indestructible anatomical models for first-aid courses and other educational purposes have been created from polyesters (2669, 2676). The rigidity and lightness of the reinforced polyesters, plus their ease of cleaning and resistance to liquids, also prompted their successful application in the manufacture of artificial limbs (2676).

The objectionable odors and breakable glass jars usually associated with the preservation of botanical and biological specimens can now be eliminated. Embedding the specimens in a liquid casting resin that sets to a clear, hard plastic preserves and displays them in their true shape and color (1930, 1931, 1932, 2663).

Clear, nonreinforced polyesters produce lenses which are very resistant to abrasion (10 to 30 times better than acrylics) and solvent and crase resistant (2680). The impact resistance (notched) and formability of these lenses, however, is poorer than those of acrylics. In photographic printing filters, they replace lacquered gelatin filters, which are generally short lived (2671). Some polyester resins have particularly good photoelastic properties and are used in making specimens for stress analysis (918, 2546).

Polyester resins are also used as molding materials for dental work (914, 915, 919).

CONSUMER ITEMS

The discovery of a new material is followed with amazing rapidity by its appearance over the counter in a multitude of products for use by the consumer. Alert manufacturers eagerly began experiments with the polyesters and reinforced polyesters as they came to their attention, and the wide range of products now available on the market is only an indication of their potentialities.

Home Furnishings and Appliances

Furniture designers were quick to note the attractiveness and durability of reinforced plastics. They have made chairs, dinette sets, and many other pieces that satisfy the modern home owner's desire for functional furniture and that are available in a wide choice of colors to fit a decorator's scheme (2711, 2722, 2731, 2754). The prize winning Eames chair is not only attractive to the eye but comfortable to sit in, because the body's weight is distributed evenly over the chair's surface and the back and the arms are permitted to rest naturally. This chair can be produced in a variety of models and in many different colors from just one mold (2389).

In homes you can also find reinforced polyesters used for bathtubs which weigh only 15 pounds and can be handled by one man, as compared to cast iron or steel tubs which weigh 150 to 300 pounds and require two to four men to lift them (2389, 2721). On a smaller scale, there are lamp shades which come in any desired shape, are flame resistant, impervious to moisture, and washable, and will not scratch, mar, dent, warp, or wrinkle (2389, 2713, 2715); as well as figurines, ash trays, book-ends, and candy and cigarette boxes in a variety of colors and shapes (2546, 2707).

In such a common household appliance as the washing machine one or two parts molded of reinforced polyester can replace as many as 22 metal parts previously needed at a cost saving as high as 25% (2702, 2747). Assembly time is cut down to a fraction of the time required to assemble metallic parts (2709). Reinforced polyesters are also used in vacuum cleaners, not as an economy measure but to reduce the weight of the finished article (2714). In one cleaner, the weight was decreased from 5.93 pounds to 1.66 pounds by the replacement of metal parts with reinforced polyesters (2714). The housewife should also be pleased to note that their application in low-cost dish washers provides tubs and lids that are immune to attack by detergents and won't rust, stain, crack, or chip (2708).

The control of humidity sensitivity by the vinyl silane type of sizes (p. 86) and recent improvements in finishing procedures (p. 126) are paving the way for the use of reinforced polyesters in refrigerator applications (2727, 2744).

Fruit juice dispensers (2726), parts of automatic ice makers (2727), and even soda bottle caps (921, 922) have been molded of reinforced polyesters.

Office Equipment

In the office furniture field, reinforced polyesters have found an entry in the construction of file drawers (2720). These drawers do not dent easily during transportation or in office handling. They slide smoothly, are light handling for girls, do not give a metallic clatter in closing, and do not slide open after closing.   They do not require lubrication as metal drawers sometimes do (2389).

Applications for reinforced polyesters in business machines are under investigation, and one of the first to prove successful is their use as dust covers for IBM clocks (2764). In giant computing machines, polyester film is used as insulation in the electrical capacitors and polyester tape as backing for magnetic tape (2725).

Sports and Entertainment

Fisherman are now equipped with casting and fly rods which not only have tremendous flexural strength and good fatigue resistance, but are nonsetting and noncorrosive (2756). They can also use a minnow bucket which is light enough to float because it is made of reinforced polyester combined with foamed polystyrene (2699). Boats made of glass fibers and polyesters, with their light weight, durability, and other advantages (p. 179), have been readily adopted by fishermen and other sportsmen.

Other sporting goods items made from reinforced polyesters are blades for hockey sticks (2688, 2748) and swimming pool ladders (2746).

The ice shows which tour the country were quick to find out that the many props required for their lavish spectacles, the "bang boards" for the skating rinks, and the orchestra stands were heavy and difficult to transport when made of conventional materials. Now they are made of strong, lightweight reinforced polyesters (2703, 2704). The movie studios too have turned to the use of these materials for everything from pseudo buildings to boulders and cactus (2749).

Miscellaneous

Light, strong, more easily handled clothing mannequins are made of reinforced polyesters (2705). Indoor and outdoor advertising displays (2698, 2730) and highway department road signs (2745) have also been made from them.

The desirable qualities of beauty, lightness, and durability are claimed for luggage made of polyesters and glass fibers (2757). The luggage also will not scratch, dent, scuff, or mildew (2710). Another advantage of luggage made of reinforced polyesters is that it needs no lining, since the interior finish is already smooth from the molding process and there are no metal clips to cause damage to anything carried in the case. A detachable lining, which can be removed easily and cleaned at will, can be selected by the purchaser (2389).

In the musical instrument field, polyesters have been used to make replicas of piano keyboards for students (2701) and mutes for trumpets (2758).

The same advantages that reinforced polyesters offer in products for grown-ups also have appeal in toys. For example, parents may be willing to pay a slightly higher price for a reinforced polyester rocking horse because it will last longer, will not break, and is light to move (2389, 2763).

FUTURE OF POLYESTERS

Although consumption of polyester resins dropped sharply at the end of World War II, since 1947 it has shown a steady increase and within recent years has even reached the proportions of a boom. Consumption in 1947 was only 4 million pounds. But in 1953 it was estimated at around 27 million pounds and by 1957 is expected to rise to about 60 million pounds (3219). Production of these resins jumped from 19 million pounds in 1952 to 26 million pounds in 1953. (The 1953 figure compares with approximately 3 billion pounds of all resins produced by the entire plastics industry). It is expected to hit a new record of 35 million pounds in 1954 (2822).

Year	Polyester resin production Pounds
1945	4,000,000
1946	400,000
1947	1,000,000
1948	2,000,000
1949	7,000,000
1950	9,000,000
1951	14,000,000
1952	19,000,000
1953	26,000,000

Since polyesters make up the major portion of plastics used in reinforced plastics, the phenomenal growth of this industry is also worth notice. Since 1950, it has expanded at a rate of between 40% and 50% a year (2832).

Despite this obviously healthy growth and the vast potential markets for polyesters pointed out by most market surveys, the picture is not entirely rosy. There are many problems still to be faced before the potential markets are turned into actual ones.

One of these is the cost problem. The cost per pound of reinforced plastics is considerably higher than that of other structural materials, such as aluminum, steel, and other metals. Some predict, however, that a combination of raw material price decreases, improved molding techniques, technical advances in resins, and increasing competition between small and large molders will effect a major reduction in the price of finished reinforced plastics products within the next 10 years (2389).

Present fabricating techniques are often not economical in volume production for mass markets. (In short production runs the low tooling cost may give reinforced polyesters a finished cost advantage.) More mechanization is needed, but there is an even more important bottleneck—

the "cure time" of the resin. Even the fastest curing of present resins ties up press, floor space, and operator for 3 to 4 minutes for each molding. As a result, even if a plastics molding operation were completely mechanized, it would still take an acre of presses to match the output of a single steel-stamping unit (1978).

The use of glass reinforcement impregnated with partially cured resin (p. 112) may provide a partial answer to the problem of speeding up cure time. This problem will probably not be fully solved, however, until a resin that cures in a split second is invented (1978). Such a resin is far from being an immediate possibility, since the polymerization reaction involved in curing takes time if a structurally strong plastic is to be created.

Finishes for polyesters that are both good and cheap are still needed, although progress has been made in this direction (p. 126). Particular attention needs to be paid to finishes for parts subject to movement, strain, or friction (2833).

Reliable design data are needed on nearly all reinforced polyester materials, so that they will continue to lose the status of "substitute" materials and be utilized in applications where their particular properties provide an advantage. As one pioneer in this field so aptly stated, "Let us beware of the word 'substitute.' It would be just as unreasonable to describe the successful application of reinforced plastics as a substitute for some accustomed material, as it would be to call the automobile a substitute for the horse and buggy, or the telephone a substitute for the carrier pigeon" (2852).

The newcomer to the polyester and reinforced polyester field should beware lest he underestimate the capital he needs. The low cost of tooling might give a false sense of the actual costs of producing a certain item and should not influence his decision before the exploration of all the hidden production costs.

Manufacturing problems are entirely different in proprietary molding as compared to custom molding, because it is up to the molder to evaluate the market and to make his own sales analysis. Also, he must take the time and make the necessary expenditures to develop and test his product adequately (2841). All of this results in a sizable outlay of cash. It has been estimated that one should have a minimum capital of $60,000, and preferably over $100,000 before entering the field (1979). Another estimate sets $100,000 as the bare minimum, and $250,000 as a more realistic approach (2389).

Not only capital is necessary but "know-how" must be learned or purchased. Not all of the information can be found in the literature, for each new item will have specific problems of its own (1979). As the price of polyester resins moves downward, resin manufacturers will be less willing to furnish a great deal of special technical services free of charge to small-scale molders.

SATURATED POLYESTERS

I. LINEAR FIBER-FORMING POLYESTERS

The ability of certain linear polymers to form high-strength fibers was recognized by W. H. Carothers in his early work (1131, 1133). This ability is evidently closely connected with high molecular weight, well in the hundred thousands, and steric configuration that permits microcrystallinity. Polymers with these properties can be stretched, or drawn, which results in alinement of the molecules in the direction of the draw.

In patents assigned to E. I. du Pont de Nemours & Co., Inc. (928), Carothers defined the conditions under which linear fiber-forming polymers are formed. He disclosed several groups of these polymers, including "polyesters derived from dibasic acids plus glycols." (As acids that may be used he mentioned carbonic, oxalic, succinic, glutaric, adipic, pimelic, sebacic, hexamethylene dicarboxylic, phthalic, etc.)

At present the terephthalate resins, whose unit structure is that of terephthalic acid and a polymethylene glycol, form the basis for the only commercial fibers produced from polyesters. These resins are also important raw materials for production of films, to which they contribute phenomenal strength characteristics. So far they have not been used successfully for molding or coating, although an attempt was made many years ago to prepare alkyd resins from terephthalic acid for use in paints and varnishes (964).

The terephthalates were first prepared in England by Whinfield and Dickson in 1941 (965, 2889, 2890). E. F. Izard of Du Pont has made important contributions to their development in this country (2861). A review of the development of polyethylene terephthalate was recently published by Izard (3230).

Because of their commercial importance this chapter is principally devoted to the preparation of terephthalates, their fabrication into film and fiber, and their applications. Linear fiber- and film-forming polyesters based on other ingredients are also covered but in less detail.

MANUFACTURE OF FIBER-FORMING POLYESTERS

Polymethylene Teraphthalates

Raw Materials. The basic raw materials used in the manufacture of polymethylene terephthalates are terephthalic acid and ethylene glycol.

The properties and preparation of ethylene glycol are described on page 26.

Chemistry of Terephthalic Acid. Terephthalic acid [$C_6H_4(COOH)_2$], or 1,4-dicarboxybenzene, is a para isomer of phthalic acid. Both carboxyl groups of terephthalic acid are capable of esterification, but the compound contains no double-bond unsaturation capable of addition polymerization.

Simple esters of terephthalic acid are obtained without difficulty, but polyesters are obtained only under exacting conditions (2890). Side reactions during the polyesterification produce by-products which discolor the resin and often make its purification difficult (2890). Since 1935, however, the work of Carothers has opened the door to accomplishing the difficult. The basic techniques utilized by the inventors of polyethylene terephthalate (934, 965) were established from his line of experimental investigation.

Synthesis and Production. Terephthalic acid is prepared by the oxidation of para-xylene (1,4-dimethylbenzene), which may be obtained from a coal tar fraction (2877). Para-xylene is difficult to obtain in a pure form from a mixture of xylenes because of the closeness of the boiling points of these compounds (ortho-xylene, 144°C.; meta-xylene, 138.8°C.; para-xylene, 138.5°C.) (1357).

In another method for the preparation of terephthalic acid para-cymene is oxidized with nitric acid to para-methylbenzoic acid, and this compound is further oxidized with potassium permanganate to terephthalic acid. The terephthalic acid produced by this method is not pure. Since it is insoluble in most organic solvents, it can only be purified by conversion to its methyl or dimethyl ester. The crude terephthalic acid is esterified, the ester distilled under reduced pressure, and the product crystallized from carbon tetrachloride.

Dimethyl terephthalate is commonly used in place of terephthalic acid to form polyesters with ethylene glycol for fiber or film manufacture. It is easier to obtain in pure form, reacts more readily, and has a lower melting point (2862, 2863). Terephthalic acid sublimes at 300°C. Dimethyl terephthalate melts with considerable sublimation at 142°C. (2871).

A new process for the production of dimethyl terephthalate from para-xylene was recently announced by Hercules Powder Co. (2863). It involves alternate additions of oxygen (air oxidation) and esterifications with methyl alcohol:

$$\text{para-xylene} \xrightarrow{O_2} \text{para-toluic acid} \xrightarrow{CH_3OH} \text{methyl para-toluate}$$

$$\xrightarrow{O_2} \text{monomethyl terephthalate} \xrightarrow{CH_3OH} \text{dimethyl terephthalate}$$

All reactions take place in the liquid phase.

Preparation of Terephthalates. *Basic Methods.* The first disclosure on the preparation of terephthalate resins was made by Whinfield and Dickson (934, 965). They described three methods of obtaining low-molecular-weight polymethylene terephthalates: (1) direct esterification of terephthalic acid with excess glycol in the presence of an esterification catalyst, such as para-toluenesulfonic acid; (2) ester interchange between a low ester of the acid and excess glycol in the presence of an ester-interchange catalyst; and (3) reaction between a dihalide of the acid and a glycol in the presence of an inert diluent, such as chloroform, and an alkaline catalyst, such as pyridine.

The low-molecular-weight products produced by any of the three methods are converted to high-molecular-weight polyesters by heating to a temperature above the boiling point of the glycol. The heating should be conducted under conditions that will prevent oxidation of the resin, for example, in an atmosphere of an inert gas such as nitrogen. During the heating, the pressure is reduced to facilitate removal of the excess glycol.

Commercial Method. The first method, in which the acid itself is poly-condensed with a glycol, is not used commercially. An industrial process requires fairly short cycles, and it was necessary, the inventors disclosed, to reflux the acid with the glycol for 72 hours until solution was effected.

In practice polyethylene terephthalates are made by ester-interchange methods. Whinfield and Dickson's disclosure contained a number of examples of this process. In one, 10 grams of methyl terephthalate, 4.85 grams of ethylene glycol, and 0.003 gram of sodium catalyst were heated at 197°C. in a stream of oxygen-free nitrogen. By the end of 3 hours, most of the methyl alcohol by-product of the ester interchange was removed. The low-molecular-weight product was heated at 280°C. under ordinary pressure for about 30 minutes and then further heated for 10 hours in a vacuum. During the heat-conversion, a slow current of nitrogen was introduced through a capillary tube. The final product of this reaction melted at 256°C.

The duration of both reactions—the glycol-methyl alcohol interchange and the self-condensation of the glycol ester—is significantly affected by the type of catalyst. For instance, in another example Whinfield and Dickson used both sodium and clean magnesium ribbon as catalysts. In this case the ester interchange required only 2 hours of heating, and it was almost completed in the first hour. The self-condensation required only 2 hours for completion at the higher temperature. With magnesium turnings as the catalyst the first reaction required only 30 minutes, and in the second reaction a polymer of molecular weight high enough to be fiber-forming was obtained in 4 hours. Suggested catalysts include sodium, lithium, potassium, calcium, magnesium, zinc, cadmium, and manganese, as well as the oxides, carbonates, borates, or other alkaline-reacting salts of various of these metals (934, 965).

The duration of the ester-interchange part of the cycle also depends on the size of the batch. (Probably the real factor here is the surface-to-volume ratio.) For a large-scale batch of about 2,000 pounds, the ester interchange usually takes from about 4 to 6 hours (951). The polycondensation step takes longer, and depends not only on the catalyst concentration and the size of the batch, but also on the desired final viscosity and the amount of surface area generated in the polymerization autoclave, that is, surface from which the glycol can evaporate. Thus, if the vessel is but partially filled, and vigorous mixing splashes the melt on the walls of the whole vessel, a larger surface area of the polymer is exposed and the glycol can be removed faster. Vigorous mixing is therefore important.

In one recorded procedure, the stainless steel autoclave in which the reaction takes place is equipped with a stainless steel double helical stirrer which scrapes close to the side of the autoclave (951). The evacuation takes place gradually through an ice trap and a dry ice trap, until a vacuum of 0.5 millimeter of mercury is obtained.

The polycondensation reaction is continued until the melt viscosity at 280° C. reaches 2000 to 5000 poises; the intended use of the polymer determines the degree of polymerization (2875).

Basic reviews on the methods and problems encountered in the preparation of polyethylene terephthalate are given by J. R. Whinfield (2889, 2890). In general, a high vacuum is required to remove excess glycol and viscosity is the logical means for control in continuous manufacture.

Improvement in Catalysts. The long periods which are necessary to remove excess glycol during the polycondensation reaction often result in the formation of glycol ethers. Diethylene glycol is often formed, and it becomes a part of the long chain of the polymer. As is always the case when different reactants are introduced, the presence of diethylene glycol in the polymer results in lowering of its melting point and general degradation of its properties.

To accelerate the polycondensation, and above all to diminish the amount of diethylene glycol formed, E. F. Izard introduced lead oxide (PbO), commonly called litharge, as a new catalyst (940). [The catalysts originally used in the production of terephthalates are given in references (934, 965).] He obtained a polymer containing less than 3% of diethylene glycol by using this catalyst.

Usually the larger the amount of the catalyst, the shorter is the reaction time, the higher is the viscosity, and the lower is the percentage of diethylene glycol in the polymer. Too high a concentration of litharge, however, causes the formation of colored by-products. If it is necessary to obtain a completely white product, the concentration of litharge should not be larger than 0.01%.

In a recent disclosure by C. H. Hofrichter, cobaltous acetate, used by itself or in combination with litharge or antimony trioxide, is claimed to accelerate both the ester interchange and the polycondensation reaction without producing discoloration (951). In amounts ranging from 0.005 to 0.15%, based on the weight of dimethyl terephthalate, this catalyst is particularly suitable for producing polymers whose intrinsic viscosity is not higher than 0.75.

W. F. Gresham used lead and zinc perborates as catalysts in an earlier patent for the production of esters of terephthalic acid and butyl alcohol. No butyl ether or other dehydration products of butyl alcohol were obtained (937).

Variation in Ingredients. A number of patents have been obtained that extend the basic patents of Whinfield and Dickson for the manufacture of terephthalates. Dickson, Huggill, and Welch found that the functional derivatives of terephthalic acid which can be used are not only the lower esters of the acid, but also its half-esters, cycloaliphatic esters, aryl esters, acid halides, and amine salts (969). The only condition is that the esters, salts, etc, be derived from alcohols, phenols, or other compounds which have a boiling point lower than the glycol used in the polycondensation. As long as this condition is fulfilled, the by-products of the ester-interchange reaction can be removed from the polymerizate without removing the glycol.

The functional derivatives of glycols can also be utilized. J. C. Cook describes a process of manufacturing polyethylene terephthalate in which excess of a glycol ester of a low-molecular-weight acid, such as acetic acid, is used with terephthalic acid or an ester of terephthalic acid (968). When the acid is used, 4 to 5% excess of glycol is preferred. With esters of terephthalic acid, it is sufficient to use 1.5 to 2.5% excess of glycol.

Monofunctional compounds, such as ethyl benzoate and ethyl terephthalate, can be added to the polymerizate to produce a more uniform molecular weight and viscosity (975). In the examples given, the final product obtained from 60 parts of dimethyl terephthalate, 89 parts of ethylene glycol, and 0.93 part of ethyl benzoate had a limiting viscosity[1] of 0.70.

---

[1]Limiting viscosity is determined as follows: 1% of the polyester is dissolved in a solution of 3 parts (by weight) of phenol and 2 parts of trichloroethane. The limiting viscosity equals the natural log of the viscosity of the dilute solution divided by the viscosity of solvent, over the concentration in grams per 100 cubic centimeters.

When 1.86 parts of ethyl benzoate were used, the limiting viscosity was 0.61.

Other Fiber-Forming Polymers

Although only polyethylene terephthalate is in commercial production, many patents have been issued on fiber-forming resins prepared from related materials.

From an economic standpoint, it appears particularly desirable to be able to prepare useful polymers from isophthalic acid. This acid is produced by oxidation of meta-xylene which is unavoidably obtained as a by-product in isolating para-xylene, the raw material for terephthalic acid. According to a recent patent issued to Flory and Leutner, a linear fiber-forming polymer is obtained by condensation of tetramethylene glycol and isophthalyl chloride (5). The process appears to be limited to the use of tetramethylene glycol; other glycols give products that are much lower melting, or that lose their orientation within a short time after drawing or heat treatment.

A research and development program on dimethyl isophthalate is being conducted by Hercules Powder Co. This chemical will be available when semiplant facilities now being used for dimethyl terephthalate are released (2862). Study of the reaction of dimethyl isophthalate with glycols has not yet progressed far enough to present data on the expected polyesters, but polyester plasticizers and laminating resins are said to be potential applications (2866).

A number of aromatic acids are claimed in the patent literature to be useful in the preparation of fiber-forming polyesters. They include: diphenoxyethane 4,4'-dicarboxylic acid (966); benzophenone 4,4'-dicarboxylic acid or its esters (984); 1,5 or 2,6 or 2,7 naphthalene dicarboxylic acids or their esters (970); acids of the formula HOOC—⬡—R—⬡—COOH, where R may be $(CH_2)_x$ (967), O, O—CH_2, O—⬡—O, etc. (971), S,

S—$(CH_2)_x$—S, etc. (972), —NH—$(CH_2)_m$—NH, or —N(—$(CH_2)_2$—)(—$(CH_2)_n$—)N—

(974); and an acid of the formula HOOC—⬡(OCH_3)—O—R—O—⬡(CH_3O)—COOH (948).

High-melting linear polyesters have been produced from aromatic dicarboxylic acids and bis(beta-oxyethyl) derivatives of diphenols (995), trans-quinitol (4), and acetylated diphenols (946).

An alcohol of the formula $H(OR)_m$—O —⟨benzene⟩— A —⟨benzene⟩— O —$(RO)_nH$
is reported to give linear polyesters with fumaric or maleic acid (949).

Compounds containing a heterocyclic ring, such as thiophene, furane, and pyridine 2,5-dicarboxylic acids, have also been used to prepare high-melting polyesters suitable for fiber-forming (941).

Polyesters capable of being cold-drawn to give fibers have been produced from hydroquinone diesters and terephthalic acid (982). These polyesters are very crystalline, however. If the hydroquinone polyesters are interpolymerized with the autocondensation products of a hydroxy-carboxylic acid of the formula HO — R —⟨benzene⟩—COOH, where R is $(CH_2)_x$ or $(CH_2)_z$—O (935, 973), more readily cold-drawn resins are obtained (985).

Polyhexahydroquinone sebacate has also been used to prepare fiber-forming polyesters (931).

Variations in Manufacturing Methods

High Polymers from Low Polymers. *Solvent Method.* Izard and Auspos disclose a method of getting high-molecular-weight polymethylene terephthalates that can be used either as the only polymerization method or as a method for getting high polymers from low polymerization products (947). In this method the reactants are polymerized in a solvent for the polyester product. The solvent reduces the viscosity of the polymerizate to such a point that the excess glycol is easily distilled off without the use of a vacuum.

Any solvent can be used which can hold the polymer in concentrations of from 50 to 90% at the temperature of the reaction. Naphthalene, tetra-hydronaphthalene, diphenyl, and their analogues are examples of such solvents. It is most convenient to use a solvent that boils at a higher temperature than the glycol used. When this is not the case, the distillate will contain both the glycol and the solvent, and it will be necessary to add more solvent as the reaction progresses. Of course, the solvent can be recaptured from the distillate and returned to the autoclave.

The reaction is continued until the viscosity of the mixture reaches the required point. The mixture is then poured into a nonsolvent, and the polymer precipitates out. (If the solvent used is one that will not hold the polymer in solution at temperatures lower than those employed during the polymerization reaction, it may suffice to cool the mixture to precipitate the polymer.) The precipitate is then filtered out, extracted with ether, and dried over phosphorus pentoxide.

This method of production has the advantage of giving the final product in the form of a fine powder, which can be used in conventional injection molding apparatus.

Interpolymerization. Another method of preparing high-molecular-weight polymers from low polymerization products is given by W. W. Triggs (992). According to his disclosure, an ordered linear polyester is prepared by interpolymerizing a low polyester prepared from one set of compounds containing an excess of hydroxyl terminal groups with another low polyester prepared from a different set of compounds containing an excess of carboxyl terminal groups. The polyester obtained in this manner is strong and tough and has a melting point which is but slightly lower than that of either of the two components. A copolymerization product of all the ingredients involved would have a much lower melting point and poor strength.

Acid Halide-Glycol Polycondensation. The Wingfoot Corp. is the assignee of many patents on the use of acid chlorides of dibasic acids for polycondensation with glycols (943, 979, 983, 990). This corporation also holds patents on condensation of terephthalic and isophthalic acid halides with glycols (5, 944, 945, 980, 991).

The inherent advantage of using the acid halide procedure is that the reaction is nonreversible. The by-product is hydrochloric acid, and no glycol or acid chloride can be regenerated by the action of hydrochloric acid on the polymer.

Not all glycols can be utilized in this reaction, however. Only those which have at least four atoms in the shortest chain between the two valence bonds to the two terminal hydroxy groups can be used. In addition, high purity is required of both reactants; they should be at least 98%, and preferably 99.5% pure.

Procedure. The dibasic acid chloride and the glycol are usually mixed in molecular proportions (it is sometimes more convenient to add the glycol in successive small portions), and the mixture is warmed gradually to a temperature of about 200°C. During the reaction, the hydrogen chloride formed is swept out by passing a stream of inert gas through the melt, since it has a tendency to etherify the glycol or to induce other types of reactions.

In one example 2.025 parts (by weight) of pure tetramethylene glycol were added to 4.473 parts of purified terephthalyl chloride (944, 980). A solid polyester was formed in about 10 minutes, after the end of a spontaneous strongly exothermic reaction. The temperature was then raised to 200°C., and the polyester melted to a clear, colorless liquid. The reaction started again at this temperature, and in 5 minutes a solid polyester was obtained. The temperature was increased to 255°C. and maintained there for 1 hour. Vacuum was applied intermittently to remove bubbles of hydrogen chloride gas. At the end of this time the melt viscosity was measured and found to be 684 poises, representing an estimated number-average molecular weight of about 15,000. The color of the melt was light amber, and the polymer had a melting point of 218° to 219°C. Strong elastic fibers could be cold-drawn from the melt.

When ethylene glycol was substituted for the tetramethylene glycol in this example, the polymer decomposed on application of vacuum.

Prevention of Glycol Decomposition. In the preceding method there is some tendency for unreacted tetramethylene glycol to decompose at the high temperatures necessary to force the reaction to completion and for side reactions to take place with some discoloration of the product. A more recent disclosure by Flory and Leutner gives a method that eliminates this difficulty by using two different glycols (945, 991). In the first step tetramethylene glycol is reacted with 2 to 10% excess of the acid chloride; at a certain point, another glycol is added in such an amount that the reactants are in stoichiometric proportions. The glycol added is one that is more stable at the higher temperatures and thus results in less discoloration of the polymer. Usually it is a higher glycol, such as pentamethylene, hexamethylene, decamethylene, or diethylene glycol.

As usual, the addition of other ingredients lowers the melting point of the polymer. When 2.7% (molar) of decamethylene glycol was added to the tetramethylene terephthalate, however, the product melted at 222° to 223.5°C., which is only about 4°C. lower than the melting point of pure tetramethylene terephthalate.

A trial and error method could be utilized in adding the higher glycol; that is, glycol could be added in small portions until the maximum obtainable viscosity is reached. The preferred method, however, depends on developing a curve that shows the relationship of excess acid chloride in the melt to the melt viscosity. Such a curve can be prepared by combining data from a series of experiments in which the amount of acid used is varied and thus can be established for a wide range of manufacturing conditions.

An alternative method for preventing glycol decomposition is one in which the tetramethylene glycol is fed to the reaction vessel in small portions. The same inlet which is used for introducing inert gas can also be used for the introduction of glycol.

MANUFACTURE OF FIBERS

Crystallization and Orientation

Polyethylene terephthalate has a rather sharp melting point of about 255°C. In its solid state it can be amorphous or possess various degrees of crystallinity, depending on its thermal history.

When the melt is quenched rapidly, the mass formed is transparent and almost completely amorphous. The polymer molecules are "quick frozen" in the position they held when they passed into the solid state. No crystallization can take place. Fibers extruded from a melting tank have this configuration, since their extreme thinness causes a very rapid cooling. X-ray examination of such fibers shows almost no crystallinity.

When amorphous polyethylene terephthalate fibers or films are heated, crystallization commences at about 80°C., which is the second order transition temperature of the polymer. At this temperature the molecules possess enough energy to permit some mobility, and the linear chains can become more ordered. A rise in temperature raises not only the total amount of crystallinity, but also the rate of crystallization.

The density of polyethylene terephthalate is an indication of its crystallinity, since the more ordered the molecules are, the more compact is the polymer's structure. In the amorphous state the density is about 1.33 grams per cubic centimeter; at 130°C. the density is 1.37 grams per cubic centimeter; at 170°C. the highest density obtainable is 1.40 grams per centimeter (2875).

Heating, however, does not in itself produce an orientation of the molecules in any particular direction. The randomly distributed molecules of amorphous polymer are now more crystalline, but they still lie in all planes. Fibers which are only annealed are very brittle.

To improve the strength of polyethylene terephthalate, it is oriented by stretching, or drawing. This operation is performed at temperatures higher than the transition point of the polymer, so that the molecules have the freedom of movement which is necessary for orientation (2875, 2890).

Fiber-Forming Procedures

Fiber-forming procedures devised for other synthetic fibers (1022) can be applied to polyethylene terephthalate. In general, a molten mass of the polymer is extruded as a ribbon, which is then cooled by a spray of water (or other coolant that does not affect the resin) and broken down into chips (1031). These chips are remelted (oxygen and moisture should be excluded) and extruded once more through orifices to give them the desired shape. In the older process for the preparation of fibers from linear polymers, two separate operations of spinning and drawing are required. A continuous process was recently developed, however, that produces fibers that are useful "as-spun" and that do not require a subsequent drawing operation (1010).

Fibers can be produced in two forms which, while identical in chemical composition, differ in their physical properties. The two forms—continuous filaments and staple—were introduced essentially to adapt polyethylene terephthalate to diverse applications.

Continuous Process. The continuous process of manufacture of fibers, which eliminates a separate drawing operation, was patented by H. H.

Hebeler (1010). The fibers made by his method have most of the desirable properties of wool, and are stronger, have better wrinkle resistance and retention of pressed-in creases, and, of course, are mothproof and bacteria-proof.

Hebeler's process can be utilized for making 100% polyethylene terephthalate fibers, or fibers in which up to 10% (mole) of another acid and (or) another glycol may be added. Suitable modifying acids include sebacic, adipic, bibenzoic, naphthalic, and hexahydroterephthalic acids. Other glycols that can be used are tetramethylene, hexamethylene, and diethylene glycols. The modifiers may be added as initial reactants or polymerized separately and then melt-blended with the polyethylene terephthalate.

Simultaneous Spinning-Drawing. Starting from the remelted and filtered polymer, the fibers are formed by forcing the melt through spinnerettes into air at room temperature. The extrusion temperature for polyethylene terephthalate is about 280° to 295°C. (a temperature range 10° to 20°C. lower is preferred for copolymers). The extruded filaments cool off and solidify several inches from the spinnerettes. At 40 to 50 inches from the spinnerettes, when the filaments are completely solidified, they are taken up by a forwarding means and drawn at the same time they are spun. The forwarding means may be a hinged roll, a jet of air, or a fast-turning wheel. Continuous filaments are usually wound on a roll. Staple fibers are prepared by forwarding the filaments by an air jet to a high-speed cutter, which chops them into fragments of desired length.

As long as the filaments are molten, the spinning-drawing operation has merely the effect of attenuating them. The filaments become thinner, but no crystallization or orientation takes place. As soon as they start to solidify, however, the pulling action results in orientation and partial crystallinity.

The drawing of the filaments in the continuous process, as well as the so-called cold drawing of the older step-wise process, has to be done at elevated temperatures. The heat supplies the linear molecules with enough energy to move so that they can orient themselves in the direction of the drawing and form crystallites. A temperature slightly above the second order transition point is used for drawing in both processes.

Crimping. The wool-like properties of fibers prepared by the continuous process are obtained by permitting the spun-drawn filaments to relax at temperatures between 90° to 200°C., preferably around 100°C. The heating medium may be hot air, hot or boiling water, steam, or various hot solutions which plasticize the filaments, such as nitric acid. The operation may be performed on the filaments as they arrive from the spinning, before they are cut into staple fibers or wound up, or on finished fabric. This heat treatment imparts a "crimp" to the fibers, which largely accounts for the wrinkle-recovery and other desirable properties of cloth woven from polyethylene terephthalate fibers (p. 219).

The crimping properties of the fibers depend on their shrinkage properties, which in turn are determined by the spinning speed. The preferred speed range is from 3,000 to 5,200 yards per minute; the lower limit is preferred for low-denier filaments. Speeds higher or lower than this range do not give fibers which attain wool-like properties when crimped.

Spinning speeds between 3,000 and 5,200 yards per minute will give fibers which will shrink between 15 and 30% when crimped in water at 90° to 100°C. Staples with less than 15% shrinkage do not crimp satisfactorily at this temperature, and those with more than 30% shrinkage will form tight, difficult-to-open wads (1010). For staple fibers of high shrinkage, a hot-air treatment as they come off the cutter in a fluffy state is more advisable than crimping in hot water. A convenient method is to blow the fibers through a pneumatic tube fed with air at about 150°C.

Bristle Manufacture. A method of making filaments that are particularly suitable for bristles and screens is given by Byers and Swallow (1027). Filaments made by this method possess high stiffness and resistance to high temperatures, bacteria, and light.

Previously made chips are melted in a heated grid, as described in British patents 533,307 (1023), 536,379 (1024), and 536,380 (1024). The resin is melted at temperatures no higher than 50°C. above its melting point, and poured through orifices of 0.003 to 0.09 inch in diameter. The fibers formed are cooled rapidly, preferably in water. For highest tensile strength the fibers are drawn at temperatures between 16°C. and 30°C. above their melting point. The fibers are also given a heat treatment at a temperature 30°C. or more below their melting point, as described in British patent 603,840 (1026).

A U. S. patent issued to W. R. McClellan gives another method of forming filaments for use as bristle material (1013). The filaments produced have good recovery from bending, which gives good resilience in bristles. This property is produced by drawing the polyethylene terephthalate filaments at 55° to 180°C. until they are 4.6 to 5.2 times their original length, heating them in relaxed state until they shrink from 5 to 10% of their drawn length, and finally heating them at 150° to 200°C. while preventing further shrinking. The intrinsic viscosity of the polymer used should be at least 0.35, preferably 0.75. The drawing can be done in two steps: The filaments are first drawn at 55° to 80°C. until they are about 3 to 4 times their original length, and then at 80° to 180°C. to a total draw of 4.6 to 5.2 times their original length.

The important consideration in this process is that the filaments should not be permitted to shrink beyond the prescribed limits. It is not important whether the filaments are drawn dry or in a nonsolvent (water, for example), or whether the nonsolvent, if it is used, swells the fiber or not. The manner in which the relaxation and shrinking is accomplished is also of little significance so long as the specified reduction of size takes place. It can be done by first winding the filaments on a roller of constant speed, passing the filaments through a bath of boiling water, and winding them again on a roller going at 90% of the speed of the first one. The final heat setting can be done while the filaments are on the roller, or otherwise held in place. The duration of the treatment is not significant either, as long as it is sufficient for complete relaxation of the filaments; somewhat longer treatment does no harm.

Improving Toughness and Other Properties of Fibers. A process for making polyethylene terephthalate fibers tougher and more resilient, and at the same time not reducing their tensile strength to a large extent, is disclosed by L. E. Amborski (1008). The usual methods of increasing elongation at the breaking point of a synthetic fiber (which causes a tougher and more resilient fiber) depend on heat relaxing of a stretched filament. These methods, however, result in a decrease of the filament's tensile strength and tenacity.

In Amborski's process the filament is treated with nitric acid solution. The concentration of the solution used depends on the duration and temperature of the treating operation, higher concentrations being required for shorter durations and lower temperatures. According to the inventor, the nitric acid penetrates the fiber and causes relaxation, which allows the crystallites in the fiber greater freedom of movement. Crystallinity and stability are thereby increased, and at the same time, better orientation along the fiber axis is produced. Greater toughness and resilience thus result. Yarns treated in this manner are particularly suited for carpets because of their high work recovery.[2]

Treatment with hydroxide is utilized by Hall, Ridge, and Whinfield (1007) to impart softness to polymethylene terephthalate fabric. When a coarsely woven fabric is immersed in a solution of sodium hydroxide (4 to 20%), an undegraded, fine, soft fabric results.

Coloring and Dyeing of Polyethylene Terephthalate Fiber

In general polyethylene terephthalate fibers can be colored by the usual dyeing methods applied to synthetic fibers.

The dyeing properties of the terephthalate fibers can be improved by some variation in the composition of the fiber. For example, if the polymer is modified with a high-molecular-weight polyalkylene oxide, the

[2]Work recovery is defined as the ratio of the amount of work done by the yarn in recovering from deformation to the amount of work performed in causing the deformation (1008).

water absorption of the fibers is increased, which permits the use of certain water-soluble dyestuffs (1034).

The fibers can be delustered by a method of British patent 504,714 (1020), as adapted by Dickson, Heath, and Reynolds (1030). Titanium dioxide, zinc sulfide, calcium sulfate, talc, mica, iron oxide, and similar pigments are dispersed in the glycol before polymerization, and fibers produced from the resulting polymer have no luster. The pigment must be finely divided and have an index of refraction different from that of the polymer itself. In British patent 596,688 an insoluble pigment dispersed in a different linear polyester, or in a linear polyesteramide, is used (1025). The addition of a different polymer, however, may result in an undesirable change in the properties of the product, such as lowering of the melting point.

The methods just described are applied to the whole batch, but in large-scale production it may not be convenient to have the whole batch of one color. A U. S. patent issued to Waters and Woods gives a process which overcomes this difficulty (1006). An organic coloring agent is used which is soluble in the polymer at the temperature of spinning and which is stable at this temperature. The coloring material used must not cause an appreciable degradation of the polymer. Substituted amino-anthraquinones and vat dyestuffs of the indigo, thioindigo, and anthraquinone series are examples of classes of dyes especially suited for this process. The powdered dyes are mixed with chips of the polymer, and the mixture is then dried, melted, and spun. The colored fibers produced have excellent fastness to light, washing, and rubbing.

MANUFACTURE OF FILM

Of the three main methods used in industry for film-forming, two are not suitable for making films from polyethylene terephthalate. The rather sharp melting point of this polyester and its low viscosity at temperatures above the melting point make calendering impractical. Solvent casting is not convenient because the polymer has but poor solubility in most commercial solvents. To be sure, a patent was granted to Swallow, Baird, and Ridge on this process (1003). According to their disclosure a thin layer of the polymer solution is cast on a smooth surface, and the solvent (e.g., cresylic acid) is evaporated slowly, so that no bubbles can form. The film is then stripped from the surface and oriented by stretching.

Commercial Production of Film

R. A. Hudson gives a good review of the commercial method of preparing polyethylene terephthalate film (2875). Other reviews amplify his remarks (2892).

Extrusion. The polyethylene terephthalate, previously prepared, is melted, filtered, and extruded through a long, narrow slot. As the film comes through the slot it is rapidly cooled in water. The viscosity of the molten terephthalate is only about one-fifth of the viscosity of the comparable grade of polyethylene used for film forming, which makes mandatory a careful control of the temperature, pressure, and die shape.

The extruded film is amorphous; it has a good surface gloss and is water-clear and fairly strong. It is unstable, however, because it crystallizes at temperatures above $80°$ C. to an opaque and brittle product.

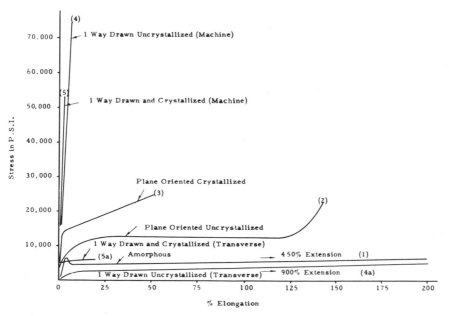

Figure No. 8.—Stress-strain relationships for polyester films produced under different drawing and crystallization conditions. Source: R. A. Hudson, *British Plastics* 26, 6–9 (1953).

Drawing. The next step in the fabrication process is "plane orientation" in order to make the film equally strong in all directions in its own plane. The film is drawn in two directions at right angles at the same time. As a result the molecules are oriented so that they lie entirely in the plane of the film, but are not oriented in this plane in any particular direction.

The draw improves most mechanical properties of the film. The larger the draw, however, the less is the elongation to which the finished film can be subjected without rupture. Thus, a compromise must be reached between the tensile strength of the film, which increases with the de-

gree of draw, and its toughness and extensibility, which decrease with
draw.

The rate of draw, which also must be determined with considerable
care, depends on the temperature used. The higher the temperature, the
faster the draw should be so as not to permit the film to flow excessively.
Excessive flow may result in a film which is not only too thin for the intended use, but also not oriented and therefore not strong.

Annealing. The final step in the manufacture of film is also the result of a compromise. The drawn film, if heated above the temperature
of drawing, will shrink. In order to "lock" the molecules in place, the
film is held so that it cannot contract and is then annealed. The film becomes more crystalline during this treatment, but the orientation of the
molecules is not considerably affected. The resultant film is stable and
will not contract when heated up to the temperature of annealing, which
is usually between 180° and 210°C. The annealing temperature cannot
be made too high, for at high temperatures the molecules would be free to
move around, and the advantages of orientation would be wiped out.

A diagram illustrating the stress-strain relationships of polyethylene
terephthalate films, varied by adjusting drawing and crystallization conditions, is given in figure No. 8.

Variation in Ingredients

For some applications films made from polyethylene terephthalate are
too insoluble and stiff. Edgar and Ellery disclose a method by which
these shortcomings may be overcome (986). Since films from adipic and
sebacic acids are soft and low melting, they combine both types of ingredients. A mixture of terephthalic acid with either adipic or sebacic
acid, or with both acids, is polymerized with ethylene glycol; 2.4 moles
of the aromatic acid are used for 1 mole of either of the other acids. The
resulting polymer gives a softer film.

The required minimum molecular weight for film-forming polymers is
10,000. Isocyanates can be used to cross-link the polymers and provide
at least that high a molecular weight.

Recovery of Waste

Since the terephthalates are thermoplastics, and soften on heating, it
is possible to reclaim some of the waste and scrap which are always
produced during fabrication. In one method for the recovery of terephthalic acid from scrap, the polymer is hydrolized by refluxing it with a
mineral acid such as nitric acid (1028). The terephthalic acid separates
and is washed and further purified by dissolving it in sodium hydroxide
solution and reprecipitating with acid.

A method for the recovery of the whole scrap, not only the acid, is also disclosed by the same inventor, R. L. Heath (1029). Waste terephthalic polymer yarn is degraded by refluxing it with ethylene glycol. After the polymer is degraded, the mixture is distilled in vacuum to remove excess glycol. It is then heated at 275°C. until the melt is suitable for fiber-drawing. The principle of this reclaiming method may also be utilized for cleaning equipment used in the manufacture and fabrication of the resin. Autoclaves, for example, can be cleaned with vapors of glycol, preferably under pressure, and the solution of the polymer and the glycol formed can be drawn off.

ELASTOMERIC TEREPHTHALATES

In addition to films and fibers, the terephthalate structural unit can also be utilized for the preparation of elastomeric plastics. Elastic yarns have been made which are stronger than any rubber thread known and which do not have the disadvantages of rubber when made into textiles, such as unpleasant odor and deterioration on exposure to light and oxygen (1038, 1039).

Preparation of Polymer

M. D. Snyder discloses a method for making a very elastic yarn from terephthalic acid, an acyclic dicarboxylic acid, and a glycol (1039). Mixtures of dicarboxylic acids can be used, but the proportion of aromatic to aliphatic dicarboxylic acid is crucial. An excess of either ingredient would increase the crystallinity of the product and decrease its elasticity. The aromatic acid should comprise from 30 to 60% by weight of all the acid used in the compound. The best results are attained if the range is from 45 to 55%.

The dimethyl esters of the acids are the usual raw materials. The polymerization is therefore preceded by an ester interchange between the acid ester and the glycol, which is catalyzed by litharge and zinc chlorate. When the methyl alcohol produced by this reaction ceases to evolve, the temperature of the polymerizate is raised to about 275°C. A vacuum is applied to help in removal of excess glycol. These conditions are maintained and the polymerizate is stirred vigorously until a polymeric melt of the desired intrinsic viscosity is produced (preferably 1.0–1.5 or above).

Yarn Formation

A ribbon of the melt is extruded on a water-cooled wheel and chopped into pieces. The pieces are remelted, and the melt is pushed through a sand-packed filter. The filtered melt is extruded at 150° to 275°C. through spinnerettes and into a cooling chamber where the filaments solidify. The filaments are tacky at this stage, and talc is used to prevent them from adhering to one another. The tackiness can be eliminated by heat treatment at a temperature about 10° C. below the sticking point[3] of the polymer.

Another way of eliminating the stickiness and imparting crystallinity is the drawing of the fiber in differential-speed rollers to about 3 times its initial length. In this case, however, the fiber is then relaxed by rewinding it, so that the final length is about 2.5 times the original. A greater draw during manufacture would reduce the elongation tolerance of the finished yarn, that is, the length to which it can be stretched without breaking. The tenacity, elastic recovery, and modulus of elasticity (the force required to extend the fiber by a certain given percent) of the yarn, however, increase with increased draw. Therefore, the drawing, relaxing, and winding conditions chosen are those that will produce the optimum relationship of yarn properties for a particular use.

The resultant yarn shrinks from 50 to 85% at elevated temperatures, which is excessive for most applications. A heat treatment of the yarn at temperatures 10° C. below its sticking point reduces the shrinkage to about 5 to 10%.

Improvement of Heat Stability

Many uses for elastic fibers require that they be undamaged during ironing. Snyder obtained fibers with a sticking point above the usual ironing temperatures by mixing an aromatic aliphatic copolyester similar to that described in U. S. patent 2,623,033 (1039) with an aromatic polyester (1038).

The two components are prepared separately by the usual procedure. In the aromatic aliphatic copolyester the aromatic acid content is about 35 to 45% of the total acid content. The aromatic polyester is mixed with the copolyester in such proportions that the final mixture contains about 45 to 55% of aromatic acid.

The copolyester and the aromatic polyester can be combined directly as melts, or each may first be cast on water-cooled wheels, broken in chips, remelted, and then blended. The blending can be continuous, which will give the product a desired uniformity because of common thermal history, or it can be done in a batch. The extent of blending is very important in this procedure. It is necessary to blend the two components until a homogeneous mass is prepared, and yet not long enough to permit a large amount of ester interchange, which would produce a true copolymer, with a lower sticking point. Inhibitors or stabilizers, such as

---

[3]Sticking point is the temperature at which a sample of polymer leaves a molten trail as it is stroked with moderate pressure across a smooth surface of a heated block of glass.

aryl esters of high molecular weight, can be added to each component before blending to prevent excessive ester interchange.

Yarns from this resin, even though their chemical composition is almost identical with that of the previously described yarns, have a sticking point of at least 130°C., which gives them a satisfactory heat stability at normal ironing temperatures.

Yarn Properties and Uses

In comparison with rubber threads, these terephthalate elastic yarns are stronger, have a higher modulus of elasticity, and can be spun readily into multifilament yarns (1038, 1039). They have good resistance to degradation by oxidation, light, soap, perspiration, and greases, can be dyed by common dyestuffs, and have good elastic recovery ("snap").

All these properties make the yarn particularly suitable for articles requiring high stretchability and high elastic recovery after stretching. Examples are wearing apparel, such as girdles and bathing suits, elastic bandages, surgical hosiery, upholstery, pile fabrics for carpets, and many other items.

PROPERTIES AND USES OF TEREPHTHALATES

Fibers

Properties. In the United States polyethylene terephthalate fibers are manufactured by E. I. du Pont de Nemours & Co., Inc., under the trade name "Dacron." The English counterpart of "Dacron" is "Terylene" fibers made by Imperial Chemical Industries, Ltd. These fibers have a unique combination of properties that make them especially valuable for apparel uses as well as many industrial uses. They have less stretchability than polyamide fibers, such as nylon, but are stronger (2971).

The properties of polyethylene terephthalate fibers may be summarized as follows (2928, 2937, 2951, 2959):

(1) Very high strength and tenacity, wet or dry.

(2) High resistance to stretching.

(3) High resistance to abrasion or rubbing.

(4) Highly resilient; keep shape, wet or dry.

(5) Outstanding resistance to acids and oxidizing agents. [Alkali attacks polyethylene terephthalate fibers. Except for aqueous ammonia, which reduces the molecular weight and tensile strength of the fiber, the alkali attack is proportionate to the exposed surface (2890).]

(6) Mothproof, mildewproof, and immune to attack by other insects or bacteria.

(7) Outstanding dielectric properties.

Table No. 27.— *Properties of Dacron polyester fibers**

Property	Filament	Staple
MECHANICAL PROPERTIES		
Specific gravity	1.38	1.38
Tensile strength		
At 21°C. and 65% relative humidity, gm. per denier	4.2–5.0	3.6–4.0
Tenacity at 21°C. and 65% relative humidity, psi	74,000–89,000	64,000–72,000
Wet, % of strength at 21°C. and 65% relative humidity	100	100
Ultimate elongation at 65% relative humidity, %	22–30	38–48
Recovery from strain		
Strain, %	2 8	......
Recovery, %	97 80	......
Modulus of elasticity		
Static method, gm. per denier	About 90	......
Velocity of sound method, gm. per denier	About 120	......
Stiffness, average, gm. per denier	14–23	7–11
Toughness index, gm.-cm. per denier cm.	0.55–0.64	0.76–0.86

CHEMICAL AND SOLVENT RESISTANCE

Effect of strong acids	Very resistant to most mineral acids. Disintegrated by 96% sulfuric acid.
Effect of weak acids	Virtually no effect.
Effect of strong alkalies	Moderate resistance when cold. Disintegrated at boil.
Effect of weak alkalies	Good resistance.
Effect of organic solvents	Generally unaffected. Soluble in some phenolic compounds.

MISCELLANEOUS PROPERTIES

Property	Filament	Staple
Moisture regain at 21°C. and 65% relative humidity, %	0.4	0.4
Swelling in water, %	Virtually none	Virtually none
Dielectric constant, 60 cycles (dry)	3.8	3.8
Softening temperature	Melts at about 480°F., sticks at 455°F.	
Effect of prolonged exposure to sunlight	Some loss of strength. No discoloration. Much more resistant behind glass.	
Resistance to moths and mildew	Not attacked	

*Source: *Modern Plastics Encyclopedia.*

(8) Outstanding heat resistance.

(9) Exceptional resistance to weather and sunlight, especially behind glass.

(10) Water-repellent and quick-drying.

(11) Warm to the touch.

Table No. 27 gives the properties of "Dacron" in detail.

Table No. 28.— *Colors produced by Dacron fibers with several identification stains**

Stain	Color produced by	
	Dacron staple	Dacron filament
Identification Stain A	Pale orange yellow	Grayish yellow
Calco Identification Stain No. 2 (American Cyanamid)	Pale grayish yellow	Grayish greenish yellow
Fibrotint GLS (Ciba)	Light grayish reddish brown	Light yellowish brown
Identification Stain GDC (General Dyestuff)	Yellowish gray	Light yellow green
Identification Stain ODDA (General Dyestuff)	Grayish yellowish pink	Grayish purplish pink
National Aniline Stain C-63807	Grayish yellow green	Light greenish yellow
Texchrome Identification Stain (Fisher Scientific)	Pale blue	Very pale blue
Testfabrics Identification Stain	Grayish yellow	Orangish green yellow
Interchemical Identification Stain	Strong yellow green and pale green	Light yellowish green
Du Pont Identification Stain No. 4	Moderate orange	Moderate orange yellow

*Source: G. L. Royer, "Identification of Synthetic Fibers by Microscopical and Dye Staining Techniques," American Cyanamid Co., Calco Chemical Division, Technical Bulletin No. 831.

A combination of stain tests and microscopical examination of cross sections can be used to distinguish Dacron from other synthetic fibers (2981). "Dacron" fibers are round in cross section, but so are nylon and several other fibers. Colors produced with various identification stains can be used to distinguish the "Dacron" fibers (table No. 28).

Applications. Fabrics made from the polyethylene terephthalate fibers (Dacron and Terylene) are a gift seemingly earmarked for travelers. Suits, dresses, shirts, and blouses made from them spring back into press even after a crushing ride in a car or train or a sudden downpour.

A garment made from Dacron has light weight, long wear, spot-cleans and washes easily, is quick-drying and needs no ironing, holds its size and shape even when wet, and has body and good drape and feel (2937).

In addition to wearing apparel, the polyethylene terephthalate fibers, particularly in staple form, can be used in felts of various kinds, including papermaker's felts, carpets, turkish towels, and similar items (1010).

Although it is still a relatively expensive fiber, the properties of polyethylene terephthalate make it efficient and economical for specialized industrial uses. These include filter cloths (which last at least five times longer than wool or cotton cloths), acid-resistant ropes, safety belts, acid-resistant clothing and footwear, anode bags, laminates, and rubberized products (2928, 2951, 2962).

Hose pipe has been made by winding fabric or yarn made from glycol-terephthalate esters on rubber or plastic tubing (1041).

A process was previously described for producing polyethylene terephthalate bristles which are flexible, strong, and curl-resistant, and which exhibit outstanding recovery from bending (1013). The modulus of elasticity of these bristles is about four times that of nylon bristles, so that small-diameter bristles can be made without loss of brush stiffness. Brushes with thin bristles have many advantages. For example, when they are used for paint brushes they increase the paint-holding capacity of the brush and reduce brush marks. In addition, the bristles are not affected by paint solvents and do not soften in water or high humidity.

Films

Properties. Polyethylene terephthalate film is manufactured in this country by Du Pont under the trade name "Mylar." Imperial Chemical Industries, Ltd. in England uses "Terylene" as the trade name for both the fiber and film produced from polyethylene terephthalate.

Table No. 29 summarizes the physical, electrical, and chemical properties of Mylar and Terylene polyester films. The data given are average values and should not be used for specifications or design purposes. The properties of "Mylar" film are given in detail in reference (2938). Information on the properties of "Terylene" film is given in references (2892, 2979).

One of the outstanding characteristics of polyethylene terephthalate film is its combination of high mechanical strength with good electrical properties over a wide temperature range. It is this characteristic that makes the film of special interest to the electrical industry.

The high strength of polyethylene terephthalate film, which is said to be from 2 to 8 times that of other commercial films, makes possible thin gages as fine as $\frac{1}{4}$ of $\frac{1}{1000}$ inch (2987).

Polyethylene terephthalate film also has high thermal stability. For example, the physical and mechanical properties of Mylar show little change over the temperature range of $-20°$ to $80°C$.; no embrittlement

Table No. 29.— *Properties (average) of Mylar and Terylene polyethylene terephthalate films**

Property	Mylar	Terylene
Melting point	250°–255°C.	265°C.
Specific gravity	1.38–1.39	1.39
Refractive index	1.655 (n_{D25})	......

MECHANICAL PROPERTIES

Tensile strength	17,000–25,000 psi	25,000 psi
Impact strength	**70 kg.-cm.	......
Elongation at breaking point	**70–130%	50%
Tear resistance	**18 gm.	120 gm.-cm. per cm. tear per 0.001 in. thickness
Bursting strength	**45 lb.	......
Yield stress at break	......	14,000 psi

ELECTRICAL PROPERTIES

Dielectric strength	***4,500 volts per mil (25°C., 60 cycles) ***3,150 volts per mil (25°C., 60 cycles)	4,500 volts per mil
Dielectric constant	3.16 (25°C., 60 cycles) 3.7 (125°C., 60 cycles) 3.12 (25°C., 1 kilocycle) 2.98 (25°C., 1 megacycle)	3.1–3.2 (60 cycles) 3.1–3.2 (1 kilocycle) 3.0–3.1 (1 megacycle)
Volume resistivity	1×10^{19} ohm.-cm. (25°C.) 1×10^{13} ohm.-cm. (150°C.)	1,017 ohms per cm.
Dissipation factor (Power loss factor given for Terylene)	0.0021 (25°C., 60 cycles) 0.0064 (150°C., 60 cycles) 0.0047 (25°C., 1 kilocycle) 0.016 (150°C., 1 megacycle)	0.002 (60 cycles) 0.004–0.006 (1 kilocycle) 0.013–0.015 (1 megacycle)
Insulation resistance	800–1,000 meg.-mics (130°C.) 80–100 meg.-mics (150°C.)	......

MOISTURE ABSORPTION AND PERMEABILITY CHARACTERISTICS

Moisture absorption	0.3% (immersion in water at 25°C. for 1 week)	0.5% by weight (prolonged immersion in water)
Water vapor permeability	**160 gm. per 100 sq. m. per hr. (39.5°C.)	30 gm. per sq. m. per day (38°C., 90% relative humidity)
Oxygen permeability	**0.90 gm. per 100 sq. m. per hr.	......

*Source: Mylar—E. I. du Pont de Nemours & Co., Inc., Film Department, Technical Bulletin No. 1-2-53; Terylene—Anonymous, *Plastics* (London) 18, 17 (1953); *Chemical Age* 68, 8 (1953).
**1-mil film.
***2-mil film.

Table No. 29.—— *Properties (average) of Mylar and Terylene polyethylene terephthalate films* (Cont'd)

Property	Mylar	Terylene
MOISTURE ABSORPTION AND PERMEABILITY CHARACTERISTICS (*Cont'd*)		
Organic vapor permeability	Marked resistance to passage	Marked resistance to passage
MISCELLANEOUS PROPERTIES		
Chemical and solvent resistance	Excellent resistance to organic solvents, greases, and oils (except phenols and cresols); good resistance to commonly used electrical varnishes (except phenolic resin and asphaltic base varnishes, which cause some degradation); rapidly embrittled under severe hydrolysis conditions.	Good resistance to mineral acids (except decomposed by concentrated sulfuric acid); moderate resistance to oxidizing agents and organic compounds (except phenols and chlorinated phenols).
Shrinkage	3–5% (150°C.)	......
Light transmission	More than 90% of incident light in visible region of spectrum	......
Fungus resistance	Very good, not attacked	Very good, not attacked
Flammability	Ignites, but burns with difficulty	Ignites, but burns with difficulty

occurs at temperatures as low as −60°C.; and the film retains useful properties up to 150° to 175°C. (2938). Terylene film remains flexible at −50°C. (2892).

Both Mylar and Terylene film have good resistance to chemicals and solvents, low moisture absorption, and high resistance to the passage of water and organic vapors.

Mylar film is difficult to heat-seal with conventional heat-sealing techniques. A temperature of 240° to 245°C. is required for heat-sealing, and at this temperature the sealed area becomes puckered and brittle. However, sealers in which the film is restrained from shrinkage throughout the heating and cooling cycle have been found to be satisfactory (2952).

Standard threads can be used for sewing "Mylar."

Applications. Because of its excellent physical and chemical properties, many applications have been suggested for polyethylene terephthalate film. It is probable that the main outlet for this film will be in the electrical industry (2875). When used in electrical equipment, it enables the bulk of insulation to be reduced and makes possible the use of higher working temperatures.

Table No. 30. —*Suggested applications for Mylar polyethylene terephthalate film**

Electrical	Nonelectrical	Glass replacement	Special packaging
Dielectric in capacitors	Base for magnetic sound-recording tape	Storm windows	Packaging of medical items and
Slot liners and face insulation for motors	Base for pressure-sensitive electrical and industrial tapes	Plastic glazing for agricultural buildings, greenhouses, etc.	other items requiring sterilization in the package
Tape insulation for motor and generator coils	Cab-lining materials		Packaging of bearings etc.
Insulation on magnet wire	Lining material for steel and fiber drums		Powder box drum heads
Barrier tapes and insulating tape in cable construction	Protective covers		Transparent inserts for window cartons
Layer insulation and insulation between turns and transformer coils	Base for metalizing with aluminum, zinc, or silver		Use of metalized Mylar film for packaging products requiring protection from light and/or requiring a wrap having a very low permeability to water vapor, organic vapors (e.g., odors and flavors), and gases. Examples of such products are: stick gum, photographic film, hygroscopic powders, dehydrated soups, frozen juice concentrates, high-fat-content foods, dried activated yeast, cigarettes, butter, and margarine.
Backing for mica fittings and integrated mica	Protective wrap on pipeline insulation, such as glass fibers, cork, magnesium, etc.		
	Metallic yarn		
	Industrial laminations with foils, paper, asbestos, glass cloth, etc.		
	Surfacing material for paneling, decorative laminates, etc.		

*Source: E. I. du Pont de Nemours & Co., Inc., Film Department, Technical Bulletin No. 1-2-53.

Mylar polyester film has replaced impregnated paper as the dielectric in capacitors used in dial telephone equipment. It is tougher and stands more voltage; the capacitors made from it require no protective housing and are much smaller and less costly (2932).

Polyester film has exceptionally high ratings in properties important for the packaging field—clarity and strength. Problems in machine handling and sealing still need to be solved, however (2943).

Polyethylene terephthalate base for photographic film (lithographic and motion picture film) is expected to be on the market in the summer of 1955 (2931). Experimental quantities made by Du Pont appeared several times stronger than present safety film base and had greater dimensional stability. The polyester film can be made 27% thinner than today's standard, thus adding 35% more film footage to a given reel.

Table No. 30 lists some specific uses for Mylar film in the electrical and other fields. U. S. patent 2,641,592 has a very long list of possible uses for polyethylene terephthalate film (951).

PRODUCTION CAPACITY

Production capacity for polyethylene terephthalate film and fibers will take a tremendous jump when plant expansion programs of the two producers—Du Pont and Imperial Chemical Industries, Ltd. (ICI)—are completed.

It is predicted that Du Pont's plant for production of Mylar polyester film at Circleville, Ohio, which started production in late 1954, will be able to supply all demands for this product for some time to come (2988, 3006). A new plant at Kingston, N. C., will produce 35,000,000 pounds per year of Dacron fiber when it reaches full production (3005).

Two new plants for the production of Terylene polyester fiber—one in England and one in Canada—are scheduled to begin production in 1955. The ICI plant under construction at Wilton, England, is expected to reach a total output of 22 million pounds by 1956 (2998). The second new ICI plant is at Milhaven, Ont. It is to be operated by Imperial Chemical Industries of Canada, a recently formed subsidiary of ICI (2999).

ICI has also licensed firms in France, Germany, Italy, the Netherlands, and Belgium for production of Terylene fibers (2994, 3004).

Dimethyl terephthalate for ICI's Canadian plant, as well as for Terylene producers in other countries, will be supplied by Hercules Powder Co's. new plant at Burlington, N. J. This plant will have an annual capacity of about 12 million pounds (3003).

II. DI-ISOCYANATE-MODIFIED POLYESTERS

Polyesters can be modified with di-isocyanates to yield a variety of resinous products ranging from tough, rubbery plastics to foams. The chemistry of isocyanate-modified polyesters and their applications as elastomers, adhesives, foams, and molding and coating compounds are discussed in this chapter.

The isocyanate-modified polyesters are primarily a German development. O. Bayer, the pioneer in this field, has given a good summary of the basic work (3012, 3013). Comprehensive reviews of more recent developments are presented by Bjorksten, Tovey, and Dollard (3014) and by Katz (3231).

CHEMISTRY

Isocyanates ($R-N=C=O$) react with compounds containing reactive hydrogen atoms. A urethane linkage is formed with compounds containing hydroxyl groups and an amide linkage with molecules containing carboxyl groups:

$$R-OH + O=C=N-R^1 \rightarrow R-O-\overset{\displaystyle O}{\overset{\displaystyle \|}{C}}-\overset{\displaystyle H}{\overset{\displaystyle |}{N}}-R^1$$

$$R-\overset{\displaystyle O}{\overset{\displaystyle \|}{C}}-OH + O=C=N-R^1 \rightarrow R=\overset{\displaystyle O}{\overset{\displaystyle \|}{C}}-\overset{\displaystyle H}{\overset{\displaystyle |}{N}}-R^1 + CO_2$$

The reaction products of di-isocyanates and polyester resins usually contain a mixture of the two types of linkages, since the terminal groups in the original polyester molecules are usually a mixture of hydroxyl and carboxyl groups. The proportions of the two types of linkages can be varied by changing the proportions of acid and glycol used in preparing the polyester. With excess glycol, the number of urethane linkages formed is correspondingly increased. Increasing the acid proportion increases the number of amide linkages.

The first step in the di-isocyanate modification of polyesters results mainly in an extension of chain length, since the reaction is usually that of adding on to the polyester chain or of linking two polyester chains together. Urethane linkages formed by hydroxyl group reaction still contain

225

an active hydrogen, which offers a point for further attack by additional di-isocyanate. By using excess of the same di-isocyanate or adding different di-isocyanates the polyesters may be modified and cross-linked to give products with a wide range of properties.

When a di-isocyanate reacts with a polyester containing a large number of carboxyl groups, or water is added to a polyester-di-isocyanate reaction product, amide linkages are formed and carbon dioxide is evolved. This reaction may be used to produce foamed polyesters. Unfortunately, it may also occur when undesired if moist air comes in contact with the di-isocyanates. For this reason many of the reactions of polyesters and di-isocyanates must be carried out in airtight apparatus, and the drums or containers of chemicals in storage should have moisture-tight closures.

Schlack, looking for fiber-forming polyurethanes, extended hydroxy polyesters with di-isocyanates in equimolecular quantities, but the melting point of the products was too low for commercial application (1046, 1047). In general, attempts to prepare artificial fibers from di-isocyanate-modified polyesters equal to or better than polyamide fibers (nylon) have not been successful (3015). The di-isocyanate-modified polyesters have melting points much lower than that of nylon; they are difficult to spin; and the range of applicable dyes is limited.

The fields of elastomers and foams are by far the most active applications for di-isocyanate-polyester resins.

ELASTOMERS

The German Vulcollans, which opened the field (3018, 3019, 3023, 3024, 3025), and Goodyear's Chemigum SL (3020), are the practical results of research on di-isocyanate-polyester elastomers.

Basically, these elastomers are prepared by combining glycol-adipic acid polyesters with naphthalene di-isocyanates to lengthen the chains, and then cross-linking the modified polyester by reaction with water, glycols (1058, 1059, 1073, 1074, 1075), diamines (1058, 1059, 3018, 3019), or amine alcohols (1057, 1058). Cross-linking can also be obtained by determining the active chemical endings in the modified polyester and reacting them with a calculated amount of additional di-isocyanate. If a glycol or diamine cross-linking agent is added in small, controlled amounts, objectionable gas formation is eliminated (1055).

Considerable attention has been given to the control of the rate of cross-linking or curing. From the standpoint of manufacturing technique the necessity for control is obvious. By proper selection of the particular glycol or diamine (or use of the proper amount of water) on the one hand, and the particular isocyanate on the other, it is possible to vary the curing time over very wide limits (1056, 1057).

Continuous production of specific articles from the polyester-derived polyurethane elastomers has, so far as is known, not yet been introduced. The mixing and addition of the cross-linking material, however, can be carried out in a warm press which has been adapted for extrusion. Therefore, continuous operation appears basically feasible. A process which avoids the use of heavy-duty mixers has been disclosed (1061).

Where batch processes require relatively slow setting, this can be accomplished by the methods given in references (1056, 1057, 1076). The liquid reaction mass may also be poured into a heated revolving form, and the cross-linking agent then added to effect the final cure.

If glycol is used as the cross-linking agent, the cross-linked product can be used for compression molding. A combined casting-pressing process is also employed, in which the completely mixed mass of di-isocyanate-modified polyester and cross-linking glycol is cooled to room temperature. It will retain its thermoplasticity for several days. Within this time it can be formed or pressed and heat cured (3022).

It is possible to cast elastomers of the urethane type in liquid form. However, this precludes compounding of the conventional type, such as by calendering (1076, 3026).

Benzoyl peroxide, nitro compounds, quinone oximes, and chromates and dichromates of potassium, ammonium, barium, and lead have been employed for curing elastomeric reaction products of polyesters and di-isocyanates (1053, 1062, 1067). Formaldehyde, or formaldehyde-producing compounds, in conjunction with compounds which are neutral at low temperatures and acidic at high temperatures, are also disclosed as curing agents for polyurethane elastomers (1049, 1052, 1063, 1064, 1065, 1066).

Proteins, partially hydrolyzed polyvinyl acetals, and cellulose derivatives have been disclosed by Harper, Smith, and White as other modifiers of elastomeric polyurethanes (1068, 1069, 1070). Sulfur can be used to vulcanize elastomers (1051, 1060).

The isocyanate-polyester elastomers have abrasion resistance, ozone resistance, and tensile strength far superior to those of natural rubber and synthetic GR-S (3222). They have excellent oil resistance, fair resistance to dry heat, but poor resistance to extremes of temperature. They are attacked by acids and alkalies. Detailed data on the properties of these elastomers are given by R. P. Dinsmore (3020).

The higher cost of the isocyanate-polyester rubbers has prevented their full commercial realization. Also, processing is difficult and adhesion and compounding problems have only been partially solved. Potential applications include heavy-duty truck, bus, and aircraft tires, conveyor and driving belts, shoe heels and soles, friction wheels, hydraulic gaskets, oil seals, and related products.

FOAMS

Preparation

The foaming process (p. 226) is applicable to elastomeric as well as to rigid urethane resins (1097). Mixtures of polyesters suitable for making foamed resins have been disclosed by Simon and Thomas (1095).

In the production of isocyanate-modified polyester foams, the manner in which water is added to the mixture is important. By adding it in predetermined quantities at carefully chosen intervals, the reaction may be regulated to give foams of a wide range of cell size and physical properties (3046). The water may be added in the form of a metal salt hydrate (1086).

The molecular weight of the polyester employed for condensation with the isocyanate also plays an important part in determining the properties of the foam (1097, 1098). For example, semielastic foams are produced if polyesters having molecular weights below 1,000 are used (1097). More rigid foams are produced from higher molecular weight polyesters.

The foaming reaction is exothermic and gives a temperature and pressure increase sufficient to complete the curing of the polyester component (1096). The temperature changes during foaming should be controlled. When the volume of foam to be produced is large, internal cooling, by means of finely powdered dry ice (solid carbon dioxide), is particularly recommended. This procedure was suggested in 1950 by E. A. Jonasch, who was with the Naval Ordnance Laboratory at that time, and was worked out on a production scale by R. Mondano of Raytheon Manufacturing Co. (3048). It makes close control of temperature possible, regardless of the thickness of the foamed section.

The best process for obtaining optimum adhesion, strength, toughness, and thermal resistance of foams will depend on the volume of foam to be produced, and the temperature and other conditions used in each case. Generally speaking, it appears advantageous to start foaming at as low a temperature as is compatible with reasonable speed of operation. In the latter part of the process the exotherm is allowed to bring up the temperature moderately in order to carry the reaction to completion (3048).

By using as the di-isocyanate component a di-isocyanate prereacted with a relatively minor proportion of the polyester material, or a polyisocyanate containing hydrolyzable chlorine, it is possible to extend the time before foaming starts (1091, 1092). This procedure also minimizes the amount of free di-isocyanate present, which constitutes a health hazard unless the shop is well ventilated.

Simon and Thomas of the Lockheed Aircraft Co. disclose the use of metal soap powders alone or with metallic leafing powders to improve

foam stability, and thus make possible a lighter foam of high final strength
(1087, 1095). A similar result is obtained by using quaternary ammonium
bentonite complexes or ethyl cellulose in preparing foamed polyester-di-
isocyanate resins (1089, 1093). Fillers also increase the compressive
strength of foams, but they increase the density as well.

The polyurethane foams are compatible with flame retardants such as
the allyl aryl phosphonates (1088).

Preparation and application of foamed material requires mixing and material handling equipment adapted to this task. An ordinary high-speed
propeller mixer is suitable when properly arranged and adapted to the
size of the mixing container.

A spraying type of mixer has been developed which mixes the di-
isocyanate and the polyester together on the one hand, and the water and
the activator on the other, and then brings these two systems together in
a final mix chamber. The mix emerges from the chamber in a low viscous
state, ready to foam (3018, 3019).

When the components are sprayed under high pressure into a very small
mixing space, it is possible to mix all the components in a single chamber
(1099). Small portable foaming tools, adaptable for use on the spot, can
therefore be used on the production line, in ship yards, or in the building
industry.

Care must be taken not to expose the polyester-di-isocyanate mixes to
atmospheric humidity before foaming, as this could cause them to gel prematurely. During foaming the production of dense foams requires a dry
atmosphere; humid air will cause the formation of light foam.

Applications

At present, many urethane-polyester foams are on the German market,
and several firms have entered the foamed resin field here (3040, 3041).

In the cushion and mattress fields these foams compete with foamed
rubber. They are used in a number of applications requiring a buoyant
material. For example, they provide a means for filling life belts and
buoyancy compartments in boats with a cellular foam that prevents flood-
ing even if the container or outer shell should be pierced; in the toy field
they provide an inexpensive, light means for filling inflatable toys perma-
nently; and in the aircraft and other lightweight structural fields they
provide a simple, effective means for stabilizing hollow, thin-skinned
constructions against "oil canning" and buckling, thus reducing fatigue
and increasing rigidity and strength. The alkyd-isocyanate foamed-in-
place types of foams are used extensively as core materials in certain
sandwich types of radomes, where exact control of facing and core thickness and uniformity of core material is necessary in order to obtain the
electronic efficiency required (3049).

ADHESIVES

The isocyanate-modified polyesters have certain properties which make them logical choices for the production of adhesives. They can be polymerized in the presence of the materials to be bonded, which generally favors a good bond. Also, the di-isocyanate component is so reactive that it is very likely to find groups on adjacent surfaces to which it can attach itself (1079, 1081). If an excess of di-isocyanate is used in preparing the adhesive, all reactive hydroxyl groups will be covered and water sensitivity therefore is reduced.

Windemuth and Bock have produced adhesives from adipic acid-glycol type of polyesters extended by reaction with toluene di-isocyanate (1082). The polyesters used have molecular weights in the order of 3,000 to 6,000 and a hydroxyl number of 40 to 50. Before use the modified polyesters are cross-linked with polyfunctional di-isocyanates, which leads to quick drying. These compounds are used in the shoe industry.

Di-isocyanate polyester resins are also used for binding cork for gaskets and floor coverings (1077), as adhesives for waxed paper (1078), for bonding synthetic fibers to rubber in automobile tires, and for bonding wood (1083).

The principal disadvantages of the isocyanate-polyester adhesives are the inconvenience of using a two-component system and the short storage life of the components. The fabricator must prepare the adhesive at the time of assembly, which involves handling the active isocyanate and using rapid production schedules. As with foams, the use of slow-acting di-isocyanate carriers makes possible some improvements in handling time and care required.

Based on the elastomer type of products, single-component adhesives have been developed from isocyanate-polyester resins (1080, 1085). These adhesives, however, have high sensitivity to moisture, which causes them to skin prematurely.

MOLDING COMPOUNDS

Molding compounds were among the first materials developed from the polyester type of urethane resins (3012). [Early patents on these compounds covered their use in phonograph records and printing plates (1101, 1102).] The basic developments were completed several years ago, and relatively few new developments have been forthcoming in recent years.

The disadvantages of the di-isocyanate-polyester resins from a molding standpoint are the limited storage life of these mixed polyester-isocyanate compounds, the toxicity of unreacted di-isocyanate, and the necessity for protecting at least the di-isocyanate component from moisture contact. For these reasons it is unlikely that the isocyanate-polyester resins will supplant the present principal injection- or compression-molding materials, even though their price becomes more attractive and their mechanical and electrical properties and heat stability are good.

For injection molding of urethane resins it is necessary to use machines in which the clearance between the heating cylinder and the torpedo is small, and the capacity is such that just enough material is heated to fill the die.

Procedures and machines for blow molding of polyurethane films are described by A. Romanowski (3050).

COATINGS

Preparation and Modification

In the surface coating field the isocyanate-modified polyester resins show excellent adhesion and resistance to chemicals and abrasion (1103, 3051). Nonetheless, they have not yet been accepted generally because of hazards in handling the isocyanate component, and because of the inconvenience of using two-component systems.

The difficulties experienced with these resins are being overcome, however. By using di-isocyanates which are not reactive at room temperatures it is possible to produce one-system coating compositions which have pot lives of a few days. Another method is to use compounds which decompose at high temperatures with formation of di-isocyanates, such as

$$C_6H_5-O-\overset{\overset{\textstyle O}{\|}}{C}-NH(CH_2)_6NH-\overset{\overset{\textstyle O}{\|}}{C}-O-C_6H_5$$

bisphenylurethanes ($C_6H_5-O-\overset{O}{\overset{\|}{C}}-NH(CH_2)_6NH-\overset{O}{\overset{\|}{C}}-O-C_6H_5$) or the adducts of di-isocyanates and malonic or acetoacetic esters

$$[(ROC)_2CH-\overset{\overset{\textstyle O}{\|}}{C}-NH(CH_2)_6NH-\overset{\overset{\textstyle O}{\|}}{C}-CH(COR)_2]$$

[$(ROC)_2CH-\overset{O}{\overset{\|}{C}}-NH(CH_2)_6NH-\overset{O}{\overset{\|}{C}}-CH(COR)_2$] (1091, 1113, 3055). Other di-isocyanate carriers which represent substantial improvements in safety, handling time, and care required are the reaction products of isocyanates with about half an equivalent of polyester material, to which tertiary amines are added (1100, 3005).

Pertinent to the coating field is a method for conversion of the hydrophilic groups in a polyester or other unsaturated alkyd resin to polar groups which are much less hydrophilic, while still obtaining a resin soluble in organic solvents. This is achieved by reacting an organic unsaturated alkyd resin that is soluble in organic solvents with 3% to 25% by weight of a primary unsaturated isocyanate, such as a vinyl or allyl benzyl isocyanate (1107).

The metallic dryers commonly used in coating compositions may also be used with isocyanate-modified polyester coatings. H. S. Rothrock obtained a patent on the use of oil-soluble metallic salts, such as cobalt naphthenate, as catalysts for compositions from isocyanates and hydrogen-containing compounds (1106).

Properties and Uses

Polyester-derived urethane coatings are generally superior to the rubber or polyvinyl chloride coatings in regard to tear strength and resistance to aging and water. They can be cured at lower temperatures than those necessary for alkyds, and they have high gas impermeability. Therefore, their use seems likely to increase, once the application methods have been streamlined further and mastered by a larger number of coating firms.

A large potential field for these resins is in can coatings and in protective coatings for magnesium, iron, and zinc, where their excellent adhesion, tenacity, and complete resistance and inertia to solvents, lard, greases, and flavors offer important advantages.

Applications such as wire coating and insulation are logical in view of the excellent dielectric properties of these resins. This problem has been attacked by D. S. Breslow and the Hercules Powder Co. on the basis of employing mixtures of a difunctional and a trifunctional di-isocyanate (1108). Compositions used for these purposes in Germany are discussed by A. Höchtlen (3022).

Di-isocyanate-modified polyesters are used as nonvolatile plasticizers in polyvinyl chloride (1109).

TESTING

Testing is of interest to almost everyone concerned with polyester manufacture and fabrication. The raw materials must meet specifications, as must the resins and the final products. This chapter summarizes the testing methods used for raw materials, resins, catalysts, fillers, and certain final products.

It is not essential that a great deal of money be spent for equipment for testing plastics. A list of the equipment that is generally needed is given on page 241.

RAW MATERIALS

The testing of raw materials is the concern mainly of the raw material supplier. A visual examination, however, is usually made of all raw materials received in the resin manufacturing plant. There are also certain rapid qualitative tests which may be run by the resin manufacturer.

Glycols should be water-white, and may be checked by comparison with distilled, glass-stored standards for discoloration or foreign particles.

Phthalic anhydride often contains potential coloring agents (1,4-naphthoquinone, for example) and may be checked by heating with stannous chloride. A pink or red discoloration indicates the presence of the impurity (1350). Other acids, if stored in nonmetallic containers, are generally checked by a visual examination for discoloration or foreign matter. Storage of these materials in metallic containers should be avoided, since the presence of metallic contaminants causes variations in the quality of the resin and may even cause premature gelation of the resin. (Metallic contaminants may also come from equipment used for making or handling the corrosive acids.)

The styrene used as a cross-linking agent should be checked for polystyrene content before use in resin manufacture. This is done by diluting a sample of the styrene with about 5 parts of methyl alcohol and visually examining the resultant solution. Any cloudiness indicates the presence of objectionable polystyrene. The amount and effectiveness of the inhibitor remaining in the styrene may be checked by inserting a test tube of styrene solution in boiling water and checking the solution for cloudiness every half hour. Most fresh styrene will show no cloudiness in 3 hours of this treatment. If cloudiness develops before 2 hours have elapsed, it is usually advisable to use the styrene as soon as possible, or to add additional inhibitor (for example, 5 parts per million of *tert.*-butyl catechol).

If dry ice (solid carbon dioxide) is used for internal cooling of a di-isocyanate-polyester foam material, it should be tested for freedom from water. This can be done by allowing 500 grams of the dry ice to sublime in a Pyrex beaker covered with a watch glass. If as much as a single drop of water is noticed in the bottom of the beaker after the dry ice sublimes, only the interior portions of the block should be used (3048).

RESINS AND PLASTICS

Process Control

Three testing procedures are normally used during the manufacture of the resin, to follow the course and extent of the reaction: (1) determination of the amount of water removed from the reaction kettle; (2) determination of the acid number; and (3) determination of viscosity.

The determination of the amount of water removed from the reaction kettle is not an absolute determination, because in some polyester reactions the amount of water evolved may be greater or less than the calculated amount required by theory (1291). In practice, the "water" removed also contains some glycol. Samples of the condensate may be taken periodically and checked in a refractometer against standards. The glycol content is then determined from standard curves showing the refractive indices of water-glycol solutions of various concentrations. By subtracting the weight of glycol from the total weight of the condensate, the weight of water removed is determined.

The second, and possibly most widely used, means of following the reaction is the determination of the acid number on periodically removed samples. The acid number may be determined by dissolving a 2- to 3-gram sample of resin in a 50:50 alcohol-benzene solution and titrating with 0.2N aqueous potassium hydroxide to a pH of 6.5 to 6.6 with brom-thymol blue indicator (3170).

Viscosity determinations should be made in the course of manufacture. They are particularly useful in the manufacture of flexible resins in which the acid number becomes so low (below 20) as to limit its usefulness as an accurate means for determination of the extent of reaction. Viscosity determinations are also used as a quality control on the final resin. In viscosity evaluations a sample is dissolved in an equal weight of solvent (usually a high-boiling hydrocarbon such as benzene, toluene, or xylene), and the viscosity is determined by Brookfield, Ostwald, or other appropriate measuring means. Automatic viscosity recording equipment is useful but not necessary.

Plant control determinations on batches of liquid resin include visual inspection for impurities, determination of color by comparison with the standard solutions given in American Society for Testing Materials (ASTM) Standard D365, and determination of specific gravity by weight per gallon cups or by ASTM Standard D70 (3103, 3170). The refractive index is sometimes determined. It is an especially important check for resins used in making translucent glass laminates. Various statistical determinations may be used as a means for standardizing resin products from different manufacturing plants, according to Werner and Nielson (3129).

Molecular weight determinations may be useful, especially in new product development and standardization. These may be made by osmotic, viscometric light scattering, or other means (1135, 1162, 1193, 1226, 1252).

The phthalic anhydride content of the resin may be determined by a fast centrifuge method (3094).

A scheme for chemical analysis of commercial filled unsaturated polyester formulations has been devised by Stafford and Shay (3120). The filled resin is extracted with acetone (or digested with benzylamine if partially cured polymer is present) to separate the filler. The polyester component and the cross-linking agent are separated by precipitation of the polyester with a nonsolvent such as petroleum ether. The various fractions can then be identified by conventional means.

Other schemes for the general identification of resins, are given by Shaw (3113), Pallaud (3108), and Speitmann (3118).

Foam-producing resins can be compared by determining the minimum size of the cells produced in the foam (3109).

Hardening Tests on Resins

Certain of the polymerization characteristics of polyesters, such as the storage life of the resin, uncatalyzed and catalyzed, and the gel time, are determined by the manufacturer. Control of those characteristics is extremely important from the user's standpoint, since his fabricating procedure will be based on the assumption that the resin he uses will set at a certain rate.

Storage Life. In the manufacturing plant, determination of the storage life of the resin is usually run under conditions agreeable to both the manufacturer and the resin consumer (3103, 3170).

Most uncatalyzed polyesters resist polymerization for from 4 to 6 months if stored at room temperature in the dark; lowering the storage temperature prolongs the usable life of the resin, and an increase in the temperature shortens it materially. Storage in sunlight, if the resin is photosensitive, may cause the resin to gel, in some cases in a matter of hours.

The storage life or "pot life" of the catalyzed resin varies with the type of resin, the type of catalyst and inhibitor system, the temperature, extent of exposure to sunlight and oxygen, and other storage conditions, and the presence of trace impurities. Some of these factors are beyond the control of the resin manufacturer. Therefore, whenever the pot life may be at all critical, it should be rechecked by the fabricator for each batch shortly before use. (This is also true for the gel time.)

It is common practice for resin manufacturers to add a higher percentage of inhibitor in the summer than in the winter, in order to compensate for the higher temperatures in storage. If some of the summer formula should be left over until winter, or stored under refrigeration, however, its pot life and setting-up characteristics would vary from the standard. Pot life tests by the consumer would discover any of this summer-formula resin.

Gel Time. In general, the gel time of a resin is the time elapsing from the point when the catalyst is added to the resin until the resin solidifies. Because plant conditions, especially temperature, vary, however, a standard test has been established in which a specific definition is given for "gel time."

The gel time test is run in the following manner: Catalyzed resin is poured into a test tube of 19 by 150 millimeters to a depth of 3 inches. The tube is suspended in a constant-temperature (180° F. unless otherwise specified) bath, with the liquid resin level below the bath level. A steel needle thermocouple is centered in the resin, and the rise in resin temperature is recorded. The gel time, by definition, is the time required for the resin temperature to rise from 150° F. to 10° F. above the bath temperature, or to 190° F. (3103, 3170). This gel time is valuable in determining the cure characteristics of a resin, and it can be used as a means of comparison among various resins.

The maximum temperature reached by the curing resin is taken from the gel time curve (3103, 3170). This temperature, called the peak exotherm, indicates to the fabricator the amount of exothermic heat developed during the polymerization. Various applications require or permit varying degrees of exothermic heat; it is especially necessary to know the amount of heat developed if articles of varying size of heat dissipation are made in the same plant. For example the peak exotherm may indicate need for caution or addition of an inhibitor in laminating thick sections where heat dissipation is slow.

The drift in gel time during storage can be important. This is determined by running gel time curves at periodic intervals on a resin stored under conditions set by the manufacturer and the resin user. The drift is recorded as the percentage difference between the initial gel time and the value after a certain storage period (3103, 3170).

An ingenious device for determining gel time has been developed by R. P. Lappala (3099). An ordinary inexpensive electric clock is hung on a hinge so that it faces downward. The second hand is replaced by a small chuck which has an expendable propeller, made by hand twisting a metal wire, attached to it. The propeller is placed in the resin to be tested, and the clock is started. When gelling occurs, the clock will stop, and the gel time can be read directly from it.

A recheck of the gel time and pot life of each resin batch shortly before use is particularly necessary when the resin is used for continuous fabrication processes. Here the form of the finished article is determined at the moment of gelation, and it is very important to have gelation occur at a time in the production cycle when the resin is held in the desired shape. This may call for split-second timing in a cycle in which the resin passes through a setting oven at high temperature.

As higher-speed and larger-volume processes mature, it would not be surprising to see more continuous-process fabricators begin to manufacture their own polyester resins, for better control of resin properties. An example of this has already been mentioned—the manufacture of Mylar film and Dacron fiber by Du Pont.

Extent of Cure. The extent of cure of a polyester resin is usually determined by hardness tests. Specific gravity and chemical resistance tests are also used. The methods used for these tests are given in table No. 31 (p. 239).

Some manufacturers use a minimum cure time test. This is the time required for the resin to obtain a set Barcol hardness (p. 238) at a selected temperature.

The rate and extent of cure of an unsaturated polyester resin have also been evaluated by determining the change in density and electrical resistance during cure (3091).

Tests on Solid Resins and Plastics

The usual tests run on solid resins are specific gravity, strength tests, hardness, heat distortion, color, water absorption, cold flow, index of refraction, chemical resistance, electrical properties, and light, heat, and flame resistance.

Specifications. These tests are usually run according to American Society for Testing Materials (ASTM) Standards or Federal Specification L-P-406, "Plastics, Organic: General Specifications, Test Methods" (3068). Table No. 31 lists the applicable ASTM Standard for each test and the corresponding method of Specification L-P-406. The ASTM and Federal Specification methods are usually, but not always, similar. The tests may be run on cured unfilled or filled resins or plastic laminates.

Military Specification MIL-R-7575A, which covers the requirements for resins used in fabricating plastic laminates for structural parts, aircraft radio and radar antenna housing, and other applications, is based largely on the methods of Specification L-P-406. Other Military Specifications applicable to the testing of polyester plastics are:

Specification	*Subject*
MIL-P-4389	Plastics Materials, Polyester Type, Molding and Plastic Parts, Molded, Thermosetting
MIL-P-7816 (AER)	Plastic Laminate; Glass Fiber-Mat Base, Low Pressure
MIL-P-8013	Plastic Materials, Glass Fabric Base, Low Pressure Laminated, Aircraft Structural
MIL-C-8073	Core Material, Plastic Honeycomb, Laminated Glass Fabric Base, for Aircraft Structural Applications
MIL-C-8087	Core Material, Foamed-in-Place, Alkyd Iso-cyanate, for Aircraft Structural Applications
MIL-S-9041	Sandwich Construction, Plastic Resin, Glass Fabric Base, Laminated Facings and Honey-comb Core for Aircraft Structural Applications
MIL-P-9400	Plastic Materials, Glass Fiber Base, Low Pressure Laminated, Aircraft Structural; Process and Inspection Requirements
MIL-P-15615 (Ships)	Plastics—Low Pressure Thermosetting Resins
MIL-P-17549 (Ships)	Plastics Materials, Fibrous Glass-Base, Laminated, Marine Craft Structural
AF (Air Force) No. 12043	Plastic Parts, Molded; General Specification for Inspection of

A proposed standard for structural reinforced plastic flat sheets has been worked out by the Society of the Plastics Industry, Reinforced Plastics Division, Standards Committee (3082). This same committee and the National Electrical Manufacturers' Association have also prepared a proposed standard for a general-purpose grade of polyester-glass mat sheet laminates for both mechanical and electrical applications (3115).

Other Test Methods. *Hardness.* In addition to the Rockwell test listed in table No. 31, the Barcol and Shore tests are often used to measure

Table No. 31.— *Tests performed on polyester plastics
and applicable specifications*

Test	ASTM Standard	Federal Specification L-P-406 Method No.
Specific gravity	D792	5011, 5012
Refractive index	D542	3011
Strength tests:		
Bearing strength	D953	1051
Compression	D695	1021, 1022
Flexure	D747, D790	1031, 1032
Impact	D256	1071
Shear	D732	1041
Tension	D638, D651	1011, 1012
Hardness (Rockwell)	D785	1081
Abrasion and mar resistance	D673, D1044, D1242	1091, 1093
Heat distortion point	D648	2011
Resistance to heat	D794	6011
Resistance to flame	D568, D635, D757	2021, 2022, 2023
Cold flow (deformation under load)	D621	1101
Chemical resistance	D543	7011
Electrical properties	D149, D150, D257, D495	4011, 4021, 4031, 4041
Water absorption	D570	7031
Resistance to light	D620	6031
Light transmission, color, haze	D791	3021

hardness of plastics. The Barcol hardness tester is manufactured by the Barber-Colman Co., Rockford, Ill. The Shore Durometer A, which is frequently used for flexible resins, is described in reference (3146); ASTM Standard D676 gives the method used in determining hardness with this instrument.

Flame and Heat Resistance. Flammability and combustibility of plastics may be tested by the Underwriters Laboratories, Inc. heat-stability and self-extinguishing test. To pass this test, a glass mat laminate made from the particular resin must be self-extinguishing in less than 20 seconds from the time of flame removal and the laminate must not burn above a height of 5 inches.

Testing of the flammability and combustibility of plastics has increased in importance with the development of much improved flame-resistant resins, such as the Hetron[1] resins. The flammability tests are partly based on requirements for structural materials, partly on requirements for paints (although a specification for fire-resistant paints is still needed), and partly on electrical requirements.

[1]Trade name of Hooker Electrochemical Co.

Flexural strength usually serves as the basis for determining the resistance of reinforced polyester parts to high temperatures, such as might be encountered in operation of high-speed aircraft. The flexural strength is measured before, during, and after exposure to high temperatures. Ebers et al. measured the thermal stability of glass cloth-polyester laminates by the rate of loss of flexural strength and hardness during aging at 260°F. (1275). The results of such tests, however, should not be taken as a direct indication of resistance to high temperatures. Such factors as the humidity and oxygen concentration of the atmosphere, thermal degradation, and post cure must be considered. For airplane parts, the effect of fast air flow over the part is another variable.

Mechanical Strength. As a test for evaluating low-pressure laminates for applications in which mechanical strength is of prime importance, Dr. G. M. Kline, National Bureau of Standards, recommends determination of the loss of flexural strength after 30 days' immersion in water at room temperature (Discussion, *Reinforced Plastics Division, Society of the Plastics Industry Conference, 8th Annual,* 1953, Section 24, p. 18). A good correlation exists between this test (Military Specification MIL-R-7575A) and determination of flexural strength after immersion in boiling water for 3 hours, although the boiling-water test (1670, 3172) is slightly more exacting.

If the polyester article is to be under strain while immersed, a test simulating this condition should be used. In warm water (say 150°F.) failures occur much more rapidly and at lower pressures than under normal conditions.

The effect of variations in the speed of the testing machine, the radius of the loading edges, and the span-depth ratios during flexural testing of plastics has been evaluated by W. A. Zinzow (3131).

Methods of evaluating tensile stress-strain data for glass fabric reinforced polyester resins are discussed by Lamb and Axilrod (3098). K. H. Boller gives methods and results of fatigue and stress-rupture tests of glass fabric-polyester laminates (3077, 3078).

Electrical Properties and Moisture Absorption. The electrical properties of a plastic material depend to some extent on the moisture content of the material and its distribution in the material. Two methods developed in Sweden for determination of insulation resistance, volume resistivity, and surface resistivity of plastics are reported to show moisture absorption of laminates almost instantly. The electrode arrangements used in these methods are described in references (3131e, 3131f).

Resistance to Chemicals and Fungi. A statistical method for laboratory testing of the chemical resistance of plastics was developed by Adams and Lebach (3071). The test is based on the establishment of ratings for the changes in weight and volume of the plastic and the appearances of the plastic and the chemical solution.

Tests for determining the resistance of plastics to fungi are described by J. M. Leonard (3100).

For reviews on the testing of plastics in general, see references (3072, 3083, 3095, 3107, 3126).

EQUIPMENT FOR TESTING PLASTICS

Suitable equipment for chemical and physical testing of plastics is listed below:

Suggested Equipment for Average Molding Plant[2]

Acetone-extraction apparatus
Balance—specific gravity
Bulk factor tester
Deflection tester
Hardness tester
Impact tester
Molding press—full size

Oven
Polarizer
Pyrometer
Sieves
Stirrers
Timers
Tensile testing machine—complete with compression and flexural fixtures

Additional Equipment for More Advanced Laboratories[2]

Abrasion tester
Adhesion tester
Aging bath
Aging bomb
Autoclave
Ball mills
Brittleness tester
Cold box
Compression fatigue cell
Compression set tester
Deformation tester
Dilatometer
Distortion tester
Fatigue tester
Flame resistance tester

Flex tester
Flow tester
Glossmeter
Hazemeter
Heaters and hot plates
High frequency heater
Light tester
Microscope
Mixers
Polariscope
Resiliometer
Salt fog cabinet
Service testing equipment
Stiffness gage
Thickness measuring gages

Some of the equipment necessary for testing of plastics may be adapted from equipment used for other purposes, or it may be built especially for this purpose. Descriptions of such equipment have been published, including a novel flexural test machine (3166), a steel-ball-impact testing

[2]Source: H. H. Bashore (Precision Scientific Company), *Industrial Plastics 1*, No. 11, 19–21, 35 (1946).

machine (3140, 3164), a torsion pendulum tester for determining shear modulus (3155), equipment for testing hardness and abrasion resistance (3142, 3150, 3152), and apparatus for determining flame resistance, ignition characteristics, and heat resistance (3144, 3148, 3158, 3160, 3161, 3163).

Equipment has also been described for making high-speed rain abrasion tests (3159), vapor diffusion tests (3157, 3165), and accelerated weathering tests of plastics (3139).

CATALYSTS

Tentative standards for the evaluation of catalysts have been prepared by the Society of the Plastics Industry, Reinforced Plastics Division, Standards Committee. These include the determination of the catalyst solubility in styrene, percent of insoluble materials, and percent of active oxygen (3170).

The catalysts used in the molding of polyesters play a large part in determining the molding cycles (see chapter on catalysis and inhibition, p. 46), which in turn may influence the physical properties of the molded products (see pp. 170-172).

GLASS FILLERS

Specifications

Tentative specifications have been established for glass fillers by the Reinforced Plastics Division of the Society of the Plastics Industry, and related to the testing of woven glass fabrics, tape, yarn, mats, and chopped strands (3170).

Woven fabrics are tested for thickness, weight, width, thread count, breaking strength, and glass content by the methods of ASTM Standard D579. Tapes are tested for thickness, width, weight, construction, bearing strength, and glass content according to ASTM Standard D580. Yarns are tested for construction, tensile strength, and glass content by ASTM Standard D578.

Test methods for glass mats and chopped strands are given in detail in reference (3170). Mats are tested for thickness, weight, binder content, type of binder, mat uniformity, strand integrity, tensile strength, and color and light fastness. Chopped fibers or cut strands are tested for length and strand integrity.

The present method for testing glass mat uniformity is not considered completely adequate, and other methods are being sought (3175). Placing a small quantity of resin on the mat and observing the uniformity of its spreading will sometimes give a good indication of the uniformity of the mat.

An apparatus for measuring the elastic properties of glass fibers and the changes in elasticity upon heat treatment is described by J. B. Murgatroyd (3174).

Sizes and Finishes

The "size" or finish of the glass fibers affects the adhesion between the glass and the polyester resin, and consequently the strength of glass reinforced plastics. A very comprehensive study of methods for determining the adhesion between glass and polyester was made by Yaeger, Henning, Marshall, and Cox (1670). Optical, dielectric, and sonic methods were tried and discarded. In tests in which laminates were pulled apart on a recording tension machine, comparison of the tensile curves at any one point of stress was difficult because of the irregularity of the curves for different laminates. Comparison of the area of the curves gave more significant results, since the area represented all the work required to pull the laminate apart.

For quick tests of sizes, a glass sheet sized with a known standard size is laminated to another glass sheet sized with an experimental size. The two sheets are then pulled apart in the tension machine. Visual inspection will easily show which sheet has the more effective size, since the bonding resin will adhere to it (1670).

For more quantitative tests, strength and other properties can be measured on sections cut from laminates made with glass fabric with various sizes (1585, 3172). Another procedure for size evaluation utilizes rovings containing the size. Rovings are impregnated with the catalyzed resin and dried. A specified amount of these rovings are then wound over two hooks and wrapped with cellophane tape to form a cylindrical rod. The rod is then cured and tested for flexural strength (1583, 1584, 3171, 3173).

Military Specification MIL-F-9084 covers finished woven glass fabrics for reinforced plastic laminates, and Military Specification MIL-F-9118 covers finishes for glass fabrics.

DESIGN DATA AND NONDESTRUCTIVE TESTS

At present the plastics industry has two needs in relation to testing of plastics. One is for design data on plastics and plastic-filler combinations (2386, 2405, 2411, 3182), and the other is for nondestructive tests that may be applied to expensive finished items such as boats (2385, 2393, 3179). Both these needs are currently known to the industry, but good solutions are still lacking.

Standard Performance Data for Plastic Laminates

A careful study of the mechanical properties and permanence of reinforced plastic laminates has been made by Dr. G. M. Kline and his associates at the National Bureau of Standards (2232, 2252, 2254, 2255, 2256). The rapid advancement of this field, particularly in glass fiber sizes and finishes (p. 84), has rendered obsolete much of these excellently presented data. It is hoped, therefore, that the Bureau of Standards will continue its activities in setting up standards for laminate strength.[3]

An important milestone in the design of laminates has already been passed—they have been made stronger than aluminum on a weight basis. The next step is to make them stronger, for straight structural parts, on a cost basis. Then the goal is to make laminates stronger than steel, on a cost basis, in flexure, tension, and compression.

One reason for the lack of reliable design data on reinforced plastic materials is the lack of standardization of cloths, lay-ups, and molding procedures for the preparation of test panels, according to Perry *et al.* (3181). Preliminary data from an investigation of the effect of variations in preparation on the flexural properties of 181 glass cloth laminate test panels led to the following conclusions:

(1) A vacuum impregnation process provides an increase of more than 10% in the average dry strength and a reduction in scatter of data, as compared to a conventional process of resin spreading in air.

(2) Positive pressure molding is superior to molding with platen stops.

(3) Variations in the assembling and testing of the panels can lead to strength variations of at least 33%; nesting (interlocking) of shafts of adjacent glass sheets adds an additional variation of 10%; and deviation from standard test specimens adds another 6% variation.

Nondestructive Testing

Evaluation of finished reinforced polyester items at present usually involves destructive testing of at least one finished object to determine the usefulness and service life of the object (2401). Promising approaches to nondestructive testing have been made, however (3182a). Voids and uneven filler distribution can easily be detected by x-ray (3177, 3178, 3180), sonic (3179), and dielectric methods. X-ray photographs will also show up any metal inserts that are out of place or bent. Some unpigmented items can be checked visually for voids and filler distribution (2393).

In reinforced plastics, however, strength depends very greatly on the bond between the reinforcement and the resin. The laminate or molded part can be completely free from voids, and still have a poor adhesion at this critical point. What is really needed, therefore, is a nondestructive test of adhesion between the reinforcement and the resin.

Generally, a high degree of transparency indicates at least good wetting of the reinforcement with the bonding resin, although this is by no means

[3]See footnote on page 175.

complete assurance for high strength. Often, however, laminates are non-transparent, highly pigmented, or laminated with metal foil.

Dielectric and sonic methods have been tried for detecting poor adhesion but with indifferent success. The sonic methods have distinguished between "no bond" and a "good bond," but they cannot distinguish dependably between laminates having a flexural strength of, say, 50,000 and 80,000 pounds per square inch.

Transducer and thermographic methods offer the most promising approaches to nondestructive testing of reinforced plastics. The transducer method has the advantage of being adapted to one-side testing, so that large objects such as tanks, silos, and boats could be checked from one side only.

In the transducer method an electromagnetic alternating current impresses movement on an iron core, which in turn contacts the object to be tested and causes vibrations to be generated in it. These vibrations are picked up by another iron core, which vibrates inside a coil and generates electric currents in it. If the transfer of motion is perfect, then theoretically the outgoing current should match the ingoing current. Any difference in electrical characteristics between the two currents will be a measure of the changes of absorption of vibrations in the test object between the iron cores. Alert observers (or an electronic relay) can use this difference to detect points of poor adhesion in the laminate.

A transducer device for testing from one side would be possible by having the iron cores in the form of an inner core with an outer ring around it. Vibrations caused by the inner core at one point in the side of an object would be transferred to other points and picked up by the outer ring.

The thermographic method developed by General Electric Co. is based on the fact that a poor bond usually means a void or incomplete contact between the reinforcement and the bonding resin and therefore poor thermoconductivity. The laminate is frozen so that moisture condenses on its surface. Heat is then allowed to reach the laminate from one side only. The frost melts fastest at the points where the bond is good and last at those points where the bond is poorest and the thermoconductivity is therefore the poorest. This method has its drawbacks, such as sensitivity to irregularities in filler distribution and to small differences in thickness. It is therefore always wise to supplement it by thickness measurements.

Another approach to nondestructive testing is to apply direct pull and measure the stress-strain relationship with an ultrasensitive strain gage. This is done within a range of forces where Hooke's law is valid. The first deviation from this law on the stress-strain curve would indicate the point of incipient bond failure, which could thus be determined short of destruction of the specimen. The Tuckerman optical type of gage, which is sensitive to strains as small as 0.000002 inch, is suitable.

A type of nondestructive test has been applied to polyester reinforced tubing. The test is run by filling the tube with water and applying external pressure. The water on the inside supports the unit so that it is not destroyed (2528, 2529).

HEALTH HAZARDS

The manufacture and fabrication of polyesters is not connected with severe health hazards. Most of the raw materials used are primary irritants and sensitizers (p. 252); some of the fillers used contain silica, which under certain conditions may cause silicosis; the glass fibers used as reinforcing agent and filler may act as a mechanical irritant; and some of the peroxide catalysts, particularly when used in conjunction with promoters and accelerators, represent a potential explosion hazard. These materials, however, are not toxic agents which may cause systemic poisoning. The application of a few simple principles of industrial hygiene will prevent the development of any serious condition.

Good ventilation and good housekeeping are the first two commandments of industrial hygiene. They are essential in storage, in manufacture, in fabrication, and in processing of the plastic product.

HAZARDS IN MANUFACTURE

The hazards in manufacture may be divided into two divisions: those involved in storage of raw materials (which the manufacturers of polyester resins share with all chemical manufacturers), and those attendant to the process of making the resin.

Storage Hazards

Fire is the principal danger in storage. National Board of Fire Underwriters Research Report No. 1 lists a number of measures designed to diminish the danger of fire when large quantities of flammable material are handled (3184). The storage tanks must be protected from external fires by fireproof insulation. Other protective steps are: emergency relief venting, diversion of spills and run-off from dyked areas, and drainage gutters located in safely isolated burning pits.

It is wise to ascertain the solubility characteristics of the stored materials in water, since these characteristics determine the method of fire fighting. Some materials may be diluted by water to a point where they become nonflammable, but others will float on water, and addition of water will only spread the fire.

247

It is also necessary to remember that the ignition points given for various materials in standard handbooks are usually based on fairly pure compounds. Many of the materials used in the manufacture of resins are of technical grade, and the impurities may vitally affect the ignition points of these materials.

The Office of Rubber Reserve has published a safety manual for copolymer plant laboratories which contains general instructions on laboratory safety in handling flammable and explosive hydrocarbon mixtures (3183).

Process Hazards

In the manufacturing process the fumes of the materials used may be dangerous. Styrene, other vinyl monomers, allyl alcohol, and maleic acids are all primary irritants and sensitizers. Phthalic acid is a sensitizer (3213). Charging of the materials through a closed system, such as pipes, will prevent escape of vapors and the building up of dangerous concentrations.

An excess of fumes is usually signaled by irritation of eyes and nose. This is a warning sign, and steps should be taken to prevent so strong a concentration. No maximum permissible concentration has been established for most of the compounds used in polyester manufacture, however. Styrene has been the subject of more study than the other compounds (1405, 3192, 3210, 3218). Latest research proposes a maximum permissible concentration of 200 parts of styrene per million parts of air.

HAZARDS IN FABRICATION

The manufacturer of the resin is usually in a better position to guard against the hazards inherent in handling the raw materials and manufacturing of the resin than the fabricator. The fabricator does not deal with obviously toxic substances. Yet the resin, until completely cured, may have the same effects as the raw materials from which it is prepared.

Precautions in Resin Handling

In the fabricator's plant the resin is handled more than in the manufacturer's plant. Dermatitis is the main danger here. Though some manufacturers claim that their resin is not prone to give dermatitis (1956), L. Schwartz reported that in one factory the use of polyesters for laminating glass fabric resulted in a turnover of labor of 600% among 85 workers in 1 year (3213). He also found that the modified alkyd resins (polyesters) which contained styrene or allyl alcohol combined with an ester of glycol and phthalic or maleic anhydride are particularly irritating in a partially polymerized state. No resistance, or "hardening," is developed to the primary irritant action of these monomers.

Schwartz makes the following preventive recommendations (3213):

(1) The persons handling resin-impregnated material should wear gloves with cut fingers so as to enable easier manipulation. Long-sleeved smocks should also be worn. The gloves should be made preferably of washable leather, and the smocks should be cleaned at least once a day. Those whose jobs require handling of the resin paste should wear long rubber gauntlets.

(2) Those employed in places where there are strong concentrations of fumes should be provided with a protective ointment for the face and neck. The ointment should be of the type which leaves a dry, adherent, water-repellent coat on the skin to shield it from fumes. This ointment may also be applied to uncovered parts of the fingers.

(3) Well-placed ventilators to draw fumes away from the workers are needed.

(4) The use of broad spatulas to smooth the resin-impregnated glass fibers down on the mold is recommended.

(5) Wash stands should be placed close to the workers, and they should be instructed to wash the resin from their hands and fingers at frequent intervals.

(6) The workers should be instructed not to touch their faces and necks with resin-soiled hands.

A. G. Cranch also stresses good ventilation, both general and local; personal cleanliness, including avoidance of unnecessary contact, frequent washing, and use of clean clothing; and use of protective clothing and protective skin cream as safety practices to be observed in the plastics industry (3193).

Similar recommendations for safeguarding health are given in the *Pennsylvania Department of Labor and Industry Safe Practices Bulletin* No. 88 (3194).

It may be possible, in some instances, to change the resin itself to make it less dangerous to handle. This is illustrated in a method disclosed by C. A. Heilberger for the production of an interpolymer of styrene, allyl alcohol, and diallyl fumarate (1115). Excess allyl alcohol, which has tear-producing effects, is removed by heating a 30% solution of the interpolymer in xylene for 1 to 2 hours at 90° to 95°C., distilling, and repeating the process three times.

Hazards from Other Materials

C. S. McKinley reports on practical experiences with materials involved in plastic production (3204). Coloring agents are used in such small amounts that they represent no hazard. The same applies to some of the organometallic compounds used, which are primary skin irritants and which will cause systemic reactions if absorbed. The lubricants used are usually oil materials and are not dangerous. There is little danger from glass fibers and other fillers if recommended safety practices are followed.

Glass Fibers. The Owens-Corning Fiberglas Corp., which is vitally interested in assuring people working with glass fibers that they present no unusual danger, cites the following facts to this effect (3186):

(1) The Aetna Insurance Co., which carries group insurance on all glass fiber employees, says that the manufacture of glass fiber products involves no hazard different from any normal manufacturing operation.

(2) The Industrial Commission of the State of Ohio, where thousands of workers have been exposed to glass fiber production for many years, states that no worker's compensation claim has ever been paid for disability due to exposure to glass fibers. Compensation rates based on the state's appraisal of the risk in the manufacture and fabrication of glass fiber products are lower than for workers in any comparable industry.

L. U. Gardner studied the effect of inhaled glass wool extensively. He found that exposure to the dust of glass wool involves no hazard to lungs because the fibrous material cannot be inhaled (3184). Apparently the tendency of the particles to form a feltlike mass prevents inhalation. Experimental animals kept for a year in high concentrations of glass wool dust showed no serious effect on the lungs.

Dermatitis is common among glass fiber workers. The small fibers of glass are mechanical irritants and, in some cases, sensitizers. Some workers become hardened, however, and can work without any change.

If hardening does not occur, transfer is indicated. Otherwise, proper clothing, protective sheaths, adequate washing, moistening of the material with binder before it is machined or cut, use of soft or lanolated soap, and adequate washing facilities should suffice. Where the glass product is machined, exhaust fans should be provided. An alert medical staff and proper indoctrination of the labor force are necessary.

W. J. Siebert also reports that the manufacture, fabrication, and application of glass fiber products are attended by no unusual occupational hazards (3215). There are no silicoses, fibroses, or dust hazards connected with working with glass fibers.

Other Fillers. Other fillers, particularly those containing silica, as in the form of silica flour, should receive special attention, reports W. R. Bradley (3189). There is a great quantity of animal experimentation showing that the inhalation of free silica (SiO_2) eventually destroys the lungs. The danger of silicosis depends upon the composition of the inhaled dust, the size of the particles, and the length of time during which particles are inhaled. Proper ventilation systems should be installed to prohibit free silica from escaping to the workroom atmosphere. If the presence of dust in the atmosphere cannot be prevented, workmen should use respiratory equipment approved by the U. S. Bureau of Mines for protection against the inhalation of toxic dust.

Asbestos in finely divided form is also capable of entering the lungs by inhalation. Asbestosis may be caused by prolonged exposure to asbestos dust. It has been recommended that the maximum permissible limit for free silica dust and for asbestos dust in the working environment is 5 million particles of dust per cubic foot of air for an 8-hour daily exposure (3189).

Clays used as fillers are mainly silicates containing relatively small amounts of free silica. They are classified as nuisance dusts and have a permissible limit for atmospheric dustiness of 50 million particles per cubic foot of air. Calcium carbonate dust is usually considered in the nuisance category from the standpoint of industrial hygiene. It has been known, however, to produce irritation of moist skin, particularly when workmen are exposed to heavy concentrations and may be perspiring freely.

Peroxide Catalysts. It may be prudent at this point to add a word of caution: the peroxides used in curing of the resins are sometimes very reactive with the various activators and promoters used (3208). It is very important to stir each ingredient completely into the mixture before adding a second one. In particular, a peroxide must not be mixed with an amine accelerator in concentrated form. A metal naphthenate type of drier should be used with a hydroperoxide catalyst, never with a peroxide catalyst.

Plastic Dust

Plastic dust is a potential danger in the processing of plastics, not only from the standpoint of dermatitis, but also because it may cause explosions. H. R. Brown describes a new U. S. Bureau of Mines standard for prevention of explosions of plastic dust (3191). The National Fire Protection Association has also published a code in this field (3185). This code discusses plant arrangement, building construction, design of equipment for handling dusts, housekeeping, and fire extinguishing systems.

STANDARDS FOR CONTROL OF HEALTH HAZARDS

The standards established for control of health hazards depend on various methods of testing the toxicity of the various materials.

For fumes the important test depends on the smallest amount in parts per million parts of air which would cause death by inhalation. An investigation is conducted on animals, and the results are reported in parts per million per gram or kilogram of body weight.

The dustiness is tested by the number of particles of dust per cubic foot of air.

The physical properties of taste and odor are not easily measured. L. C. Barail says that excellent results can be obtained by the use of an osmometer for the measurement of odors (3188). This instrument, however, has found little acceptance industrially.

The toxicity of plastics can be tested in three ways: (1) intravenous injection, (2) intraperitoneal injection, and (3) feeding an extract either in drinking water or mixed with solid food.

Skin irritation and sensitization are tested by four methods: (1) patch tests on animals, (2) hypodermic injection into animals; (3) intradermal injection into animals, and (4) intradermal injection into man.

Plastics which will cause dermatitis at the first application are said to contain primary skin irritants. Those which cause dermatitis only after the second or third application are said to contain sensitizers. The patch test of the U. S. Public Health Service is the only method accepted by government agencies as being conclusive. Since it is of long duration and expensive, however, plastics manufacturers have been looking for less costly and more rapid screening tests.

Systematic work on range finding of toxicity data is done by various investigators (3217). Literature searches may therefore be fruitful when new materials are to be used in production.

ANNOTATED BIBLIOGRAPHY

This annotated bibliography covers the published literature pertaining to polyesters and reinforced polyesters up to June 1, 1954. Patents, books, articles, and manufacturers' publications are included. The majority of the references have been classified according to their principal topic. The classifications follow closely the chapter headings and subheadings in the text. Those references which are cited in the text have been placed in the classification corresponding to the chapter and section in which they are first cited. Some pertinent references published after June 1, 1954 are listed in an unclassified section at the end of the bibliography.

A. PATENTS

THEORETICAL CONSIDERATIONS

	Patent Number	Patentee	Assignee
1.	U.S. 2,388,319	C. S. Fuller	Bell Telephone Laboratories, Inc.
2.	U.S. 2,410,073	J. B. Howard	Bell Telephone Laboratories, Inc.
3.	U.S. 2,423,093	C. J. Frosch	Bell Telephone Laboratories, Inc.
4.	U.S. 2,621,167	J. W. Fisher and J. Lincoln	Celanese Corp. of America
5.	U.S. 2,623,034	P. J. Flory and F. S. Leutner	Wingfoot Corp.
6.	Brit. 623,309	J. W. Fisher and J. Lincoln	British Celanese, Ltd.

THEORETICAL CONSIDERATIONS

Concerning

Cross-linking of linear polyesters, *e.g.*, from ethylene glycol, maleic acid, and succinic acid, by heating with an organic peroxide. Cross-linked polyester can be used in covering for electrical wires.

Preparation of fiber-forming polymers. Esterification time shortened by use of catalysts, *e.g.*, ZnCl$_2$, continuous agitation, and large excess of glycol.

Polyesters with high degree of linearity from ethylene glycol, isopropylene glycol, sebacic acid, and aconitic acid (0.025–5 mol. %).

Trans-quinitol-succinic acid polyesters. High melting points.

Isophthalate polyester. Tetramethylene isophthalate can be made highly oriented, melting at 142°C., becoming crystalline on casting from solution or annealing. Fibers do not shrink below 135°C.

See U.S. 2,621,167 in this section.

UNSATURATED POLYESTERS

Acids

	Patent Number	Patentee	Assignee
7.	U. S. 1,284,888, U. S. 1,285,117	C. Conover and H. D. Gibbs	
8.	U. S. 2,114,798	H. B. Foster	National Aniline & Chemical Co.
9.	U. S. 2,154,079	J. M. Weiss	Calorider Corp.
10.	U. S. 2,191,786	A. M. Aronow	C. A. Miketta (20%)
11.	U. S. 2,194,362	A. D. Macallum	E. I. du Pont de Nemours & Co., Inc.
12.	U. S. 2,194,363	A. D. Macallum	E. I. du Pont de Nemours & Co., Inc.
13.	U. S. 2,205,402	H. B. Foster and J. H. Crowell	National Aniline & Chemical Co.
14.	U. S. 2,208,519	L. U. Spence and J. C. Mitchell	Rohm & Haas Co.
15.	U. S. 2,215,070	J. Z. Miller	Hercules Powder Co.
16.	U. S. 2,215,095	O. Drossbach	General Aniline & Film Corp.
17.	U. S. 2,215,498	C. S. Fazel	Solvay Process Co.
18.	U. S. 2,215,968	J. W. Livingston	Monsanto Chemical Co.
19.	U. S. 2,222,283	J. H. Crowell	National Aniline & Chemical Co.
20.	U. S. 2,223,493– 2,223,494	D. J. Loder	E. I. du Pont de Nemours & Co. Inc.
21.	U. S. 2,226,357	J. F. Olin and F. D. Fritsch	Sharples Solvents Corp.
22.	U. S. 2,228,261	E. K. Ellingbal	E. I. du Pont de Nemours & Co., Inc.
23.	U. S. 2,250,091	G. B. Campbell and F. Porter	Solvay Process Co.
24.	U. S. 2,291,211	R. M. Cavanaugh	E. I. du Pont de Nemours & Co., Inc.
25.	U. S. 2,294,130	F. Porter	Solvay Process Co.
26.	U. S. 2,298,387	W. O. Kenyon and G. V. Heyl	Eastman Kodak Co.
27.	U. S. 2,302,888	F. Porter	Solvay Process Co.
28.	U. S. 2,316,543	W. J. Amend	E. I. du Pont de Nemours & Co., Inc.

I. RAW MATERIALS

Concerning

Preparation of phthalic anhydride by catalytic vapor-phase oxidation (with vanadium pentoxide catalyst) of naphthalene.

Preparation of maleic acid and anhydride by catalytic vapor-phase oxidation of biphenyl.

SiO$_2$ or Al$_2$O$_3$ catalysts for vapor-phase partial oxidation of aromatic compounds, e.g., production of maleic anhydride from benzene.

Preparation of adipic acid by oxidation of cyclohexanol with nitric acid.

Preparation of adipic acid by catalytic hydrogenation of propiolic acid or its salts.

Preparation of acetylenic acids, e.g., propiolic acid, by treatment of an alkali metal acetylide homolog with carbon dioxide.

See Brit. 508,489 in this section.

Production of fumaric acid by heating an aqueous solution of maleic acid and a soluble thiocyanate, e.g., KCNS.

Vapor-phase oxidation of benzene to maleic anhydride.

Production of maleic acid from catalytic oxidation of dihydrofuran or tetrahydrofuran.

Control of vapor-phase reactions, e.g., oxidation of naphthalene to phthalic anhydride and of benzene to maleic anhydride.

Recovery of phthalic anhydride from products of catalytic oxidation of naphthalene with air.

Continuous method for formation of maleic anhydride from maleic acid.

Production of aliphatic dibasic acids, e.g., adipic acid, cyclic alcohols, and ketones by catalytic oxidation of saturated cyclic hydrocarbons, e.g., cyclohexane.

Production of polycarboxylic acids, e.g., adipic acid, by oxidation of a cycloaliphatic sulfate, e.g., cyclohexyl disulfate.

Production of adipic acid by oxidation of cyclohexane with nitric acid.

Production of maleic anhydride by dehydration of maleic acid.

Oxidation of alicyclic ketones and their allyl derivatives with nitric acid, as in the production of adipic acid from cyclohexanone.

Use of phosphates with vanadium-containing catalysts to reduce by-product formation and the violence of the reaction in production of dicarboxylic anhydrides, e.g., maleic and phthalic, by vapor-phase oxidation of hydrocarbons.

Oxidation of alcohols, aldehydes, or ketones with NO$_2$, as in the production of adipic acid from cyclohexanol.

Production of maleic anhydride by contact of maleic acid with the hot gaseous products from a maleic anhydride converter.

Catalytic oxidation of ketones, as in the production of adipic acid from cyclohexanone.

Acids (Continued)

	Patent Number	Patentee	Assignee
29.	U.S. 2,323,861	C. N. Zellner	Tide Water Associated Oil Co.
30.	U.S. 2,326,986	S. A. Waksman	Merck & Co. & Chas. Pfizer & Co.
31.	U.S. 2,327,191	J. H. Kane, A. Finlay, and P. F. Amann	Merck & Co. and Chas. Pfizer & Co.
32.	U.S. 2,340,739	C. R. Downs	Calorider Corp.
33.	U.S. 2,341,288	H. Prückner	E. I. du Pont de Nemours & Co., Inc.
34.	U.S. 2,352,461	J. F. Walker	E. I. du Pont de Nemours & Co., Inc.
35.	U.S. 2,358,775	H. D. Finch and T. W. Evans	Shell Development Co.
36.	U.S. 2,365,631	W. L. Faith	Sharples Chemicals, Inc.
37.	U.S. 2,365,703	E. J. Jahn	Shell Development Co.
38.	U.S. 2,385,518	R. M. Isham	Danciger Oil & Refineries, Inc.
39.	U.S. 2,386,736	H. A. Bruson	Resinous Products & Chemical Co.
40.	U.S. 2,393,352	L. Winstrom	Allied Chemical & Dye Corp.
41.	U.S. 2,414,066	W. Scott	Wingfoot Corp.
42.	U.S. 2,415,531	F. Porter	Solvay Process Co.
43.	U.S. 2,421,428	E. R. Nielsen	Quaker Oats Co.
44.	U.S. 2,494,049	D. Levin	Chemical Concentrates Corp.
45.	U.S. 2,500,260	L. W. Newton	Union Carbide and Carbon Corp.
46.	U.S. 2,510,803	W. C. Cooper	Pittsburgh Coke & Chemical Co.
47.	U.S. 2,580,931	F. W. Lane	E. I. du Pont de Nemours & Co., Inc.
48.	U.S. 2,589,648	F. T. Wadsworth	Pan American Refining Corp.
49.	U.S. 2,594,570	C. B. Linn	Universal Oil Products Co.
50.	U.S. 2,601,223	M. J. Roedel	E. I. du Pont de Nemours & Co., Inc.

Concerning

Preparation of dibasic acids, e.g., adipic, by catalytic oxidation of hydrocarbons, e.g., cyclohexene, with nitric acid.

Preparation of fumaric acid by fermentation of a carbohydrate, e.g., glucose, with *Mucorales*.

Preparation of fumaric acid by fermentation of a carbohydrate, e.g., glucose, with *Rhizopus nigricans*.

Drying the air used in vapor-phase catalytic oxidation of benzene to maleic anhydride.

Catalytic oxidation of ketones, as in production of adipic acid from cyclohexanone.

Unsaturated dibasic acids formed, e.g., by reaction of butadiene, sodium, and carbon dioxide.

Production of fumaric acid by the catalytic oxidation of a fraction from the pyrolytic conversion of dichlorobutane to butadiene.

Production of maleic and fumaric acids and anhydrides by catalytic oxidation of haloaliphatic compounds, e.g., products from commercial chlorination of pentane.

Saturated mono-olefin-maleic anhydride reaction products, e.g., alkyl succinic acids. Useful in manufacture of alkyd resins.

Production of maleic and succinic acids by catalytic oxidation of butyrolactone.

Cyanoethylation of ketones with acrylonitrile to give products, e.g., 2-(2-cyanoethyl) cyclohexanone, useful in preparation of mono- and polycarboxylic acids.

Production of fumaric acid by introducing converter gases from the oxidation of benzene, which contain maleic anhydride, into a solution of hydrochloric acid.

Conversion agents for isomerization of *cis* forms of unsaturated acids and esters to *trans* form, e.g., thiazoles, thiazolines, thiuram disulfide, dithiocarbamates.

Utilization of effluent reaction vapors to cool catalyst chamber in production of phthalic (and maleic) anhydride by oxidation of naphthalene.

Production of maleic anhydride and maleic acid by catalytic oxidation of furfural.

Production of fumaric acid by heating monosodium maleate from the scrub liquor of a phthalic anhydride plant in a hydrochloric acid solution.

Preparation of fumaric acid by heating a 50% solution of maleic acid in maleic anhydride. (An equimolar mixture of water and maleic anhydride may be used as the equivalent of maleic acid.)

Vanadium pentoxide catalyst for vapor-phase oxidation of naphthalene to phthalic anhydride and benzene to maleic anhydride.

Alkaline pyrolysis of castor oil to obtain sebacate salts and acid.

Production of alkane dicarboxylic acids by oxidation of cycloalkanes, e.g., adipic acid from cyclohexane.

Cycloalkanones as catalysts for conversion of *cis* forms of alpha, beta-unsaturated acids to *trans* forms, e.g., maleic acid to fumaric acid.

Preparation of dibasic carboxylic acids by treating a peroxide compound obtained from hydrogen peroxide and a cyclic ketone with a redox reducing agent.

Acids (*Continued*)

	Patent Number	Patentee	Assignee
51.	U.S. 2,609,910	S. H. Herzfeld, R. E. Lidov, and H. Bluestone	Velsicol Corp.
52.	U.S. 2,625,554	J. R. Darby	Monsanto Chemical Co.
53.	U.S. 2,649,477	D. I. H. Jacobs, D. J. Hadley, and R. Heap	Distillers Co., Ltd.
54.	U.S. 2,662,901	M. E. Bailey	Allied Chemical & Dye Corp.
55.	U.S. 2,670,325	H. J. West and K. Goodemoot	American Cyanamid Co.
56.	U.S. 2,670,355	G. Barsky and S. Gottfried	
57.	U.S. 2,671,054	A. H. Bump, R. Marotta, and R. D. Swisher	Monsanto Chemical Co.
58.	U.S. 2,671,090	M. L. Kalinowski and F. H. MacLaren	Standard Oil Corp. of Indiana
59.	U.S. 2,674,582	J. R. Darby	Monsanto Chemical Co.
60.	Austrian 174,375		"Chemin," Chemische Hilfsstoffe G.m.b.H.
61.	Belg. 445,813		Deutsche Hydrierwerke A.-G.
62.	Brit. 508,489	H. B. Foster and J. H. Crowell	National Aniline & Chemical Co., Inc.
63.	Brit. 547,594		Chas. Pfizer & Co.
64.	Brit. 566,110	E. I. du Pont de Nemours & Co., Inc.	Imperial Chemical Industries, Ltd.
65.	Brit. 578,867	P. G. Carter and H. Plimmer	Imperial Chemical Industries, Ltd.
66.	Brit. 588,545	P. Eaglesfield	Distillers Co., Ltd.
67.	Brit. 633,814	C. H. B. Jarl	Beck, Koller & Co., Ltd.
68.	Brit. 659,786		Standard Oil Development Co.
69.	Brit. 677,624	D. J. Hadley, R. Heap, and D. I. H. Jacobs	Distillers Co., Ltd.
70.	Brit. 684,649		California Research Corp.
71.	Brit. 688,033	D. J. Hadley, R. Heap, and D. I. H. Jacobs	Distillers Co., Ltd.

Concerning

Preparation of a Diels-Alder adduct of a hexahalocyclopentadiene and a dieno-
phile selected from maleic anhydride, cyclopentadiene, butadiene, styrene, etc.

Oxidation of benzene to maleic anhydride in presence of vanadium catalyst on
silica-glass carrier.
Oxidation of butenes or butadiene to maleic acid in presence of phosphorus-
molybdenum oxide catalyst.
Purification of crude phthalic anhydride containing naphthoquinone-type impurities by heating in presence of a bisulfite, metabisulfite, hydrosulfite, or sul-
foxylate of sodium or potassium.
Removal of color- and odor-forming impurities from crude phthalic anhydride by
distillation in presence of an alkali metal phthalate.
Fractional condensation method for recovery of maleic anhydride from mixture of
maleic anhydride vapor and water vapor.
Purification of crude phthalic anhydride containing color and odor impurities by
heating with a sodium or lithium salt of an inorganic acid, followed by fractional distillation.
Purification of phthalic anhydride by heating with molten asphalt.

Catalyst for vapor-phase oxidation of benzene to maleic anhydride: finely divided
silica and glass impregnated with vanadium catalyst.
Process for production of phthalic anhydride by catalytic oxidation of naphthalene.

Production of adipic acid by oxidation of cyclohexane with nitric acid.

Production of maleic anhydride by heating ($160°-400°$ C.) maleic acid.

Production of fumaric acid by fermentation of carbohydrates; rate of aerobic fermentation increased by bubbling air through and mechanically agitating
substrate.
Production of aliphatic carboxylic acids by catalytic oxidation of ketones, e.g.,
adipic acid from cyclohexanone.
Products of Diels-Alder reaction between maleic acid or derivatives and dicyclopentadiene. Resin intermediates; improve air-drying properties.
Recovery of fumaric acid from aqueous fermentation products.
Recovery of maleic anhydride from a 40–60% aqueous solution by azeotropic removal of water with xylene.
Preparation of maleic acid by catalytic oxidation of 2-methyl- and 4-methyl-1,3-
pentadiene.
Catalysts for production of maleic acid by oxidation of various types of compounds: activated mesh alumina or silica gel soaked in phosphomolybdic acid
and dried.
Purification of phthalic anhydride by contact with a granular heat-exchange
material.
Preparation of maleic acid by air oxidation of mixture of 1- and 2-butenes in
presence of phosphorus and molybdenum oxide catalyst.

Acids (Continued)

	Patent Number	Patentee	Assignee
72.	Brit. 697,506		E. I. du Pont de Nemours & Co., Inc.
73.	Can. 414,474	S. A. Waksman	Merck & Co.
74.	Fr. 803,443		Carbide & Carbon Chemicals Co.
75.	Ger. 717,952	H. Hopff and W. Rapp	I. G. Farbenind. A.-G.
76.	Ger. 719,134	H. Hopff and W. Rapp	I. G. Farbenind. A.-G.
77.	Ger. 724,758	O. Drossbach	I. G. Farbenind. A.-G.
78.	Ger. 740,333	R. Hilpert, A. Baumann, C. Beck, and E. Jagla	I. G. Farbenind. A.-G.
79.	Ger. 805,641	W. Rippe and W. Schweckendick	Badische Anilin- & Soda-Fabrik (I. G. Farbenind. A.-G. "In Auflösung")
80.	Ger. 861,840	F. Hölscher	Badische Anilin- & Soda-Fabrik (I. G. Farbenind. A.-G. "In Auflösung")
81.	Japan. 137,755	K. Takahasi	Sankyo K. K.
82.	Japan. 1412 ('52) 2115 ('52)	H. Sveta et al.	Nippon Chemical Industries Co.
83.	Japan. 3070 ('52)	H. Oka et al.	Mitsubishi Chemical Industries Co.
84.	Japan. 4573 ('52)	M. Hosoya	Nippon Chemical Industries Co.
85.	Japan. 5617 ('51)	O. Hibino and S. Morita	Yawata Iron Manufacturing Co.
86.	Russ. 50,394	Y. S. Zal'kind and L. F. Markov	

Alcohols

	Patent Number	Patentee	Assignee
87.	U.S. 2,060,880	W. A. Lazier	E. I. du Pont de Nemours & Co., Inc.
88.	U.S. 2,071,395	H. Dreyfus	
89.	U.S. 2,072,015	M. W. Tamele and H. P. A. Groll	Shell Development Co.
90.	U.S. 2,072,016	M. W. Tamele and H. P. A. Groll	Shell Development Co.
91.	U.S. 2,130,891	N. M. Mnookin	Synthetic Products, Inc.
92.	U.S. 2,148,304	J. D. Ruys and H. R. McCombie	Shell Development Co.

Concerning

Dibasic carboxylic acids (see U.S. 2,601,223 in this section).

Production of fumaric acid by fungal fermentation of carbohydrates; acid is partially neutralized (pH 5.0–6.5) as formed to prevent crystallization.

Production of maleic acid by oxidation of butadiene, butylenes, or normal and secondary butyl alcohols.

Production of adipic acid and related compounds by oxidation of hexahydroacetophenone, its homologs, or halo-substituted products.

Production of adipic acid and related compounds by oxidation of hexahydroacetophenone, its homologs, or halo-substituted products.

Production of maleic anhydride by catalytic oxidation of succinic acid or its anhydride.

Production of adipic acid by oxidation of cyclohexylamine with nitric acid.

Production of alpha, beta-unsaturated carboxylic acids and derivatives by treatment of compounds of acetylene series and carbon monoxide with compounds containing reactive hydrogen atoms, e.g., $HC \equiv CH + H_2O + CO = $ acrylic acid.

Alkylamines, such as dimethylamine, diethylamine, or dibutylamine, or di- or triethanolamines as catalysts for *cis-trans* rearrangement of olefin dicarboxylic acids, e.g., maleic to fumaric acid.

Production of fumaric acid by heating furfural in chlorate solution in presence of oxidation catalyst.

Preparation of phthalic anhydride by air oxidation of naphthalene in presence of a catalyst comprising V_2O_5, K_2SO_4, and SiO_2 gel.

Process for purification of phthalic anhydride containing naphthoquinone and 1-$C_{10}H_7OH$ as impurities.

Process for air oxidation of crude naphthalene to phthalic anhydride.

Production of phthalic anhydride by vapor-phase oxidation of a fluorine-containing coal-tar fraction in presence of a vanadium pentoxide catalyst mixed with molybdenum, tin, and chromium oxides.

Production of adipic acid by oxidation of cyclohexane with potassium dichromate.

Production of ethylene glycol by catalytic hydrogenation of diethyl oxalate.

Production of polyhydric alcohols, e.g., ethylene glycol, by catalytic oxidation of gaseous olefins, e.g., ethylene.

See Can. 357,070, in this section.

Production of allyl alcohol by hydrolysis of allyl chloride.

Production of glycol by heating a mixture of ethylene dichloride and water under pressure.

Production of ethylene glycol by hydrolysis of ethylene dichloride.

Alcohols (Continued)

	Patent Number	Patentee	Assignee
93.	U.S. 2,159,507	G. H. Law and R. W. McNamee	Carbide & Carbon Chemicals Co.
94.	U.S. 2,176,055	E. C. Britton and G. H. Coleman	Dow Chemical Co.
95.	U.S. 2,236,919	A. F. A. Reynhart	Shell Development Co.
96.	U.S. 2,255,411	C. A. Cohen and C. M. Beamer	Standard Alcohol Co.
97.	U.S. 2,271,083	E. J. Lorand	Hercules Powder Co.
98.	U.S. 2,285,448	D. J. Loder	E. I. du Pont de Nemours & Co., Inc.
99.	U.S. 2,305,104	F. W. Pardee, Jr.	E. I. du Pont de Nemours & Co., Inc.
100.	U.S. 2,318,033	G. H. Van de Griendt, K. E. Marple, and L. M. Peters	Shell Development Co.
101.	U.S. 2,325,206	L. A. Stengel	Commercial Solvents Corp.
102.	U.S. 2,325,207	L. A. Stengel and W. K. O'Loughlin	Commercial Solvents Corp.
103.	U.S. 2,378,104	C. F. Reed	C. L. Horn
104.	U.S. 2,395,638	N. A. Milas	Research Corp.
105.	U.S. 2,398,157	A. S. Ramage	A. A. F. Maxwell
106.	U.S. 2,418,290	H. A. Bruson and W. D. Niederhauser	Resinous Products & Chemical Co.
107.	U.S. 2,607,805	W. F. Gresham	E. I. du Pont de Nemours & Co., Inc.
108.	U.S. 2,617,835	G. F. Curtin, Jr.	E. I. du Pont de Nemours & Co., Inc.
109.	U.S. 2,654,786	W. F. Gresham	E. I. du Pont de Nemours & Co., Inc.
110.	Brit. 555,240	F. W. Pardee	E. I. du Pont de Nemours & Co., Inc.
111.	Brit. 610,613		British Celanese, Ltd.
112.	Can. 357,070	M. W. Tamele and H. P. Groll	Shell Development Co.
113.	Fr. 774,186		Société carbochimique, S.A.

Concerning

Catalytic isomerization of 1,2-alkylene oxides having 2-4 C atoms to produce aldehydes and alcohols, e.g., allyl alcohol.

Recovery of allyl alcohol from wood-spirits residue by treatment with hydrochloric acid.

Production of ethylene glycol from ethylene oxide and water.

Production of glycols by hydration of cooled olefin oxides, e.g., ethylene glycol from ethylene oxide.

Production of polyhydric alcohols, e.g., ethylene glycol, by catalytic hydrogenation of sugars of 2-4 C atoms.

Production of polyhydric alcohols, e.g., ethylene glycol, by catalytic hydrogenation of an aliphatic alcohol ester of a partially dehydrated glycolic acid, e.g., ethyl glycolate.

Catalytic hydrogenation of alkyl glycolates, as in the production of ethylene glycol from methyl hydroxyacetate.

Production of alcohols, e.g., allyl alcohol, by hydrolysis of the corresponding halogenated hydrocarbon, e.g., allyl halide.

Method of effecting catalytic hydrogenation, e.g., in production of propylene glycol from molasses and methyl alcohol, by hydrogenating in presence of precipitated copper hydroxide.

Process similar to U.S. 2,325,206, in which coprecipitated ferric hydroxide or magnesium hydroxide or both are used together with the precipitated copper hydroxide.

Production of polyhydric alcohols by chlorination of olefins and saponification of the resultant chlorohydrin, e.g., ethylene glycol from ethylene.

Production of glycols, aldehydes, ketones, quinones, or acids by oxidation of aromatic hydrocarbons with hydrogen peroxide, e.g., phthalic acid from naphthalene.

Preparation of ethylene glycol and ethyl acetate by heating $Pb(C_2H_3O_2)_2 \cdot 2Pb(OH)_2$ in ethyl alcohol with ethylene chloride.

Preparation of unsaturated 1,3-glycols by reaction of an alpha, gamma-dialkyl crotonaldehyde with formaldehyde.

Conversion of glycolic acid to ethylene glycol by liquid-phase hydrogenation over a ruthenium hydrogenation catalyst.

Mixtures of polyhydric alcohols (e.g., pentanediol and hexanediol) suitable as raw materials for polyester plasticizers and produced by catalytic hydrogenation of esterified by-products obtained in the catalytic air oxidation of cyclohexane or cyclohexanone to adipic acid.

Preparation of polyethylene glycols by esterifying and etherifying hydroxyacetic acid with a glycol and then hydrogenating the resulting complex ether-ester.

Production of ethylene glycol by vapor-phase catalytic hydrogenation of hydroxyacetic acid and its derivatives.

Production of allyl alcohol by electrolytic reduction of acrolein.

Production of unsaturated alcohols by hydrolysis of corresponding unsaturated halides, e.g., isobutenol from isobutenyl chloride.

Production of ethylene glycol from dichloroethane.

Alcohols (Continued)

	Patent Number	Patentee	Assignee
114.	Fr. 844,415		Hinkel & Cie. G.m.b.H.
115.	Ger. 695,997		Société carbochimique, S.A.
116.	Japan. 664 ('53)	T. Haga and H. Takahashi	Mitsubishi Chemical Industries Co.
117.	Japan. 2272 ('52)	E. Ishida	
118.	Swiss 213,251		Bombrini Parodi-Delfino

Styrene and Other Vinyl Derivatives of Benzene

	Patent Number	Patentee	Assignee
119.	U.S. 2,228,788–2,228,791	F. J. Soday	United Gas Improvement Co.
120.	U.S. 2,241,770	R. R. Dreisbach, S. M. Stoesser, and A. W. Hanson	Dow Chemical Co.
121.	U.S. 2,314,466	H. L. Thwaites	Jasco, Inc.
122.	U.S. 2,318,211	S. G. Foord	International Standard Electric Corp.
123.	U.S. 2,318,212	S. G. Foord	International Standard Electric Corp.
124.	U.S. 2,361,538	R. A. Franz	United Gas Improvement Co.
125.	U.S. 2,364,027	A. L. Marshall	Monsanto Chemical Co.
126.	U.S. 2,370,346	E. W. Gluesenkamp	Monsanto Chemical Co.
127.	U.S. 2,376,533	G. Egloff	Universal Oil Products Co.
128.	U.S. 2,376,734	C. L. Thomas	Universal Oil Products Co.
129.	U.S. 2,376,985	V. Voorhees	Standard Oil Co. of Indiana
130.	U.S. 2,377,074	G. Egloff	Universal Oil Products Co.
131.	U.S. 2,377,221	A. W. Francis and E. E. Reid	Socony-Vacuum Oil Co.
132.	U.S. 2,383,043	E. L. Cline	Allied Chemical and Dye Corp.

Production of polyhydric alcohols by hydrogenation of carbohydrates in aqueous alcohol solutions or suspensions in presence of a cobalt catalyst.
See Fr. 774,186 in this section.

Preparation of allyl alcohol by treating propargyl alcohol, water, and zinc dust with sodium hydroxide.
Preparation of allyl alcohol by heating propargyl alcohol with Raney nickel catalyst.
Production of glycerol and propanediol by catalytic hydrogenation of carbohydrates, e.g., glucose and other sugars.

Removal of color-forming compounds from light-oil styrene fractions by treatment with sulfuric acid; sulfuric acid and a boron compound, e.g., boric acid; a sulfonic acid, e.g., benzenesulfonic acid; or oxalic, formic, acetic, chloroacetic, citric, lactic, tartaric, succinic, or propionic acid.
Stabilization of styrene against polymerization during storage and distillation by treatment with phenylacetylene.

Triphenyl stibine, arsine, or bismuthine as polymerization and condensation inhibitors for styrene.
Stabilization of styrene against polymerization in storage by addition of hexamine.

Stabilization of styrene against polymerization in storage by addition of hydroxylamine hydrochloride.
Stabilization of aromatic olefins, e.g., styrene, against oxidation and polymerization by adding a mixture of a basic compound, e.g., a primary amine, and a phenolic compound, e.g., 4-tertiary-butyl pyrocatechol.
Stabilization of polystyrene against discoloration under ultraviolet radiation with an aromatic hydrocarbon having adjacent hydroxyl and carbonyl groups on the nucleus, e.g., salicylaldehyde.
Purification of styrene, to remove oxidation products, by refluxing with an amine, e.g., 2-naphthylamine, under reduced pressure.
Catalyst for production of styrene by alkylation of benzene with ethylene.

Composite catalyst for production of styrene by alkylation of benzene with ethylene.
Conversion of butadiene dimer to styrene by heating in contact with a metallic oxide catalyst, e.g., V, Cr, Mo, W oxides.
Production of styrene from benzene and ethylene.

Separation of styrene from ethylbenzene by 2-stage extraction with aqueous silver nitrate and pentane.
Stabilization of polymerizable monomers, e.g., styrenes, acrylates, vinyl esters, against polymerization in storage, with hematoxylin or hematein.

Styrene and Other Vinyl Derivatives of Benzene (Continued)

	Patent Number	Patentee	Assignee
133.	U.S. 2,383,179	G. Egloff	Universal Oil Products Co.
134.	U.S. 2,383,772	N. K. Chaney and E. L. Hall	United Gas Improvement Co.
135.	U.S. 2,384,984	C. Weizmann	
136.	U.S. 2,385,166	H. M. Singleton and T. B. McCullock	Standard Oil Development Co.
137.	U.S. 2,389,444	W. J. Mattox	Universal Oil Products Co.
138.	U.S. 2,389,793	J. W. Livingston	Monsanto Chemical Co.
139.	U.S. 2,389,801	W. J. Mattox	Universal Oil Products Co.
140.	U.S. 2,392,289	C. R. McCullough and W. H. Gehrke	Monsanto Chemical Co.
141.	U.S. 2,392,910	R. A. Franz	United Gas Improvement Co.
142.	U.S. 2,392,960	C. W. Watson	Texas Co.
143.	U.S. 2,399,395	L. C. Shriver	Carbide & Carbon Chemicals Co.
144.	U.S. 2,400,774	G. A. Nesty and W. A. Klingelhoefer	Solvay Process Co.
145.	U.S. 2,406,319	L. A. Brooks and M. Nazzewski	Sprague Electric Co.
146.	U.S. 2,410,408	J. R. Durland	Monsanto Chemical Co.
147.	U.S. 2,412,504	G. Goldfinger	Godfrey L. Cabot, Inc.
148.	U.S. 2,416,990	M. H. Gorin and E. Gorin	Socony-Vacuum Oil Co., Inc.
149.	U.S. 2,419,198	R. E. Bowman	
150.	U.S. 2,420,862	T. S. Chambers	Standard Oil Development Co.
151.	U.S. 2,426,848	M. H. Tuttle	Max B. Miller & Co., Inc.
152.	U.S. 2,458,494	J. R. Durland	Monsanto Chemical Co.
153.	U.S. 2,650,899	R. Nobbs and E. T. Borrows	Petrocarbon Ltd.
154.	Brit. 572,045	A. L. Mond	Universal Oil Products Co.
155.	Brit. 575,769	C. Weizmann	

Concerning

Production of styrene from benzene and ethylene or ethane using an aluminum-chromium oxide catalyst.

Production of styrene by "relatively homogeneous" cracking of a primarily naphthenic petroleum product.

Production of styrene and ethylbenzene by passing olefins, usually with 2-5 C atoms, over a metallic hydrogenating-dehydrogenating catalyst, e.g., copper wire gauze.

Recovery of styrene by extraction of an alkylated benzene fraction with furfural and dehydrogenation of the extract.

Production of styrene by alkylation of benzene with ethylene and dehydrogenation of the resultant ethylbenzene.

Recovery of styrene from pyrolysis products of ethylbenzene by fractional distillation and static crystallization.

Production of styrene by passing ethylcyclohexane over a metallic oxide catalyst, e.g., Al, Cr, and Mg oxides.

Production of styrene by dehydrogenation of ethylbenzene in presence of sulfur vapor.

Four-stage process to free a light-oil styrene fraction from phenylacetylene and color-imparting materials.

Production of styrene by dehydrogenation of a butadiene dimer.

Production of styrene by catalytic dehydration of para-methylphenyl carbinol.

Simultaneous synthesis of butadiene and styrene from benzene and ethylene.

Preparation of dihalogenated styrene compounds. Polymers and copolymers, e.g., with maleic anhydride, of these compounds provide good electrical insulation.

Phenolic sulfides, e.g., di(para-tertiary-butyl catechol) monosulfide, and their polymers as polymerization inhibitors for styrene.

Removal of polymerization inhibitors from monomers, e.g., styrene, by heating the monomer in the presence of carbon black.

Production of styrene by pyrolysis of isopropylbenzene and alpha-methyl styrene.

Dehydrohalogenation of organic compounds. Production of styrene from chloromethylbenzene and trichloromethane, using a magnesium iodide complex as catalyst.

Stabilization of vinyl aromatic compounds, such as styrene, against polymerization by treating with highly volatile dienes or acetylenes, e.g., butadiene, acetylene.

Production of styrene by cracking of hydrocarbons in presence of coke.

Stabilization of vinyl compounds against polymerization in storage, shipment, and distillation with phenolic sulfides, e.g., dicatechol, di-meta-cresol monosulfides.

Stabilization of styrene during storage or distillation with 2-furfurylidene malononitrile.

Production of styrene by selective catalytic dehydrogenation of ethylbenzene in a mixture with xylene.

Production of styrene and other aromatic compounds by catalytic dehydrogenation of solvent naphtha.

Styrene and Other Vinyl Derivatives of Benzene (Continued)

	Patent Number	Patentee	Assignee
156.	Brit. 586,537	E. R. Erickson	Mathieson Alkali Works, Inc.
157.	Can. 407,428	J. W. Britton, R. F. Prescott, and R. C. Dosser	Dow Chemical Co.
158.	Can. 442,478	R. L. Heider	Monsanto Chemical Co.
159.	Russ. 59,055	N. D. Zelinskii, A. A. Balandin, and G. M. Marukyan	

Other Cross-Linking Agents

160.	U.S. 2,370,565– 2,370,566	L. E. Muskat and F. Strain	Pittsburgh Plate Glass Co.
161.	U.S. 2,370,573	L. E. Muskat and F. Strain	Pittsburgh Plate Glass Co.
162.	U.S. 2,370,574	L. E. Muskat and F. Strain	Pittsburgh Plate Glass Co.
163.	U.S. 2,384,115	L. E. Muskat and F. Strain	Pittsburgh Plate Glass Co.
164.	U.S. 2,385,931– 2,385,932	L. E. Muskat and F. Strain	Pittsburgh Plate Glass Co.
165.	U.S. 2,385,933	L. E. Muskat and F. Strain	Pittsburgh Plate Glass Co.
166.	U.S. 2,385,934	L. E. Muskat and F. Strain	Pittsburgh Plate Glass Co.
167.	U.S. 2,387,530	W. W. Prichard	E. I. du Pont de Nemours & Co., Inc.
168.	U.S. 2,403,112	L. E. Muskat	Pittsburgh Plate Glass Co.
169.	U.S. 2,403,113	L. E. Muskat and F. Strain	Pittsburgh Plate Glass Co.
170.	U.S. 2,411,136	S. B. Luce	Monsanto Chemical Co.
171.	U.S. 2,415,366	L. E. Muskat	Marco Chemicals, Inc.
172.	U.S. 2,426,863	G. F. Deebel	Monsanto Chemical Co.

Concerning

Stabilization of styrene and its derivatives with 2,5-alkoxy hydroquinones, e.g.,
2,5-diethoxy, 2,5-di(beta-methoxyethoxy), 2,5-di-n-propoxy hydroquinones.
Stabilization of styrene against polymerization with 0.01–5.0% of sulfur.

Stabilization of styrene with 0.005–0.05% of para-amino phenol, para-tertiary-
butyl phenol, 2-hydroxy biphenyl, or 2-amino 5-hydroxy biphenyl.
Production of styrene by catalytic dehydrogenation of ethylbenzene in a carbon
dioxide atmosphere.

Polybasic acid-polyhydric alcohol esters, e.g., glycol bis(allyl carbonate),
bis(allyl maleate), bis(allyl phthalate).
Production of polymerizable unsaturated esters by reaction of chloroformates of
glycolates with unsaturated alcohols or of chloroformates of unsaturated alcohols with glycolates of unsaturated alcohols.
Diesters of carbonic acid and an unsaturated alcohol ester of glycolic acid, e.g.,
allyl glycolate gives bis(carballyloxymethyl) carbonate.
Preparation of polymerizable complex mixed esters from polyhydric compounds
(glycerols, glycols, etc.) and acid esters of carbonic acid and unsaturated
alcohols.
Preparation of polymerizable unsaturated esters, e.g., resorcinol bis(allyl carbonate), from esters of hydroxy acids or other appropriate hydroxy compounds
and alcohol chloroformates.
Unsaturated alcohol esters of triethylene glycol bis(acid carbonate) and polymers thereof.
Preparation of polymerizable allyl carbonates of glycerol lactates, e.g., bis(allyl
carbonate) of ethylene glycol dilactate, from alcohol chloroformates.
Insolubilization of linear polymers, e.g., polyester amides, by heating with a
cyclic anhydride of a dibasic acid having an acyclic chain of at least 4 atoms
between the carboxyl groups, e.g., adipic anhydride. Cross-linking agents.
Molding materials from polymerized unsaturated esters, e.g., ethylene glycol
bis(allyl carbonate).
Diesters of a glycol containing at least 3 C atoms in a continuous chain and a
half-ester of carbonic acid and an unsaturated alcohol, e.g., glycol bis(allyl
carbonates).
Preparation of esters of unsaturated acids and allylic-type alcohols, e.g., methallyl maleate. Alkali metal silicate catalyst used.
Polymerizable monomers obtained from 1 molecule of glycol and 2 molecules of
the ester of an unsaturated dicarboxylic acid and a saturated alcohol, e.g.,
diethylene glycol bis(methyl fumarate).
Cross-linking agent for synthetic resins: diallyl ether of 2-butene-1,4-diol prepared by reaction of 1,4-dichloro-2-butene with an alkali metal alcoholate of
allyl alcohol.

Other Cross-Linking Agents (Continued)

	Patent Number	Patentee	Assignee
173.	U.S. 2,437,508	G. F. D'Alelio	General Electric Co.
174.	U.S. 2,462,042	A. M. Howald and J. L. Jones	Libbey-Owens-Ford Glass Co.
175.	U.S. 2,474,686	H. T. Neher, E. H. Kroeker, and W. J. Croxall	Rohm & Haas Co.
176.	U.S. 2,482,706	H. M. Day	American Cyanamid Co.
177.	U.S. 2,504,052	R. H. Snyder	U.S. Rubber Co.
178.	U.S. 2,510,503	E. L. Kropa	American Cyanamid Co.
179.	U.S. 2,514,354	D. E. Adelson and H. Dannenberg	Shell Development Co.
180.	U.S. 2,515,132	C. R. Milone	Wingfoot Corp.
181.	U.S. 2,521,303	H. T. Neher, E. H. Kroeker, and W. J. Croxall	Rohm & Haas Co.
182.	U.S. 2,545,184	L. N. Whitehill and E. C. Shokal	Shell Development Co.
183.	U.S. 2,557,667	E. L. Kropa	American Cyanamid Co.
184.	U.S. 2,583,980	L. W. Whitehill and W. M. McLamore	Shell Development Co.
185.	U.S. 2,591,020	A. E. Smith	United States of America
186.	U.S. 2,598,664	E. Kropa	American Cyanamid Co.
187.	U.S. 2,631,148	R. G. Nelb	U.S. Rubber Co.
188.	Brit. 497,175		Ellis Foster Co.
189.	Brit. 574,606		Pittsburgh Plate Glass Co.
190.	Brit. 586,520		Pittsburgh Plate Glass Co.
191.	Brit. 592,172	A. H. Stevens	Pittsburgh Plate Glass Co.
192.	Brit. 596,467	F. J. H. Mackereth	Imperial Chemical Industries, Ltd.

Concerning

Allyl and methallyl ether esters as cross-linking agents to convert thermoplastic material to thermoset resins, e.g., allyl allyloxyacetate as cross-linking agent for ethylene glycol maleate.

Preparation of unsaturated substances, e.g., fumaryl bis(allyl lactate), by copolymerization of the reaction product of an acid, e.g., fumaric, and $SOCl_2$ with an unsaturated ester, e.g., allyl lactate.

Preparation of allyl diglycolate from diglycolic anhydride and allyl alcohol. Forms cross-linked polymers with high flexural and impact strengths.

Diallyl isopropylidene bis(para-phenoxyacetate), which may be copolymerized with unsaturated alkyd resins to form copolymers with low dielectric constants.

Copolymerizable interpolymers of allylic fumarates and allylic alcohols.

Basic patent. Triallyl cyanurate type of heat-resistant polyester resins.

Clear, hard copolymers of diallyl carbonate with other diallyl esters, e.g., diallyl phthalate and diallyl adipate.

Diallyl esters of diethyl ether dicarboxylic acids. Can be copolymerized with other monomers, e.g., styrene.

Copolymers of allyl succinyl allyl glycolate and acrylic esters.

Polymerizable diallyl esters of acyloxylated aliphatic dicarboxylic acids, e.g., diallyl tartrate diacetate. Can be copolymerized with polyesters, etc.

Reaction product of a cyanuric triester and a polyhydric alcohol. Can be copolymerized with unsaturated alkyd resins, etc.

Polymerizable unsaturated diesters of hydrazodicarbonic acids, e.g., N,N-dicarboallyloxyhydrazine, by treating unsaturated chloroformates with hydrazine.

Allylated trimethylene trisulfones. Cross-linking agents for polyesters, styrene, etc.

Allyl carbamate and substituted allyl carbamates as compounds that will copolymerize with alkyl resins to give clear, colorless gels.

Manufacture of triallyl cyanurate by adding alkali metal hydroxide to a slurry of cyanuric chloride in allyl alcohol.

Cross-linking of unsaturated alkyds with methyl acrylate, methyl methacrylate, or vinyl acetate.

Preparation of polymers of complex esters from phosgene and allyl esters, e.g., allyl lactate, methallyl lactate.

Preparation of unsaturated carbonate esters $[CH_3CH(CO_2R)OCO_2CH(CO_2R^1)CH_3]$ from lactic acid esters of unsaturated alcohols and phosgene. Polymers of esters high in tensile strength and shattering resistance.

Preparation of polymerizable complex esters from (a) a chloroformate of an unsaturated alcohol ester of a monohydroxy monocarboxylic acid and a glycol or glycerol or (b) a polychloroformate of a glycol or glycerol and an unsaturated alcohol ester of a monohydroxy monocarboxylic acid.

Preparation of polymerizable doubly unsaturated tetraesters; e.g., condensation of chloroformate of allyl glycolate with ethylene glycol to give glycol di(allyl glycolyl carbonate).

Other Cross-Linking Agents (Continued)

	Patent Number	Patentee	Assignee
193.	Brit. 599,837	F. J. H. Mackereth	Imperial Chemical Industries, Ltd.
194.	Brit. 606,716–606,717	R. Hammond	Imperial Chemical Industries, Ltd.
195.	Brit. 607,888	R. Hammond	Imperial Chemical Industries, Ltd.
196.	Brit. 611,529	J. A. Bralley and F. B. Pope	B. F. Goodrich Co.
197.	Brit. 618,295		N. V. de Bataafsche Petroleum Maatschappij
198.	Brit. 622,235		Wingfoot Corp.
199.	Brit. 650,144		U. S. Rubber Co.
200.	Brit. 691,041	E. M. Evans and J. E. S. Whitney	British Resin Products, Ltd.
201.	Brit. 683,645		Wingfoot Corp.
202.	Dutch 64,140		N. V. de Bataafsche Petroleum Maatschappij
203.	Dutch 66,160		N. V. de Bataafsche Petroleum Maatschappij

Concerning

Polymerizable unsaturated hexaesters, e.g., glycol di(allyl glycolyl succinate); form hard, scratch-resistant transparent polymers.

Preparation of polyesters from dihydric alcohols and chloroformates of half-esters of dihydric alcohols with acrylic acids.

Polymerizable unsaturated esters prepared by treating acrylic or alpha-substituted acrylic acid, acid chloride, anhydride, or methyl, ethyl, or butyl esters with dihydric polyesters.

Preparation of polyunsaturated polyesters, e.g., 1,4-bis(allyl carbonato) 2,3-dichlorobenzene, by condensation of alkenyl chloroformates with polyphenolic compounds, e.g., 2,3-dichlorohydroquinone, and alkali.

Speeding up thermosetting of diallyl phthalate by copolymerizing with methyl methacrylate.

Cross-linking of unsaturated alkyd resins with allyl carbamate.

Cross-linking of unsaturated alkyd resins with 2,5-dichlorostyrene to increase fire resistance.

Ortho- and meta-vinyl phenols as cross-linking agents for certain polyesters. Impart improved adhesive properties.

Cross-linking of polyesters or polyamides with N-acyl polylactams prepared by treating polyacyl halides with a lactam, e.g., N,N^1-terephthalylbiscaprolactam from caprolactam and terephthalyl chloride.

Polymerizable monomers containing an epoxide and an olefinic group, e.g., esters of dicarboxylic acids such as glycidyl allyl phthalate.

Polymerizable ethereal oxygen-containing carboxylic acid esters of unsaturated alcohols, e.g., diallyl diglycolate.

	Patent Number	Patentee	Assignee
204.	U.S. 1,975,750	M. M. Safford	General Electric Co.
205.	U.S. 2,057,766	M. M. Brubaker	E. I. du Pont de Nemours & Co., Inc.
206.	U.S. 2,273,891	M. A. Pollack, I. E. Muskat, and F. Strain	Pittsburgh Plate Glass Co.
207.	U.S. 2,286,062	F. E. Condo, C. J. Krister, and W. E. Lundquist	E. I. du Pont de Nemours & Co., Inc.
208.	U.S. 2,375,256	F. L. Soday	United Gas Improvement Co.
209.	U.S. 2,377,095	I. E. Muskat	Pittsburgh Plate Glass Co.
210.	U.S. 2,391,393	R. I. Coffmann and R. M. Marks	E. I. du Pont de Nemours & Co., Inc.
211.	U.S. 2,454,539	E. M. Beavers	Rohm & Haas Co.
212.	U.S. 2,483,960	M. Baer	Monsanto Chemical Co.
213.	U.S. 2,484,415	C. G. Malm and L. D. Bearden	Eastman Kodak Co.
214.	U.S. 2,491,350	D. W. Young and W. Sparks	Standard Oil Development Co.
215.	U.S. 2,492,086	M. Baer	Monsanto Chemical Co.
216.	U.S. 2,494,133	A. W. Jefts	American Cyanamid Co.
217.	U.S. 2,496,222	E. C. H. Kolvoort and G. Akkerman	N. V. de Bataafsche Petroleum Maatschappij
218.	U.S. 2,543,335	B. Phillips, Jr., and W. M. Quattlebaum, Jr.	Union Carbide and Carbon Corp.
219.	U.S. 2,595,679	B. W. Lew	Atlas Powder Co.
220.	U.S. 2,613,201	J. W. Anderson, J. W. McCorney, and G. E. Ham	Shell Development Co.
221.	U.S. 2,629,713	M. T. Goebel	E. I. du Pont de Nemours & Co., Inc.
222.	U.S. 2,629,716	P. W. Morgan	E. I. du Pont de Nemours & Co., Inc.
223.	Brit. 570,331		E. I. du Pont de Nemours & Co., Inc.
224.	Brit. 668,998		N. V. de Bataafsche Petroleum Maatschappij

II. RESIN MANUFACTURE

277

	Patent Number	Patentee	Assignee
225.	Brit. 672,224	J. S. Wakely	Imperial Chemical Industries, Ltd.
226.	Brit. 684,334	F. Dean	Imperial Chemical Industries, Ltd.
227.	Dutch 61,145	W. L. J. de Nie and R. H. M. Meyer	N. V. de Bataafsche Petroleum Maatschappij
228.	Dutch 64,718	E. C. H. Kolvoort and G. Akkerman	N. V. de Bataafsche Petroleum Maatschappij
229.	Dutch 64,982	W. L. J. de Nie	N. V. de Bataafsche Petroleum Maatschappij
230.	Dutch 71,996		N. V. de Bataafsche Petroleum Maatschappij
231.	Ger. 738,276	H. Lange	I. G. Farbenind. A.-G.
232.	Swiss 251,877	F. Schmocker	

Concerning

One-step production of styrene-modified alkyd resin by heating styrene, a polybasic acid, e.g., phthalic anhydride, and a partial ester of glycerol or pentaerythritol.

Method for preparing colorless esters, e.g., dialkyl phthalates, from solid acids or anhydrides.

Method for polymerizing in a watery emulsion substances of different polymerizing capacity, e.g., maleic acid anhydride or fumaric acid esters and acrylic or methacrylic compounds.

Emulsion polymerization process for polymerizable materials, e.g., styrene and fumaric acid esters. Materials emulsified in nonacid aqueous medium; acid added to bring pH below 3; emulsion then polymerized.

Emulsion polymerization of unsaturated compounds, e.g., fumaric and maleic acid esters.

Prevention of formation of colored contaminants in preparation of esters by conducting sulfur dioxide gas through esterification reaction mixture.

Prevention of stoppage of vacuum pumps by polymerized material by adding polymerization inhibitors to the pump lubricant.

Homogenization of reaction mixture under pressure in making maleic esters from alcohols and maleic anhydride.

Catalysts, Accelerators, Promoters

	Patent Number	Patentee	Assignee
233.	U.S. Pat. Appl. 723,449	J. L. Jones	Libbey-Owens-Ford Co.
234.	U.S. 2,209,246	W. Bauer and E. Trommsdorff	Rohm & Haas Co.
235.	U.S. 2,258,423	J. B. Rust	Ellis-Foster Co.
236.	U.S. 2,319,576	M. C. Agens	General Electric Co.
237.	U.S. 2,367,805	R. B. Semple	Monsanto Chemical Co.
238.	U.S. 2,367,810	V. H. Turkington and L. R. Whiting	Bakelite Corp.
239.	U.S. 2,374,789	F. Strain	Pittsburgh Plate Glass Co.
240.	U.S. 2,380,473– 2,380,477	W. D. Stewart	B. F. Goodrich Co.
241.	U.S. 2,380,618	W. D. Stewart and B. M. G. Zwicker	B. F. Goodrich Co.
242.	U.S. 2,380,710	W. D. Stewart	B. F. Goodrich Co.
243.	U.S. 2,381,702	W. D. Stewart	B. F. Goodrich Co.
244.	U.S. 2,391,920	M. D. Peterson	E. I. du Pont de Nemours & Co., Inc.
245.	U.S. 2,403,758	F. F. Rust, F. H. Dickey, and E. R. Bell	Shell Development Co.
246.	U.S. 2,403,771	W. E. Vaughan and F. F. Rust	Shell Development Co.
247.	U.S. 2,419,347	V. L. Folt and F. W. Shaver	B. F. Goodrich Co.
248.	U.S. 2,426,476	W. E. Vaughan and F. F. Rust	Shell Development Co.

III. CATALYSIS AND INHIBITION

Concerning

Photopolymerization of unsaturated polyesters by actinic light (from ultraviolet to infrared) in presence of a vicinal diketone catalyst, *e.g.*, diacetal or benzil, at room temperature to $100\,^{\circ}C$.

Tetralin peroxide as an accelerator of the polymerization of styrene and other vinyl compounds.

Ascaridol as aid to copolymerization of vinyl derivatives, *e.g.*, styrol or methyl methacrylate, with glycol-maleic acid esters.

Peroxidized esters of polycarboxylic acids and alcohol-ethers, *e.g.*, peroxidized tetrahydrofurfuryl maleate. Useful as accelerators for polymerization of styrene and other vinyl compounds.

Hydroperoxides of general formula R——O——O——H, where R is the radical of an alcohol, *e.g.*, tertiary-butyl hydroperoxide, as polymerization catalysts for styrene.

Polymerization catalysts for styrene and its derivatives: mixture of oxalic acid and a borate, *e.g.*, H_3BO_3, HBO_3, B_2O_3, $Na_2B_4O_7$, $MnH_4(BO_3)_2$, etc.

Preparation of alkyl monoperoxycarbonates, useful as polymerization catalysts, *e.g.*, for diallyl phthalate, by reaction of alkyl hydroperoxides with alkyl chloroformates.

Catalysts for addition polymerization comprising water-soluble heavy metal salts, *e.g.*, Co, Cu, or Fe salts, combined with various types of compounds, *e.g.*, salts and esters of P oxyacids; aliphatic, keto-substituted carboxylic acids such as levulenic acid; aliphatic compounds containing 1–2 bivalent S atoms, such as glutathione; sugars; natural compounds containing a substituted cyclopentenophenanthrene ring such as cholesterol.

Polymerization catalyst containing the $\diagdown N$——CS——$N\diagup$ structure, *e.g.*, thiobarbituric acid, phenylthiohydantoic acid, trithiocyanuric acid.

Polymerization catalyst comprising dicyanodiamidine alone or in a mixture with a water-soluble heavy metal salt.

Alkali metal periodates as polymerization initiators. Vitamins (thiamine chloride) and plant hormones (beta-indole-3-propionic acid) act as catalysts for periodate-initiated reaction.

Dialkyl peroxides as polymerization catalysts for ethylene and vinyl compounds.

Asymmetrical ditertiary peroxides, useful as polymerization catalysts for unsaturated compounds, from reaction of tertiary hydroperoxides with tertiary alcohols, *e.g.*, tertiary-amyl alcohol with tertiary-butyl hydroperoxide.

Ditertiary-alkyl peroxides, useful as polymerization catalysts, produced by oxidation of tertiary hydrocarbons, *e.g.*, isobutane, or by treating tertiary hydroperoxides with the corresponding alcohol.

Alkoxybenzoyl peroxides, *e.g.*, diethoxybenzoyl peroxide, as catalysts for polymerization of vinyl compounds in aqueous emulsion. More effective than benzoyl peroxide.

Ditertiary-alkyl peroxides as polymerization catalysts. Relatively stable and do not discolor the resin.

Catalysts, Accelerators, Promoters (Continued)

	Patent Number	Patentee	Assignee
249.	U.S. 2,429,060	W. R. Hoover and R. M. Paulsen	U.S. Rubber Co.
250.	U.S. 2,439,528	M. Roedel	E. I. du Pont de Nemours & Co., Inc.
251.	U.S. 2,440,498	D. W. Young and H. B. Kellog	Standard Oil Development Co.
252.	U.S. 2,449,299	E. C. Hurdis	U.S. Rubber Co.
253.	U.S. 2,450,552	E. C. Hurdis	U.S. Rubber Co.
254.	U.S. 2,452,669	M. M. Levine	Cornell Aeronautical Laboratory
255.	U.S. 2,464,062	F. Strain	Pittsburgh Plate Glass Co.
256.	U.S. 2,466,800	C. F. Fisk	U.S. Rubber Co.
257.	U.S. 2,467,033	E. C. Hurdis	U.S. Rubber Co.
258.	U.S. 2,467,526	R. R. Harris	American Cyanamid Co.
259.	U.S. 2,467,527	R. R. Harris	American Cyanamid Co.
260.	U.S. 2,468,111	J. A. Robertson	E. I. du Pont de Nemours & Co., Inc.
261.	U.S. 2,471,959	M. Hunt	E. I. du Pont de Nemours & Co., Inc.
262.	U.S. 2,475,296	E. C. Shokal and F. A. Bent	Shell Development Co.
263.	U.S. 2,480,928	E. C. Hurdis	U.S. Rubber Co.
264.	U.S. 2,488,298– 2,488,299	W. Lange and R. Livingston	Ozark-Mahoning Co.
265.	U.S. 2,492,763	P. S. Pinkney	E. I. du Pont de Nemours & Co., Inc.
266.	U.S. 2,503,291	W. W. Odell	

Concerning

Hydrazine or aromatic hydrocarbon-substituted hydrazine as promoter for peroxide-catalyzed polymerization of dihydric alcohol esters of alpha-olefinic dicarboxylic acids with ethylenic monomers.

Azines, e.g., benzal azine ($C_6H_5CH=NN=CHC_6H_5$), as polymerization catalysts for olefins, e.g., ethylene or other mono-olefins up to 4 C atoms.

Catalyst for low-temperature ($-160°$ to $0°C.$) polymerization, e.g., of iso-olefins of 1-7 C atoms; a double salt of a Friedel-Crafts metal halide catalyst and a titanium alkoxy compound.

N-monoalkyl mono(monocyclic aryl) secondary monoamines, e.g., N-ethyl-meta-toluidine, as promoters for peroxide-catalyzed polymerization of unsaturated alkyd resins with ethylenic compounds.

Aliphatic polyamines, e.g., ethylenediamine, or aldehyde derivatives as promoters for peroxide-catalyzed copolymerization of unsaturated alkyd resins with ethylenic monomers.

Promoters, e.g., triethanolamine and tri-isopropanolamine, for peroxide-catalyzed polymerization of polyesters with vinyl compounds, e.g., styrene.

Peroxydicarbonates as catalysts for low-temperature ($0°-60°C.$) polymerization of unsaturated compounds containing the nonaromatic group $—C=C—$

Sulfhydryl compounds, e.g., dodecyl mercaptan, as promoters for peroxide-catalyzed polymerization of polyesters.

Accelerators for peroxide catalysts: methylene poly-(N,N-dialkylarylamine), e.g., 4,4-[tetramethyl (or ethyl or propyl) diamino] diphenylmethane.

Ferrous chloride and ferrous salt of diethylene glycol monomaleate as promoters for curing of copolymers of unsaturated alkyd resins and compounds containing the $CH_2=C=$ group, e.g., styrene.

Stannous chloride as promoter for curing of copolymers of unsaturated alkyd resins and compounds containing the $CH_2=C=$group, e.g., styrene.

Azodisulfonic acid salts, e.g., potassium azodisulfonate, as catalysts for polymerization of ethylenic compounds, e.g., styrene.

Azo compounds of class $R—N=N—R'$ (R and R' = aliphatic or cycloaliphatic) as polymerization catalysts for ethylenic compounds. Do not oxidize polymer or affect dyes.

Copper as catalyst for polymerization at temperatures above $215°C.$ (Inhibits polymerization at lower temperatures.)

Dialkyl monoaryl tertiary amines, e.g., diethylaniline, as promoters for peroxide-catalyzed polymerization of unsaturated alkyd resins with ethylenic monomers.

Production of hexafluophosphoric acid (HPF_6), useful as polymerizing and esterifying catalyst, from hydrogen fluoride and a compound containing pentavalent phosphorus, e.g., $H_3PO_4 PF_5$.

Preparation of azobis(alpha-cycloalkyl acetonitriles), useful as polymerization catalysts for unsaturated compounds, e.g., styrene, diallyl diglycolate, diallyl phthalate, from $N_2H_4·H_2O$ and cycloalkyl ketones, e.g., methyl cyclopropyl ketone.

Method of catalyzing chemical reactions, e.g., polymerization, by passing a fluidized stream of reactants through stratified layers of different finely divided solid catalysts.

Catalysts, Accelerators, Promoters (Continued)

	Patent Number	Patentee	Assignee
267.	U.S. 2,508,734	J. E. Troyan	Phillips Petroleum Co.
268.	U.S. 2,516,309	G. L. Fraser	Monsanto Chemical Co.
269.	U.S. 2,520,601	M. M. Lee	
270.	U.S. 2,524,536	B. W. Nordlander and J. A. Loritsch	General Electric Co.
271.	U.S. 2,529,214	R. R. Harris	American Cyanamid Co.
272.	U.S. 2,537,375	W. G. Simons and E. H. Dafter, Jr.	American Cyanamid Co.
273.	U.S. 2,543,635– 2,543,636	J. A. Loritsch	General Electric Co.
274.	U.S. 2,553,325	J. A. Loritsch	General Electric Co.
275.	U.S. 2,554,567	H. L. Gerhart and W. H. Lycan	Pittsburgh Plate Glass Co.
276.	U.S. 2,566,206	J. B. Hyman	Catalin Corp. of America
277.	U.S. 2,568,331	V. J. Frilette	
278.	U.S. 2,578,690	H. L. Gerhart	Pittsburgh Plate Glass Co.
279.	U.S. 2,594,560	E. G. Howard, Jr.	E. I. du Pont de Nemours & Co., Inc.
280.	U.S. 2,601,293	E. G. Howard, Jr.	E. I. du Pont de Nemours & Co., Inc.
281.	U.S. 2,608,570	D. Harman	Shell Development Co.
282.	U.S. 2,628,210	P. T. Etchason and H. F. Jones	General Electric Co.
283.	U.S. 2,631,997	W. D. Steward	B. F. Goodrich Co.
284.	U.S. 2,642,410	H. A. Hoppens	Libbey-Owens-Ford Glass Co.

Concerning

Polymerization of unsaturated compounds of general form $CH_2:C\big\langle$ using as activator a dihydroxy aromatic compound of general type $R_2Ar(OH)_2$ where Ar is an aromatic nucleus and the R's are hydrogen, alkyl, aryl, cycloalkyl, or aralkyl.

1-Hydroxy-1-cyclohexyl hydroperoxide as a polymerization catalyst for unsaturated polyester resins.

Organic phosphines, e.g., dibutyl phosphine, as promoters for peroxide-catalyzed copolymerization of unsaturated alkyd resins with ethylenic compounds.

List of catalysts functioning adjacent to copper surfaces (e.g., electrical wire) without retardation.

Aromatic sulfonic acids as catalysts for cure of polyester at high temperatures but not at room temperature. The system contains a peroxide catalyst and a phenolic inhibitor.

Organic hydroperoxides and peracids as polymerization catalysts; permit not only gelation but also complete cure of polyesters at room temperature.

Organic reducing agents, such as phenyl phosphinic acid, diphenylphenol phosphinate, dibutyl sulfite, as promoters for peroxide catalysts.

Organic reducing compounds, e.g., ascorbic or isoascorbic acid, as promoters for peroxide-catalyzed polymerization of ethylenic compounds, e.g., styrene, or esters of alpha-unsaturated, alpha,beta-polycarboxylic acids, e.g., diethyl fumarate.

Method for quickly and completely dispersing a peroxide catalyst in polyester resins in absence of styrene, to paste consistency.

Catalyst for copolymerization of styrene and unsaturated polyesters: mixture of peracetic acid and organic peroxide results in crack-free and bubble-free compositions.

Acceleration of peroxide-catalyzed polyester-styrene copolymerization with Ba, Sr, Ca, or Mg oxide or hydroxide. Transparency is impaired. Sulfur has opposite effect.

Aldehyde amines, e.g., butyraldehyde aniline, as accelerators of gelation.

Polymerization initiator: an azide and an oxidant containing one of the following ions: MnO_4^-, ClO^-, IO_4^-, BrO_3^-, or Ce^{4+}.

Initiator system for polymerization of ethylenically unsaturated monomers: hydrazone, cupric sulfate or halide, and peroxide.

Preparation of organic peroxyesters, e.g., tertiary-butyl peroxyacetate, useful as polymerization initiators and catalysts.

Oxygenated derivatives of a compound of the general formula $CH_2=CR'C(=O)O-[(CH_2)_m(CHR'')_pCHRO_n]C(=O)CR'=CH_2$ as a polymerization accelerator, e.g., for copolymerization of styrene and polyesters, or as a copolymerizable material itself, e.g., with diallyl phthalate.

Catalysts for polymerization of unsaturated organic compounds: an aminosulfite compound and an oxidant. Cause polymerization at temperatures below $30°$ F.

Catalyst system for laminating, casting, or foaming processes involving polymerization of unsaturated polyesters: allyl or cyclohexyl hydroperoxide and a metallic drier, e.g., Co, Cu, or Mn naphthenate, linoleate, or resinate.

Catalysts, Accelerators, Promoters (Continued)

	Patent Number	Patentee	Assignee
285.	U.S. 2,647,878	M. M. Lee	
286.	U.S. 2,661,363	F. H. Dickey	Shell Development Co.
287.	Brit. 456,934		Standard Oil Development Co.
288.	Brit. 560,663	H. S. Rothrock	E. I. du Pont de Nemours & Co., Inc.
289.	Brit. 582,719		E. I. du Pont de Nemours & Co., Inc.
290.	Brit. 582,890		Imperial Chemical Industries, Ltd.
291.	Brit. 586,796		Imperial Chemical Industries, Ltd. and E. I. du Pont de Nemours & Co., Inc.
292.	Brit. 589,861		Standard Oil Development Co.
293.	Brit. 591,543	F. F. Rust, F. H. Dickey, and E. R. Bell	Shell Development Co.
294.	Brit. 595,061		Pittsburgh Plate Glass Co.
295.	Brit. 596,190	R. R. Harris	American Cyanamid Co.
296.	Brit. 596,779		Pittsburgh Plate Glass Co.
297.	Brit. 598,777	D. Brundit and J. A. D. Hickson	Imperial Chemical Industries, Ltd.
298.	Brit. 598,871		U.S. Rubber Co.
299.	Brit. 599,472	M. C. Ashworth, R. C. R. Bacon, and L. B. Morgan	Imperial Chemical Industries, Ltd.
300.	Brit. 603,324		U.S. Rubber Co.
301.	Brit. 603,325		U.S. Rubber Co.
302.	Brit. 603,546		U.S. Rubber Co.
303.	Brit. 604,544	E. C. Shokal, L. N. Whithill, and C. W. Schroeder	Shell Development Co.

Concerning

Heterocyclic amines, *e.g.*, 1-(2-hydroxyethyl)1,2,3,4-tetrahydroquinoline, alone or with peroxides as polymerization catalysts and accelerators.

Vinyl polymerization catalysts: peresters of nonaromatic peroxy-carboxylic acids and aromatic substituted aliphatic alcohols. Low-temperature reactive; do not cause discoloration.

Polyesters prepared by autocondensation of monocarboxylic acids having alcohol groups in the presence of a carboxylic acid having a dissociation constant greater than 3×10^{-5}.

Polymerization of an ester of an unsaturated monohydric alcohol in the presence of a metallic drier, *e.g.*, lead naphthenate.

N-chlorinated hydantoins, *e.g.*, 1,3-dichloro-5,5-dimethylhydantoin, as catalysts for polymerization of acrylic acid and its derivatives.

Dialkyl peroxides (ROOR) as catalysts (0.0001-5.0%) for ethylenic compounds.

Catalyst for polymerization of ethylenic compounds; 0.01-5% of an oxygen-yielding substance and 0.001-5% of a water-soluble compound containing the : S : O group, *e.g.*, para-toluenesulfonic acid.

Phenylated lower aliphatic hydrocarbons as free-radical-forming catalysts for polymerization of unsaturates, *e.g.*, unsaturated esters.

Preparation of ditertiary-alkyl peroxides (useful as polymerization catalysts) by treating tertiary-alkyl hydroperoxides with aliphatic tertiary alcohols.

Catalyst for preparation of mixed unsaturated esters from partial esters of unsaturated alcohols and polycarboxylic acids and ethylene: mercury compound, boron trifluoride, and hydrofluoric acid.

Multivalent metal compounds capable of oxidation to higher state, *e.g.*, $SnCl_2$ or ferrous salt of diethylene glycol monomaleate, as promoters for peroxide-catalyzed copolymerization of styrene and unsaturated alkyd resins.

Peroxycarbonate esters, *e.g.*, ethyl peroxydicarbonate. Useful as catalysts for polymerization of ethylenic compounds.

Polymerization catalyst for unsaturated compounds, *e.g.*, olefins, carboxylic acids, esters: peroxy compound plus water-soluble copper salt (0.01-2.0 p.p.m. Cu.).

Promoters for addition polymerization: aliphatic polyamines such as propylene diamine, tetraethylene pentamine, etc.

Polymerization catalyst for ethylenic substances: water-soluble persulfate, water-soluble salt of an oxy acid of sulfur, and a water-soluble metal salt (0.1-1.0%), *e.g.*, $CuSO_4$.

Dialkyl aryl amines, *e.g.*, diethyl aniline, as promoters for addition polymerization.

Methylene dialkyl aryl amines, *e.g.*, $(CH_3)_2NC_6H_4CH_2C_6H_4N(CH_3)_2$, as promoters for addition polymerization.

Monoalkyl aryl amines, *e.g.*, monoethyl aniline, as promoters for addition polymerization.

Polymerization of unsaturated compounds by heating in presence of 2 or more organic peroxide catalysts which have their maximum catalytic efficiencies at different temperatures.

Catalysts, Accelerators, Promoters (Continued)

	Patent Number	Patentee	Assignee
304.	Brit. 604,580		E. I. du Pont de Nemours & Co., Inc.
305.	Brit. 618,168	I. Marshall, I. Harris, and K. B. Garrett	Imperial Chemical Industries, Ltd.
306.	Brit. 658,522	D. Harman	N. V. de Bataafsche Petroleum Maatschappij
307.	Brit. 658,741		British Thomson Houston, Ltd.
308.	Brit. 688,937		N. V. de Bataafsche Petroleum Maatschappij
309.	Can. 441,872	W. R. Hoover, R. M. Paulsen, and S. V. Landgraf	Dominion Rubber Co., Ltd.
310.	Can. 443,297	D. A. Swedlow	Shellmar Products Corp.
311.	Dutch 66,834		N. V. de Bataafsche Petroleum Maatschappij
312.	Dutch 67,013		N. V. de Bataafsche Petroleum Maatschappij
313.	Fr. 854,115		Société anon. des manufactures des glaces et produits chimiques de Saint-Gobain, Chauny & Cirey.
314.	Swiss 255,978		De Trey freres S. A.

Inhibitors and Stabilizers

	Patent Number	Patentee	Assignee
315.	U.S. 2,075,251	H. A. Winkelmann	Marbon Corp.
316.	U.S. 2,255,313	C. Ellis	Ellis-Foster Co.
317.	U.S. 2,307,157	W. M. Quattlebaum, Jr., and C. A. Noffsinger	Carbide amd Carbon Chemicals Co.
318.	U.S. 2,313,757	L. A. Matheson and R. F. Boyer	Dow Chemical Co.
319.	U.S. 2,373,464	H. R. Dittmar	E. I. du Pont de Nemours & Co., Inc.
320.	U.S. 2,381,771	P. I. Paul	U.S. Rubber Co.
321.	U.S. 2,393,899	E. W. Cook and W. D. Thomas, Jr.	American Cyanamid Co.

Concerning

Organic polyperoxide catalysts for polymerization of ethylenic compounds, prepared by reaction of hydrogen peroxide with a ketone, aldehyde, or mixtures of the two.

Esters of hyponitrous acid ($H_2N_2O_2$) as catalysts for polymerization of ethylenic compounds, e.g., methyl, ethyl, propyl, butyl, oleyl, etc.

Polar-substituted tertiary-alkyl peroxides from olefinic compounds containing an activated double bond, e.g., methyl acrylate, and a tertiary organic hydroperoxide.

Phenyl phosphinic acid as a promoter for addition polymerization.

Preparation of tertiary-alkyl peroxides by reaction of a peroxy acid with a tertiary alkylating agent, e.g., a tertiary alcohol, a tertiary-alkyl ester of a mineral acid. Compounds are useful as polymerization catalysts.

Phenyl hydrazine as promoter for peroxide catalyst in polymerization of mixture of ethylenic monomer and resinous ester of an unsaturated organic acid with a polyhydric alcohol.

Use of light-sensitive catalysts (peroxides, amines) and irradiation with light before heat treatment to prevent resin from collecting in pockets during heat treatment of glass fabric-plastic laminates.

Bis(tertiary-alkyl) peroxides, e.g., bis(tertiary-butyl) peroxide. Useful as catalysts for polymerization of unsaturated compounds.

Catalyst system of at least 2 peroxides having catalytic effectiveness over different temperature ranges, preferably 25 °C. apart; e.g., mixtures of benzoyl peroxide with tertiary-butyl peroxide or hydroperoxide.

Preparation of a polymerization catalyst consisting of a peroxide in an anhydrous medium. Process applicable to polymerization of styrene.

Sulfinic acids ($R.SO_2H$) as catalysts for polymerization of vinyl and acrylic esters and styrene and its derivatives, e.g., ortho- and para-toluenesulfinic acids.

Good list of stabilizers for rubber.

Basic patent. Resins produced by copolymerization of unsaturated acid-glycol polyester with a liquid monomeric unsaturated polymerizable compound, e.g., vinyl acetate. Fillers used as inhibitors.

Heat stabilization of vinyl resins by adding an olefinic carboxylic acid salt, e.g., dibutyl tin fumarate.

Allyl esters of dicarboxylic acids, e.g., diallyl sebacate or maleate, as stabilizers for polymeric vinylidene products.

Atmospheric and pure oxygen as polymerization inhibitors for methacrylic acid and its derivatives.

Para-substituted-arylamino-2,2,4-trialkyl-1,2-dihydroquinolines as antioxidants, e.g., for synthetic resins.

N,N'-dicycloalkyl para-phenylenediamines, useful as antioxidants and stabilizers for synthetic resins.

Inhibitors and Stabilizers (Continued)

	Patent Number	Patentee	Assignee
322.	U.S. 2,433,616	K. E. Marple, and E. C. Shokal	Shell Development Co.
323.	U.S. 2,437,046	D. A. Rothrock, Jr., and R. F. Coyne	Resinous Products & Chemical Co.
324.	U.S. 2,437,232	D. A. Rothrock, Jr., and R. F. Coyne	Resinous Products & Chemical Co.
325.	U.S. 2,445,189	E. C. Shokal	Shell Development Co.
326.	U.S. 2,493,343	H. L. Gerhart	Pittsburgh Plate Glass Co.
327.	U.S. 2,516,309	G. L. Fraser	Monsanto Chemical Co.
328.	U.S. 2,532,475	T. F. Anderson	Libbey-Owens-Ford Glass Co.
329.	U.S. 2,559,837– 2,559,838	T. F. Anderson	Libbey-Owens-Ford Glass Co.
330.	U.S. 2,566,739	S. A. Moore and P. Kass	Interchemical Corp.
331.	U.S. 2,570,269	E. E. Parker	Pittsburgh Plate Glass Co.
332.	U.S. 2,577,414	G. L. Fraser and H. F. Park	Monsanto Chemical Co.
333.	U.S. 2,593,787	E. E. Parker	Pittsburgh Plate Glass Co.
334.	U.S. 2,606,161	P. E. Marling	Monsanto Chemical Co.
335.	U.S. 2,607,756	T. F. Anderson	Libbey-Owens-Ford Glass Co.
336.	U.S. 2,610,168	T. F. Anderson	Libbey-Owens-Ford Glass Co.
337.	U.S. 2,610,961	R. E. Burnett	General Electric Co.
338.	U.S. 2,612,488	J. F. Nelson	Standard Oil Development Co.
339.	U.S. 2,619,479	D. M. McQueen	E. I. du Pont de Nemours & Co., Inc.
340.	U.S. 2,623,025	W. C. Dearing and A. M. Howald	Libbey-Owens-Ford Glass Co.

Concerning

Stabilization of esters, e.g., diallyl phthalate, against discoloration during peroxide-catalyzed polymerization by polymerization in presence of an alkyl halide (0.5-1%), preferably methyl iodide. Hardness of product somewhat diminished.

Stabilizers. Flexible polyester for hot-melt applications. Conventional polyester is partly polymerized, then reacted with an alkyl phosphite or tricresyl phosphite.

Flexible polyester for hot melt applications. Conventional polyester is partly polymerized, then reacted with a phosphorous acid, tricresyl phosphite, or other polyfunctional ester formers.

Prevention of discoloration of polyesters produced by peroxide-catalyzed polymerization by conducting polymerization in presence of a hydrogen halide, e.g., bromide, chloride, iodide, fluoride.

Prevention of premature gelation of maleic anhydride-diethylene glycol-styrene polymerizable mixtures by gradual liberation of air bubbles or oxygen at bottom of container. Aeration is stopped just before polymerization.

Polyester casting resin. Inhibitor system composed of, e.g., tertiary-butyl catechol, cobalt or manganese naphthenate, and 1-hydroxycyclohexyl hydroperoxide-1 permits use for embedding biological specimens.

Stabilization of polyester-catalyst mixture with N-aryl-hydroxy-3-naphthamide on inert filler in contact with air. Resin does not gel until cured.

Stabilization of thermosetting polyester compositions with dihydroxy diphenyls, e.g., 4,4′-dihydroxy diphenyl or 4,4′-dihydroxy-3,3-dimethyl diphenyl, or thiophenols, e.g., thio-beta-naphthol.

Obtaining proper polymerization even in contact with copper by inclusion of a hydroxy polycarboxy acid, e.g., tartaric or malic acid.

Premature gelation retarded by phenylhydrazine hydrochloride or analogues.

Use of a solubilizer such as sodium sulfonate of dioctyl succinate and analogues to disperse or dissolve haze in resins and thus improve clarity.

Salts of quaternary ammonium hydroxides as gelation inhibitors: still permit rapid cure.

Incorporation of an aromatic monocarboxylic acid (35-81%) in a styrene-alkyd resin copolymer to improve solvent and heat resistance.

Stabilization of ethylene glycol-maleic anhydride polyesters with 1-(arylazo) naphtholsulfonic acids.

Polyester with catalyst added, yet nongelling for several weeks at room temperature; readily cured by heat. Stabilizer: thymoquinone monoxime or similar benzoquinone oximes or chlorimines.

Stabilizer for thixotropic compositions (polyesters with quinone) consisting of an alkyl resin containing tertiary-butyl catechol, a polymerization catalyst, and a filler.

Aryl polyphosphites as stabilizers of synthetic rubber and lubricating oils.

Stabilizers for polymers, e.g., nitroxides, hydrazyls, and phenazyls.

Methods for dispersing air throughout a resin to make it nongelling until heated, even after compounding with catalyst.

Inhibitors and Stabilizers (Continued)

	Patent Number	Patentee	Assignee
341.	U.S. 2,623,029	W. C. Dearing and A. M. Howald	Libbey-Owens-Ford Glass Co.
342.	U.S. 2,623,030	D. E. Cordier	Libbey-Owens-Ford Glass Co.
343.	U.S. 2,626,943	L Skeist and S. B. McFarlane	Celanese Corp. of America
344.	U.S. 2,632,751	T. F. Anderson	Libbey-Owens-Ford Glass Co.
345.	U.S. 2,632,753	T. F. Anderson	Libbey-Owens-Ford Glass Co.
346.	U.S. 2,635,089	T. F. Anderson	Libbey-Owens-Ford Glass Co.
347.	U.S. 2,643,985	E. E. Parker	Pittsburgh Plate Glass Co.
348.	U.S. 2,646,416	E. E. Parker	Pittsburgh Plate Glass Co.
349.	U.S. 2,664,413	E. E. Parker	Pittsburgh Plate Glass Co.
350.	U.S. 2,676,947	E. E. Parker	Pittsburgh Plate Glass Co.
351.	U.S. 2,679,493	T. F. Anderson	Allied Chemical & Dye Corp.
352.	Brit. 510,899		Resinous Products & Chemical Co.
353.	Brit. 540,167		American Cyanamid Co.
354.	Brit. 571,496		British Thomson Houston, Ltd.
355.	Brit. 575,649		Wingfoot Corp.
356.	Brit. 585,215		Wingfoot Corp.
357.	Brit. 588,833–588,834		Resinous Products & Chemical Co.
358.	Brit. 630,158		Bakelite Corp.

Polyester with catalyst added, yet nongelling until heated. Peroxide dispersed in solid form; air also dispersed throughout resin.

Use of zinc or cadmium peroxide to improve polyester resistance to temperature and humidity, particularly retention of insulation resistance.

Stabilization of polymerized methylvinyl ketone by neutralizing persulfate catalyst with sodium bicarbonate.

Stabilization of thermosetting polyester compositions with nuclearly substituted phenols, e.g., guaiacol, cresol, monobenzyl ether of hydroquinone, para-hydroxybiphenyl, 2-chloro-5-hydroxytoluene, etc. Polymerization is retarded at atmosphere temperatures.

Stabilization of compositions containing an unsaturated polyester and an organic peroxide or ozonide catalyst with para-benzoquinone. Curability is not decreased.

Hydroxybenzoic acid as stabilizer for polyester compositions containing a polymerization catalyst.

4-Phenethyl catechol as stabilizer for propylene maleate phthalate-styrene polyester.

Salts of amines (0.01–2.0%) as gelation inhibitors for polyesters dissolved in a vinylic monomer. Do not inhibit gelation when peroxides are added, even at room temperature.

Prevention of premature polymerization of polyester-styrene mixture by adding oxalic acid and a vinyl polymerization inhibitor.

3-Isopropyl catechol as gelation inhibitor for polyesters.

Stabilization of granular polyester-filler compositions with phenol, a halophenol, or an aminophenol.

Fatty acid modified alkyd resins prepared by process similar to Brit. 588,833–4 (in this section) using organic phosphorus-containing esters to prevent cross-linking.

Inhibitors for polymerization of polyhydric alcohol polyesters of unsaturated polycarboxylic acids with ethylenic substances, e.g., phenols, aromatic amines, tannin, benzaldehyde, etc.

Polymerization of diallyl phthalate in presence of benzoyl peroxide and a bright blue copper complex formed by initially heating diallyl phthalate with peroxide in the presence of bright copper turnings. Any desired viscosity can be produced without gelation occurring.

Stabilization of vinyl halide resin films against discoloration with 2-10% of antimony potassium tartrate.

Prevention of thermal discoloration of vinyl chloride-dialkyl fumarate copolymers by using alkali metal sulfides as stabilizers.

Linear polyesters of high molecular weight and stability from condensation of dihydric alcohols, e.g., alkylene glycols, with dicarboxylic acids, e.g., phthalic, in the presence of a trivalent phosphorus compound, e.g., H_3PO_4 and esters. Phosphorus compounds prevent cross-linking.

Complexes of a drier metal (Zn, Cd, Pb, Co, Mn, V, Ni) prepared in form of clear liquids from the metal, a phenol, and a nitrogen compound (e.g., an amine). Can be incorporated into polyesters for insulating coatings for copper wire.

Inhibitors and Stabilizers (Continued)

	Patent Number	Patentee	Assignee
359.	Brit. 677,203		Union Carbide & Carbon Corp.
360.	Ger. 706,509	G. F. D'Alelio	Allgemeine Elektricitats-Gesellschaft.

Concerning

Improvement over Brit. 630,158 (also in this section). Halogenated phenols and additional nitrogen compounds, e.g., imino or ammonia (NH_3 or NH_4OH) compounds, may be used.

Ascorbic and isoascorbic acids as polymerization retarders for vinyl compounds and derivatives.

Reinforcing Fillers

	Patent Number	Patentee	Assignee
361.	U.S. 2,196,033	H. Schuhmann	General Electric Co.
362.	U.S. 2,343,180	O. Hehn	Hehn-Hitner Developing Corp.
363.	U.S. 2,356,161	R. K. Iler	E. I. du Pont de Nemours & Co., Inc.
364.	U.S. 2,403,872	K. J. Miller	Owens-Corning Fiberglas Corp.
365.	U.S. 2,428,654	H. W. Collins	Owens-Corning Fiberglas Corp.
366.	U.S. 2,437,799	N. R. Yorke	St. Regis Paper Co.
367.	U.S. 2,446,119	E. White, R. Steinman, and L. P. Biefeld	Owens-Corning Fiberglas Corp.
368.	U.S. 2,456,228	W. I. Weaver	Libbey-Owens-Ford Glass Co.
369.	U.S. 2,477,407	J. A. Grant and D. E. Babcock	Owens-Corning Fiberglas Corp.
370.	U.S. 2,482,142	G. H. Chidester *et al.*	United States of America
371.	U.S. 2,500,092	L. Parker and B. J. Zach	H. L Thompson Co.
372.	U.S. 2,513,268	R. Steinman	Owens-Corning Fiberglas Corp.
373.	U.S. 2,534,617	H. W. Mohrman	Monsanto Chemical Co.
374.	U.S. 2,544,666, 2,544,667, 2,544,668	M. T. Goebel and R. K. Iler	E. I. du Pont de Nemours & Co., Inc.
375.	U.S. 2,552,910	R. Steinman	Owens-Corning Fiberglas Corp.
376.	U.S. 2,563,288	R. Steinman	Owens-Corning Fiberglas Corp.
377.	U.S. 2,563,289	R. Steinman	Owens-Corning Fiberglas Corp.
378.	U.S. 2,577,214	G. Slayter	Owens-Corning Fiberglas Co.
379.	U.S. 2,577,936	J. H. Waggoner	Owens-Corning Fiberglas Corp.

IV. FILLERS AND REINFORCEMENTS

Concerning

Synthetic resin molding composition with filaments of glass dispersed throughout to increase the strength of the resin.

Coating for improving strength of fabrics, e.g., woven glass, containing amyl acetate, recinus oil, sodium nitrate, paraffin, nitroglycerine, boric acid, and ether.

Complex chromium compounds of Werner type for waterproofing or other purposes, e.g., lubricants for glass fibers in glass cloth.

Improvement of strength of plastic laminates by applying a resorcinol-formaldehyde resin to the glass fibers, drying the fiber, and then impregnating them with thermosetting resin.

Reinforced plastic laminate of glass fabric bonded with a resin containing short, fine glass fibers.

Craze-resistant coating for paper or cotton sheets, asbestos, or glass cloth: a thermosetting resin, e.g., phenolic, melamine, urea, or alkyl, dissolved in a suitable solvent, and thin glass fibers.

Process for increasing the adhesion between glass fibers and resin binders in reinforced plastics by coating the fibers with dextrinized starch and heating to fix the starch to the fibers.

Dispersing a solid polymerization catalyst in a thermosetting sirup by impregnating inert fibers, e.g., alpha-cellulose, with the catalyst and stirring the fibers into the resin.

Improvement of adhesion of phenolic and cresylic resins to glass fiber fabric by (1) treating the fabric with a binding agent, e.g., gelatin, (2) dehydrating the fibers, e.g., with aluminum chloride solution, and (3) roughening the surface, e.g., with hydrofluoric acid.

Structural material of compressed resin-impregnated paper sheets. Thermosetting resins used.

Process for leaching batted, resin-bonded glass fibers to remove oxides, except SiO_2, and heating to remove resin.

Improvement of bondability of unsaturated polyesters to glass fibers by adding methallyl silicate to the polyester.

Laminated unidirectional glass fabric having specified polyester type of binder.

Werner complexes.

Werner complexes as finish to promote adhesion between glass fibers and resins.

Organosilicon sizes for glass fibers in reinforced plastics, e.g., ethoxysilanes (allyl, methallyl), allyl trichlorosilane.

Coating glass fibers with an amino polymer and a resin with free amino groups that can be converted into an onium compound or an ionizable salt.

Glass mat for reinforcing plastics in which the twisted glass fiber strands are in the form of loops held together by a binder.

Coloring of glass fibers by contact with vapors of a decomposible salt of a polyvalent metal, e.g., chlorides, bromides, iodides of Sb, As, Ba, Be, Bi, Cu, Pb, Hg, Sn, Ti, and Zn. Colored fibers are treated with a polysiloxane.

297

Reinforcing Fillers (Continued)

	Patent Number	Patentee	Assignee
380.	U.S. 2,604,688	G. Slayter	Owens-Corning Fiberglas Corp.
381.	U.S. 2,608,499	C. J. Straka	Westinghouse Electric Corp.
381a.	U.S. 2,610,957	R. Steinman and H. C. Courtright	Owens-Corning Fiberglas Corp.
382.	U.S. 2,611,718	R. Steinman	Owens-Corning Fiberglas Corp.
383.	U.S. 2,613,397	G. W. Borkland	Owens-Corning Fiberglas Corp.
384.	U.S. 2,619,475	L. A. Kovreg	Owens-Corning Fiberglas Corp.
385.	U.S. 2,625,499	R. J. Nebesar	Universal Moulded Products Corp.
386.	U.S. 2,632,744	A. M. Howald	Libbey-Owens-Ford Glass Co.
387.	U.S. 2,637,673	R. H. Barnard	Reconstruction Finance Corp.
388.	U.S. 2,640,797	C. G. Evans and P. H. H. Bishop	British Minister of Supply
389.	U.S. 2,645,553	C. L. Lawsberg	General Aniline & Film Corp.
390.	U.S. 2,649,396	R. K. Witt, W. G. Carson, and B. L. Raskin	
391.	U.S. 2,663,903	C. J. Stalego	Owens-Corning Fiberglas Corp.
392.	U.S. 2,663,906	D. Labino	Glass Fibers, Inc.
393.	U.S. 2,665,261	T. C. Baker	Allied Chemical and Dye Corp.
394.	U.S. 2,666,720	E. H. Balz	Glass Fibers, Inc.
395.	U.S. 2,667,430	J. R. Wells	U.S. Rubber Co.
396.	U.S. 2,667,465	R. J. Nebesar	Universal Moulded Products Corp.
397.	U.S. 2,668,789	E. H. Phreaner	⅓ to H. C. White
398.	U.S. 2,671,033	J. H. Waggoner	Owens-Corning Fiberglas Corp.

Concerning

Vapor-permeable, water-repellent glass fabrics treated with organo-silicon compounds, e.g., octadecyl trichlorosilane or diphenyl polysiloxane.

Glass fabric laminates with phenylmethyl siloxane binder.

Glass fibers bonded with an acid salt of aluminum, phosphoric acid, an inorganic base, and an organic resinous binder.

Complexes of trivalent chromium with unsaturated acids of 3–7 C atoms, e.g., methacrylate chromic chloride, as finish to promote adhesion of plastic binder to glass fiber.

Molding compositions containing low-pressure thermosetting resinous binder.

Binder for glass fibers containing furfuryl alcohol and starch carbamate.

Treating glass fibers for reinforcing with polyethylene or polymonochlorotrifluoroethylene.

Resin compositions prepared from an unsaturated polyester and a cellulose filler impregnated with a formaldehyde-urea type of product. Have greater strength and water resistance than compositions prepared from nonimpregnated cellulose.

Nonwoven film-coated fabric from staple glass fibers.

Method of making asbestos reinforced synthetic resin material.

Coloring woven glass fibers by treatment with sodium hydroxide, crude lignosulfonic acid, and specific coloring agents.

Bonded structure of glass fabric, fibers, mat, or sheet bonded to plastics (including polyester resins) or other materials with a silane bonding agent, e.g., monovinyltriethoxysilane, monoallyltrimethoxysilane, triallylmonoethoxysilane.

Apparatus for producing glass fibers.

Method for producing extremely fine staple glass fibers which can be used for producing extremely fine mats of uniform distribution.

Molding composition containing filler of cellulose fibers coated with octadecyl oxymethyl pyridinium chloride; has improved impact resistance.

Removal of starch lubricant from the binder on glass cloth by treatment with an aqueous solution of urea and a wetting and detergent agent.

Very transparent resin-impregnated glass fabric obtained by coating the fabric with (1) a urea-formaldehyde-butyl alcohol condensation product and (2) a polyester-styrene mixture.

Molding composition: polyester; ingredient selected from vinyl acetate, vinyl chloride, and amyl acrylate; asbestos fibers. Asbestos fibers prevent weak, resin-rich spots.

Rubber-polyester laminates made by using either a rubber that contains oxidizing material or an intermediate layer of oxidizing rubber.

Treatment of glass fibers with salt of Sb, Zn, Sn, Pb, Ti, or Ba at high temperature to form white reaction product on fiber surfaces which improves anchorage of coloring agents.

Reinforcing Fillers (Continued)

	Patent Number	Patentee	Assignee
399.	U.S. 2,671,744	L. P. Biefeld and J. P. Stalego	Owens-Corning Fiberglas Corp.
400.	U.S. 2,671,745	G. Slayter	Owens-Corning Fiberglas Corp.
401.	U.S. 2,674,548–2,674,549	E. H. Balz	Glass Fibers, Inc.
402.	U.S. 2,676,128	J. A. Piccard	E. I. du Pont de Nemours & Co., Inc.
403.	Brit. 481,126	S. A. Pollock	
404.	Brit. 481,286	A. L. Forster	Chance Brothers & Co. Ltd.
405.	Brit. 481,690		N. V. Maatschappij tot Beheer en Exploitatie Van Octrooien.
406.	Brit. 482,085		N. V. Maatschappij tot Beheer en Exploitatie Van Octrooien.
407.	Brit. 482,090		N. V. Maatschappij tot Beheer en Exploitatie Van Octrooien.
408.	Brit. 497,175	W. W. Triggs	Ellis-Foster Co.
409.	Fr. 977, 079	H. George	
410.	Ger. 816,215	R. G. Terreil	Algemeene Kunstvezel Maatschappij N. V.
411.	Ger. 822,004	W. Schuller	
412.	Japan. 2434('51)	D. Suge, *et al.*	Furukawa Electro Industries Co.
413.	Russ. 78,248	N. S. Teitel	

Bulk Fillers

	Patent Number	Patentee	Assignee
414.	U.S. 2,448,572	B. S. Biggs	Bell Telephone Laboratories, Inc.
415.	U.S. 2,505,353	C. F. Fisk	U.S. Rubber Co.
416.	U.S. 2,549,732	W. I. Weaver	Libbey-Owens-Ford Glass Co.
417.	U.S. 2,577,618	D. W. Jayne, Jr., and H. M. Day	American Cyanamid Co.
418.	U.S. 2,610,958	B. W. Nordlander and J. A. Loritsch	General Electric Co.

Concerning

Sizing of glass fibers with a composition consisting of a polyamide formed by reaction between dimerized and trimerized fatty acids and diamines and nitrocellulose.

Process for making looped glass fiber mats which give high impact and flexural
strength when used for reinforcing resins.

Removal of oil and starch binder from glass cloth by impregnating with an alkali
or alkaline earth metal chlorate and then heating to burn off the binder.

Preparation of nonwoven fabrics by matting staple nylon fabrics, mixing with a
dry linear copolyester of ethylene glycol sebacate and ethylene glycol terephthalate, and heating under pressure to make the copolyester adhesive.

Drawing and stranding of glass fibers.

Apparatus for making glass threads and forming them into mats.

Manufacture of glass fibers from molten glass.

Drawing of glass fibers from molten glass.

Drawing of glass fibers from molten glass.

Material for laminating by heat and pressure consisting of paper or canvas impregnated with a copolymer of a polyester, e.g., diethylene glycol maleate,
and an alpha-substituted ethylenic compound, e.g., styrene, a methacrylic
ester, a vinyl ketone.

Preparation of surface of glass fibers for dyeing by heating with steam under
pressure.

Apparatus for manufacture of mats of glass fibers.

Process and apparatus for the manufacture of glass fibers.

Improvement of adhesion of glass to glass, metals, porcelains, or plastics by
coating with organic silicon compound, followed by adhesive.

Apparatus for drawing thin glass fibers.

Addition of insoluble alkaline carbonate, preferably calcium carbonate, to increase elastic life of cured polyester synthetic rubber compounds.

Microporous resin sheets from maleic anhydride-diethylene glycol polyester,
styrene, and sodium silicate or hydrous silica gel. Useful as battery separators.

Fibers of crystalline anhydrous silicates of divalent metals as fillers in polyester resins; ratio 100 : 1 to 1 : 6. List of such silicates.

Use of calcium silicate as filler to increase resilience and tensile strength of
rubberlike polyester.

Addition of a moisture-containing oxide of Fe, Cr, Zn, or Ti to a polyester resin
to make the resin thixotropic and thus prevent flowing after application.

Bulk Fillers (Continued)

	Patent Number	Patentee	Assignee
419.	U.S. 2,610,959– 2,610,960	B. W. Nordlander	General Electric Co.
420.	U.S. 2,624,714	M. H. Bigelow	Libbey-Owens-Ford Glass Co.
421.	U.S. 2,624,720– 2,624,721	D. B. Hatcher and R. H. Bunnell	Libbey-Owens-Ford Glass Co.
422.	U.S. 2,624,722	E. L. Kropa and A. S. Nyquist	American Cyanamid Co.
423.	U.S. 2,628,209	C. F. Fisk	U.S. Rubber Co.
424.	U.S. 2,632,752	T. F. Anderson	Libbey-Owens-Ford Glass Co.
425.	U.S. 2,641,586– 2,641,587	B. W. Nordlander, J. A. Loritsch, and R. E. Burnett	General Electric Co.
426.	U.S. 2,642,409	D. E. Cordier	Libbey-Owens-Ford Glass Co.
427.	U.S. 2,645,626	B. W. Nordlander and R. E. Burnett	General Electric Co.
428.	U.S. 2,665,263	A. M. Howald	Allied Chemical & Dye Corp.
429.	Brit. 587,160		Westinghouse Electric International Co.
430.	Ger. 737,520	O. Groening	O. Groening and O. Weigel
		Special Fillers	
431.	U.S. 2,433,992	M. E. Hughes	Shell Development Co.
432.	U.S. 2,579,375	J. B. Eisen	Monsanto Chemical Co.
433.	U.S. 2,643,983	C. Dangelmajer	Eimsig Manufacturing Co.
434.	Brit. 582,899– 582,900	J. W. Coates and J. W. C. Crawford	Imperial Chemical Industries, Ltd.

Concerning

Thixotropic unsaturated alkyd resin compositions containing a filler of silica aerogel or vermiculite. Do not flow after application.

Use of graphite as filler in polyester-glass fiber plastic to impart high abrasion resistance, probably by reduction of friction.

Silicon-containing alkyd resins with good moisture and weather resistance.

Silicon-containing alkyd resins.

Increasing the viscosity and hardness of a vinyl alkyd copolymer, as well as its resistance to solvents and heat distortion, by incorporation of 1–15% of finely powdered magnesium oxide. No sacrifice in clarity; run-off during curing prevented.

Production of polymers with improved water resistance and electrical properties from composition containing a polymerizable unsaturated polyester and dehydrated kaolin.

Thixotropic polyester compositions containing a filler selected from Georgia kaolin, catalpo clay, bucca clay, Kentucky ball clay, and bentonite.

Coating of kaolin filler for polyester molding compounds with a thin film of melamine-formaldehyde resin. Improves electrical insulation property and lowers water absorption of molded products.

Thixotropic coating comprising a liquid unsaturated alkyd resin, a polymerizable ester of methacrylic acid, and a filler selected from Fe_2O_3, Cr_2O_3, ZnO, TiO_2, Ni_2O_3, and SiO_2.

Addition of an oxide of Mg, Ca, Sr, Zn, Cd, or Hg to a polyester-filler molding composition to reduce stickiness, impart stiffness, and reduce corrosive effect on molds. Also improves water resistance and electrical properties of molded product.

Mica impregnated with the resinous reaction product of pentaerythritol, maleic acid, and phthalic acid for electrical insulation purposes.

Xylite, a natural wood product, as a filler for plastics and synthetic resins.

Method for coloring plastics involving milling the pigment with a polyester oil and dissolving the pigment mix in the monomer or polymer to be polymerized.

Nonelectrostatic plastics prepared by incorporating in the molding powder a lipophilic quaternary ammonium salt, e.g., didodecyl dipropyl ammonium bromide.

Plastic articles with a sheen, suitable for buttons. Polyesters are prepolymerized until maximum viscosity obtainable without gelation is achieved; pearl essence is added; and the polyester is combined with styrene and cast.

Colored synthetic resins obtained by polymerizing solutions of chelated compounds of Cr, Mo, V, Mn, Fe, Co, Ni, and Cu and beta-ketones in compounds containing a $\diagdown C = C \diagdown$ group.

Molds and Other Shaping Equipment

	Patent Number	Patentee	Assignee
435.	U.S. 2,347,600	J. H. Goode	
436.	U.S. 2,362,672	E. C. Sloan	Rudolph Wurlitzer Co.
437.	U.S. 2,368,717	C. F. Marschner	McDonnel Aircraft Corp.
438.	U.S. 2,392,108	E. L. Vidal and W. A. Taylor	Vidal Corp.
439.	U.S. 2,618,310	R. W. Kerr and W. C. Koenig	
440.	U.S. 2,625,498	K. A. Koch	Owens-Corning Fiberglas Corp.
441.	U.S. 2,638,428	J. E. Gordon and C. G. Evans	British Minister of Supply
442.	U.S. 2,679,473	C. K. Swartz	Consolidated Molded Products Corp.
443.	Brit. 561,625	S. C. Smith	
444.	Brit. 597,214		International Polaroid Corp.
445.	Ger. 738,832	W. Schönherr	Dynamit A.-G. vorm. Alfred Nobel & Co.
446.	Ger. 742,682	G. Barchfeld	Dynamit A.-G. vorm. Alfred Nobel & Co.
447.	Ger. 816,859	W. Mehdorn	

Heating Methods and Equipment

448.	U.S. 2,385,143	A. C. Levine	
449.	Brit. 507,768		Bakelite Ltd.

Molding and Laminating Methods

450.	U.S. 1,195,949	M. R. Carney	
451.	U.S. 1,195,951	M. R. Harrison (nee Carney)	
452.	U.S. 2,222,470	R. B. Barnes	American Cyanamid Co.
453.	U.S. 2,323,191	C. E. Bennett	Okonite Co.
454.	U.S. 2,335,930	O. F. Freeland and J. J. Yopst	Anaconda Wire and Cable Co.
455.	U.S. 2,370,562	V. Meunier	Pittsburgh Plate Glass Co.

V. SHAPING

Molding and Laminating Methods (Continued)

	Patent Number	Patentee	Assignee
456.	U.S. 2,379,247–2,379,248	L. E. Muskat	Pittsburgh Plate Glass Co.
457.	U.S. 2,391,489	A. J. Stamm and H. D. Turner	United States of America
458.	U.S. 2,420,720	A. Pechukas and P. J. Gegner	Pittsburgh Plate Glass Co.
459.	U.S. 2,456,093	D. A. Swedlow	Shellmar Products Corp.
460.	U.S. 2,459,279	R. W. Holden	Laminating Specialties, Inc.
461.	U.S. 2,489,985	F. Y. Speight, Jr.	American Cyanamid Co.
462.	U.S. 2,495,640	L. E. Muskat	Marco Chemicals, Inc.
463.	U.S. 2,517,698	L. E. Muskat	Marco Chemicals, Inc.
464.	U.S. 2,545,832	J. K. Wagers and E. C. Shokal	
465.	U.S. 2,554,471	D. G. Patterson and W. F. Turner	American Cyanamid Co.
466.	U.S. 2,554,471	E. L. Kropa, L. E. Craig, and A. S. Nyquist	American Cyanamid Co.
467.	U.S. 2,579,949	F. L. Minnear	Continental Can Co., Inc.
468.	U.S. 2,596,162	L. E. Muskat	Marco Chemicals, Inc.
469.	U.S. 2,602,037	R. G. Nelb	U.S. Rubber Co.
470.	U.S. 2,602,959	J. M. Fenlin	
471.	U.S. 2,625,497	J. Cadgene	
472.	U.S. 2,628,144	F. R. Loetscher	Farley and Loetscher Manufacturing Co.
473.	U.S. 2,631,955	L. E. Muskat	Marco Chemicals, Inc.

Concerning

Preparation of shaped (curved) sheets by (1) polymerizing diallyl or dimethallyl esters of dicarboxylic acids in suitably shaped vessels, removing polymer from mold, heating mildly, shaping mechanically while still warm, and cooling, or (2) conducting final stages of polymerization in curved mold.

Method of molding laminated materials involving precompressing of resin-impregnated sheets before placing them in the mold.

Protection of polyester coating while curing with film of polyvinyl alcohol or other water-soluble resin.

Molding polyester-fibrous base laminates in closed, compressible cell.

Pregelling of polyester resins with infrared or ultraviolet light to eliminate resin squeeze-out and entrapping of air bubbles when resin-filler laminates are formed.

Impregnation of fibrous material with unsaturated alkyd resin and styrene. Cellophane covering used to reduce loss of styrene.

Method for molding fiber-reinforced resinous parts. Suitable resins include polyesters of unsaturated dibasic acids and polyhydric alcohols.

Preparation of fiber-reinforced resinous parts by impregnating fabric sheets with resin, e.g., polymer of dialkyl phthalate, and curing between glass sheets without substantial pressure.

Method for producing a laminate from sheets of water-absorptive cellulosic fibers and a polyester. Metal molds are used.

Method for applying polyester surface (including decorative paper or fibers) to wood.

Structural materials of low density and high strength with resinous interlayer prepared from alkyd resin foamed with a gas-liberating agent, e.g., diguanylurea salt of diazotized toluidine, ammonium bicarbonate or carbonate, potassium carbonate, etc.

Moisture- and heat-resistant laminated product with outer plies of paper sheets impregnated with a flexible thermosetting polyester contact-pressure resin and an inner ply of glass fiber cloth.

Fabricating method comprising partially polymerizing a polyester in continuous fibrous sheet between flexible air excluders (e.g., cellophane), shaping it when plastic, and curing.

Self-extinguishing laminates prepared by sandwiching polyester-impregnated glass cloth between single plies of glass fiber sheet impregnated with melamine-formaldehyde resin and curing by heat and pressure.

Mandrel-type apparatus for continuously producing reinforced plastic tubing from woven glass fiber and thermoplastic or thermosetting resins.

Process for fusing thermoplastic fabric sheets to each other.

Resin-metal laminate.

Production of shaped laminates by impregnating fabric sheets with a polymerizable liquid, e.g., diallyl phthalate containing 5% of benzoyl peroxide, and setting and compacting the sheet in layers by compression within flexible nonporous envelopes, e.g., cellophane.

Molding and Laminating Methods (Continued)

	Patent Number	Patentee	Assignee
474.	U.S. 2,639,213	R. M. Barth	Price Driscoll Corp.
475.	U.S. 2,639,248	R. L. Overholt	U.S. Plywood Corp.
476.	U.S. 2,642,370	G. B. Parsons and D. Depew	Fairchild Engine and Airplane Corp.
477.	U.S. 2,647,851	R. E. Schwartz	Vibradamp Corp.
478.	U.S. 2,653,887	G. Slayter	Owens-Corning Fiberglas Corp.
479.	U.S. 2,655,459	J. E. Gordon and C. R. Evans	British Minister of Supply
480.	U.S. 2,655,978	D. Gonda and A. A. Hodge	Holoplast Ltd.
481.	U.S. 2,666,685	M. C. Hommel and C. C. Currie	Dow Corning Corp.
482.	U.S. 2,674,557	H. D. Boggs	H. D. Boggs Co., Ltd.
483.	U.S. 2,676,729	H. Neville, Jr., and O. G. R. Ferguson	Laminex Corp.
484.	Brit. 561,625	S. C. Smith	
485.	Brit. 670,224	D. H. Powers	Monsanto Chemical Co.
486.	Dutch 70,585		N. V. Bataafsche Petroleum Maatschappij
487.	Fr. 810,665		Imperial Chemical Industries, Ltd.

Preforming

488.	U.S. 2,653,473	A. L. Simison	Owens-Corning Fiberglas Corp.

Casting

489.	U.S. 2,318,959	I. E. Muskat, M. A. Pollack, F. Strain, and W. A. Franta	Pittsburgh Plate Glass Co.
490.	U.S. 2,370,587	M. A. Pollack, I. E. Muskat, and F. Strain	Pittsburgh Plate Glass Co.
491.	U.S. 2,379,218	W. R. Dial and C. Gould	Pittsburgh Plate Glass Co.
492.	U.S. 2,392,578	A. G. Chenicek	Pittsburgh Plate Glass Co.

Concerning

Application of a mold release agent, e.g., silicone-base oil, by spraying a fine mist of a dispersion of the agent in liquefied gas, e.g., chlorodifluoroethylene.

Reinforced plastic radomes made by molding a sandwich arrangement of skins of moistureproofed glass fiber cloth and cellulosic netting with a styrene-polyester resin.

Preparation of polyethylene-glass fiber laminates suitable as protective coatings for aircraft or chemical tank liners. Polyesters can be used for bonding.

Production of resilient laminated glass fiber mat which will withstand relatively high load stresses without crumbling. Thermosetting resin is used as binder.

Production of fiber-reinforced plastic tubing.

Molding process for production of aerofoil structures and other aircraft parts having a core and a laminated skin of glass cloth and thermosetting resin.

Manufacture of corrugated plastic laminates.

Mold release emulsion consisting of organosiloxane fluids, finely divided silica, emulsifying agent, and water.

Continuous mandrel-wrapping process for manufacture of pipe from glass mat and thermosetting resin.

Process for molding reinforced plastic tanks and containers.

Shaping of laminated sheet material. Two-part mold used.

Laminating method in which laminae of cellulosic fabrics are treated with colloidal silica and bonded with a contact-pressure type of resin.

Improvement of adhesion of polymeric unsaturated esters, e.g., diallyl esters of phthalic acid, to metals by polymerization *in situ* in presence of unsaturated dicarboxylic acids, e.g., maleic acid.

Making of molded articles: mold and its contents are subjected to centrifugal force during polymerization of the molding materials.

Apparatus for testing suitability of resins for binding preforms and glass mat.

Artificial glass made by simultaneously polymerizing sheets of a polymer, e.g., of methallyl crotonate, to a hard, infusible state on the surface and to a lesser extent in the interior.

Prevention of bubble formation, cracking, warping, etc., in cast or pressure molding of plastics by partial polymerization of monomer to fusible, soluble monomer but not gel state, addition of unreacted monomer to prevent haze, and polymerization of mixture to final state.

Casting esters of vinyl, allyl, and other alcohols of 2–10 C atoms with polycarboxylic acids, e.g., oxalic, phthalic, at room temperature.

Reduction of internal strain in cast objects by polymerizing the resin in the mold only to the gel state, removing the part from the mold, and heating to final cure.

Casting (Continued)

	Patent Number	Patentee	Assignee
493.	U.S. 2,462,158	J. Boyd and R. A. Bice	Westinghouse Electric Corp.
494.	Brit. 460,240		E. I. du Pont de Nemours & Co., Inc.
495.	Brit. 572,670	H. P. Staudinger and H. M. Hutchinson	Distillers Co., Ltd.
496.	Brit. 595,058	A. G. Chenicek	Pittsburgh Plate Glass Co.
497.	Fr. 852,977	G. Schorsch	

Foamed Plastics and Honeycomb Structures

498.	U.S. Pat. Appl. 638,894	E. B. McMillan and D. F. Straubel	United States of America
499.	U.S. 2,371,707	E. T. Rainier and D. M. French	U.S. Rubber Co.
500.	U.S. 2,376,653	R. V. Boyer	General Electric Co.
501.	U.S. 2,461,761	L. E. Nye	U.S. Rubber Co.
502.	U.S. 2,461,942	W. T. L. Ten Broeck, Jr.	Wingfoot Corp.
503.	U.S. 2,498,621	E. L. Kropa, L. E. Craig, and A. S. Nyquist	American Cyanamid Co.
504.	U.S. 2,518,454	M. A. Elliott	
505.	U.S. 2,529,512	J. B. Ott	Monsanto Chemical Co.
506.	U.S. 2,532,240	J. B. Ott	Monsanto Chemical Co.
507.	U.S. 2,628,945	W. J. Wayne	E. I. du Pont de Nemours & Co., Inc.
508.	U.S. 2,629,698	R. F. Sterling	Westinghouse Electric Corp.
509.	U.S. 2,634,243	H. D. Glenn	U.S. Rubber Co.
510.	Can. 449,275	G. L. Dorough and H. J. Richter	Canadian Industries Inc.

Swelling-resistant bearing staves made by impregnating laminated fabric with heat-hardenable resin, swelling it with water, air drying, and machining to size.

Apparatus for casting materials that shrink during solidification, especially organic liquids.

Large castings produced by swelling a small cast object with a monomer and polymerizing the monomer. Suitable for optical glasses.

See U.S. 2,392,578 in this section.

Large castings produced by swelling a small cast object with a monomer and polymerizing the monomer. Suitable for optical glasses.

Laminated structures for enclosing antennas made from skins of material containing low-pressure thermosetting resin and a core of cellular hard rubber or other porous or foamed hard resins or plastics.

Nitrogen-generating chemicals, for use as blowing agents in making foamed plastics, made in form of thixotropic gels containing MgO and NH_4NO_2.

Lightweight rigid material made by foaming thermosetting resins, with or without fibrous filler, between laminated sheets or boards.

Foamed resin from copolymer of unsaturated alkyds and monomeric compounds, e.g., styrene and polyethylene glycol maleate.

Sponges prepared from copolymers of vinyl chloride and esters of unsaturated dicarboxylic acids, e.g., diethyl fumarate, and a blowing agent, e.g., a bicarbonate compounds.

Foamed resins produced by heating unsaturated alkyd resins, vinyl compounds, e.g., styrene, gas-liberating materials, e.g., NH_4HCO_3, and polymerization catalysts.

Coating for water-sealing a cable, consisting of a heat-polymerizable material, e.g., "Plastisol" XE-777, and a blowing agent, e.g., diazoaminobenzene, that emits a gas when heated and thus causes a foam that fills the spaces between elements in the cable.

Tough, soluble forms from typical saturated or unsaturated polyesters foamed with monoaryl azides.

Usual polyester compound foamed with diphenyl-4,4^1-di(sulfonylazide). Tough, soluble, fusible foam; can be cured to insoluble state.

Cyclic ethylene carbonate as a blowing agent for making cellular polyesters and other cellular polymers.

Cellular thermoset resins.

Mixture of urea and oxalic acid as blowing agent for preparation of expanded rubber and plastics, including alkyd resins.

Foamed plastic prepared from a copolymer of vinyl chloride and a dialkyl fumarate with a plasticizer, and a material that evolves gas at high temperatures, e.g., $(NH_4)_2CO_3$.

UNSATURATED POLYESTERS

Surface Treatments

Patent Number	Patentee	Assignee
511. U.S. 2,392,158	H. T. Lacey and W. E. Ness	American Cyanamid Co.
512. U.S. 2,400,720	H. P. Staudinger and H. M. Hutchinson	Distillers Co., Ltd.
513. U.S. 2,461,612	H. C. Olpin and A. J. Wesson	Celanese Corp. of America
514. U.S. 2,562,140	E. H. Dafter, Jr.	American Cyanamid Co.
515. U.S. 2,578,665	J. A. Bjorksten, S. O. Fiedler, and L. L. Yaeger	Nash-Kelvinator Corp.
516. U.S. 2,578,683	J. A. Bjorksten, S. O. Fiedler, and L. L. Yaeger	Nash-Kelvinator Corp.
517. U.S. 2,607,729	W. L. Dills	E. I. du Pont de Nemours & Co., Inc.
518. U.S. 2,617,269	R. Smith-Johannsen	General Electric Co.
519. U.S. 2,617,748	J. A. Bjorksten and L. L. Yaeger	Nash-Kelvinator Corp.
520. U.S. 2,624,725	J. A. Bjorksten and J. B. Eisen	Monsanto Chemical Co.
521. U.S. 2,628,176	S. A. Simon and A. H. Drelich	Chicopee Manufacturing Co.
522. U.S. 2,628,923	L. L. Yaeger	Nash-Kelvinator Corp.
523. U.S. 2,640,817	E. G. Sheridan, L. L. Yaeger, and J. A. Bjorksten	Nash-Kelvinator Corp.
524. Brit. 558,386		Sandoz Ltd.
525. Brit. 575,912	H. C. Olpin and A. J. Wesson	

VI. FINISHING

Oil-soluble dyes for coloring plastics. Dye condensed with ester formed from fatty acid, e.g., oleic, and the reaction product of a trialkylolamine and an alkylene oxide.

Treatment of plastic surfaces with SO_3, H_2SO_4, or HSO_3Cl to make them dye more readily or provide for better adhesion.

Method of dyeing resins, e.g., polymerized diallyl phthalate, with a water-insoluble dye dissolved in a polyhydric alcohol.

Surface-coating agents for articles requiring molding or pressing as final step: Polyester dissolved in solvent, catalyst added, polyester gelled, cooled, and inhibited at desired gel state. Dye or pigments may be added.

Coatings for polystyrene or styrene copolymers, prepared from acrylate or methacrylate resins or combinations of these resins with cellulose esters. Increase abrasion, scratch, and solvent resistance of plastics.

Cellulose esters which are aromatic polycarboxylic acid esters of partially esterified cellulose acetate or cellulose propionate and which contain at least 1 free carboxyl group, e.g., cellulose acetate hydrogen phthalate; used in the coatings of U.S. 2,578,665.

Flame-resisting composition for textiles from Sb_2O_3 and $TiCl_4$. Particularly effective on acrylonitrile polymers.

Coating of polymeric monochlorotrifluoroethylene for reducing the adhesion of certain surfaces, e.g., plastics, to ice.

Ultraviolet screening coating for polystyrene consisting of phenyl, methyl, or benzyl salicylate, a cellulose ester of an acrylic acid, and a cellulose ester containing acetyl groups. Eliminates yellowing or darkening of plastic on exposure to light.

Aliphatic amines with at least 6 C atoms in one radical, e.g., octadecyl dimethylamine, plus acid, e.g., phosphoric, as antistatic agents for resinous molding compounds.

Antistatic coatings for resins.

Polystyrene coated with a cellulose mixed ester.

Antistatic coating for plastics: polychlorobiphenyl, an acrylate polymer or copolymer, and an amine type of destaticizing agent.

Anthraquinone derivatives for coloring plastics.

Coloring of articles of infusible, insoluble synthetic resins with solution of dyes in polyhydric alcohols or their esters or ethers.

Resin Patents

	Patent Number	Patentee	Assignee
526.	U.S. 1,860,730	B. T. Brooks and E. J. Cardarelli	
527.	U.S. 1,897,260	R. H. Kienle and H. C. Rohlfs	General Electric Co.
528.	U.S. 1,897,977	C. Ellis	Ellis-Foster Co.
529.	U.S. 1,945,307	H. B. Dykstra	E. I. du Pont de Nemours & Co., Inc.
530.	U.S. 1,950,468	F. Zwilgmeyer	National Aniline & Chemical Co., Inc.
531.	U.S. 1,975,246	F. Zwilgmeyer	National Aniline & Chemical Co. Inc.
532.	U.S. 2,036,009	J. G. E. Wright	General Electric Co.
533.	U.S. 2,047,398	A. Voss and E. Dickhäuser	I. G. Farbenind. A.-G.
534.	U.S. 2,087,852	C. Ellis	Ellis-Foster Co.
535.	U.S. 2,155,639	T. F. Bradley	American Cyanamid Co.
536.	U.S. 2,166,542	T. F. Bradley	American Cyanamid Co.
537.	U.S. 2,187,817	H. Hopff, G. Steinbrunn, and H. Freudenberger	I. G. Farbenind. A.-G.
538.	U.S. 2,195,362	C. Ellis	Ellis-Foster Co.
539.	U.S. 2,202,846	B. S. Garvey and C. H. Alexander	B. F. Goodrich Co.
540.	U.S. 2,206,171	C. Ellis	Ellis-Foster Co.
541.	U.S. 2,208,321	T. F. Bradley	American Cyanamid Co.
542.	U.S. 2,213,201	E. C. Britton and G. H. Coleman	Dow Chemical Co.
543.	U.S. 2,218,439	H. S. Rothrock	E. I. du Pont de Nemours & Co., Inc.
544.	U.S. 2,220,855	H. R. Slagh	Dow Chemical Co.
545.	U.S. 2,211,662	H. S. Rothrock	E. I. du Pont de Nemours & Co., Inc.
546.	U.S. 2,221,663	H. S. Rothrock	E. I. du Pont de Nemours & Co., Inc.

VIII. TAILOR-MAKING POLYESTERS

Resins from condensation of Δ–4 cyclohexane 1,2-dicarboxylic acid with glycerol or a glycol.

Alkyd resins prepared in presence of glycol succinate to give flexibility.

Artificial resins from polyhydric alcohols and polybasic carboxylic acids or anhydrides, e.g., glycol and maleic acid.

Interpolymers of esters of dicarboxylic acids and vinyl compounds.

Alkyd resins from a polyhydric alcohol, an organic polycarboxylic acid, and a partially esterified polycarboxylic acid.

Products and process of polymerizing a polyhydric alcohol and polycarboxylic acid. Resulting intermediate is copolymerized with an unsaturated aliphatic acid, e.g., acrylic acid.

Synthetic resins prepared from polyesters and vinyl chloride. Zinc oxide used as catalyst.

Resins made by copolymerizing an alpha, beta-unsaturated acid derivative with styrene or other vinyl monomers.

Coating resin from reaction of substituted aromatic organic acids, e.g., chlorine-substituted phthalic acid, with glycerol.

Flexible product obtained by reacting a long-chain (at least 8 atoms) glycol, e.g., polyethylene glycol, with the reaction product of an unsaturated polycarboxylic acid, e.g., maleic anhydride, and a terpene or diene compound, e.g., d-limonene.

Truly water-soluble polyesters from alcohols having at least 3 ether linkages and no more than 3 hydroxyls, e.g., hexaethylene glycol.

Interpolymers of vinyl chloride and maleic acid esters of a saturated alcohol suitable for coating fabrics.

Maleic polyesters and analogues copolymerized with styrene and analogues and polymerization catalyst.

Copolymers of polyallyl esters and a compound containing the polymerizable group $=C=CH_2$, e.g., vinyl acetate.

Soluble resins from polyesters modified with drying oils, e.g., linseed oil.

Rubberlike polymers from esterification of a polyterpene (e.g., $C_{20}H_{32}$)-maleic anhydride reaction product with glycol.

Molding compound consisting of a copolymer of styrene and, as a plasticizing agent, a bis(halophenyl)alkane, e.g., 1,2-bis(4-chlorophenyl)ethane.

Resinous polymer of dimethallyl adipate.

Fumaric acid esters, e.g., diallyl fumarate. Useful in preparation of resins and as modifying agents for vinyl resins.

Polymerizable esters from dimethyl fumarate and propargyl alcohol.

Resinous polymer of dimethallyl maleate.

Resin Patents (Continued)

	Patent Number	Patentee	Assignee
547.	U.S. 2,224,035	J. H. Long	Hercules Powder Co.
548.	U.S. 2,230,240	H. L. Gerhart	United Gas Improvement Co.
549.	U.S. 2,235,447	T. F. Bradley and W. B. Johnston	American Cyanamid Co.
550.	U.S. 2,238,030	T. F. Bradley	American Cyanamid Co.
551.	U.S. 2,238,684– 2,238,685	C. Ellis	Ellis-Foster Co.
552.	U.S. 2,240,516	E. L. Kropa	American Cyanamid Co.
553.	U.S. 2,249,768	E. L. Kropa	American Cyanamid Co.
554.	U.S. 2,251,765	B. E. Sorenson	E. I. du Pont de Nemours & Co., Inc.
555.	U.S. 2,252,393	T. F. Bradley and W. B. Johnston	American Cyanamid Co.
556.	U.S. 2,253,681	T. F. Bradley and W. B. Johnston	American Cyanamid Co.
557.	U.S. 2,256,444	I. Rosenblum	
558.	U.S. 2,260,005	G. F. D'Alelio	General Electric Co.
559.	U.S. 2,275,494	H. Bennett	
560.	U.S. 2,275,951	E. H. Farmer	British Rubber Producers Research Assoc.
561.	U.S. 2,280,242	E. L. Kropa and T. F. Bradley	American Cyanamid Co.
562.	U.S. 2,280,256	D. G. Patterson	American Cyanamid Co.
563.	U.S. 2,281,394	B. E. Sorenson	E. I. du Pont de Nemours & Co.
564.	U.S. 2,282,002	T. R. Scott and M. C. Field	International Standard Electric Co.
565.	U.S. 2,282,088	M. A. Pollack	Pittsburgh Plate Glass Co.
566.	U.S. 2,288,315	G. F. D'Alelio	General Electric Co.
567.	U.S. 2,299,189	D. Swan	Eastman Kodak Co.
568.	U.S. 2,306,071	J. G. McNally and R. H. Van Dyke	Eastman Kodak Co.

Concerning

Adhesive for laminating, comprising mixture of 2 or more synthetic resins which are esterification products of glycols, *e.g.*, ethylene, diethylene, and triethylene glycols, with a terpene-maleic anhydride product.

Synthetic resins formed from components such as styrene and maleic anhydride.

Condensation products of fumaric acid, a nonconjugated terpene of the $C_{10}H_{16}$ series, and a glycol, *e.g.*, fumaric acid, alpha-pinene, and triethylene glycol. Method used prevents decomposition of fumaric acid at high temperatures.

Copolymers of vinyl acetate and diallyl fumarate; suitable for casting and coating.

Modified alkyd resins. ·"Recipe" given for maleic polyester.

Polyester-polyamide resins prepared from monoalkylolamines, *e.g.*, ethanolamine, and dibasic acids, *e.g.*, terephthalic acid, and modified with amino acids, hydroxy acids, or proteins to increase water resistance.

Allyl esters from allyl alcohols and polycarboxylic acids, *e.g.*, fumaric acid.

Polymerizable esters from an alkyl ester of an unsaturated dicarboxylic acid, *e.g.*, dimethyl maleate, and an olefinic monohydric alcohol, *e.g.*, methallyl alcohol.

Reaction products of terpene hydrocarbons, *e.g.*, dipentene, and a fumaric acid ester, *e.g.*, dibutyl fumarate.

Copolymers of polyesters with conjugated terpene.

Maleic anhydride-polyhydric alcohol-natural resin products.   Suitable for use in lacquers.

Interpolymers of allyl crotonate and unsaturated alkyd resins.

Esters of polymerized polyhydric alcohols, *e.g.*, ethylene glycol, with organic acids, *e.g.*, stearic.

Modified rubber derivatives or resins from reaction of maleic anhydride with rubber and styrene, vinyl acetate, etc.

Maleic anhydride-ethylene glycol-methallyl alcohol resins.

Resin from maleic acid, linseed oil, fatty acids, ethylene glycol, and allyl alcohol.   Can be used in manufacture of laminated paper or cloth electrical insulation.

Hydroxy esters of alpha,beta-unsaturated acids and alcohols.   Suitable for enamels.

Incorporation of polymerized mono-olefins in polymerized styrene.

Chloroacrylic esters prepared by esterification of alpha-chloroacrylic acid, *e.g.*, with allyl, methallyl, or crotyl alcohol.   Polymers of esters can be used in laminated glass products.

Interpolymers of a diallyl ether with an unsaturated alkyd resin for moldings, coatings, and adhesives.

Details for the production of a copolymer of vinyl methyl formal and maleic anhydride.

Resins produced from a monohydric alcohol, *e.g.*, ethyl or propyl, and the lactone of a heteropolymer of vinyl alcohol and an unsaturated alpha, beta-dicarboxylic acid, *e.g.*, maleic acid. Suitable for making films.

Resin Patents (Continued)

	Patent Number	Patentee	Assignee
569.	U.S. 2,306,136	I. E. Muskat	Pittsburgh Plate Glass Co.
570.	U.S. 2,306,918, 2,306,919, 2,306,920	J. M. Weiss and R. P. Weiss	Research Corp.
571.	U.S. 2,308,236	M. A. Pollack, I. E. Muskat, and F. Strain	Pittsburgh Plate Glass Co.
572.	U.S. 2,308,494	G. F. D'Alelio	General Electric Co.
573.	U.S. 2,308,495	G. F. D'Alelio	General Electric Co.
574.	U.S. 2,311,327	T. F. Bradley	American Cyanamid Co.
575.	U.S. 2,314,972	H. Dreyfus	Celanese Corp. of America
576.	U.S. 2,319,798	G. F. D'Alelio	General Electric Co.
577.	U.S. 2,319,799	G. F. D'Alelio	General Electric Co.
578.	U.S. 2,320,724	H. L. Gerhart and W. W. Bauer	Pittsburgh Plate Glass Co.
579.	U.S. 2,321,750	I. W. Humphrey	Hercules Powder Co.
580.	U.S. 2,323,706	G. F. D'Alelio	General Electric Co.
581.	U.S. 2,330,527	H. P. Staudinger	Distillers Co., Inc.
582.	U.S. 2,331,263	E. C. Britton, G. H. Coleman, and J. W. Zemba	Dow Chemical Co.
583.	U.S. 2,331,869	D. E. Adelson and H. Dannenberg	Shell Development Co.
584.	U.S. 2,332,898	G. F. D'Alelio	General Electric Co.
585.	U.S. 2,340,109	G. F. D'Alelio	General Electric Co.
586.	U.S. 2,341,175	E. C. Britton, H. B. Marshall, and W. J. LeFevre	Dow Chemical Co.
587.	U.S. 2,343,483	B. E. Sorenson	E. I. du Pont de Nemours & Co., Inc.
588.	U.S. 2,345,948	F. G. Pellett	General Electric Co.
589.	U.S. 2,349,768	F. Strain	Pittsburgh Plate Glass Co.

Concerning

Polymerization of unsaturated alcohol diesters of oxalic acid, *e.g.*, diallyl, dimethallyl, or dioleyl oxalate.

Resins from an anhydride of a polybasic aliphatic acid, *e.g.*, maleic anhydride, and a primary, secondary, or tertiary aliphatic amine.

Polymerization of polyhydric alcohol esters of monocarboxylic acids, *e.g.*, glycerol polycinnamate.

Interpolymers of unsaturated alkyd resins with a polycrotyl ester of a saturated or aromatic polycarboxylic acid, *e.g.*, dicrotyl phthalate.

Interpolymers of an unsaturated alkyd resin and a monoallyl ester of a nonvinylic monocarboxylic acid, *e.g.*, allyl furoate.

Resin suitable for molding or coating, prepared by heating mixture of polymerization catalyst, *e.g.*, benzoyl peroxide, and diallyl fumarate sebacate, succinate, adipate, or phthalate.

Linear high polymers from esterification of amino sugars with dicarboxylic acids or acid halides.

Interpolymers of an unsaturated alkyd resin and a phthalic, adipic, or similar diester of 2-chloroallyl alcohol.

Interpolymers of an unsaturated alkyd resin and a poly(1-halogenoallyl) ester.

Coating resins prepared by addition polymerization of styrene and an unsaturated dicarboxylic acid, partial esterification with a monohydric alcohol, and esterification of the remaining carboxyl groups with a monohydric alcohol ester of a polyhydroxy alcohol and an unsaturated higher fatty acid.

Maleic anhydride-diterpene $[(C_{10}H_{16})_2]$ synthetic resin suitable for use with glycols in making flexible varnish and lacquer resins.

Interpolymers of an unsaturated alkyd resin and a 3-hydroxy alkene-1 polyester of a polycarboxylic acid, *e.g.*, di(buten-1-yl-3) succinate.

Polymerization of styrene and styrene polymers in the presence of vinyl or other esters of crotonic acid having at least 2 double bonds.

Insoluble, nonbenzene-swellable copolymers of styrene with diallyl esters of maleic acid.

Polymerization of mono-olefinic halides, *e.g.*, allyl chloride, of not more than 15 C atoms in the presence of boron trifluoride as catalyst.

Partially thermoplastic composition obtained by cross-linking an unsaturated polyester with the usual monomer, *e.g.*, styrene, and then simultaneously hydrolyzing the cross-linked product with an acid catalyst and acetalizing or

ketalizing the hydroxyl groups with compounds containing $O{=\!\!=}C\diagdown$ groups,

e.g., formaldehyde, butyraldehyde, acetone. Utilized in electrical insulation.

Copolymer of polyester with divinylbenzene.

Moldable copolymers of styrene and *e.g.*, allyl cinnamate.

Interpolymers of styrene and the reaction products of maleic esters with relatively nonconjugated drying oils.

Condensation products of 3,6-endomethylene tetrahydrophthalic acid or anhydride ("carbic anhydride") and a polyhydric alcohol, *e.g.*, glycerol, ethylene glycol.

Resinous polymers of polyhydric alcohol polyesters of acrylic and alpha-substituted acrylic acids, *e.g.*, ethylene glycol dimethacrylate.

Resin Patents (Continued)

	Patent Number	Patentee	Assignee
590.	U.S. 2,361,019	H. L. Gerhart	Pittsburgh Plate Glass Co.
591.	U.S. 2,371,990	W. E. Hanford	E. I. du Pont de Nemours & Co., Inc.
592.	U.S. 2,373,527	M. C. Agens	General Electric Co.
593.	U.S. 2,386,999	D. E. Adelson and H. Dannenberg	Shell Development Co.
594.	U.S. 2,387,931– 2,387,932	I. E. Muskat and F. Strain	Pittsburgh Plate Glass Co.
595.	U.S. 2,392,139	H. L. Gerhart	Pittsburgh Plate Glass Co.
596.	U.S. 2,392,621	F. Strain	Pittsburgh Plate Glass Co.
597.	U.S. 2,392,756	C. J. Mighton	E. I. du Pont de Nemours & Co., Inc.
598.	U.S. 2,395,581	H. J. Richter	E. I. du Pont de Nemours & Co., Inc.
599.	U.S. 2,398,688– 2,398,700	J. B. Rust	Montclair Research Corp.
600.	U.S. 2,399,214	T. W. Evans and D. E. Adelson	Shell Development Co.
601.	U.S. 2,399,285	I. E. Muskat and F. Strain	Pittsburgh Plate Glass Co.
602.	U.S. 2,401,581	I. E. Muskat and F. Strain	Pittsburgh Plate Glass Co.
603.	U.S. 2,403,791	G. F. D'Alelio	General Electric Co.
604.	U.S. 2,404,780	H. W. Arnold	E. I. du Pont de Nemours & Co., Inc.
605.	U.S. 2,407,479	G. F. D'Alelio	General Electric Co.
606.	U.S. 2,409,633	E. L. Kropa	American Cyanamid Co.
607.	U.S. 2,411,599	W. J. Sparks and A. H. Gleason	Standard Oil Development Co.
608.	U.S. 2,413,275	F. E. Wilson, G. J. Esselen, and G. F. D'Alelio	Pro-phy-lac-tic Brush Co.

Resinous copolymer of styrene, an ester of a polyhydric alcohol and an unsaturated dicarboxylic acid or its anhydride, e.g., diethylene glycol maleate, and an unsaturated dicarboxylic acid or anhydride, e.g., maleic acid.

Linear polyesters of methylene glycols from saturated aliphatic monoaldehydes, e.g., formaldehyde, and a polyanhydride of a dicarboxylic acid, e.g., polyadipic anhydride.

Treatment of maleic acid or its monoesters with cyclic amines, e.g., pyridine, to decarboxylate and give rapidly air-drying products (alkyd type).

Transparent, practically colorless resins from allyl esters, e.g., diallyl diglycolate.

Polymerizable unsaturated complex esters of (1) an unsaturated ester of a hydroxy acid, e.g., allyl lactate, and (2) an acid ester of a polybasic acid and an unsaturated alcohol, e.g., monoallyl phthalate.

Conjoint polymerization of dicarboxylic compounds and vinylic compounds in the presence of aliphatic or cyclic ketone plasticizers.

Transesterification method of polyesterification. Production of esters from glycols and esters of unsaturated acids, e.g., diethylene glycol and diethyl fumarate.

Freeze-resistant synthetic rubber from copolymers of halogenated dienes with unsaturated alcohol esters of unsaturated dicarboxylic acids.

Modified vinyl chloride-fumaric ester copolymer.

Preparation of resins for varnishes by heating rosin esters with unsaturated alcohol esters of unsaturated dicarboxylic acids.

Heat- or oxygen-convertible alkyd resins from unsaturated ethers of glycerol or glycidol, e.g., allyl ethers, and a dicarboxylic acid or anhydride, e.g., phthalic acid.

Unsaturated polyesters containing 3–10 ester groups of unsaturated hydroxy acids and unsaturated alcohols, e.g., from an unsaturated monohydric alcohol, an unsaturated monobasic acid, and an ester hydroxy acid.

Unsaturated salicylic acid esters and their polymers.

Interpolymers of a methylene malonic ester and an unsaturated alkyd resin, e.g., diethylene glycol maleate.
See Brit. 570,331 in this section.

Interpolymers of a monohydric alcohol polyester of an unsaturated polycarboxylic acid and the esterification product of a monohydric alcohol, a polyhydric alcohol, and polycarboxylic acids.

Insoluble, infusible resins from polymerization of polyester resin, e.g., ethylene glycol maleate resin, with an allyl compound, e.g., diallyl esters such as diallyl fumarate, maleate, phthalate, or succinate.

Interpolymers of unsaturated esters, e.g., methyl acrylate, with iso-olefins, e.g., isobutylene. Clear, transparent, flexible resins.

Polyvinyl acetal maleates, suitable for hot molding, produced by heating polyvinyl alcohol, maleic anhydride, and an aldehyde.

Resin Patents (Continued)

	Patent Number	Patentee	Assignee
609.	U.S. 2,415,400	R. T. Armstrong	U.S. Rubber Co.
610.	U.S. 2,418,633	C. Gould	Marco Chemicals, Inc.
611.	U.S. 2,418,688	F. C. Atwood	National Dairy Products Corp.
612.	U.S. 2,421,876	H. L. Gerhart	Pittsburgh Plate Glass Co.
613.	U.S. 2,423,042	I. E. Muskat	Marco Chemicals, Inc.
614.	U.S. 2,426,325	P. O. Tawney	U.S. Rubber Co.
615.	U.S. 2,426,902	R. B. Seymour	Monsanto Chemical Co.
616.	U.S. 2,427,640	L. N. Whitehill and E. C. Shokal	Shell Development Co.
617.	U.S. 2,428,787	G. F. D'Alelio	General Electric Co.
618.	U.S. 2,428,788	G. F. D'Alelio	General Electric Co.
619.	U.S. 2,430,109	G. F. D'Alelio	Pro-phy-lac-tic Brush Co.
620.	U.S. 2,430,313	C. A. Vana	E. I. du Pont de Nemours & Co., Inc.
621.	U.S. 2,431,373	G. F. D'Alelio	Pro-phy-lac-tic Brush Co.
622.	U.S. 2,431,374	G. F. D'Alelio	Pro-phy-lac-tic Brush Co.
623.	U.S. 2,436,926	R. A. Jacobson	E. I. du Pont de Nemours & Co., Inc.
624.	U.S. 2,437,962	E. L. Kropa	American Cyanamid Co.
625.	U.S. 2,439,227	R. B. Seymour and J. R. Kispersky	Monsanto Chemical Co.
626.	U.S. 2,439,953	J. Swiss and N. C. Foster	Westinghouse Electric Corp.
627.	U.S. 2,441,799	G. F. D'Alelio	General Electric Co.
628.	U.S. 2,443,735	E. L. Kropa	American Cyanamid Co.
629.	U.S. 2,443,736	E. L. Kropa	American Cyanamid Co.
630.	U.S. 2,443,737	E. L. Kropa	American Cyanamid Co.

Concerning

Copolymers of methallyl alkyd ethers with maleic anhydride. Yield cross-linked resins with polyhydric alcohols.

Polymerizable materials of low viscosity, from reaction of alkyd resin with a monohydric alcohol, e.g., propanol, and then with a carboxylic acid, e.g. acetic up to tung oil.

Elastic polymers made by milling and heating glycol with a copolymer of an alkyd acrylate and maleic anhydride.

Copolymer of styrene and a polyester of endomethylene tetrahydrophthalic acid and a glycol.

Production of polyesters from specified proportions of constituents. Phthalic acid or anhydride (5–35%) is added before polymerization to prevent crystallization.

Interpolymers of diallyl ether (cross-linking agent), a saturated monohydric alcohol ester of an acrylic acid, e.g., methyl methacrylate, and a saturated monohydric alcohol ester of an ethylenic dicarboxylic acid, e.g., diethyl fumarate.

Higher alkyl esters of chloromaleic acid, e.g., bis(2-ethylhexyl) chloromaleate. Form copolymers with resins.

Polymers of esters of sulfonyl-containing carboxylic acids with unsaturated alcohol, e.g., diallyl sulfonyl diglycolate. Clear, transparent, almost colorless resins.

Copolymer of a polyester and an ester of a saturated polybasic acid with allyl alcohol or its analogues.

Copolymers of unsaturated alkyd resins modified with a saturated polycarboxylic acid and monohydric alcohol esters of unsaturated polycarboxylic acids.

A heat-curable copolymer of divinylbenzene and a maleic acid type of ester.

Copolymerization of monoethylenic hydrocarbons with maleic anhydride type of materials.

Copolymers of divinylbenzene and monohydric alcohol esters of itaconic acid.

Copolymers of diallyl maleate and saturated monohydric alcohol esters of maleic or fumaric acid.

Polymerization in aqueous solution of acrylonitriles with, e.g., ethylenic dicarboxylic acids and derivatives.

Copolymers of allyl esters of polybasic acids, e.g., diallyl succinate, with saturated monohydric alcohol esters of unsaturated polycarboxylic acids, e.g., diethyl fumarate.

Ternary interpolymers of styrene, maleic anhydride, and acrylonitrile.

Resin of low power and loss factors, infusible at $250\,^{\circ}$C., from reaction of styrene (75–95%) with castor oil-maleic anhydride reaction product.

Copolymers of nonethylenic-modified unsaturated alkyd resins with monohydric alcohol esters of unsaturated polycarboxylic acids.

Copolymers of unsaturated alkyd resins with allyl esters.

Copolymer of diallyl phthalate and unsaturated alkyd resin.

Basic patent on copolymers of unsaturated alkyd resins with alkyl esters of saturated polycarboxylic acids.

Resin Patents (Continued)

	Patent Number	Patentee	Assignee
631.	U.S. 2,443,738	E. L. Kropa	American Cyanamid Co.
632.	U.S. 2,443,739	E. L. Kropa	American Cyanamid Co.
633.	U.S. 2,443,740	E. L. Kropa	American Cyanamid Co.
634.	U.S. 2,443,741	E. L. Kropa	American Cyanamid Co.
635.	U.S. 2,443,915	J. L. Jones	Libbey-Owens-Ford Glass Co.
636.	U.S. 2,444,817	R. G. Fordyce	Monsanto Chemical Co.
637.	U.S. 2,445,764	G. F. D'Alelio	General Electric Co.
638.	U.S. 2,445,799	R. C. Morris and E. C. Shokal	Shell Development Co.
639.	U.S. 2,446,314	J. K. Wagers and E. C. Shokal	
640.	U.S. 2,448,259	H. de V. Finch	Shell Development Co.
641.	U.S. 2,448,531	W. O. Kenyon and C. C. Unruh	Eastman Kodak Co.
642.	U.S. 2,448,584	C. J. Frosch	Bell Telephone Laboratories, Inc.
643.	U.S. 2,448,585	C. S. Fuller	Bell Telephone Laboratories, Inc.
644.	U.S. 2,450,682	B. W. Nordlander	General Electric Co.
645.	U.S. 2,453,167	A. D. F. Toy	Victor Chemical Works
646.	U.S. 2,457,657	S. E. Glick	Monsanto Chemical Co.
647.	U.S. 2,468,769	R. C. Morris and J. L. Van Winkle	Shell Development Co.
648.	U.S. 2,473,801	E. L. Kropa	American Cyanamid Co.
649.	U.S. 2,475,557	D. Swern and G. B. Dickel	United States of America
650.	U.S. 2,475,731	G. S. Weith	Bakelite Corp.
651.	U.S. 2,476,922	E. C. Shokal, L. N. Whitehill, and C. V. Wittenwyler	Shell Development Co.
652.	U.S. 2,478,015	J. B. Rust and W. B. Canfield	Montclair Research Corp. (½) and Ellis-Foster Co. (½)

Concerning

Copolymer of unsaturated alkyd resin and alkyl derivatives.

Copolymer of modified unsaturated alkyd resin and polyallyl ester.

Compositions of unsaturated alkyd resins and polyallyl esters.

Copolymers of unsaturated alkyd resins and compatible unsaturated polycarboxylic acids, e.g., allyl lactocarbonate or tetra-allyl pentaerythritol sebacate.

Copolymer of styrene with an ester of an unsaturated dicarboxylic acid and a hydroxy acid esterified with an unsaturated alcohol.

Cast objects of high strength, high heat resistance, and good resistance to solvents, prepared by polymerizing a mixture of vinyl acetate and a diallyl or dimethallyl ester of maleic, fumaric, succinic, or adipic acid.

Copolymers of unsaturated alkyd resins, e.g., diethylene glycol maleate phthalate, with esters, e.g., diallyl maleate or itaconate.

Organic sulfer-containing polyesters prepared from sulfolanyloxy-substituted carboxylic acids, e.g., allyl 3-sulfolanyl carbonate. Copolymers of these polyesters with diallyl phthalate are more easily removed from molds and are lighter in color than diallyl phthalate polymer.

Soluble polymers of unsaturated esters of polycarboxylic acids.

Resinous polymers of esters from substituted adipic acids, e.g., trimethyl adipic acid, and unsaturated alcohols, e.g., allyl alcohol.

Copolymers of isopropenyl acetate and monohydric alcohol esters of maleic and fumaric acids.

Curable rubbery polyesters based on controlled use of disecondary glycols. Criteria for high tensile strength described.

Synthetic polyester rubber from ethylene glycol-isopropylene glycol-sebacic acid-maleic acid polyester cured with benzoyl peroxide. Criteria for high tensile strength described.

Copolymers of unsaturated alkyd resins, e.g., diethylene glycol maleate, with diallyl tetrachlorophthalate.

Copolymers of dialkenyl arylphosphonates with vinyl acetate.

Polymerizable composition for impregnating castings: styrene and a reaction product of diethylene glycol, maleic acid, and linseed oil acids.

Adducts of unsaturated dicarboxylic acids with cyclic polymers of hexadienes. Produce very reactive polyesters.

Polymerizable emulsified mixtures of unsaturated polyesters, e.g., polyhexa-ethylene glycol maleate, with vinyl monomers, e.g., diallyl maleate, diallyl phthalate, styrene,

Copolymers of unsaturated esters of 9,10-dihydroxystearic acid, e.g., isomeric allyl ester, with an olefinic monomer, e.g., vinyl acetate.

Copolymers of styrene with glycol maleate resins modified with a diolefin-maleic adduct to give effective reaction control.

Two-step polymerization ($8°$, $65°C.$) of dicarboxylic acid esters of glycidal and allyl or vinyl alcohols, e.g., glycidyl allyl phthalate.

Unsaturated polymerizable ester from pentaerythritol and monoallyl maleate or phthalate. May be copolymerized with styrene and other vinyl compounds.

Resin Patents (Continued)

	Patent Number	Patentee	Assignee
653.	U.S. 2,479,486	H. L. Gerhart	Pittsburgh Plate Glass Co.
654.	U.S. 2,479,522	F. Strain	Pittsburgh Plate Glass Co.
655.	U.S. 2,480,551	D. D. Coffmann and H. W. Jacobson	E. I. du Pont de Nemours & Co., Inc.
656.	U.S. 2,482,087	N. C. Foster	Westinghouse Electric Corp.
657.	U.S. 2,483,194	C. E. Gleim	Wingfoot Corp.
658.	U.S. 2,483,726	D. E. Floyd	General Mills, Inc.
659.	U.S. 2,484,216	N. C. Foster	Westinghouse Electric Corp.
660.	U.S. 2,484,529	M. J. Roedel	E. I. du Pont de Nemours & Co., Inc.
661.	U.S. 2,485,294	E. L. Kropa	American Cyanamid Co.
662.	U.S. 2,486,201	D. G. Patterson	American Cyanamid Co.
663.	U.S. 2,489,711	D. W. Jayne, Jr., and M. M. Day	American Cyanamid Co.
664.	U.S. 2,491,409	D. L. Kropa and A. S. Nyquist	American Cyanamid Co.
665.	U.S. 2,493,948	R. E. Davies and A. R. Esterly	Catalin Corp. of America
666.	U.S. 2,496,271	J. A. Cottrell, D. H. Hewitt, and F. Armitage	Sherwin-Williams Co.
667.	U.S. 2,496,933	J. R. Caldwell	Eastman Kodak Co.
668.	U.S. 2,497,433	E. S. Blake	Monsanto Chemical Co.
669.	U.S. 2,498,084	J. G. Kuderna and R. H. Snyder	U.S. Rubber Co.
670.	U.S. 2,498,099	P. O. Tawney and J. G. Kuderna	U.S. Rubber Co.
671.	U.S. 2,498,533	L. H. Dimpfl	California Research Corp.
672.	U.S. 2,500,222	H. E. Weaver and E. G. King	Armstrong Cork Co.
673.	U.S. 2,501,610	R. C. Morris and A. V. Snider	Shell Development Co.

<hr>

Concerning

<hr>

Esters of tetrahydrophthalic acid and analogues as replacements for conventional polyester ingredients in whole or in part. Products are hard, tough, thermosetting.

Clear, colorless copolymers of unsaturated polycarboxylic esters, such as diallyl phthalate, with maleic anhydride.

Hydrolyzed interpolymer of ethylene vinyl acetate and diethyl fumarate.

Polymerization of styrene and monoallyl maleate. Laminating and casting resin produced.

Polymer of allyl carbonate and its copolymer with diethylene glycol bis(allyl carbonate).

Polyesters from polyhydric alcohols and alkylmalonic esters of lower monohydric alcohols.

Copolymers of metallic salts of alkyl half-esters of unsaturated dibasic acids with liquid monomers having a reactive group, e.g., zinc isopropyl maleate with styrene.

Decreasing the thermoplasticity of polyesters, polyamides, and other polymers by mixing with ketones that dissociate into free radicals when excited with ultraviolet light, e.g., acetophenone, and exposing to ultraviolet light.

Copolymers of tetrahydroabietyl alcohol-modified unsaturated alkyd resins and vinyl compounds (alcohol acts as diluent or plasticizer of resin).

Resins suitable for surface coating of wood and low-pressure paper-base laminates, prepared by blending an alkylated melamine-formaldehyde condensation product with a glycol-fumaric acid polyester resin and styrene.

Rubberlike polyester obtained from omega-hydroxy decanoic acid or analogues, ethylene glycol monoethyl ester, and conventional polyester ingredients.

Copolymers of styrene with reaction product of a glycol, a dicarboxylic acid, and an adduct of alloöcimene with the glycol and acid. Insulating materials of low power factor.

Styrene-diallyl fumarate copolymers. Produce clear "popcorn"-free castings.

Polymerizable esters from allyl alcohols and the Diels-Alder reaction product of maleic anhydride with, e.g., conjugated terpenes, conjugated cycloaliphatic polyenes, etc.

Linear polyesters of hydroquinone, saturated aliphatic glycols, and dicarboxylic acids (succinic through sebacic). Tough, waxlike to hard, brittle products.

Alkyl esters of glycol polycarboxylic acid esters, e.g., mono-oleyl ester of ethylene diacid succinate.

Copolymers of diallyl fumarate with allyl chloride or a homolog.

Copolymers of diallyl fumarate with allyl chloride and styrene.

Mixture of polyesters with short curing time, e.g., ethylene glycol polyesters from 3,5-cyclohexadiene 1,2-dicarboxylic acid and maleic anhydride.

Unsaturated polyesters prepared by pyrolyzing ($250°-300°C.$) a dicarboxylic acid and a dihydric alcohol.

Polymers of diallyl 3,5-dimethylphthalate and analogous esters containing at least 1 allyl-type alcohol group.

<hr>

Resin Patents (Continued)

	Patent Number	Patentee	Assignee
674.	U.S. 2,503,209	A. S. Nyquist and E. L. Kropa	American Cyanamid Co.
675.	U.S. 2,507,871	P. O. Tawney	U.S. Rubber Co.
676.	U.S. 2,510,902	S. T. Putnam	Hercules Powder Co.
677.	U.S. 2,514,141	D. S. Phillips	American Cyanamid Co.
678.	U.S. 2,516,012	H. F. Minter and F. J. Nagel	Westinghouse Electric Corp.
679.	U.S. 2,521,575	C. F. Fisk	U.S. Rubber Co.
680.	U.S. 2,524,921	H. F. Minter	Westinghouse Electric Corp.
681.	U.S. 2,528,235	J. A. Loritsch	General Electric Co.
682.	U.S. 2,530,315	J. B. Rust and W. B. Canfield	Montclair Research Corp. (½) and Ellis-Foster Co. (½)
683.	U.S. 2,531,275	J. L. Jones	Libbey-Owens-Ford Glass Co.
684.	U.S. 2,532,498	H. A. Hoppens	Libbey-Owens-Ford Glass Co.
685.	U.S. 2,538,810	A. D. F. Toy	Victor Chemical Works
686.	U.S. 2,546,798	P. O. Tawney	U.S. Rubber Co.
687.	U.S. 2,547,696	F. J. Foster	U.S. Rubber Co.
688.	U.S. 2,547,701	R. A. Gregg	U.S. Rubber Co.
689.	U.S. 2,551,767	L. Shechter and A. S. Burhans	Union Carbide and Carbon Corp.
690.	U.S. 2,555,551	E. L. Kropa	American Cyanamid Co.
691.	U.S. 2,555,595	R. C. Morris and J. L. Van Winkle	Shell Development Co.
692.	U.S. 2,557,189	E. P. Irany, I. Skeist, and V. F. Maturi	Celanese Corp. of America
693.	U.S. 2,560,119	J. W. McCaslin and J. C. Hillyer	Phillips Petroleum Co.

Concerning

Polymerizable compound formed by reaction of an unsaturated alkyd resin and an unsaturated isocyanate.

Interpolymers of allyl alcohols and alkyd diesters of an unsaturated dicarboxylic acid.

Copolymer of maleic anhydride and 10-hendecenoic acid. Can be used in preparation of polyesters and polyamides.

Filled unsaturated polyester casting resin adhesives for glass-to-metal bonds, e.g., ethylene glycol-diethylene glycol-tetrachlorophthalate-fumarate resin cut with styrene.

Fast-curing resinous compositions: an unsaturated alkyd resin, a polyhydroxy-benzene-aldehyde condensation product, a diester of monohydric alcohol, an acid half-ester of a polyhydric alcohol, a dibasic acid, and a metallic drier. Useful as varnishes for electrical equipment.

Flexible copolymer of 2-ethyl hexanediol-1,3-maleic acid polyester (95%) and styrene (5%) (with 20–80% styrene, copolymer is rigid). Excellent clarity.

Copolymers having intermediate thermoplastic stage but becoming thermoset on curing: alkyl half-esters of ethylene glycol dimaleate and analogues.

Polyester modified with a polyvinyl formal resin (15–75%) to shorten time of cure in press. Can give nontacky impregnated tape or sheet; heat curable at convenience.

A solvent-stable drying oil-alkyd resin, which is a mixture of alkyd, drying oil fatty acid, allyl ester, and polyester ingredients.

Copolymer of polyester (100 parts) and allyl methacrylyl glycolate (20–40 parts) or analogues.

Polyester from ethylene and propylene glycols with maleic or fumaric acids in specified proportion. High compressive strength.

Nonflammable, hard, tough copolymers of diallyl esters of dicarboxylic acids, e.g., oxalic, sebacic, adipic, phthalic, succinate, with di(beta,gamma-unsaturated alkenyl) aryl phosphonates, e.g., diallylphenyl phosphonate.

Soluble copolymers of allylic maleates with allylic alcohols.

Soluble, fusible, unsaturated halogen-containing resins from di-2-alkenyl maleate, di-2-alkenyl fumarate, and bromomethane compound. Copolymers with styrene are flame-resistant.

Resins prepared by polymerizing di-2-alkenyl esters of an ethylenic dicarboxylic acid in presence of a bromomethane compound, for flame-proofing purposes.

Laminating resins prepared from sorbic acid and other acids, e.g., adipic, or a cyclopentadiene-maleic anhydride adduct, glycerol, and toluene.

Copolymers of para-isopropenyltoluene and unsaturated alkyd resins, e.g., glycol ester of unsaturated dicarboxylic acid.

Esters and polyesters from low-molecular-weight cyclic polymers, unsaturated dicarboxylic acids, and alcohols or alkyl halides.

Copolymers of esters of organic acids with unsaturated alcohols, e.g., allyl acetate, and esters of saturated alcohols with unsaturated acids, e.g., diethyl maleate.

Tetrahydrophthalic anhydride resins. Useful as adhesives and coatings.

Resin Patents (Continued)

	Patent Number	Patentee	Assignee
694.	U.S. 2,561,153–2,561,154	P. O. Tawney	U.S. Rubber Co.
695.	U.S. 2,563,133	J. C. Patrick and H. R. Ferguson	Thiokol Corp.
696.	U.S. 2,564,395	H. Dannenberg and T. F. Bradley	Shell Development Co.
697.	U.S. 2,584,315	R. J. Agnew	Texas Co.
698.	U.S. 2,584,316	R. J. Agnew	Texas Co.
699.	U.S. 2,585,323	W. E. Elwell and D. C. McGowan	California Research Corp.
700.	U.S. 2,586,884	A. D. F. Toy and L. V. Brown	Victor Chemical Works
701.	U.S. 2,586,885	A. D. F. Toy and L. V. Brown	Victor Chemical Works
702.	U.S. 2,593,411	J. R. Caldwell	Eastman Kodak Co.
703.	U.S. 2,594,145	P. J. Flory	Wingfoot Corp.
704.	U.S. 2,595,625	R. J. Agnew	Texas Co.
705.	U.S. 2,598,663	E. L. Kropa	American Cyanamid Co.
706.	U.S. 2,603,625	R. C. Feagin and D. Bandel	Mathieson Chemical Corp.
707.	U.S. 2,606,172	P. O. Tawney	U.S. Rubber Co.
708.	U.S. 2,608,549	R. J. Wolf	B. F. Goodrich Co.
709.	U.S. 2,608,550	C. S. Rowland and A. G. Chenicek	Interchemical Corp.
710.	U.S. 2,609,353	L. C. Rubens and R. F. Boyer	Dow Chemical Co.
711.	U.S. 2,609,354	O. L. Polly	Union Oil Co.
712.	U.S. 2,609,358	H. F. Pfann and E. L. Kropa	American Cyanamid Co.
713.	U.S. 2,612,491	T. W. Evans, D. E. Adelson, and L. N. Whitehill	Shell Development Co.

Concerning

Copolymers of poly-2-alkenyl esters of polybasic acids, e.g., diallyl fumarate, and 2-alkenyl ethers or esters, e.g., methallyl ethyl ether (styrene may be included as third ingredient). Can be used for coating and molding.

Polythioesters prepared by reaction of a polymercapto compound and a polycarboxylic acid, e.g., reaction of maleic acid with dimercaptoethane. Can be copolymerized with polyesters.

Copolymers of diallyl phthalate and diallyl esters of dimerized unsaturated fat acids (preferably di- to penta-ene).

Copolymer of diallyl ester of 4-chloro, 1,2,3,6-tetrahydrophthalic acid (30%) and an unsaturated polyester, e.g., of ethylene glycol and maleic and phthalic anhydrides.

Copolymers of diallyl endomethylene tetrahydrophthalate (30%) and an unsaturated mixed polyester (70%), e.g., of ethylene glycol and maleic and phthalic anhydrides.

Linear pyromellitic polyester including pentaerythritol esters. Thermoplastic products soluble in alcohols, ketones, esters; when heated (over 200 $^\circ$C.); insoluble products result. Water-swellable products included.

Copolymers of polyesters with diallyl or dimethallyl isobutenyl phosphonate and analogues.

Copolymers of polyesters with diallyl or dimethallyl phenyl phosphonate. Fireresistant, thermosetting resins for lamination or coating.

Polyesters of bis[p-(2-hydroxyalkoxy)-phenyl] sulfones and polybasic carboxylic acids, e.g., phthalic, adipic. Impart surface hardness and moisture resistance to coatings.

N-acyl polyimides used to cross-link polyesters having free hydroxy or amino groups and thus increase molecular weight.

Copolymers of polyesters and conjugated dienes.

Copolymers of polyesters and acrylamido compounds. Clear, hard resins.

Copolymers of dichlorostyrene and mixed esters of olefin polycarboxylic acids, preferably esters of maleic or fumaric acid. Resins have low water absorption, low cold flow, and high softening point.

Interpolymers of di-2-alkenyl maleate, a styrene, and a 2-alkenyl alcohol.

Interpolymers of vinyl chloride, a higher alkyl acrylate, and a dialkenyl ester of olefinic dicarboxylic acid, e.g., diallyl maleate. Do not require plasticizers during processing.

Resins from reaction of unsaturated dicarboxylic acid derivatives, e.g., chloromaleic anhydride, with cyclopentadiene polymers.

A resin using the maximum amount of styrene (up to 85%) consistent with polyester-type properties.

Modified resins from polystyrene and esters of saturated dicarboxylic acids and unsaturated alcohols.

Alkyd resins produced through use of a polymerized alcohol.

Mixed polycarboxylic acid esters of alkylidene glycols, e.g., ethylidene acetate allyl maleate. High polymers of esters are insoluble, infusible, crack free, light stable, and heat stable.

Resin Patents (Continued)

	Patent Number	Patentee	Assignee
714.	U.S. 2,612,492	P. O. Tawney	U.S. Rubber Co.
715.	U.S. 2,614,120	J. R. Caldwell	Eastman Kodak Co.
716.	U.S. 2,617,787	P. O. Tawney	U.S. Rubber Co.
717.	U.S. 2,624,754	E. S. Blake	Monsanto Chemical Co.
718.	U.S. 2,625,526	W. J. Sparks and D. W. Young	Standard Oil Co.
719.	U.S. 2,626,223	F. A. Sattler, J. Swiss, and J. G. Ford	Westinghouse Electric Corp.
720.	U.S. 2,626,944	H. W. Coover, Jr., and J. B. Dickey	Eastman Kodak Co.
721.	U.S. 2,628,215	M. J. Hunter and L. A. Rauner	Dow Corning Corp.
722.	U.S. 2,628,220	E. Arundale and F. W. Banes	Standard Oil Co.
723.	U.S. 2,628,221	F. D. Marsh	E. I. du Pont de Nemours & Co., Inc.
724.	U.S. 2,628,922	F. J. Carlin	U.S. Rubber Co.
725.	U.S. 2,628,946	W. Juda, G. Jones, and N. Altman	Albi Manufacturing Co.
726.	U.S. 2,628,958	J. A. Bittles	E. I. du Pont de Nemours & Co., Inc.
727.	U.S. 2,630,419	H. F. Wakefield, S. J. Schultz, and S. H. Richardson	Union Carbide & Carbon Corp.
728.	U.S. 2,631,141	D. Swern and E. F. Jordan, Jr.	United States of America
729.	U.S. 2,632,755	R. H. Bunnel	Libbey-Owens-Ford Glass Co.
730.	U.S. 2,636,020	H. Zenftman and R. McGillivray	Imperial Chemical Industries, Ltd.
731.	U.S. 2,646,410	J. W. Kneisley	Hercules Powder Co.
732.	U.S. 2,650,207	J. B. Rust and W. B. Canfield	Montclair Research Corp. and Ellis-Foster Co.
733.	U.S. 2,650,211	H. Dannenberg and J. R. Scheibli	Shell Development Co.

Concerning

Soluble copolymers of diallylic phthalates and allylic alcohols. Capable of
  further polymerization, e.g., with diethyl or diallyl fumarate, to form laminating
  or casting resins.

Linear polyesters prepared by reacting 2-hydroxyalkyl diesters of dicarboxydi-
  phenyl sulfones with glycols or dibasic acids, e.g., succinic, sebacic, fumaric,
  maleic, itaconic, phthalic, or terephthalic acids.

Quaternary interpolymers of unsaturated polyacids, monovinyl benzenes, unsaturated esters, and alkenyl alcohols.

Dialkyl esters of a glycol bis(alkylene-dicarboxylic acid) ester prepared by (1)
  treating a dicarboxylic acid anhydride with a glycol and a monohydric alcohol
  and (2) condensing the product with additional anhydride.

Polyvinyl chloride-dienenitrile-polyester composition.

Resinous reaction product of a combined polyesteramide and a complex resinous
  epoxide.

Polymers of alpha-acylamido acrylic acids.

Phenylmethyl dialkoxy silane-polyhydric alcohol-dicarboxylic acid copolymer.

Alkyl maleate-vinyl ester copolymer.

Copolymers of vinyl esters and tertiary-amino nitrogen compounds.

Polymer with improved adhesion to glass surfaces, prepared by heating an unsaturated polymer of a 2-alkenyl or 2-alkenyl-oxyalkyl ester containing 2 or
  more ethylenic linkages, e.g., diallyl phthalate, with a small amount of ammonium fluoride or bifluoride.

Fire-retardant cyanamide resins.

Polymerizable esters of alpha-methylene carboxylic acids.

Polyesters modified with complex metal-phenol-nitrogen compounds to improve
  flexibility, toughness, adhesion, and cohesion at elevated temperatures.

Copolymers of unsaturated esters of phthalic acid with allyl esters of long-chain
  aliphatic acids.

Copolymers of a silane and esters of maleic or fumaric acids.

See Brit. 653,489 in this section.

Heat-convertible, water-soluble polyester from partial esterification of maleic
  acid with pentaerythritol, glycerol, or their mixtures with ethylene glycol.

Copolymers of vinylimides with unsaturated alkyds.

Polyesters of alkenyl succinic acids.

Resin Patents (Continued)

	Patent Number	Patentee	Assignee
734.	U.S. 2,652,382– 2,652,383	J. F. Davis	American Cyanamid Co.
735.	U.S. 2,658,849	B. W. Lew	Atlas Powder Co.
736.	U.S. 2,662,069	P. Kass	Atlas Powder Co.
737.	U.S. 2,662,070	P. Kass and B. W. Lew	Atlas Powder Co.
738.	U.S. 2,664,411	R. S. Cooper	Diamond Alkali Co.
739.	U.S. 2,671,070	R. L. Knapp	U.S. Rubber Co.
740.	U.S. 2,673,151	H. L. Gerhart	Pittsburgh Plate Glass Co.
741.	U.S. 2,675,376	J. R. Caldwell	Eastman Kodak Co.
742.	Austrian 171,161		Spokel Pro Chemickow A Hutni Vyrobu, Warodni Podnik, Prague
743.	Brit. 455,922	H. L. Cox and T. F. Carruthers	Carbide and Carbon Chemicals Co.
744.	Brit. 483,908	T. F. Bradley	American Cyanamid Co.
745.	Brit. 500,547	S. L. M. Saunders	Pinchin, Johnson, & Co., Ltd.
746.	Brit. 505,651		W. W. Groves (I. G. Farbenind. A.-G.)
747.	Brit. 528,760		Kodak, Ltd.
748.	Brit. 537,709		Kodak, Ltd.
749.	Brit. 540,168– 540,169		American Cyanamid Co.

Concerning

Modification of unsaturated polyester resins with butylated phenol-formaldehyde resins.   Gives crater-free coating of improved hardness, acid-, alkali-, and solvent-resistance, and glass and color retention.

Binding resins for glass fiber mats comprising a powdered or granular mixture of an ethylene glycol fumarate polyester and a fumaric acid ester prepared from 2,2-bis[4-(2-hydroxyethoxy)-phenyl] propane, fumaric acid, hydroquinone, and glycerol.

Linear polyester resin from 2,2-bis[4-(hydroxypropoxy) phenyl]propane, ethylene glycol, fumaric acid, and hydroquinone.

Linear polyester resin from 2,2-bis[4-(2-hydroxyethoxy) phenyl] propane, ethylene glycol, fumaric acid, and hydroquinone.

Flame-resistant plastics comprising a transparent plastic (can be a polyester resin such as glycerol-phthalic anhydride type), chlorinated paraffin wax, and triphenyl stibine.

Alkyd resin prepared from dicyclopentadiene, maleic acid, and ethylene glycol.

Photosensitive resins prepared from a polyester, styrene for cross-linking, and a sulfur-containing photosensitizing agent, e.g., tetramethyl thiuram.

Preparation of polyesters by reacting a saturated or unsaturated aliphatic dicarboxylic acid or a monocyclic dicarboxylic aromatic acid of 4=10 C atoms with bis(4-beta-hydroxyethoxyphenyl) ketone.

Resins for lacquers, varnishes, insulating, etc., from 1,2-cyclohexanediol and polybasic acids or anhydrides.

Mixed esters from reaction of ester of an aliphatic dicarboxylic acid, e.g., succinic, with a glycol and a saturated aliphatic monocarboxylic acid, e.g., acetic.

Resinous acid anhydride produced from maleic acid or anhydride or homologs with polyterpenes of the formula $(C_{10}H_{16})_x$.   Can be esterified with polyhydric alcohols.

Polyhydric alcohol–polybasic acid condensation products; may contain driers such as Co and Mn linoleates.   Rapid-hardening compositions suitable for coating, molding, or binding.

Plastic for shaped articles prepared from hydrophilic polyvinyl compound and ester of polyhydric alcohol and aliphatic polycarboxylic or hydroxycarboxylic acid, e.g., saponified interpolymer of vinyl chloride with maleic anhydride and 1,3-butylene glycol maleate.

Resinous compositions containing a dicarboxylic anhydride–terpene condensation product and a cyclo-olefin resin, a styrene resin, or a halogenated rubber.

Synthetic resins formed by heating a heteropolymer of a vinyl ester of an organic acid and an unsaturated dicarboxylic acid or its anhydride with a monohydric alcohol, e.g., methyl, ethyl, in the presence of strong mineral acid. Especially suitable for photographic films.

Interpolymers of a polyhydric alcohol ester of an unsaturated organic acid with a high-boiling substance containing at least 1 allyl group or other ethylenic substances.

Resin Patents (Continued)

	Patent Number	Patentee	Assignee
750.	Brit. 544,057	B. D. Scott	British Thomson-Houston Co. Ltd.
751.	Brit. 547,328		British Thomson-Houston Co., Ltd.
752.	Brit. 548,137		American Cyanamid Co.
753.	Brit. 549,682		E. I. du Pont de Nemours & Co., Inc.
754.	Brit. 552,228		E. I. du Pont de Nemours & Co., Inc.
755.	Brit. 557,159		British Thomson-Houston Co., Ltd.
756.	Brit. 559,209	V. T. Wallder	Standard Telephones & Cables, Ltd.
757.	Brit. 558,656		British Thomson-Houston Co., Ltd.
758.	Brit. 562,092		E. I. du Pont de Nemours & Co., Inc.
759.	Brit. 563,554	E. G. Peterson	Hercules Powder Co.
760.	Brit. 570,216		Wingfoot Corp.
761.	Brit. 572,671	J. R. Whinfield and W. K. Birtwistle	
762.	Brit. 576,944		British Thomson-Houston Co., Ltd.
763.	Brit. 578,266– 578,267		Pittsburgh Plate Glass Co.
764.	Brit. 583,482		Imperial Chemical Industries, Ltd.
765.	Brit. 586,457		U.S. Rubber Co.
766.	Brit. 587,492		Wingfoot Corp.
767.	Brit. 588,018		Imperial Chemical Industries, Ltd.

Concerning

Interpolymers of polycrotyl esters of a saturated polycarboxylic acid and modified or unmodified polyhydric alcohol esters of unsaturated, polycarboxylic acids, e.g., maleic acid.

Interpolymers of crotonic acid esters with polyhydric alcohol esters of unsaturated polycarboxylic acids.

Polyester resins from esterification, by heat treatment, of dicarboxylic acids or anhydrides simultaneously with polyhydric alcohols and allyl alcohol or a derivative.

Water-soluble polymeric materials from interpolymerization of maleic anhydride

with a compound containing a single $\diagdown C \!=\! CH_2$ group.

Manufacture and polymerization of esters of maleic acid and unsaturated alcohols.

Synthetic resins prepared by heating a copolymer of vinyl organic esters and unsaturated alkyd resins with an aldehyde or ketone.

Insulating coating for electrical conductors composed of fibrous materials impregnated with a polyester obtained from a glycol, a saturated dicarboxylic acid, and a small proportion of maleic, fumaric, itaconic, citraconic, or dihydromuconic acid.

Resin prepared by treating endomethylene tetrahydrophthalic anhydride with a polyhydric alcohol in the presence of air or oxygen.

Polymers soluble in aqueous alkali from interpolymerization ($70°$-$150°C$.) of maleic anhydride with ethylene in presence of benzoyl peroxide and an inert diluent.

Alkyd resins produced by heating together a polymerized resin, a polycarboxylic acid or anhydride, e.g., phthalic anhydride, and a polyhydric alcohol.

Aralkyl esters of monochloromaleic acid and their copolymers with butadiene, styrene, etc.

Rubberlike substances obtained by treating a dialkylol tertiary amine with a dicarboxylic acid.

Copolymer of a partial polymer of para- or meta-divinyl benzene and an unsaturated alkyd resin.

Thermosetting polymers formed by modifying polymers of unsaturated alcohols and esters, e.g., allyl esters, with an unsaturated acid, aldehyde, or alcohol, e.g., acrylic acid. Catalyst: para-toluenesulfonic acid and (or) hydroquinone.

Copolymers of tetrafluoroethylene with ethylenic compounds, e.g., vinyl acetate, diethyl fumarate.

Interpolymers of a diallyl ether, a saturated monohydric alcohol ester of an acrylic acid, and a saturated monohydric alcohol ester of an ethylenic dicarboxylic acid. Can be used for priming leather; as coating, adhesive, or impregnating resin.

Preparation of allyl diesters of dicarboxylic acids, and their polymerization and copolymerization with vinyl compounds.

Mixtures of alkane dithiols, e.g., 1,2-ethanedithiol, with solvent-soluble unsaturated polymers, e.g., ethylene glycol maleate. Products are deposited from solvents and set into insoluble coatings on heat curing.

Resin Patents (Continued)

	Patent Number	Patentee	Assignee
768.	Brit. 592,046	E. L. Kropa	American Cyanamid Co.
769.	Brit. 592,604	K. E. Marple and E. C. Shokal	Shell Chemical Co.
770.	Brit. 595,447		Distillers Co., Ltd.
771.	Brit. 595,758	L. N. Whitehill and F. A. French	Shell Development Co.
772.	Brit. 595,881	R. Hammond	Imperial Chemical Industries, Ltd.
773.	Brit. 597,793	J. R. Whinfield and W. K. Birtwistle	
774.	Brit. 606,080		U.S. Rubber Co.
775.	Brit. 606,400	S. D. Kaganoff	Standard Telephones & Cable Ltd.
776.	Brit. 607,888	R. Hammond	Imperial Chemical Industries, Ltd.
777.	Brit. 612,311–612,312	J. A. Cottrell and D. H. Hewitt	Lewis Berger & Sons, Ltd.
778.	Brit. 613,506		Pittsburgh Plate Glass Co.
779.	Brit. 620,034		Bakelite, Ltd.
780.	Brit. 621,971	J. G. N. Drewitt and J. Lincoln	
781.	Brit. 625,877	R. Hammond	Imperial Chemical Industries, Ltd.
782.	Brit. 627,037		American Cyanamid Co.
783.	Brit. 627,235		B. F. Goodrich Co.
784.	Brit. 629,019	R. Hammond	Imperial Chemical Industries, Ltd.
785.	Brit. 629,093	A. M. Howard *et al.*	Libbey-Owens-Ford Glass Co.
786.	Brit. 630,370	R. Hammond	Imperial Chemical Industries, Ltd.

Concerning

Copolymers of aryl vinyl compounds, e.g., styrene, with unsaturated alkyd resins modified by a saturated aliphatic or aryl dicarboxylic acid to promote compatibility with the vinyl compounds.

Copolymers of unsaturated esters of an ethereal oxygen-containing polycarboxylic acid and an organic compound containing 2 unconjugated unsaturated C-C linkages, e.g., diallyl phthalate and diallyl diglycolate. Give transparent laminates with glass cloth due to similar index of refraction.

Heat- and light-stable copolymers of a halogen-containing ethenoid compound with an ester or ether-ester containing a glycidyl radical and an unsaturated aliphatic group.

Fire-resistant resins from polymerization of unsaturated esters of halogenated dicarboxylic acids of C_6H_6, e.g., tetrachlorophthalic acid, alone or with other unsaturated compounds, e.g., styrene.

Tetraesters prepared by reaction of a monoacrylic or alpha-substituted monoacrylic ester of a dihydric alcohol, e.g., ethylene glycol, with a dicarboxylic acid, e.g., oxalic, maleic, succinic, phthalic, in the presence of an "inhibitor-catalyst," e.g., hydroquinone disulfonic acid.

Manufacture of rubberlike polyesters from a dialkylol amine $[HO-(CH_2)_n-HR-(CH_2)_n-OH]$, a dicarboxylic acid, and one or more elements of Group II of the periodic system.

Interpolymers of styrene, a monomeric allyl fumarate, and a monomeric allyl alcohol. Alcohol prevents loss by gelation on cooling and purification.

Low-temperature halogenation of polymers, e.g., bromination of polystyrene at temperatures below 10° C.

Polymerizable monomers prepared by treating acrylic acids or their derivatives, e.g., esters, acid chlorides, anhydrides, with dihydric alcohol polyesters, e.g., diethylene glycol-maleic anhydride, ethylene glycol-phthalic anhydride.

Polymerizable allyl methallyl alcohol esters of Diels-Alder adducts of maleic anhydride and unsaturated compounds, e.g., dipentene, cyclopentadiene, alpha-terpinene.

Polymerization of diallyl phthalate.

Preparation of unsaturated alkyd resins from 3,6-endomethylene tetrahydrophthalic anhydride.

Polycondensation of a glycol and a heterocyclic dicarboxylic acid whose dimethyl ester has a melting point above 100° C.

Soluble thermoplastic resins from acrylic dihydroxy esters and dicarboxylic compounds, e.g., maleic acid.

Preparation of unsaturated alkyds. Glycols containing only primary alcohol groups (i.e., $-CH_2OH$) are preferred.

Copolymers of halomaleic acid and 1-ethylenic compounds.

Resins from polyhydric alcohols, e.g., ethylene glycol, and acrylic acid derivatives, e.g., chloroformates of acrylic, methacrylic, or alpha-haloacrylic monohydroxy esters of dihydric or polyhydric alcohols.

Preparation of unsaturated alkyds. Discusses effects of various ingredients on resin properties.

Method for preparation of organic polymers described in Brit. 607,888 in this section.

Resin Patents (Continued)

	Patent Number	Patentee	Assignee
787.	Brit. 632,983		Pittsburgh Plate Glass Co.
788.	Brit. 642,828	T. Evans and D. F. Adelson	N. V. de Bataafsche Petroleum Maatschappij
789.	Brit. 644,287		American Cyanamid Co.
790.	Brit. 644,468	H. Zenftman and A. McLean	Imperial Chemical Industries, Ltd.
791.	Brit. 644,984		Spolek Pro Chemickov A Hutni Vyrobo, Warodni, Podnik, Prague
792.	Brit. 650,002	S. F. Marrian	Imperial Chemical Industries, Ltd.
793.	Brit. 653,489	H. Zenftman and R. McGillivray	Imperial Chemical Industries, Ltd.
794.	Brit. 656,138		American Cyanamid Co.
795.	Brit. 662,365		Canadian Industries, Ltd.
796.	Brit. 663,559		Dow Corning, Ltd.
797.	Brit. 675,076	M. J. Hunter and L. A. Launer	Dow Corning, Ltd.
798.	Brit. 685,449	A. A. K. Whitehouse	Bakelite, Ltd.
799.	Brit. 685,649		N. V. de Bataafsche Petroleum Maatschappij
800.	Brit. 689,622		Dow Corning, Ltd.
801.	Brit. 691,014– 691,015		Dow Corning, Ltd.
802.	Brit. 691,041	E. M. Evans and J. E. S. Whitney	British Resin Products, Ltd.
803.	Brit. 700,617		Farbenfabriken Bayer
804.	Brit. 704,299		N. V. de Bataafsche Petroleum Maatschappij
805.	Dutch 66,784		N. V. de Bataafsche Petroleum Maatschappij
806.	Dutch 67,273		N. V. de Bataafsche Petroleum Maatschappij

Concerning

Condensation product of allyl acid carbonate (CH_2=CH. CH_2OCOOH) and a glycol.

Preparation of alkyd resins from a dicarboxylic acid and a compound of the formula R—O—R′ where R is an unsaturated group with an olefinic bond and R′ is glycerol or glycidol minus 1 hydroxyl group.

Crystalline unsaturated alkyd resin produced from fumaric acid and a glycol of the formula $HO(CH_2)_xOH$ (x = 2−18) or a symmetrical dialkyl derivative thereof.

Resinous polyesters from condensation of aryloxy phosphoryl dichloride with a dihydroxy aromatic compound, e.g., hydroquinone, resorcinol, dihydroxybiphenyl.

Alkylol resins from esterification of cyclohexanediol-1,2 with polybasic acids or their anhydrides in the presence of a solvent and other acids (resin acids, fatty acids).

Film-forming polyesters from pentaerythritol and alkyl carbonates.

Thermosetting polyester resins of low flammability from reaction of dihydroxy aryl compounds, e.g., dihydroxybiphenyl, hydroquinone, with a cycloparaffinic phosphonyl dichloride, e.g., cyclohexylphosphonyl dichloride.

Increase in molecular weight of alkyd resins obtained by heating with a polyfunctional alcohol or acid. Resulting resin can be copolymerized with styrene.

Polyesters from 4-vinylcyclohexene dioxide, a monocarboxylic acid, and phthalic anhydride. Useful as film-forming ingredients in coatings.

Organo-silicon modified alkyd resins prepared by reaction of one or more silanes with a polyhydric alcohol and reaction of the product with a polycarboxylic acid or anhydride.

Copolymers of a silane, a dihydric alcohol, and a polycarboxylic acid or anhydride: silane plus alcohol gives polyester with SiOC linkages which is reacted with acid to give cross-linked insoluble gel.

Unsaturated alkyd resins from esterification of a glycol mixture of low-molecularweight glycol and octadecanediol with unsaturated dibasic acid.

Polyesters from a succinic acid or anhydride containing a C_{18}-C_{26} hydrocarbon radical and an aliphatic saturated dihydric alcohol containing 2–10 C atoms, e.g., 1-octadecenylsuccinic anhydride and ethylene glycol.

Manufacture of thermosetting resins from a glycerine ester of a dicarboxylic acid and a silane or silane mixture.

High temperature resistant coatings prepared by reacting a polysiloxane with glycerine and then reacting the product with a dicarboxylic acid or anhydride thereof.

Copolymerization of vinyl phenols with a polyhydric alcohol ester of an unsaturated polycarboxylic acid.

Production of moldable or adhesive polyester compositions.

Resins prepared from the glycidyl ethers of dihydric phenols.

Polymerization of allyl alcohol or its homologs. Polymers form alkyd resins with polycarboxylic acids.

Copolymers of unsaturated esters of ethereal oxygen-containing polycarboxylic acids with other unsaturated compounds, each containing 2 or more unconjugated olefinic groups, e.g., diallyl diglycolate with diallyl phthalate.

Resin Patents (Continued)

	Patent Number	Patentee	Assignee
807.	Dutch 70,514		N. V. de Bataafsche Petroleum Maatschappij
808.	Fr. 814,093		I. G. Farbenind. A.-G.
809.	Fr. 831,241		I. G. Farbenind. A.-G.
810.	Fr. 841,527		I. G. Farbenind. A.-G.
811.	Fr. 849,985		I. G. Farbenind. A.-G.
812.	Fr. 967,916	V. Dolgopaloff	
813.	Fr. 977,285	M. L. A. Fluchaire and G. Collardeau	Société des usines chimiques Rhône-Poulenc
814.	Ger. 601,323		Allegemeine Elektricitäts-Gesellschaft
815.	Ger. 695,756	H. Hopff and W. Rapp	I. F. Farbenind. A.-G.
816.	Ger. 699,445	H. Hopff and C. Rautenstrauck	I. G. Farbenind. A.-G.
817.	Ger. 708,441	W. Hever	I. G. Farbenind. A.-G.
818.	Ger. 712,277		I. G. Farbenind. A.-G.
819.	Ger. 745,031	H. T. Neher	Rohm & Haas Co.
820.	Japan. 1393('53)	E. Ishida and I. Shimizu	
821.	Japan. 1897('53)	S. Watanabe	Ryoka Industries Co.
822.	Japan. 4156('52)	M. Umemura and G. Nanin	Daihachi Chemical Industries Co.
823.	Swiss 284,090		Ciba, Ltd.
824.	Russ. 51,154	S. N. Ushakov	
825.	Swiss 284,090		Ciba, Ltd.

Concerning

Polymers of mixed esters of polycarboxylic acids, *e.g.*, allyl vinyl phthalate, prepared by reaction of allyl monoesters, *e.g.*, monoallyl phthalate, with vinyl acetate or propionate, or with ethylene. Clear, hard, transparent resins.

Polymers obtained from aqueous emulsion of vinyl chloride and a derivative of an ethylene dicarboxylic acid, *e.g.*, neutral or acid esters of fumaric or maleic acid.

Condensation of polyhydric alcohol with polybasic carboxylic acids in presence of polyvinyl esters of carboxylic acids of low molecular weight, *e.g.*, an acetate, propionate, or butyrate.

Molding compositions prepared from cork dust and a binder obtained by condensation of a polybasic carboxylic acid, *e.g.*, adipic or alkylated adipic acid, with a polyhydric alcohol.

Process for preparation of high-molecular-weight condensation products from polyvalent alcohols and polybasic carboxylic acids. By choice of reactants, products of different properties, such as viscous oils, sticky compositions, waxes, rubberlike products, or hard resins, can be produced.

Esterification or etherification of polyethylene glycol under reduced pressure, *e.g.*, with isolinoleic acid and para-toluenesulfonic acid.

Polymers of diesters of hexahydrophthalic acids and allyl alcohols. Fusible polymers are adhesives.

Combination of alkyds with polymerized vinyl chloride.

Mixed polymers. Addition products of dienes and compounds with activated double bond can be polymerized with polymerizable compounds, *e.g.*, cyclopentadiene, maleic anhydride, and styrene.

Polymerization of fumaric esters.

Interpolymers of an organic vinyl ester, 2-chloro 1,3-butadiene, and a maleic acid ester.

Copolymers of acetylene carboxylic acid or its esters with compounds containing an aliphatic double bond.

Copolymerization of monoesters of maleic acid with vinyl, acrylo, or methacrylo compounds in methyl alcohol.

Rubberlike polyester-type substance prepared from $(CH_3)_2C(OH)CH_2CH_2CH(OH)CH_3$, $HOCH_2CH=CHCH(OH)CH_3$, tetramethylene glycol, adipic acid, maleic anhydride, and suberic acid.

Polyester-type synthetic resin from ethylene glycol, phthalic anhydride, and succinic acid. Suitable as hard rubber substitute, adhesive, or coating.

Mixed ester of dibasic acid glycolate: product of treatment of phthalic anhydride and butyl alcohol with ammonia reacted with $ClCH_2CO_2C_4H_9$ to give o-$C_6H_4(CO_2C_4H_9)CO_2CH_2CO_2C_4H_9$.

Elastic polyesters prepared by heating a polyester with a compound containing more than 1 epoxy group per molecule, *e.g.*, reaction product of 4,4'-dihydroxydiphenyldimethyl methane, epichlorohydrin, and aqueous sodium hydroxide.

Copolymers of a vinyl compound, *e.g.*, styrene, with the condensation product of a polybasic acid or anhydride and a polyhydric alcohol.

Rubberlike resins from heating polyesters whose reactive groups are separated by at least 14 links with epoxy compounds.

UNSATURATED POLYESTERS

Transportation

Patent Number	Patentee	Assignee
826. U.S. 2,500,607	T. W. Evans, D. E. Adelson, and L. N. Whitehill	Shell Development Co.
827. U.S. 2,614,059	L. S. Cooper	Rubatex Products Inc.
828. U.S. 2,653,525	J. S. McGuire	
829. Ger. 683,673	K. Riechers	Deutsche Versuchsanstalt für Luftfahrt E. V.

Electrical Applications

Patent Number	Patentee	Assignee
830. U.S. 2,282,003	T. R. Scott, R. E. Milder, and T. E. D. Menzies	International Standard Electric Corp.
831. U.S. 2,322,756	V. T. Wallder	Bell Telephone Laboratories, Inc.
832. U.S. 2,477,791	N. C. Foster, L. R. Hill, R. H. Runk, and E. L. Schulman	Westinghouse Electric Corp.
833. U.S. 2,482,086	N. C. Foster	Westinghouse Electric Corp.
834. U.S. 2,482,515	F. A. Sattler	Westinghouse Electric Corp.
835. U.S. 2,495,172	C. B. Leape	Westinghouse Electric Corp.
836. U.S. 2,516,030	J. Swiss	Westinghouse Electric Corp.
837. U.S. 2,577,005	A. DiGiacomo	Micamold Radio Corp.
838. U.S. 2,581,862	J. S. Johnson and E. L. Schulman	United States of America (Atomic Energy Commission)
839. U.S. 2,602,829	M. M. Fromm and J. S. Johnson	Westinghouse Electric Corp.
840. U.S. 2,636,018	L. C. Rubens and R. F. Boyer	Dow Chemical Co.
841. U.S. 2,656,290	L. J. Berberick and H. M. Philofsky	Westinghouse Electric Corp.

IX. FINAL PRODUCTS

Concerning

Lightweight, tough, and hard resinous copolymers of diallyl phthalate with al-lylvinyl phthalate. Suitable for aircraft windows.

Radar domes molded from glass fibers, rubber, and alkyd resin.

Glass fiber reinforced plastic mat for aircraft landing strip.

Airplane covering: web of wire of 150–120 meshes per square centimeter impregnated with synthetic resin.

Insulation of electric cables with fibrous tape and material that is polymerized *in situ*.

Covering strands, such as electrical wires, with fibrous insulating material impregnated with linear polyesters, such as polyethylene sebacate.

Insulation for electrical apparatus composed of glass cloth, a typical polyester cross-linked with styrene, mica flakes, and glass fibers.

Thermosetting resin from polymerization of reaction product of linseed oil, castor oil, and maleic anhydride with styrene. Potting compound for electrical applications.

Addition of a nonsolvent diluent, e.g., ethyl alcohol, petroleum, to a cresol solution of a polyesteramide to lower the viscosity so that the solution may be used in wire coating.

Synthetic resins from unsaturated dicarboxylic acids, polyhydric alcohols, and aliphatic diamines, e.g., ethylenediamine. Excellent insulation for enameled wire.

Insulation of wire coils for high temperature applications by applying a coating of an organopolysiloxane resin over a cross-linking polyesteramide resin enamel.

Molded electrical condenser case from vinyl compound-polyester molding composition.

Insulator for electrical machine consisting of asbestos tape and polyester (ethylene glycol-maleic anhydride) binding material.

Rope of inorganic fibers, e.g., asbestos, impregnated with polyester resin, for blocking end coils in electrical generator.

Casting composition from copolymerization of styrene and an unsaturated alkyd resin, in presence of polyisobutylene, chlorinated biphenyl resin, divinylbenzene, para-tertiary-butyl catechol, and lauroyl peroxide. Useful as electrical insulation.

Insulation of electrical coils with mica and polyester resin, e.g., adipic acid-fumaric acid-propylene glycol resin, sebacic acid-maleic anhydride-diethylene glycol resin.

Electrical Applications (Continued)

	Patent Number	Patentee	Assignee
842.	U.S. 2,661,307	N. C. Foster	Westinghouse Electric Corp.
843.	U.S. 2,661,390	M. J. Gelpi	Westinghouse Electric Corp.
844.	Brit. 535,742		Western Electric Co.
845.	Can. 435,968	N. C. Foster, L. R. Hill, E. L. Schulman, and R. H. Runk	Canadian Westinghouse Co.

Industrial Uses

846.	U.S. 2,252,271	C. H. Mathis	Phillips Petroleum Co.
847.	U.S. 2,609,319	H. E. Boge	Mathieson Chemical Corp.
848.	U.S. 2,625,748	H. E. Renaud	Renaud Plastics
849.	U.S. 2,627,482	G. C. Martin and A. J. Sears	General Electric Co.
850.	U.S. 2,629,894	H. D. Boggs	H. D. Boggs

Coatings, Adhesives, Plasticizers, Lubricants

851.	U.S. 2,005,414	H. B. Dykstra	E. I. du Pont de Nemours & Co., Inc.
852.	U.S. 2,012,267	W. H. Carothers	E. I. du Pont de Nemours & Co., Inc.
853.	U.S. 2,234,236	D. E. Edgar	E. I. du Pont de Nemours & Co., Inc.
854.	U.S. 2,298,078	W. Wolff	General Aniline and Film Corp.
855.	U.S. 2,305,224	D. G. Patterson	American Cyanamid Co.
856.	U.S. 2,319,826	F. G. Pellett	General Electric Co.
857.	U.S. 2,324,740	W. N. Stoops and W. A. Denison	Carbide & Carbon Chemicals Co.
858.	U.S. 2,339,058	G. F. D'Alelio	General Electric Co.
859.	U.S. 2,354,572	T. F. Bradley	American Cyanamid Co.

Concerning

Method for coating electrical coils and armatures with polyester resin.

Molded cylindrical electrical insulator comprising a tubular outer shell of glass fiber impregnated with polyester resin and a core of macerated glass, cotton, or asbestos fibers impregnated with polyester resin.

Insulating coating for an electrical conductor comprising a superpolyester having a molecular weight of at least 8,000.

Electrical insulator: mica flakes bonded with copolymer of a glycol ester of an alpha-unsaturated dibasic acid, a monostyrene, and(or) a methyl-substituted monostyrene.

Plugging oil or gas wells, tanks, dams, etc., by introducing into the opening a liquid mixture that contains a polyester and controlling the time of setting of the mixture by addition of benzoyl peroxide catalyst.

Laminated glass cloth-polyester resin piping.

Three-dimensional plastic templet.

Gasket of glass fibers bonded with heat-curable resin.

Molded fiber-filled threaded plastic pipe.

Esters of polycarboxylic acids of at least 5 C atoms, e.g., crotyl butyl phthalate, as plasticizers for cellulose derivatives.

Microcrystalline polyesters of dibasic acids $HOOC(CH_2)_nCOOH$ and glycols $HO(CH_2)_mOH$ where m and n are greater than 2, e.g., trimethylene succinate, decamethylene sebacate. Useful as plasticizers for pyroxylin and bases for pharmaceuticals.

Laminated materials formed by joining layers of cloth with a thermoplastic cement comprising cellulose nitrate and a polyhydric alcohol-polybasic acid resin.

Plastic products suitable for binders in floor coverings, etc., from, e.g., diethylene glycol divinyl ether and the ester of glycerol with tall oil.

Coating for inside of food and beverage cans consisting of copolymer of a diallyl ester with a maleic acid-glycol polyester.

Heat-hardenable adhesives containing a polyvinyl acetate, the reaction product of 3,6-endomethylene Δ-4-tetrahydrophthalic anhydride and a polyhydric alcohol, and a maleic anhydride-polyhydric alcohol polyester.

Coating composition: dispersion in aqueous ammonia of a copolymer of styrene, vinyl acetate, or vinyl chloride with maleic acid or anhydride and a polyalkylene glycol.

Coating composition: partially polymerized diallyl ester of a saturated dicarboxylic acid, e.g., phthalic acid, and an allyl ester of the general formula $R(CH_2:)CCH_2OC(:O)R'$.

Coatings for floor covering material prepared from a filled oxygen-convertible alkyd resin.

Coatings, Adhesives, Plasticizers, Lubricants (Continued)

	Patent Number	Patentee	Assignee
860.	U.S. 2,357,221	C. Opp	Interchemical Corp.
861.	U.S. 2,269,689	N. P. Robie and O. L. Mahlman	Carborundum Co.
862.	U.S. 2,384,595	C. M. Blair, Jr.	Petrolite Corp., Ltd.
863.	U.S. 2,386,144	J. B. Rust	Ellis-Foster Co.
864.	U.S. 2,403,213	G. F. D'Alelio	Pro-phy-lac-tic Brush Co.
865.	U.S. 2,404,192	K. G. Ries, N. P. Robie, and P. V. Doenhoff	Carborundum Co.
866.	U.S. 2,430,564	P. Gordon	American Waterproofing Co.
867.	U.S. 2,433,097	M. O. Debacher	Monsanto Chemical Co.
868.	U.S. 2,435,555	L. Coes, Jr.	Norton Co.
869.	U.S. 2,453,665– 2,453,666	E. L. Kropa	American Cyanamid Co.
870.	U.S. 2,460,181	W. P. Marshall	Pittsburgh Plate Glass Co.
871.	U.S. 2,460,186	E. W. Moffett	Pittsburgh Plate Glass Co.
872.	U.S. 2,469,737	J. G. McNab and H. W. Rudel	Standard Oil Development Co.
873.	U.S. 2,479,090	H. P. Wohnsiedler	American Cyanamid Co.
874.	U.S. 2,486,804– 2,486,806	R. B. Seymour and G. M. Schroder	Henry H. Frede & Co.
875.	U.S. 2,496,234	N. P. Robie	Carborundum Co.
876.	U.S. 2,496,934	C. M. Carson	Wingfoot Corp.
877.	U.S. 2,497,432	E. S. Blake	Monsanto Chemical Co.
878.	U.S. 2,505,347	W. F. Brucksch, Jr.	U. S. Rubber Co.
879.	U.S. 2,512,722– 2,512,723	W. M. Lanham	Union Carbide & Carbon Corp.
880.	U.S. 2,526,427	E. Sewin and F. W. Thomas	Lockheed Aircraft Corp.

Concerning

Plasticizer for cellulose acetate: sebacic and succinic acids, ethylene glycol, and glycerol.

Binder for abrasive consisting of a copolymer of a glycol-unsaturated polybasic acid polyester and vinyl monomer, e.g., styrene.

Use of condensation polymers of unsaturated dicarboxylic acids, e.g., maleic acid, with unsaturated aliphatic alcohols, e.g., oleyl alcohol, to increase viscosity index of mineral oils.

Polyester of an unsaturated dicarboxylic acid and a polyhydric alcohol (sorbitol) as textile size.

Copolymers of diallyl maleate and styrene as bonding agents for abrasives.

Combination resin-bonded abrasive articles. Example of resin binder: polymer of allyl ester, e.g., diethylene glycol bis(allyl carbonate).

Coating resins from vinyl acetate and a dialkyl ester of maleic acid.

Polyvinyl acetals plasticized with partial esters of unsaturated aliphatic acids, e.g., glycerol mono-9-octadecanoate. Useful for extrusion applications.

Mixed alkyd-phenolic resins for bonding abrasives, formed by treating acetals of polyhydric alcohol with a mixture of a phenol and a polybasic acid anhydride.

Copolymer of maleic or fumaric acid polyester with an ethylenic substance having an index of refraction of at least 1.5, e.g., styrene. Adhesives for optical members.

Adhesive calking tape from a polybasic acid-polyhydric alcohol synthetic resin, asbestos fiber, zinc chromate, polyvinyl butyral, and dibutyl phthalate.

Coating composition: an amide-aldehyde resin and, as plasticizer, a polyester of 2-ethyl hexanediol-1,3 and a dicarboxylic acid, e.g., phthalic acid.

Polymerized unsaturated acid esters as stabilizers for motor fuels containing lead tetra-acetate, e.g., copolymers of decyl maleate and vinyl acetate.

Glycol-dibasic acid (or anhydride) polyesters as plasticizers for melamine-formaldehyde thermosetting resins.

Coating for cellulosic textiles consisting of maleic anhydride-styrene interpolymer and solid polyethylene glycol.

Abrasives bonded with a polymer of the ester of an unsaturated alcohol, e.g., allyl alcohol, and a polybasic acid, e.g., phthalic anhydride.

Polyester adhesive containing a polyester of a dihydric alcohol with a fatty acid dimer and resinous cyclized rubber.

Antirusting compounds for turbine oils made by condensing alcohols and glycols with dibasic acids, e.g., mono-9-octadecenyl esters of ethylene bis(acid succinate).

Coating resin prepared by treating fumaric acid-diethylene glycol-ethylene glycol product with diallyl phthalate. Useful for impregnating fabrics to prevent fraying when cut.

As plasticizers for vinyl resins, liquid polyesters of 2-ethyl-1,3-hexanediol and saturated aliphatic dicarboxylic acids (4–10 C atoms). Acids of molecular weight of 1,000–2,000 preferred for desired flexibility and resistance to oil extraction.

Heat-resistant mixture for sealing aircraft parts of porous metal: a polyester resin, triphenyl phosphate, and zinc oxide.

Coatings, Adhesives, Plasticizers, Lubricants (Continued)

	Patent Number	Patentee	Assignee
881.	U.S. 2,544,691	J. H. Kugler and W. E. Lundquist	Minnesota Mining & Manufacturing Co.
882.	U.S. 2,555,062	K. W. Small and P. A. Small	Imperial Chemical Industries, Ltd.
883.	U.S. 2,557,047	G. J. Goepfert and E. E. Howard	Carborundum Co.
884.	U.S. 2,576,392	D. T. Downes	Pittsburgh Plate Glass Co.
885.	U.S. 2,611,756	I. Pockel	Cambridge Industries Co.
886.	U.S. 2,616,849	J. J. Giammaria	Socony-Vacuum Oil Co.
887.	U.S. 2,616,851	J. J. Giammaria	Socony-Vacuum Oil Co.
888.	U.S. 2,626,934	C. C. Kesler	Penick and Ford Ltd., Inc.
889.	U.S. 2,628,207	P. V. Smith, Jr., D. W. Young, and R. G. Newberg	Standard Oil Development Co.
890.	U.S. 2,628,974	R. T. Sanderson	Texas Co.
891.	U.S. 2,647,098	W. M. Smith, Jr., and R. J. Reid	Firestone Tire & Rubber Co.
892.	U.S. 2,647,099	W. M. Smith, Jr.	Firestone Tire & Rubber Co.
893.	U.S. 2,649,433	H. Hönel and H. Manzano	
894.	U.S. 2,650,184	L. P. Biefeld	Owens-Corning Fiberglas Corp.
895.	U.S. 2,652,382– 2,652,383	J. F. Davis	American Cyanamid Co.
896.	U.S. 2,668,133	J. J. Brophy and R. R. Perron	United Shoe Machinery Corp.
897.	U.S. 2,674,648	P. O. Nicodemus	General Electric Co.
898.	Austrian 176,021	H. Hönel	
899.	Brit. 563,624		British Thomson-Houston Co., Ltd.
900.	Brit. 586,826		Resinous Products & Chemical Co.

Concerning

Coatings for porous sheet materials, e.g., leather, paper; copolymers of acrylic esters and dicarboxylic acid esters, e.g., maleates or fumarates.

Vinyl chloride polymers plasticized with polyesters having a specified viscosity and a ratio of total number of C atoms to COOH groups of at least 4.5 to 1, e.g., polypentamethylene glutarate, sebacate, and adipate, and polytetramethylene adipate.

Abrasive with mixed polyester resins as binder and asbestos or fused quartz as filler.

Mastic for holding laminated window in place: polyester-styrene copolymer, aluminum powder filler, and neutral filler.

Polyesters, e.g., of adipic acid or succinic anhydride with diethylene or dipropylene glycol, as plasticizers for polyvinyl resins.

Copolymers of maleic anhydride with diesters of itaconic acid and aliphatic alcohols having 10–18 C atoms. Useful as pour-point depressants and viscosity-index improvers for lubricating oils.

Esters of copolymers of maleic anhydride and vinyl acetate with saturated aliphatic alcohols of 12–18 C atoms. Useful as pour-point depressants and viscosity-index improvers for lubricating oils.

Resin-modified starch adhesive.

Terephthalate esters, e.g., di-isooctyl terephthalate, as plasticizers for polymers and copolymers of vinyl chloride.

Glycol-dicarboxylic acid polyesters as synthetic lubricants. Viscosity of oils determined by acid to glycol ratio, e.g., high ratio, light oils.

Linear polyester plasticizers for vinyl chloride resins.

Linear polyester plasticizers for vinyl chloride resins.

Hardenable resins, suitable as coatings, prepared by combining a phenolformaldehyde resol with an alkyd resin, e.g., ester obtained from adipic acid and trimethylolpropane.

Glass fiber cloth coated on both sides with polyester resin but with minimum adhesion between fibers and resin. Coating method increases strength, puncture resistance, and flexural endurance of product.

Polyester coating compositions.

Curing of adhesives (including polyester adhesives) for bonding leather by radiation from microwave cavity or d.c. electron accelators.

Insulating coating for a magnet tape consisting of a fibrous inorganic tape permeated with copolymerized acrylate resins and coated with the condensation product of an ethoxylene resin and an acidic unsaturated polyester.

Polyester resins for paints prepared from polybasic aliphatic carboxylic acids, monobasic fatty acids, and a polyalcohol.

Adhesives containing an alkyd resin and a polyvinyl ester.

Linear polyesters of 1,2-propylene glycol and sebacic acid as nonmigrating plasticizers for ethenoid polymers, e.g., polyvinyl chloride, polyvinyl acetate.

Coatings, Adhesives, Plasticizers, Lubricants (Continued)

Patent Number	Patentee	Assignee
901. Brit. 684,400	O. B. Edgar and H. G. White	Imperial Chemical Industries, Ltd.
902. Brit. 689,667		Industrial Tape Corp.
903. Brit. 690,921	W. L. Beears	B. F. Goodrich Co.
904. Can. 437,995–437,996	E. L. Kropa	American Cyanamid Co.
905. Fr. 866,766		Societé anon. des Avions Caudron
906. Ger. 645,103	W. Heyn	Duco A.-G.
907. Japan. 1600('53)	K. Shintani, et al.	Kansai Paint Co.

Building Industry

908. U.S. 2,537,520	E. Eyer	U. S. Rubber Co.
909. U.S. 2,627,297	C. R. Faelten	Pittsburgh Plate Glass Co.
910. Brit. 540,939–540,940		Pittsburgh Plate Glass Co.
911. Brit. 654,146	P. A. Norris	General Motors Co.
912. Brit. 671,832	C. B. Joseph	Ashdowns, Ltd.

Military Uses

913. Ger. 742,920	G. Renwanz and O. Wernicke	Auergesellschaft A.-G.

Scientific Uses

914. U.S. 2,318,845	R. C. Feagin and C. H. Prange	Austenal Laboratories, Inc.
915. U.S. 2,477,268	J. A. Saffir	Dentists' Supply Co. of New York
916. U.S. 2,495,173	C. B. Leape	Westinghouse Electric Corp.

Concerning

Coating, impregnating, or adhesively uniting articles with polyester compositions.

Adhesive tape or sheet with a backing of polyester resin or other material and a pressure-sensitive adhesive coating over a thin primer coating.

Polyesters from 3,5,5-trimethyl-1-hexanol and aromatic polycarboxylic acids, e.g., phthalic acid. Used as plasticizers for polyvinyl chloride and other vinyl polymers.

Copolymers of fumaric acid or maleic acid polyesters with an ethylenic substance having an index of refraction of at least 1.5, e.g., styrene, as adhesives for optical apparatus.

Plasticizers for resins from phenol-, urea-, and aniline-aldehyde condensations: a long-chain compound, e.g., a polyester resin, and a common plasticizer for vinyl resins, e.g., tritolyl phosphate.

Synthetic resin lacquer components from heating, under pressure, a solution of a polyhydric alcohol-polycarboxylic acid resin in a volatile solvent, e.g., xylene.

Unsaturated polyester resin for use as coating or adhesive, prepared from maleic anhydride, diethylene glycol, and castor oil.

Substitute for ceramic wall tile consisting of a polyester-styrene copolymer filled with calcium carbonate.

Panel composed of resins and fibrous filler.

Artificial glass comprising a hard surface film of a polymerized polyhydric alcohol polyester of an unsaturated acid, e.g., cinnamic, crotonic, on a transparent flexible plastic base.

Molded sheet material suitable for door panels, etc., formed from polyester resin reinforced with a sheet of cloth that is sealed and impregnated with a water-soluble carboxy or hydroxy methylcellulose.

Sheet material impregnated with low-pressure synthetic resins, e.g., diallyl phthalate resin or compatible copolymers of polyester resins with or without styrene.

Protection of skin against war gases with a textile or paper web impregnated with unhardened intermediate and powdered condensation products of aliphatic and aromatic dicarboxylic acids and polyhydric alcohols.

Dental resin from polymerized mixture of ethyl alpha-methacrylate, diallyl itaconate, and styrene.

Dental molding compounds from glass fiber reinforced diallyl resins.

Polyesteramide film, e.g., from maleic anhydride, succinic acid, adipic acid, ethylene glycol, and ethylenediamine, used as sample holder for x-ray diffraction tests.

Scientific Uses (Continued)

	Patent Number	Patentee	Assignee
917.	U.S. 2,579,596	H. F. Minter and M. M. Leven	Westinghouse Electric Corp.
918.	U.S. 2,583,150	H. F. Minter, N. C. Foster, and M. M. Leven	Westinghouse Electric Corp.
919.	Brit. 589,701	S. A. Leader and J. J. Gordon	Portland Plastics Ltd.

Consumer Items and Miscellaneous

920.	U.S. 2,220,621	C. Ellis	Ellis Laboratories, Inc.
921.	U.S. 2,406,227	E. G. King	Armstrong Cork Co.
922.	U.S. 2,406,298	E. C. King	Armstrong Cork Co.
923.	U.S. 2,411,954	W. J. Burke	E. I. du Pont de Nemours & Co., Inc.
924.	U.S. 2,511,695	W. B. Canfield	Ellis-Foster Co. (½) and Montclair Research Corp. (½)
925.	U.S. 2,609,255	D. E. Winkler	Shell Chemical Co.
926.	U.S. 2,647,848–2,647,849	P. J. Douglas, P. V. Palmquist, and J. D. Grove	Minnesota Mining & Manufacturing Co.
927.	Ger. 742,754	H. Sonnenfeld and E. Strunk	Deutscher Verlag

---

Concerning

Casting method and device for making large specimens for photoelastic studies. Very detailed claims.

Resinous products of any size for photoelastic studies. Conventional polyester compositions; special casting device.

X-ray opaque synthetic resins, e.g., methyl methacrylate, diallyl phthalate, containing brominated hydrocarbons, e.g., vinyl bromide. For dental work.

Printing inks from straight-chain polyesters and a pigment. Polyesters used may be cross-linked with styrene. Cobalt naphthenate used as a catalyst gives quick-drying ink.

Bottle cap from polyester composition containing adipic acid.

Bottle cap from polyester of propylene glycol with usual unsaturated acids.

Mixtures of polymeric polyunsaturated compounds, e.g., polyesters and polythiols. Means of making rubbers insoluble in organic solvents.

Shoe polish consisting of a wax and a copolymer of butyl and ethyl methacrylates with diallyl maleate.

Stabilization of vinyl halides with unsaturated polyesters.

Lettering film comprising (1) a decorative weather-resistant film, e.g., a heat-cured blend of alkyd resin and aminoaldehyde resin or an air-drying alkyd resin, and (2) a nontacky waterproof adhesive.

Printing plates from nonflammable, insoluble plastics produced by polycondensation or polymerization.

Manufacture of Fiber-Forming Polyesters

	Patent Number	Patentee	Assignee
928.	U.S. 2,071,250–2,071,253	W. H. Carothers	E. I. du Pont de Nemours & Co., Inc.
929.	U.S. 2,224,037	M. M. Brubaker, R. E. Christ, and D. D. Coffman	E. I. du Pont de Nemours & Co., Inc.
930.	U.S. 2,249,950	C. S. Fuller	Bell Telephone Laboratories, Inc.
931.	U.S. 2,315,613	C. J. Frosch	Bell Telephone Laboratories, Inc.
931a.	U.S. 2,363,581	C. J. Frosch	Bell Telephone Laboratories, Inc.
932.	U.S. 2,388,318	C. J. Frosch	Bell Telephone Laboratories, Inc.
933.	U.S. 2,453,150	C. L. Mehltretter	United States of America
934.	U.S. 2,465,319	J. R. Whinfield and J. T. Dickson	E. I. du Pont de Nemours & Co., Inc.
935.	U.S. 2,471,023	J. G. Cook, J. T. Dickson, and A. R. Lowe	Imperial Chemical Industries, Ltd.
936.	U.S. 2,479,067	W. F. Gresham	E. I. du Pont de Nemours & Co., Inc.
937.	U.S. 2,491,660	W. F. Gresham	E. I. du Pont de Nemours & Co., Inc.
938.	U.S. 2,499,613	H. C. Miller and B. C. Pratt	E. I. du Pont de Nemours & Co., Inc.
939.	U.S. 2,518,283	E. F. Casassa	E. I. du Pont de Nemours & Co., Inc.
940.	U.S. 2,534,028	E. F. Izard	E. I. du Pont de Nemours & Co., Inc.
941.	U.S. 2,551,731	J. G. N. Drewitt and J. Lincoln	Celanese Corp. of America

I. LINEAR FIBER-FORMING POLYESTERS

Concerning

(Early polyester patents.) Linear condensation "superpolymers" suitable for production of pliable, strong, elastic fibers. Initial materials specified, e.g., polyesters, polyamides, polyethers, polyanhydrides, polyacetals.

Preparation of fiber-forming polyesteramides by reaction of mixtures of diamines, dibasic acids, and glycols in specified proportions. Products have greater solubility and stretchability than straight fiber-forming polyesters or polyamides.

Linear polyesters capable of cold drawing produced by esterification of dihydric alcohols, e.g., ethylene, decamethylene, or trimethylene glycol, with dicarboxylic acids, e.g., sebacic, succinic, suberic, azelaic, or glutaric, in the presence of a nonoxidizing salt of a heavy metal with a strong mineral acid, e.g., $CaCl_2$, $ZnCl_2$, $AlCl_3$, $SrBr_2$, or of diethyl sulfate.

Fiber-forming polyesters made from polyhexahydroquinone sebacate.

Cold-drawing polyesters from esterification of a glycol containing 2 hydroxyl groups joined by a straight-chain aliphatic polymethylene radical with a dicarboxylic acid, e.g., succinic acid. Esterification carried out in presence of 0.025–1% (mol.) of glycerol.

Fiber-forming linear polyester from a polymethylene glycol and a dicarboxylic acid containing a nonconjugated olefinic bond, particularly dihydromuconic acid. Nonconjugation of double bond avoids cross-linking difficulties associated with use of acids containing conjugated bonds, e.g., maleic acid.

Linear polyesters produced from dimethylene d-gluconic acid. Useful in coating compositions, fibers, and adhesives.

Basic patent. Polymeric linear terephthalic esters from esterification of a glycol with terephthalic acid, an acid ester, e.g., methyl terephthalate or a terephthalic acid dihalide.

See Brit. 604,985 in this section.

Terephthalic acid from catalytic oxidation of para-toluic acid.

Esters from terephthalic acid and butyl alcohol. Catalysts: $PbO-ZnO$, ZnB_4O_7, or PbB_4O_7.

Modification of polyester resins, etc., with inorganic polyisocyanates or polyisothiocyanates of silicon or titanium. Products dry faster and harder, gel slower, and are less affected by water; may be used for fibers and films.

Use of $3ZnO \cdot 2B_2O_3$ as catalyst in making polyethylene terephthalate from ethylene glycol and dimethyl terephthalate.

Litharge as catalyst in making polyethylene terephthalates.

High-melting polyesters from compounds of the general formula X-R-Y where X and Y are hydroxy or carboxy groups and R is a divalent radical having a heterocyclic ring, e.g., thiophene, furane, and pyridine 2,5-dicarboxylic acids. Useful in fiber-forming.

Manufacture of Fiber-Forming Polyesters (Continued)

	Patent Number	Patentee	Assignee
942.	U.S. 2,551,732	J. G. Drewitt and J. Lincoln	Celanese Corp. of America
943.	U.S. 2,589,687	P. J. Flory and F. S. Leutner	Wingfoot Corp.
944.	U.S. 2,589,688	P. J. Flory and F. S. Leutner	Wingfoot Corp.
945.	U.S. 2,594,144	P. J. Flory and F. S. Leutner	Wingfoot Corp.
946.	U.S. 2,595,343	J. G. N. Drewitt and J. Lincoln	Celanese Corp. of America
947.	U.S. 2,597,643	E. F. Izard and L. A. Auspos	E. I. du Pont de Nemours & Co., Inc.
948.	U.S. 2,630,454	L. H. Bock	Rayonier Inc.
949.	U.S. 2,634,251	P. Kass	Atlas Powder Co.
950.	U.S. 2,636,899	L. A. Burrows, R. M. Cavanaugh, and W. M. Nagle	E. I. du Pont de Nemours & Co., Inc.
951.	U.S. 2,641,592	C. H. Hofricher, Jr.	E. I. du Pont de Nemours & Co., Inc.
952.	U.S. 2,643,989	L. A. Auspos and J. B. Dempster	E. I. du Pont de Nemours & Co., Inc.
953.	U.S. 2,646,420	P. W. Morgan	E. I. du Pont de Nemours & Co., Inc.
954.	U.S. 2,647,885	H. R. Billica	E. I. du Pont de Nemours & Co., Inc.
955.	U.S. 2,650,213	C. H. Hofrichter, Jr.	E. I. du Pont de Nemours & Co., Inc.
956.	U.S. 2,651,922	B. L. Graham	Phillips Petroleum Co.
957.	U.S. 2,656,377	M. A. Pino	California Research Corp.
958.	U.S. 2,657,194	J. C. Butler and D. C. McGowan	California Research Corp.
959.	U.S. 2,657,195	W. G. Toland, Jr.	California Research Corp.

Concerning

Bis(beta-hydroxyethyl) terephthalate prepared from reaction of sodium terephthalate and ethylene chlorohydrin in the presence of sodium iodide as catalyst.

Fiber-forming condensation products of dibasic acid chlorides, both aliphatic and araliphatic, with glycols.

Preparation of a linear polymer by condensation of terephthalyl chloride or analogues with glycols.

Suppression of undesired side reaction in making terephthalate or isophthalate esters by using a small proportion of a higher glycol (C_4 and up).

Production of high-melting polyesters suitable for fiber-forming from dicarboxylic acids and acetylated diphenols, e.g., hydroquinone diacetate; give a smoother reaction and lighter-colored products than free diphenols.

Polymerization of polymethylene terephthalate in solvent (e.g., diphenyl-diphenyl oxide); polymer precipitates as fine powder.

An acid of the formula

useful for making fiber-forming polyesters.

Linear polyester resins from an alcohol of the formula

and maleic or fumaric acid.

Preparation of terephthalic acid by treating para-dialkyl benzenes, e.g., paraxylene, para-cymene, with dilute nitric acid.

Use of cobaltous acetate as catalyst in making polyethylene terephthalates.

Cerium catalysts, e.g., metallic Ce, Ce oxide, or a Ce alloy, for production of glycol terephthalate by ester interchange.

Linear fiber-forming polyesters prepared by polymerizing difunctional monomers of the type $(YR')_2RP:X$, where X is O or S, R is a univalent hydrocarbon radical, R' is a bivalent hydrocarbon radical, and Y is a functional radical (COOR, COOH, NH_2, OH, etc.).

Antimony trioxide catalyst for polyethylene terephthalate polymerization.

Production of polyethylene terephthalate.

Rotary crystallizer for continuous separation of binary mixtures of organic compounds, e.g., mixtures of meta-xylene and para-xylene.

Separation of mixtures of lower alkyl alcohol diesters of isophthalic and terephthalic acids by selective extraction with solvents for each ester.

Fiber-forming linear polyesters with improved dye receptivity from reaction of a stilbene dicarboxylic acid (or ester) with a polyalkylene glycol, e.g., diethylene or triethylene glycol.

Reaction of stilbene dicarboxylic acid (or ester) with glycol, e.g., ethylene glycol, diamine, or amino alcohol.   Preparation of ethylene para,para'-stilbenedicarboxylic terephthalate is described.

Manufacture of Fiber-Forming Polyesters (Continued)

	Patent Number	Patentee	Assignee
960.	U.S. 2,662,093	H. R. Billica	E. I. du Pont de Nemours & Co., Inc.
961.	U.S. 2,662,871	L. H. Bock	Rayonier Inc.
962.	U.S. 2,664,440	W. G. Toland, Jr.	California Research Corp.
963.	U.S. 2,666,786	M. Kulka and R. H. F. Manske	U. S. Rubber Co.
964.	Brit. 415,665	W. C. Fairweather	Singer Sewing Machine Co.
965.	Brit. 578,079	J. R. Whinfield and J. T. Dickson	Imperial Chemical Industries, Ltd.
966.	Brit. 579,462	J. T. Dickson	
967.	Brit. 588,497	J. G. Cook, J. T. Dickson, and H. P. W. Huggill	Imperial Chemical Industries, Ltd.
968.	Brit. 590,417	J. G. Cook	Imperial Chemical Industries, Ltd.
969.	Brit. 590,451	J. T. Dickson, H. P. W. Huggill, and J. C. Welch	Imperial Chemical Industries, Ltd.
970.	Brit. 604,073	J. G. Cook, H. P. W. Huggill, and A. Regenwald	Imperial Chemical Industries, Ltd.
971.	Brit. 604,074	J. G. Cook, H. P. W. Huggill, and A. Regenald	Imperial Chemical Industries, Ltd.
972.	Brit. 604,075	A. R. Lowe	Imperial Chemical Industries, Ltd.
973.	Brit. 604,985	J. G. Cook, J. T. Dickson, A. R. Lowe, and J. B. Whinfield	Imperial Chemical Industries, Ltd.
974.	Brit. 609,792	W. K. Birtwistle	
975.	Brit. 610,138	J. R. Lewis and R. J. W. Reynolds	Imperial Chemical Industries, Ltd.
976.	Brit. 610,140	J. T. Dickson and R. J. W. Reynolds	Imperial Chemical Industries, Ltd.
977.	Brit. 623,669	A. C. Farthing	Imperial Chemical Industries, Ltd.

Concerning

Monomeric glycol terephthalates prepared by treating $HO(CH_2)_nOH$ ($n = 2 - 10$) with alkyl (1–4 C atoms) terephthalates in presence of a LiH, NaH, or CaH_2 catalyst.

Linear fiber-forming polyesters made from dibasic acids derived from vanillin.

Fractional crystallization process for separation of mixture of isophthalic and terephthalic acids.

Preparation of terephthalic acid by refluxing a mixture of para-xylylene dichloride, nitric acid, and a saturated aliphatic monocarboxylic acid of 2–6 C atoms.

Alkyd resin from terephthalic acid, glycerol, and drying oils.

One of first patents on preparation of terephthalate resins from terephthalic acid or its low aliphatic esters, e.g., methyl terephthalate, and glycols.

Fiber-forming polyesters from diphenoxyethane 4,4[1]-dicarboxylic acid and glycols.

Fiber-forming polyesters from an acid of the formula $HOOC\text{---}C_6H_4\text{---}(CH_2)_x\text{---}C_6H_4\text{---}COOH$ and glycols.

Extension of Brit. 578,079. In addition to glycols, esters of glycols with low-molecular-weight acids, e.g., acetic, can be used with terephthalic acid or its esters to make resins.

Extension of Brit. 578,079. Half-esters, cycloaliphatic esters, aryl esters, acid halides, amine salts, etc. of terephthalic acid can be used to make fiber-forming polyesters if their boiling points are lower than the glycols used.

Fiber-forming polyesters from glycols and 1,5-, 2,6-, or 2,7-naphthalene dicarboxylic acids or their ester-forming derivatives.

Fiber-forming polyesters from glycols and an acid of the formula $HOOC\text{---}C_6H_4\text{---}R\text{---}C_6H_4\text{---}COOH$, where R is O, $O\text{---}CH_2$, $O\text{---}C_6H_4\text{---}O$, etc., or its ester-forming derivatives.

Fiber-forming polyesters from glycols and an acid of the same formula as in Brit. 604,074 except that R is S, $S(CH_2)_xS$, etc.

Fiber-forming polyesters from heating of hydroxycarboxylic acids of the general

formula $HO\text{---}R\text{---}\langle\ \rangle\text{---}COOH$, where R is $(CH_2)_x$ or $(CH_2)_x\text{---}O$, e.g.,

para-(beta-hydroxy-ethoxy)benzoic acid.

Fiber-forming polyesters from polymethylene glycol and an acid of the formula $HOOC\text{---}C_6H_4\text{---}R\text{---}C_6H_4\text{---}COOH$ where R is $\text{---}NH\text{---}(CH_2)_m\text{---}NH$, m =

$$2 - 10, \text{ or } \text{---}N\begin{array}{c}(CH_2)_2\\ \diagup\quad\diagdown\\ \diagdown\quad\diagup\\ (CH_2)_n\end{array}N\text{---}, \text{ n} = 1, 2, \text{ or } 3.$$

Stabilization of terephthalic acid polyesters in molecular weight and intrinsic viscosity with 5 or less % (mol.) of a monofunctional compound, e.g., ethyl benzoate, ethyl terephthalate, cetyl alcohol, etc.

Process for melt blending of terephthalic acid polyesters with polyamides, interpolyamides, polyesters, or interpolyesters.

Bis(2-hydroxyethyl) terephthalate from esterification of mixture of terephthalic acid and its salts with ethylene oxide.

Manufacture of Fiber-Forming Polyesters (Continued)

	Patent Number	Patentee	Assignee
978.	Brit. 623,836	C. H. Bowden, G. M. Henderson, and S. R. Robinson	Imperial Chemical Industries, Ltd.
979.	Brit. 627,270		Wingfoot Corp.
980.	Brit. 630,992		Wingfoot Corp.
981.	Brit. 634,609	J. G. N. Drewitt and J. Lincoln	
982.	Brit. 636,429	E. R. Wallsgrove and F. Reeder	Courtaulds, Ltd.
983.	Brit. 642,423		Wingfoot Corp.
984.	Brit. 643,388	R. H. Griffith and J. H. G. Plant	Gas, Light, and Coke Co.
985.	Brit. 648,513	A. S. Carpenter, F. Reeder, and E. R. Wallsgrove	Courtaulds, Ltd.
986.	Brit. 650,358	O. B. Edgar and E. Ellery	Imperial Chemical Industries, Ltd.
987.	Brit. 651,762	F. Reeder and E. R. Wallsgrove	Courtaulds, Ltd.
988.	Brit. 652,024	A. S. Carpenter, E. R. Wallsgrove, and F. Reeder	Courtaulds, Ltd.
989.	Brit. 652,030	A. S. Carpenter, E. R. Wallsgrove, and F. Reeder	Courtaulds, Ltd.
990.	Brit. 655,377		Wingfoot Corp.
991.	Brit. 662,682	R. J. Flory and F. S. Leutner	Wingfoot Corp.
992.	Brit. 673,066	W. W. Triggs	Wingfoot Corp.
993.	Brit. 675,169	S. O. Greenlee	Devoe and Reynolds Co., Inc.
994.	Brit. 676,372	O. B. Edgar and B. Jacob	Imperial Chemical Industries, Ltd.
995.	Brit. 678,264		British Celanese Corp.
996.	Brit 681,455		N. V. de Bataafsche Petroleum Maatschappij

---

Concerning

Terephthalic acid from oxidation of para-xylene by air with cobalt naphthenate as catalyst.

Linear polyesters from acid chlorides of dibasic acids and glycols, e.g., decamethylene glycol and sebacyl chloride. Faster reaction, higher-molecular-weight products than with acids.

Linear polyesters from condensation of terephthalic and isophthalic acid halides with glycols, e.g., terephthalyl chloride and tetramethylene glycol.

Fiber-forming polyesters prepared from reaction product of a halogenhydrin of a volatile glycol and a sodium or other salt of a dicarboxylic acid of the formula

HOOC — X — COOH, where X is $\left[-\bigcirc-\right]_n$ or $\left[-\bigcirc-Y-\bigcirc-\right]$,

n is 1 or 2, and Y is alkylene or a hetero group.

Polyesters from hydroquinone and terephthalic acid. Capable of being cold drawn into fibers.

Polycondensation of acid chlorides of dibasic acids with glycols.

Fiber-forming polyesters from glycols and benzophenone 4,4¹-dicarboxylic acid or its esters.

Interpolymerization of hydroquinone polyesters from Brit. 636,429 with polyesters from autocondensation of, e.g., 2-(para-carboxyphenoxy)ethanol (Brit. 604,985).

Soft, low-melting films by polymerization of terephthalic acid, adipic acid, and (or) sebacic acid, and ethylene glycol.

Polymeric esters from condensation of hydroquinone bis(2-hydroxyethyl)ether with terephthalic acid or other dicarboxylic acids and their diesters.

Fiber-forming thermoplastic resins prepared from dihydric phenol and epichlorohydrin.

Fiber-forming thermoplastic resins prepared from (1) epichlorohydrin and para-monohydroxy benzoic acid or (2) epichlorohydrin, a mixture of para- and meta-monohydroxy benzoic acids, and a phenolic dihydroxy compound.

Polyesters from condensation of acid chlorides of dibasic acids with glycols. See U.S. 2,594,144, in this section.

Tough, strong, high-molecular-weight polyesters by interpolymerization of low-molecular-weight polyesters with terminal hydroxyl groups and low-molecular-weight polyesters with terminal carboxyl groups.

Fiber-forming resins from condensation of polyhydric phenols and halogenhydrins.

Fiber-forming copolyesters made from ethylene glycol, terephthalic acid, and a saturated aliphatic dibasic acid of the formula $C_nH_{2n}(COOH)_2$ where n = 2- 8.

High-melting-point polyesters from aromatic dicarboxylic acids and bis(beta-oxyethyl) derivatives of diphenols.

Preparation of isophthalic or terephthalic acid by catalytic oxidation of mixture of meta-xylene and meta-toluic acid or para-xylene and para-toluic acid, respectively.

Manufacture of Fiber-Forming Polyesters (Continued)

	Patent Number	Patentee	Assignee
997.	Danish 63,874		I. G. Farbenind. A.-G.
998.	Dutch 63,987		N. V. de Bataafsche Petroleum Maatachappij
999.	Swed. 126,464	G. A. Nyman	A. Ahlström Osakeyhtiö

Manufacture of Fibers and Films

	Patent Number	Patentee	Assignee
1000.	U.S. 2,035,528	M. M. Brubaker	E. I. du Pont de Nemours & Co., Inc.
1001.	U.S. 2,253,146	E. W. Spanagel	E. I. du Pont de Nemours & Co., Inc.
1002.	U.S. 2,465,150	J. T. Dickson	E. I. du Pont de Nemours & Co., Inc.
1003.	U.S. 2,497,376	J. C. Swallow, D. K. Baird, and B. P. Ridge	Imperial Chemical Industries, Ltd.
1004.	U.S. 2,503,251	E. G. Edwards and R. J. W. Reynolds	Imperial Chemical Industries, Ltd.
1005.	U.S. 2,515,136	W. T. Pigott	Wingfoot Corp.
1006.	U.S. 2,571,319	E. Waters and L. Wood	Imperial Chemical Industries, Ltd.
1007.	U.S. 2,590,402	J. D. Hall, B. P. Ridge, and J. R. Whinfield	Imperial Chemical Industries, Ltd.
1008.	U.S. 2,597,557	L. E. Amborski	E. I. du Pont de Nemours & Co., Inc.
1009.	U.S. 2,604,667	H. H. Hebeler	E. I. du Pont de Nemours & Co., Inc.
1010.	U.S. 2,604,689	H. H. Hebeler	E. I. du Pont de Nemours & Co., Inc.
1011.	U.S. 2,605,555	E. L. Griggs, Jr., and E. F. Taylor	E. I. du Pont de Nemours & Co., Inc.
1012.	U.S. 2,611,923	H. F. Hume	E. I. du Pont de Nemoùrs & Co., Inc.
1013.	U.S. 2,615,784	W. R. McClellan	E. I. du Pont de Nemours & Co., Inc.
1014.	U.S. 2,627,449	H. Luttringhaus, H. R. Mautner, and A. A. Arcus	
1015.	U.S. 2,647,104	J. C. Shivers, Jr.	E. I. du Pont de Nemours & Co., Inc.
1016.	U.S. 2,663,612	J. W. Gibson, Jr.	E. I. du Pont de Nemours & Co., Inc.

Concerning

Cross-linking of terephthalic acid-tetramethylene glycol polyesters with di-isocyanates.

Aromatic dicarboxylic acids from oxidation of mixture of isomeric aromatic hydrocarbons to monocarboxylic acids, separation of isomers, and oxidation of isolated acids, e.g., xylene isomers + O_2 = toluic acids; para-toluic acid + O_2 = terephthalic acid.

Cumic acid and dimethyl-para-tolyl carbinol from oxidation of cymene. Terephthalic acid is a by-product.

Synthetic resins from polyhydric alcohols and polybasic acids, plus a high-molecular-weight alcohol (or alcohols), e.g., carnaubyl, ceryl, dodecyl, heptyl, etc. Give strong films.

Methacrylic size for synthetic linear polymer yarns (polyesters, polyamides, polyethers) for making knitted stocking fabric.

Formation of high-melting filaments from linear polyesters derived from diphenoxy-alkane 4,4^1-dicarboxylic acids and glycols.

Film cast from cresylic acid solution of quenched polyethylene terephthalate; solvent evaporated, polyester quenched again and drawn.

Production of filaments and fibers from highly polymeric linear polyesters, e.g., polyethylene esters of terephthalic acid.

Melting of condensation polymers, e.g., linear polyesters, by radiation of heat in a furnace.

Coloring of polyethylene terephthalate fibers and filaments.

Immersion of coarsely woven polymethylene terephthalate in sodium hydroxide solution (4–20%) to form undegraded, fine, soft fabric.

Improvement of elongation of drawn oriented polyethylene terephthalate fibers by nitric acid treatment.

Process for spinning polyester yarns from a melt, e.g., containing polyethylene terephthalate, another glycol, and (or) another dicarboxylic acid.

Spinning process for terephthalate resin and fiber.

Spinning apparatus for solvent spinning of cellulose acetate fibers.

Apparatus for drawing and heat treating of heat-stretchable yarns and filaments on single heated roll.

Terephthalate bristles—details of drawing and heat treating.

Dyeing of polyester fibers with acid leuco vat dyes.

Making ethylene terephthalate more receptive to dyes by introduction of basic nitrogen atoms into its structure, e.g., by heating with an amino alcohol in diphenyl ether.

Process for coloring polyethylene terephthalate fibers.

Manufacture of Fibers and Films (Continued)

	Patent Number	Patentee	Assignee
1017.	U.S. 2,670,263	H. Luttringhaus and A. A. Arcus	General Dyestuff Corp.
1018.	Belg. 446,549		I. G. Farbenind. A.-G.
1019.	Belg. 447,428		I. G. Farbenind. A.-G.
1020.	Brit. 504,714		E. I. du Pont de Nemours & Co., Inc.
1021.	Brit. 527,532		E. I. du Pont de Nemours & Co., Inc.
1022.	Brit. 533,306		E. I. du Pont de Nemours & Co., Inc.
1023.	Brit. 533,307		E. I. du Pont de Nemours & Co., Inc.
1024.	Brit. 536,379–536,380		E. I. du Pont de Nemours & Co., Inc.
1025.	Brit. 596,688	J. L. Moilliet, R. J. W. Reynolds, and W. Todd	Imperial Chemical Industries, Ltd.
1026.	Brit. 603,840	L. Leben and A. Little	Imperial Chemical Industries, Ltd.
1027.	Brit. 609,796	J. S. Byers and J. C. Swallow	Imperial Chemical Industries, Ltd.
1028.	Brit. 610,135	R. L. Heath	Imperial Chemical Industries, Ltd.
1029.	Brit. 610,136	R. L. Heath	Imperial Chemical Industries, Ltd.
1030.	Brit. 610,137	J. T. Dickson, R. L. Heath, and R. J. W. Reynolds	Imperial Chemical Industries, Ltd.
1031.	Brit. 610,139	J. T. Dickson, R. L. Heath, and R. J. W. Reynolds	Imperial Chemical Industries, Ltd.
1032.	Brit. 614,625	G. W. I. Sheavyn	
1033.	Brit. 672,449		E. I. du Pont de Nemours & Co., Inc.
1034.	Brit. 682,866	D. Coleman	Imperial Chemical Industries, Ltd.
1035.	Ger. 739,339	J. B. Miles, Jr.	I. G. Farbenind. A.-G.
1036.	Ger. 809,936	A. Jasicek	Vereinigte Glanzstoff-Fabriken A.-G.
1037.	Swiss 279,165		A. Maurer, S. A.

Concerning

Composition for dyeing polyethylene terephthalate fibers consisting of an acid-vat dye, a carrier selected from chlorobenzene, dichlorobenzene, and trichlorobenzene, and a dispersing agent.

Improvement of folding resistance of fibers of linear polymers, e.g., polyesters, by coating with polyamides or polyurethanes.

Roughening or delustering the surface of yarn, fibers, sheets, etc. made of polyesters or other linear polymers with neutral or slightly acid solvents.

Production of polyester fibers without luster.

Method for forming films or filaments from polyamides.

Melt-spinning method. Molten mass is extruded as a ribbon and cooled by a spray of water.

Fiber formation. Previously made resin chips are melted in grid and extruded.

Improved process and apparatus for the melt spinning of filaments.

Production of polyester fibers without luster by incorporating an insoluble pigment dispersed in a different linear polyester or a linear polyesteramide in the glycol before polymerization.

Heat treatment of fibers.

Method of making polyethylene terephthalate filaments particularly suitable for bristles and screens, e.g., melted resin extruded and cooled rapidly; drawn fibers given heat treatment.

Recovery of terephthalate acid from scrap glycol-terephthalic acid polymers by hydrolysis of the polymers with mineral acid.

Degradation of waste or scrap yarn to recover terephthalic acid polyesters by refluxing with ethylene glycol.

Production of polyester fibers without luster by incorporating pigments, e.g., titanium dioxide, in the glycol before polymerization.

Application of melt-spinning method of Brit. 533,306 to terephthalic acid polyesters.

Uniform linear condensation polymers, e.g., polyesters, prepared by heating a film of reactants by infrared rays at 220°–270° C. under stream of inert gas, e.g., nitrogen.

Drawing process and heat treatment for polyethylene terephthalate bristles.

Modification of polyethylene terephthalate fibers with high-molecular-weight polyalkylene oxide to improve water absorption and thus help in dyeing.

Application of pressure to fiber-forming polymers at temperature below softening point to orient molecules and thus improve mechanical properties.

Manufacture of twined filaments from linear superpolymers, such as polyamides, polyurethanes, or polyureas.

Apparatus for producing a synthetic fiber.

Manufacture of Fibers and Films (Continued)

	Patent Number	Patentee	Assignee
1038.	U.S. 2,623,031	M. D. Snyder	E. I. du Pont de Nemours & Co., Inc.
1039.	U.S. 2,623,033	M. D. Snyder	E. I. du Pont de Nemours & Co., Inc.

Properties and Uses of Terephthalates

	Patent Number	Patentee	Assignee
1040.	U.S. 2,399,184	W. W. Heckert	E. I. du Pont de Nemours & Co., Inc.
1041.	U.S. 2,512,433	L. Leben	Imperial Chemical Industries, Ltd.
1042.	U.S. 2,627,088	F. P. Alles and W. R. Saner	E. I. du Pont de Nemours & Co., Inc.
1043.	U.S. 2,649,622	J. A. Piccard	E. I. du Pont de Nemours & Co., Inc.
1044.	U.S. 2,652,353	M. W. Wilson	B. F. Goodrich Co.
1045.	U.S. 2,673,826	A. B. Ness	E. I. du Pont de Nemours & Co., Inc.

Concerning
Elastic fiber obtained by melt-blending copolymer of terephthalic acid or analogues, an aliphatic dibasic acid, and a glycol with the polymer from terephthalic acid and a glycol.
Fiber-forming elastic copolymer of terephthalic acid, dibasic aliphatic acid, and a glycol.
Lightweight armor plate for airplanes constructed of steel and laminates of a linear "superpolymer" (e.g., polyester) woven fabric bonded with a resin.
Hose pipe made by winding fibers, yarns, or fabrics based on glycol—terephthalate polyesters on rubber or plastic tubing.
As a film support, oriented plastic films produced by coating a cast ethylene glycol-terephthalic acid polyester with a thin layer of a vinylidene chloride copolymer and biaxially stretching the coated film.
Phonograph records made by compression molding of amorphous polyethylene terephthalate.
Synthetic fibrous materials (nylon, rayon, or terephthalate) bonded to rubber with adhesive consisting of rubber latex-phenolic resin mixture. Bonded material used in tires, belts, etc.
Laminates of polymethylene terephthalate film and other materials, such as aluminum, nylon, and cotton.

General

Patent Number	Patentee	Assignee
1046. Ger. patent application J66330(1940)	P. Schlack	
1047. Fr. 869,243	P. Schlack	I. G. Farbenind. A.-G.

Elastomers

1048. U.S. 2,381,063	F. E. Küng	B. F. Goodrich Co.
1049. U.S. 2,422,271	G. T. Vaala and C. E. Frank	E. I. du Pont de Nemours & Co., Inc.
1050. U.S. 2,424,883	B. J. Hapgood, D. A. Harper, and B. J. Reynolds	Imperial Chemical Industries, Ltd.
1051. U.S. 2,424,884	J. G. Cook, *et al.*	Imperial Chemical Industries, Ltd.
1052. U.S. 2,424,885	J. M. Buist, *et al.*	Imperial Chemical Industries, Ltd.
1053. U.S. 2,431,921	J. G. Cook and R. C. Seymour	Imperial Chemical Industries, Ltd.
1054. U.S. 2,432,148	W. Furness, L. E. Perrins, and W. F. Smith	Imperial Chemical Industries, Ltd.
1055. U.S. 2,511,544	H. Rinke, H. Schild, and W. Siefken	Vested in the U.S. Attorney General
1056. U.S. 2,620,516	K. E. Müller	Farbenfabriken Bayer A.-G.
1057. U.S. 2,621,166	F. W. Schmidt and K. E. Müller	Farbenfabriken Bayer A.-G.
1058. U.S. 2,625,531– 2,625,532	N. V. Seeger	Wingfoot Corp.
1059. U.S. 2,625,535	T. G. Mastin and N. V. Seeger	Wingfoot Corp.
1060. Brit. 573,811	J. G. Cook, *et al.*	Imperial Chemical Industries, Ltd.
1061. Brit. 574,134	D. H. Coffey, J. G. Cook, and W. H. G. Lake	Imperial Chemical Industries, Ltd.
1062. Brit. 579,857	J. G. Cook and R. C. Seymour	Imperial Chemical Industries, Ltd.

II. DI-ISOCYANATE-MODIFIED POLYESTERS

Concerning

Extension of hydroxy polyesters with di-isocyanates.

Extension of hydroxy polyesters with di-isocyanates.

Cross-linking agents for synthetic resins, e.g., polymethylene di-isocyanates, and the corresponding dinitriles, di-isonitriles, di-thiocyanates, and di-isothiocyanates. Other agents are listed.

Urea-formaldehyde monomeric alcohol reaction products as curing agents for polyesteramides modified with polyisocyanates. Give tough, durable elastomers.

Para-formaldehyde-modified reaction products of di-isocyanates with linear polyester polyamides.

Vulcanization of di-isocyanate-modified polyesters or polyamides with sulfur.

See Brit. 581,144 in this section.

Curing of polyester isocyanates with peroxides, nitro compounds, or quinone oximes.

Phenol-formaldehyde condensation products as curing agents for di-isocyanate-modified polyesters or polyesteramides. Give improved heat-aging properties.

Cross-linking of di-isocyanates with glycols or diamines. Gas formation eliminated.

Elastomers of good stability from properly selected linear hydroxyl-containing esters, a di-isocyanate, and a diamine.

Reaction of linear isocyanate-modified polyester with reaction product of an organic polyisocyanate and a diamine, diglycol, or amino alcohol. Retards activity of isocyanate so as to permit storage.

Modification of polyesters with di-isocyanates and a difunctional additive, e.g., amines, amino alcohols, dibasic acids, ureas, guanidines, thioureas, amino acids, hydroxy acids. Product can be cross-linked with additional di-isocyanate without gas formation.

Elastomers from polyesters made with excess of glycol or amino alcohol and cross-linked with di-isocyanates. Can be stored for long periods.

See U.S. 2,424,884 in this section.

Process for modification of polyesters and polyesteramides with organic di-isocyanates. Avoids use of heavy-duty mixers.

Nitro compounds, peroxides, and quinone oximes as curing agents for di-isocyanate-modified polyesters or polyesteramides, e.g., di- and tri-nitrobenzene, benzoyl peroxide, quinone dioxime.

Elastomers (Continued)

	Patent Number	Patentee	Assignee
1063.	Brit. 580,524	B. J. Hapgood, D. A. Harper, and R. J. W. Reynolds	Imperial Chemical Industries, Ltd.
1064.	Brit. 580,526	D. A. Harper and H. P. W. Huggill	Imperial Chemical Industries, Ltd.
1065.	Brit. 581,143	J. M. Buist, *et al.*	Imperial Chemical Industries, Ltd.
1066.	Brit. 581,144	W. Furness, L. E. Perrins, and W. F. Smith	Imperial Chemical Industries, Ltd.
1067.	Brit. 581,146	D. H. Coffey, W. F. Smith, and H. G. White	Imperial Chemical Industries, Ltd.
1068.	Brit. 581,410	D. A. Harper and W. F. Smith	Imperial Chemical Industries, Ltd.
1069.	Brit. 585,083	W. F. Smith and H. G. White	Imperial Chemical Industries, Ltd.
1070.	Brit. 585,205	D. A. Harper and W. F. Smith	Imperial Chemical Industries, Ltd.
1071.	Brit. 696,449– 696,450		Wingfoot Corp.
1072.	Brit. 700,608– 700,611		Farbenfabriken Bayer A.-G.
1073.	Ger. patent application D90260	H. Pinten	Dynamit-Nobel A.-G.
1074.	Ger. patent applications F 2824 39/c and F 2972 39/c		
1075.	Ger. 831,772	E. Muller, H. F. Piepenbrink, and E. Weinbrenner	Farbenfabriken Bayer A.-G.
1076.	Ger. 838,826	E. Muller	Farbenfabriken Bayer A.-G.

Adhesives

1077.	U.S. 2,365,508	P. R. Austin	E. I. du Pont de Nemours & Co., Inc.
1078.	U.S. 2,393,987	J. Harmon	E. I. du Pont de Nemours & Co., Inc.
1079.	U.S. 2,430,479	B. C. Pratt and H. S. Rothrock	E. I. du Pont de Nemours & Co., Inc.

Concerning

Formaldehyde or formaldehyde-producing compounds as curing agents for di-isocyanate-modified polyesters or polyesteramides. Give improved rubber-like properties.

Compounds that are neutral at low temperatures and acidic at high temperatures ($100^{\circ}-150^{\circ}$ C.), e.g., halogenated esters, nitriles, amides, as curing agents for mixtures of di-isocyanate-modified polyesters or polyesteramides and formaldehyde. (See Brit. 580,524 in this section.)

Prevention of scorching of di-isocyanate-modified polyesters or polyesteramides in presence of para-formaldehyde by use of acid-accepting compounds, e.g., mono-ethanolamine, sodium acetate, etc.

See U.S. 2,432,148 in this section.

Potassium, ammonium, barium, and lead chromates and dichromates as curing agents for di-isocyanate-modified polyesters or polyesteramides.

Proteins as modifiers for di-isocyanate-modified polyesters or polyesteramides. Give polymers of rubberlike properties, also suitable for adhesives, lacquers, and leather substitutes.

Partially hydrolyzed polyvinyl acetals as modifiers for di-isocyanate-modified polyesters and polyesteramides. Give elastomers of good resistance to organic fluids and low permeability to gases.

Cellulose derivatives as modifiers of di-isocyanate-modified polyesters or polyesteramides.

Elastomeric isocyanate-modified polyesters (see U.S. 2,625,531 and 2,625,532 in this section).

Di-isocyanate-modified linear polyesters.

Elastomeric di-isocyanate-modified polyester.

Reactions between glycols and isocyanates. Speed varies, depending on isocyanate selected.

Polyester isocyanates cross-linked with glycols.

Di-isocyanate-polyester-diamine reaction. Diamines and di-isocyanates are selected to provide slow reactivity, so that product can be used in liquid form and heat cured.

Adhesives for binding cork to form gaskets; low-molecular-weight polyesteramides cross-linked with di-isocyanates.

Adhesive for waxed paper from di-isocyanate-modified polyesteramides.

Bonding of laminates with isocyanates. Fifteen examples.

Adhesives (Continued)

	Patent Number	Patentee	Assignee
1080.	U.S. 2,650,212	E. Windemuth	Farbenfabriken Bayer A.-G.
1081.	Brit. 573,932		Imperial Chemical Industries, Ltd.
1082.	Ger. patent application June 21, 1952	E. Windemuth and E. Bock	
1083.	Ger. patent application 73,726 (PB Report 20,544)		
1084.	Ger. 821,934	W. Tischbein	Farbenfabriken Bayer A.-G.
1085.	Ger. 826,641	E. Windemuth	Farbenfabriken Bayer A.-G.

Foams

	Patent Number	Patentee	Assignee
1086.	U.S. 2,577,279	E. Simon and F. W. Thomas	Lockheed Aircraft Corp.
1087.	U.S. 2,577,280	E. Simon and F. W. Thomas	Lockheed Aircraft Corp.
1088.	U.S. 2,577,281	E. Simon and F. W. Thomas	Lockheed Aircraft Corp.
1089.	U.S. 2,591,884	E. Simon and F. W. Thomas	Lockheed Aircraft Corp.
1090.	U.S. 2,676,157	I. L. Newell	United Aircraft Corp.
1091.	U.S. 2,602,783	E. Simon and F. W. Thomas	Lockheed Aircraft Corp.
1092.	U.S. 2,620,349	R. J. Slocombe	Monsanto Chemical Co.
1093.	U.S. 2,634,244	E. Simon and F. W. Thomas	Lockheed Aircraft Corp.
1094.	U.S. 2,639,252	E. Simon, F. W. Thomas, and E. H. Burkart	Lockheed Aircraft Corp.
1095.	U.S. 2,642,403	E. Simon and F. W. Thomas	Lockheed Aircraft Corp.
1096.	Ger. patent application F 8030 XII/39a.	P. Hoppe and E. Weinbrenner	
1097.	Ger. patent application F5581 IV c/39b (1951)	E. Muller and P. Hoppe	

Concerning

Adhesives prepared from isocyanate polyesters with catalytic amounts of reactive hydrogen-free tertiary amines. Stable when kept anhydrous; set rapidly on addition of water.

Polyisocyanates as adhesives for materials with which they form polyurethane linkages.

Adhesives from reaction of linear polyester with toluene di-isocyanate. Product sets rapidly upon addition of a polyfunctional isocyanate, e.g., tri(para-isocyanyl phenyl)methane, or the reaction product of toluene di-isocyanate with trimethylol propane.

Adhesive for wood from cellulose acetate, di-isocyanate, and polyester.

Laminated plastics prepared by applying one or more layers of a mixture of polyvinyl compounds (or cellulose derivatives, etc.), low-molecular-weight polyesters, and polyisocyanates (tolylene di-isocyanate) to a support, e.g., cotton fabric, and drying with heat.

See U.S. 2,650,212 in this section.

Preparation of foamed polyester di-isocyanate resins using metallic salt hydrates (as water-releasing agents).

Use of metal soaps and metallic leafing powders to stabilize foams, for smaller bubbles and higher strength.

Urethane foams containing flame retardants, such as allyl aryl phosphonates.

Ethyl cellulose, polymeric acetate, and polymeric chlorinated natural rubber as stabilizers for foamed polyester-di-isocyanate resins.

Foamed resin prepared from a polyester-aldehyde reaction product and a polyisocyanate or polyisothiocyanate.

Foamed plastic with small, uniform cells from reacting a polyester with the reaction product of di-isocyanates and compounds containing labile hydrogen.

Controlling the foaming of alkyd-di-isocyanate resin by using polyisocyanates containing hydrolyzable chlorine to slow down the reaction.

Use of quaternary ammonium bentonites to stabilize foamed urethane plastics, for smaller bubbles and higher strength.

Method for simultaneous formation of core and molding of plastic housings from alkyd resin-polyisocyanate copolymers.

Mixture for producing foamed resins: saturated linear polyester, unsaturated polyester, ethylene cross-linking agent, metallic leafing powders, and di-isocyanates.

Use of heat evolved in foaming reaction to cure polyester component.

Semielastic foams from polyesters with molecular weights below 1,000.

Foams (Continued)

Patent Number	Patentee	Assignee
1098. Ger. patent application F6821 IV c/39c (1952)	E. Windemuth	
1099. Ger. patent application F7986 IV c/39b (1951)	C. Muhlhauser, *et al.*	
1100. Ger. patent application F8233 IV c/39b (1952)	E. Muller and P. Hoppe	

Molding Compounds

1101. U.S. 2,302,037	L. Kollek	Vested in Alien Property Custodian
1102. U.S. 2,342,679	H. Mediger	Vested in Alien Property Custodian

Coatings

1103. U.S. 2,333,639	R. E. Christ and W. E. Hanford	E. I. du Pont de Nemours & Co., Inc.
1104. U.S. 2,333,917	R. E. Christ and W. E. Hanford	E. I. du Pont de Nemours & Co., Inc.
1105. U.S. 2,333,922	H. Foster	E. I. du Pont de Nemours & Co., Inc.
1106. U.S. 2,374,136	H. S. Rothrock	E. I. du Pont de Nemours & Co., Inc.
1107. U.S. 2,503,209	A. S. Nyquist and E. L. Kropa	American Cyanamid Co.
1108. U.S. 2,531,392	D. S. Breslow	Hercules Powder Co.
1109. U.S. 2,606,162	D. H. Coffey, *et al.*	Imperial Chemical Industries, Ltd.
1110. U.S. 2,657,151	H. Gensel and E. Windemuth	Farbenfabriken Bayer A.-G.
1111. U.S. 2,676,164	W. Charlton and E. G. Rutter	Imperial Chemical Industries, Ltd.
1111a. Brit. 547,672	H. S. Rothrock	E. I. du Pont de Nemours & Co., Inc.
1112. Brit. 692,045		Farbenfabriken Bayer A.-G.
1113. Ger. patent application 72,804 (PB Rept. 20,544)		

Polyester-di-isocyanate reaction products in which polyester component has molecular weight above 1,000. Polyglycol ethers having at least 2 hydroxyl groups may be used in the reaction.

Portable mixers for producing foamed urethane-polyester mixtures, based on high-pressure spraying of all components into one small mixing chamber.

Polyester di-isocyanates containing cocondensed compounds containing tertiary nitrogen atoms. Excellent adhesion characteristics.

Printing plates made from superpolyurethanes. Fractureproof, easily cleaned, nonflammable, resistant to wear and chemicals, and give good, sharp reproduction.

Unbreakable, wear-resistant phonograph records made from synthetic materials, *e.g.*, polyurethane.

Resins for films and coatings prepared from di-isocyanate-modified low-molecular-weight polyesters or polyesteramides.

Coating of objects, *e.g.*, upholstery, hospital sheeting, clothing, etc., with a polyesteramide, after treatment with polyisocyanate. Makes them flexible and less apt to cold-crack.

Coating of insulated electrical conductors with polyesteramide cross-linked with polyisocyanate. Coating is easy to apply, resistant to exposure, common solvents, and cold-cracking, and flexible.

Use of metallic drier (oil-soluble metallic salt) as catalyst in preparing coating compositions from isocyanates and hydrogen-containing substances.

Treatment of alkyd resins with 3–25% of a primary unsaturated di-isocyanate, *e.g.*, vinyl benzyl isocyanate. Hydrophilic groups converted to less hydrophilic groups, but solubility in organic solvents still retained.

Wire-coating composition obtained by reacting a glycol with a mixture of di- and tri-isocyanates.

Di-isocyanate-modified polyesters as nonvolatile plasticizers in polyvinyl chloride.

Coating of fabrics with isocyanate-modified polyesters. Cross-linking agent (water and a diamine) is applied as a vapor.

Coating of nylon fabric with a composition containing a polyester prepared from adipic acid, ethylene glycol, and glycerol, and an aromatic hydrocarbon-di-isocyanate.

Modified alkyd resins, useful in coating and molding, prepared by treatment with an organic polyisocyanate or polyisothiocyanate.

Coating of textiles with emulsion of polyesters and di-isocyanates. Cross-linking agent (water or aqueous solution of an aliphatic diamine or amino alcohol) is applied first.

Mixture of alkyd with reaction product of di-isocyanate and di-phenylamine, etc. Di-isocyanate reagent not reactive at room temperatures but will release the di-isocyanate at high temperatures.

TESTING

	Patent Number	Patentee	Assignee
1114.	Japan. 4359 ('51)	E. Mukoyama and M. Watanabe	Oriental Rayon Co.

HEALTH HAZARDS

	Patent Number	Patentee	Assignee
1115.	U.S. 2,461,735	C. A. Heilberger	U. S. Rubber Co.

TESTING

Determination of molecular weight of high molecules by determination of electrical conductivity and temperature of fused liquid during heat polymerization.

HEALTH HAZARDS

Freeing interpolymers of styrene, allyl alcohol, and diallyl fumarate of allyl alcohol, which has tear-producing effects, by heating in xylene 1-2 hours, distilling, and repeating 3 times.

B. ARTICLES, BOOKS, MANUFACTURERS' LITERATURE

General Concepts

Author	Reference
1116. Anon.	*J. Polymer Sci.* **8**, 257–77 (1952).
1117. Anon.	*J. Polymer Sci.* **10**, 129–48 (1953).
1118. Alexander, J.	*Colloid Chemistry*, Vol. 6, Reinhold, New York, 1946, 855–9.
1119. Alfrey, T., Jr.	*Trans. N. Y. Acad. Sci.* **10**, 298–303 (1948).
1120. Alfrey, T., Jr., Bohrer, J. J., and Mark, H. F.	*Copolymerization*, Vol. 8, Interscience High Polymers Series, New York, 1952, 279 pp.
1121. Alfrey, T., Jr., and Lewis, C.	*J. Polymer Sci.* **4**, 767–8 (1949).
1122. Alfrey, T., Jr., and Merz, E.	*Polymer Bull.* **1**, 86–9 (1945).
1123. Alfrey, T., Jr., Merz, E., and Mark, H. F.	*J. Polymer Research* **1**, 37–43 (1946).
1124. Bartlett, P. D., and Nozaki, K.	*J. Am. Chem. Soc.* **68**, 1495–1504 (1946).
1125. Blum, J. J., and Morales, M. F.	*J. Chem. Phys.* **20**, 1822 (1952).
1126. Bolle, J.	*Mém. services chim. état* (Paris) **31**, 293–8 (1944).
1127. Bueche, F.	*J. Chem. Phys.* **21**, 205–8 (1953).
1128. Burk, R. E.	*Ind. Eng. Chem.* **30**, 1054–63 (1938).
1129. Carothers, W. H.	*J. Am. Chem. Soc.* **51**, 2548–59 (1929).
1130. Carothers, W. H., and Arvin, J. A.	*J. Am. Chem. Soc.* **51**, 2560–70 (1929).
1131. Carothers, W. H., and Hill, J. W.	*J. Am. Chem. Soc.* **54**, 1559–66 (1932).
1132. Carothers, W. H., and Hill, J. W.	*J. Am. Chem. Soc.* **54**, 1566–9 (1932).
1133. Carothers, W. H., and Hill, J. W.	*J. Am. Chem. Soc.* **54**, 1579–87 (1932).
1134. Cerf, R., and Scheraga, H. A.	*Chem. Revs.* **51**, 185–261 (1952).
1135. Chelnokova, G. N., Rafikov, S. R., and Korshak, V. V.	*Izvest. Akad. Nauk S.S.S.R., Otdel Khim. Nauk* 1949, 205–11.
1136. Chenicek, A. G.	*J. Chem. Education* **21**, 495–501 (1944).
1137. Cleereman, K. J., et al.	*Modern Plastics* **30**, No. 9, 119 (1953).
1138. Debye, P.	*J. Applied Phys.* **15**, 338–42 (1944).
1139. Debye, P.	*J. Phys. Colloid Chem.* **51**, 18–32 (1947).
1140. Doak, K. W.	*J. Am. Chem. Soc.* **70**, 1525–7 (1948).
1141. Doty, P.	*Chem. Weekblad* **43**, 422–4 (1947).

THEORETICAL CONSIDERATIONS

Concerning

Report on nomenclature in field of macromolecules (International Union of Pure and Applied Chemistry).

Molecular weight measurements by different methods. Report from International Union of Pure and Applied Chemistry.

Theory of behavior of plastics.

General review of copolymerization of monomers by a free radical mechanism.

Mathematical analysis of side-chain copolymerization of a vinyl monomer and a linear polymer.

Relative polymerization reactivities of unsaturated compounds, e.g., styrene and maleic anhydride and derivatives.

Experimental study of copolymerization, e.g., styrene and diethyl maleate.

Mechanism of peroxide-induced polymerization of allyl acetate with maleic anhydride.

Light scattering of polymers. Mathematical and theoretical.

Molecular weights in mixed polymerization. Theory of action of inhibitors in polymerization.

Effect of interactions of segments of polymer chain on molecular size.

Theories on mechanism of polymerization.

Polymerization and ring formation. I. Theory of condensation polymers.

Polymerization and ring formation. II. Preparation and properties of some polyesters.

Studies of polymerization and ring formation. XII. Linear superpolyesters.

Studies of polymerization and ring formation. XIII. Polyamides and mixed polyester-polyamides.

Artificial fibers from synthetic linear condensation superpolymers. Theory.

Flow birefringence in solutions of macromolecules. Review with 197 references.

Determination of mean molecular weight of polyesters by end groups.

Factors affecting properties of resins. Functionality of molecules.

Polystyrene monofilaments and bristles. Theory of orientation and birefringence.

Light scattering in solutions of polymers. Application to determination of molecular weight.

Molecular weight determination by light scattering.

Monomer reactivity ratios for some copolymerizations of chloroethylenes.

Review of recent physical investigations of polymer molecules.

General Concepts (Continued)

	Author	Reference
1142.	Doty, P. M., and Mark, H. F.	*Ind. Eng. Chem.* **38**, 682–6 (1946).
1143.	Dreher, E.	*Kunststoffe* **27**, 137–43, 221–8 (1937).
1144.	Dreher, E.	*Kunststoffe* **28**, 35–7, 114–7 (1938).
1145.	D'yachenko, P. F., and Vlodaveta, I. N.	*Kolloid Zhur.* **14**, 338–45 (1952).
1146.	Enoksen, B.	*J. Polymer Sci.* **3**, 314 (1948).
1147.	Ferigle, S. M., and Meister, A. G.	*Am. J. Phys.* **20**, 421–8 (1952).
1148.	Fleck, H. R.	*Plastics, Scientific and Technological,* 3d ed., Temple Press, London, 1951, 414 pp.
1149.	Flory, P. J.	*J. Am. Chem. Soc.* **61**, 3334–40 (1939).
1150.	Flory, P. J.	*J. Am. Chem. Soc.* **62**, 1057–70 (1940).
1151.	Flory, P. J.	*J. Phys. Chem.,* **46**, 132–40 (1942).
1152.	Flory, P. J.	*J. Phys. Chem.* **46**, 870 (1942).
1153.	Flory, P. J.	*Principles of Polymer Chemistry,* Cornell Univ. Press, Ithaca, N. Y., 1953, 688 pp.
1154.	Fox, T. G., and Flory, P. J.	*J. Phys. Chem.* **55**, 221–34 (1951).
1155.	Fox, T. G., and Flory, P. J.	*J. Am. Chem. Soc.* **73**, 1915–20 (1952).
1156.	Fox, T. G., Flory, P. J., and Bueche, A. M.	*J. Am. Chem. Soc.* **73**, 285–9 (1951).
1157.	Frisch, H. L., and Stannett, V.	*Chem. & Ind.* 1953, 1036.
1158.	Frisman, E. V., and Tsvetkov, V. N.	*Zhur. Eksptl. i Teoret. Fiz.* **23**, 690–702 (1952).
1159.	Frost, A. A., and Pearson, R. G.	*Kinetics and Mechanism. A Study of Homogeneous Chemical Reactions,* Wiley, New York, 1953, 343 pp.
1160.	Gonikberg, M. G.	*Doklady Akad. Nauk S.S.S.R.* **86**, 297–9 (1952).
1161.	Hohenstein, W. P.	*Polymer Bull.* **1**, 60–8 (1945).
1162.	Houwink, R.	*J. prakt. Chem.* **157**, 15–8 (1940).
1163.	Hultzsch, K.	*Kunststoffe* **42**, 385–90 (1952).
1164.	Hultzsch, K.	*Mitt. Chem. Forsch.-Lusts. Wirtsch. Österr.* **6**, 1 (1952).
1165.	Ichimura, H.	*J. Phys. Soc. Japan* **7**, 182–5 (1952).
1166.	Inuoe, I.	*Chem. High Polymers* (Japan) **9**, 316–25 (1952).

Concerning

Review of indirect methods for determining size and shape of polymer molecules: ultracentrifuge, osmotic pressure, light scattering, streaming birefringence.

Review on chemistry of polymers, mechanism of polymerization, types of polymers, and influence of molecule constitution on polymerization.

Review of chemistry of polycondensation reactions, e.g., esterification of polyhydric alcohols with polybasic acids.

Determination of molecular weight of casein by light-scattering method.

"Osmotic balance" for molecular weight determination.

Selection rules for vibrational spectra of linear molecules.

Effects of molecular weight and viscosity on reaction rate of polyesterification.

An exact relation between viscosity and chain length. Use for molecular weight determination.

Constitution of 3-dimensional polymers and theory of gelation.

Viscosities of polyester solutions. Melt viscosity-molecular weight relationship.

Polymer properties, polymerization and copolymerization mechanisms, relation of structure of polymers to properties.

Melt viscosity of polyisobutylene. Method for determination of molecular weight.

Intrinsic viscosity relationships for polystyrene.

Treatment of osmotic pressure and light-scattering data. Determination of molecular weight.

Initial composition of polyesters in copolymerization reaction. Theoretical.

Dynamic birefringence and geometric dimensions of macromolecules in solution.

Theory of stepwise polymerization under pressure.

Mechanisms of polymerization and polycondensation and structure of high polymers. Literature reviewed.

Relation between degree of polymerization of polyesters as determined by viscometric and osmotic methods.

Methods of producing macromolecular compounds: polycondensation, polymerization, and polyaddition.

Recent developments in field of polycondensation and polyaddition products.

High-polymer solution theory.

Theory of condensation polymerization. Mathematical.

General Concepts (Continued)

Author	Reference
1167. Ivanov, V. I., and Zakharov, B. A.	*Uspekhi Khim.* **22**, 686–711 (1953).
1168. Izard, E. F.	*J. Polymer Sci.* **8**, 503–18 (1952).
1169. Izard, E. F.	*J. Polymer Sci.* **9**, 35–9 (1952).
1170. Jellinek, H. H. G.	*J. Polymer Sci.* **9**, 369–80 (1952).
1171. Jenckel, E., and Cossmann, G.	*Kolloid-Z.* **127**, 83–97 (1952).
1172. Jordan, D. O., and Mathieson, A. R.	*J. Chem. Soc.* (London) 1952, 2354–8.
1173. Kaneko, G., Noboru, N., and Furichi, J.	*Busseiron Kenkyû* No. 57, 90–100 (1952).
1174. Kawai, R.	*J. Inst. Elec. Engrs. Japan* **63**, 303–6 (1943).
1175. Kern, W.	*Chem.-Ztg.* **76**, 667–72 (1952).
1176. Kienle, R. H.	*Ind. Eng. Chem.* **22**, 590 (1930).
1177. Kienle, R. H.	*J. Soc. Chem. Ind.* **55**, 229T (1936).
1178. Kirkwood, J. G., and Brown, R. A.	*J. Am. Chem. Soc.* **74**, 1056–8 (1952).
1179. Klein, E., and Jenckel, E.	*Z. Naturforsch.* **7a**, 800–7 (1952).
1180. Kogan, A. I.	*Zhur. Priklad. Khim.* **9**, 1070–81, 1446–55 (1936).
1181. Kogan, G. M.	*Zhur. Priklad. Khim.* **21**, 676 (1948).
1182. Korshak, V. V.	*Uspekhi Khim.* **21**, 121–74 (1952).
1183. Korshak, V. V.	*Izvest. Akad. Nauk S.S.S.R., Otdel Khim. Nauk* 1953, 321–35.
1184. Korshak, V. V., and Rogozhin, S. V.	*Izvest. Akad. Nauk S.S.S.R., Otdel Khim. Nauk* 1952, 509–15.
1185. Korshak, V. V., and Rogozhin, S. V.	*Khim. i Fiz.-Khim. Vysokomolekul. Soedinenii Doklady 7-oi Konf. Vysokomolekul. Soedineniyan* 1952, 11–8.
1186. Korshak, V. V., and Vinogradova, S. V.	*Izvest. Akad. Nauk S.S.S.R., Otdel Khim. Nauk* 1952, 193–7 (Engl. translation).
1187. Korshak, V. V., and Vinogradova, S. V.	*Izvest. Akad. Nauk S.S.S.R., Otdel Khim. Nauk* 1952, 1109–15; *Zhur. Obshchel. Khim.*, **22**, 1176 (1952).
1188. Kraemer, E. O., Bartell, F. E., and Kistler, S. S., editors.	*Advances in Colloid Science*, Vol. I, Interscience, New York, 1942, 269–317.
1189. Krigbaum, W. R., and Flory, P. J.	*J. Polymer Sci.* **9**, 503–8 (1952).
1190. Krigbaum, W. R., and Flory, P. J.	*J. Chem. Phys.* **20**, 873–6 (1952).
1191. Krigbaum, W. R., and Flory, P. J.	*J. Polymer Sci.* **11**, 37–51 (1953).

Concerning

Osmometric method for determining molecular weight.

Effect of chemical composition on selected physical properties of linear polymers.
Effect of chemical structure on physical properties of isomeric polyester.
Degradation of long-chain molecules as a reverse polymerization process. Kinetic equations are derived.
Swelling and shrinking of cross-linked polymers, e.g., polystyrene and polymethyl methacrylate.
Kinetics and mechanism of catalytic polymerization of alpha-methylstyrene. Molecular weight distribution in polar polymerization.
Absorption and velocity of supersonic waves on concentrated solutions of linear polymers, e.g., polystyrene. Mechanism compared to that of birefringence.
Dielectric absorption of fusible resin. Theoretical.

Review, with 15 references, of polycondensation and polyaddition reaction mechanisms.
General theory of polymer formation, based on polyester studies.
Theory of polymer formation.
Diffusion-convection, a new method for fractionation of macromolecules.

Dependence of the modulus of elasticity of high polymers on temperature.

Investigations of reactions between phthalic anhydride and glycerol and polyglycerols.
Possibility of secondary anhydride formation in the preparation of alkyd resins.
Review of available literature on formation of high polymers by polycondensation. 155 references.
Nomenclature and classification of high-molecular-weight compounds.

Decarboxylation of dicarboxylic acids during polycondensation.

Causes of cessation of chain growth in polyesterification.

High molecular compounds. Significance of acidolysis and polyesterification reaction.
Interaction between polyester macromolecules. Effect on molecular weight and polydisperity.

Birefringence of macromolecules and its use for determining the size and shape of macromolecules.

Mathematical treatment of osmotic-pressure data.

Statistical mechanics of ternary mixtures of 2 polymers and a solvent.

Dependence of intrinsic viscosity of polymer solutions on molecular weight of polymer.

General Concepts (Continued)

Author	Reference
1192. Krigbaum, W. R., Mandelkern, L., and Flory, P. J.	*J. Polymer Sci.* **9**, 381–4 (1952).
1193. Krüger, H. E., and Broser, W.	*J. makromol. Chem.* **1**, 225–34 (1943).
1194. Lamb, J. J., Albrecht, I., and Axilrod, B. M.	*Natl. Advisory Comm. Aeronaut. Tech. Note* No. 1054, 30 pp. (1946).
1195. Lever, A. E.	*Plastics* (London) **18**, 395–7, 445–7 (1953).
1196. Lewis, F. M., *et al.*	*J. Am. Chem. Soc.* **70**, 1519–23 (1948).
1197. Lewis, F. M., *et al.*	*J. Am. Chem. Soc.* **70**, 1527–9 (1948).
1198. Lewis, F. M., and Mayo, F. R.	*J. Am. Chem. Soc.* **70**, 1533–6 (1948).
1199. Losev, I. P., and Trostyanskaya, E. B.	*Uspekhi Khim.* **14**, 395–412 (1945).
1200. McLaren, A. D., and Hofrichter, C. H., Jr.	*Paper Trade J.* **125**, No. 19, 96, 98–100 (1947).
1201. McLeod, L. A., and McIntosh, R.	*Can. J. Chem.* **29**, 1104–14 (1951).
1202. McNabb, J. W.	*Offic. Dig. Federation Paint & Varnish Production Clubs* No. 332, 605–11 (1952).
1203. Mark, H. F.	*Record Chem. Progress* **7**, 27–31 (1946).
1204. Mark, H. F.	*Trans. Faraday Soc.* **43**, 447–62 (1947).
1205. Mark, H. F.	*Monatsch. für Chem.* **81**, 140–50 (1950).
1206. Mark, H. F., and Proskauer, E. S., editors.	*The Science of Plastics,* Interscience, New York, 1948.
1207. Mark, H. F., and Raff, R.	*High Polymeric Reactions,* Vol. 3, Interscience High Polymers Series, New York, 1941, 23.
1208. Mark, H. F., and Whitby, G. S., editors.	*Collected Papers of Wallace Hume Carothers on High Polymeric Substances,* Vol. 1, Interscience High Polymers Series, New York, 1940, 3–270.
1209. Marvel, C. S., and Frank, R. L.	*J. Am. Chem. Soc.* **64**, 1675–8 (1942).
1210. Masson, C. R., and Melville, H. W.	*J. Polymer Sci.* **6**, 21 (1951).
1211. Matsumoto, M.	*Chem. High Polymers* (Japan) **8**, 382–7 (1951).
1212. Maurer, K.	*Angew. Chem.* **54**, 389–92 (1941).
1213. Mayo, F. R., *et al.*	*J. Am. Chem. Soc.* **70**, 1523–5 (1948).
1214. Mayo, F. R., Lewis, F. M., and Walling, C.	*J. Am. Chem. Soc.* **70**, 1529–33 (1948).
1215. Meeske, C. J.	*Am. Ink Maker* **25**, No. 11, 23–5, 27, 65, 67 (1947).

Concerning

Dependence of intrinsic viscosity of polymer solutions on molecular weight of polymer.

Relation between viscosity and concentration of organic high polymers.

Impact strength and flexural properties of laminated plastics. Includes polyester laminates reinforced with glass fibers.

Review, with 88 references, on formulation of thermoplastic materials by copolymerization.

Copolymerization. Effect of temperature and solvents on monomer reactivity ratios.

Monomer reactivity ratios for some copolymerizations of styrene and other compounds.

Copolymerization. Comparison of reactivity of *cis* and *trans* isomers, e.g., diethyl fumarate and maleate.

Review of measurement of molecular weight and degree of polymerization, preparation, properties, and uses of various plastics.

Theory of adhesion of high polymers to cellulose.

Osmotic-pressure measurements of polyvinyl acetate systems. Use for calculation of molecular weight.

Definition and theory of copolymerization.

A review on polymer research up to 1945. 116 references.

Mechanical properties of high polymers. Theoretical discussion.

Viscosity and molecular weight of macromolecular solutions.

Review of original literature for 1942–46.

Definitions of most important average values for molecular weight of high polymers.

Studies on polymerization and ring formation.

Copolymerization of alkyl acrylates and maleates. Kinetic studies.

"Osmotic balance" for molecular weight determination.

Mechanism of high polymerization. Differentiating various types of radicals.

Review of chemistry of polyesters and polyamides.

Monomer reactivity ratios for some copolymerizations of vinyl acetate.

Relation between structure and monomer reactivity in copolymerization.

Functionality concepts of fatty acid modified alkyd resins. Some historical information given.

General Concepts (Continued)

	Author	Reference
1216.	Melville, H. W., and Burnett, G. M.	*J. Polymer Sci.* **13**, 417–26 (1954).
1217.	Mizushima, S., Morino, Y., and Inoue, Y.	*Bull. Chem. Soc. Japan* **12**, 136 (1937).
1218.	Müller, A.	*Kunststoffe* **42**, 301–2 (1952).
1219.	Nichols, F. S., and Flowers, R. G.	*Ind. Eng. Chem.* **42**, 292–5 (1950).
1220.	Porod, G.	*J. Polymer Sci.* **10**, 157–66 (1953).
1221.	Redfarn, C. A.	*Brit. Plastics* **14**, 6–16, 18–21 (1942).
1222.	Ruggli, P.	*Ann.* **392**, 92–100; **399**, 174–82 (1912).
1223.	Sakurada, I.	*Chem. High Polymers* (Japan) **2**, 165–72 (1945).
1224.	Schultz, A. R.	*J. Polymer Sci.* **11**, 93–6 (1953).
1225.	Schulz, G. V.	*Z. physik Chem.* **A182**, 127–44 (1938).
1226.	Schulz, G. V.	*J. makromol. Chem.* **1**, 131–46 (1944).
1227.	Schulz, G. V.	*Kolloid-Z.* **115**, 90–103 (1949).
1228.	Schulz, G. V., Cantow, H. J., and Meyerhoff, G.	*J. Polymer Sci.* **10**, 79–96 (1953).
1229.	Scott, R. L.	*J. Polymer Sci.* **9**, 423–32 (1952).
1230.	Shkol'man, E. E., and Zeidler, I. I.	*Zhur. Priklad. Khim.* **26**, 736–42, 840–7 (1953).
1231.	Shkol'man, E. E., and Zeidler, I. I.	*Zhur. Priklad. Khim.* **26**, 1205–12 (1953).
1232.	Simha, R., and Budge, M.	*Natl. Bur. Standards Letter Circ.* LC922, 49 pp. (1948).
1233.	Singer, S.	*Polymer Bull.* **1**, 79–85 (1945).
1234.	Spurlin, M. M.	*J. Polymer Sci.* **3**, 714–34 (1948).
1235.	Staudinger, H. P.	*Berichte* **53B**, 1073–85 (1920).
1236.	Staudinger, H. P.	*J. Soc. Dyers Colourists* **63**, 313–91 (1947).
1237.	Staudinger, H. P.	*Makromol. Chem.* **4**, 289–307 (1950).
1238.	Stockmayer, W. H.	*J. Polymer Sci.* **9**, 69–71 (1952).
1239.	Stockmayer, W. H.	*J. Polymer Sci.* **11**, 424 (1953).
1240.	Stoeckhert, I. K.	*Kunststoffe* **43**, 36–7 (1953).
1241.	Svedberg, T., and Fåhraeus, R.	*J. Am. Chem. Soc.* **48**, 430–8 (1926).
1242.	Svedberg, T., and Nichols, J. B.	*J. Am. Chem. Soc.* **49**, 2920–34 (1927).
1243.	Svedberg, T., and Rinde, H.	*J. Am. Chem. Soc.* **46**, 2677–93 (1924).

Concerning

Table of rate constants for polymerization reactions.

Polymerization of styrene as revealed by Raman spectra.

Historical review on polyamides and polyesters.
Prediction of shrinkage in addition polymerization of vinyl- or allyl-type monomers.
X-ray and light scattering by chain molecules in solution. Relation to shape of chain molecules.
Review of chemical structure of plastics. Functionality theory.
Triple-bond ring compounds from reactions normally producing polymers.
Termination mechanism of chain polymerization—3 types of collision between molecules.
Maximum precipitation temperature of a heterogeneous polymer. Use for determination of molecular weight.
Formation of polymers by condensation equilibrium. Progress depends on rate of by-product removal.
Determination of molecular weights of polymers. Distribution function and average degree of polymerization.
Present state of viscometric molecular weight determinations.
Determination of diameter of coiled chain molecules from light diffusion and viscosity number.

Thermodynamics of high-polymer solutions. The compatibility of copolymers.
Kinetics of the polyesterification of acid esters of glycerol and phthalic acid.

Kinetics of reaction of polyesterification of acid esters of ethylene glycol and phthalic acid.
Bibliography of some recent research in field of high polymers.

Molecular weight averages of polymers from sedimentation velocity and diffusion measurements. Mathematical relationships.
Properties of polymer solutions. Molecular weight determination.
Mechanism of true polymerization and ring formation.
General theory of chemistry of high polymers.
Roentgenographic and viscometric determination of chain length of threadlike molecules.
Molecular distribution in condensation polymers.
Correction of equation for molecular weight of condensation polymers.
Molecular weight determination of high polymers. Constant for characterization of average molecule size.
Determination of molecular weight by sedimentation equilibrium method.

Application of oil-turbine type of centrifuge to study of stability region of carbon monoxide-hemoglobin.
Use of ultracentrifuge for determination of size and distribution of colloid particles.

General Concepts (Continued)

Author	Reference
1244. Tabuchi, D.	*Chem. High Polymers* (Japan) **9**, 41–9 (1952).
1245. Takayanagi, M., Ishii, K., and Saramoto, J.	*J. Soc. Chem. Ind. Japan* **54**, 387–9 (1951).
1246. Takayanagi, M., and Kuriyama, S.	*Kogaku Shuho, Kyushu Univ.* **25**, 139–42 (1953).
1247. Thinius, K.	*Kunststoffe* **37**, 36–8 (1947).
1248. Wakeman, R. L.	*Chemistry of Commercial Plastics,* Reinhold, New York, 1947.
1249. Walling, C.	*J. Am. Chem. Soc.* **65**, 441–7 (1945).
1250. Walling, C., *et al.*	*J. Am. Chem. Soc.* **70**, 1537–42, 1544–7 (1948).
1251. Walling, C., *et al.*	*J. Am. Chem. Soc.* **70**, 1543–4 (1948).
1252. Waser, J., Badger, R. M., and Schomaker, V.	*J. Chem. Phys.* **14**, 43–5 (1946).
1253. Wilde, M. C., and Smets, G.	*J. Polymer Sci.* **5**, 253–8 (1950).
1254. Winding, C. C., and Hasche, R. L.	*Plastics Theory and Practice: The Technology of High Polymers,* McGraw-Hill New York, 1947.
1255. Zhurkov, S. N.	*Trudy Konferentsii Vysokomolekulyar Soedineniyam, Akad. Nauk S.S.S.R., Otdel Khim. Nauk i Otdel. Fiz.-Mat. Nauk* **2**, 66–76 (1944) (pub. 1945).
1256. Zimm, B. H., and Bragg, J. K.	*J. Polymer Sci.* **9**, 476–8 (1952).

Polyesters

Author	Reference
1257. Abramov, S. A.	*Legkaya Prom.* **9**, No. 9, 16–9 (1949).
1258. Bacon, C. E.	Paper presented Jan. 24, 1947, at Low Pressures Industries Meeting of Society of the Plastics Industry. (Abst. in *Prod. Eng.* **18**, No. 6, 125–6 (1947).)
1259. Baker, W. O.	*J. Am. Chem. Soc.* **69**, 1125–30 (1947).
1260. Barron, H.	*Rubber Age & Synthetics* **34**, 211–3 (1953).
1261. Batzer, H.	*Makromol. Chem.* **10**, 13–29 (1953).
1262. Batzer, H., and Mohr, B.	*Makromol. Chem.* **8**, 217–33 (1952).
1263. Beaman, R. G.	*J. Polymer Sci.* **9**, 470–2 (1952).
1264. Beavers, E. M.	*Reinforced Plastics Div., Soc. Plastics Ind. Confer., 4th Annual,* 1949; *Modern Plastics* **26**, No. 7, 154–6 (1949).

Polyesters (Continued)

	Author	Reference
1265.	Bevan, E. A.	*Varnish Making, Oil & Colour Chem. Assoc.* 1939, 34–60.
1266.	Boyer, R. F., and Spencer, R. S.	*J. Applied Phys.* **16**, 594–607 (1945).
1267.	Bradley, T. F.	*Ind. Eng. Chem.* **29**, 440–5 (1937).
1268.	Bradley, T. F.	*Ind. Eng. Chem.* **29**, 579–84 (1937).
1269.	Bradley, T. F.	*Ind. Eng. Chem.* **30**, 689 (1938).
1270.	Bradley, T. F., Kropa, E. L., and Johnston, W. B.	*Ind. Eng. Chem.* **29**, 1270–6 (1937).
1271.	Breitenbach, J. W.	*Experientia* **3**, 239–41 (1947).
1272.	Brennecke, W.	*Melliand Textilber.* **33**, 946–50 (1952).
1273.	Dannenberg, H., Bradley, T. F., and Evans, T. W.	*Ind. Eng. Chem.* **41**, 1709–11 (1949).
1274.	Dunbrook, V. R. F.	*India Rubber World* **117**, 745–8 (1948).
1275.	Ebers, E. S., *et al.*	*Ind. Eng. Chem.* **42**, 114–9 (1950).
1276.	Edgar, O. B., and Ellery, E.	*J. Chem. Soc.* (London) 1952, 2633–43.
1277.	Edgar, O. B., and Hill, R.	*J. Polymer Sci.* **8**, 1–22 (1952).
1278.	Flory, P. J.	*J. Am. Chem. Soc.* **62**, 2261–4 (1940).
1279.	Fuller, C. S.	*J. Am. Chem. Soc.* **70**, 421–3 (1948).
1280.	Gee, G.	*Proc. XIth Intern. Congr. Pure and Appl. Chem.* (London) **5**, 305–9 (1937) (pub. 1953).
1281.	Hadert, H.	*Fette und Seifen* **53**, 161 (1951).
1282.	Hill, R., and Walker, E. E.	*J. Polymer Sci.* **3**, 609–30 (1948).
1283.	Hsiao, C. C.	*Applied Phys.* **23**, 1189–90 (1952).
1284.	Hudson, B. J. F., and Robinson, R.	*J. Chem. Soc.* (London) 1941, 715–22.
1285.	Jarrijon, A.	*Ind. plastiques modernes* **3**, No. 1, 33–5; No. 2, 3–5 (1951).
1286.	Jenckel, E.	*Kunststoffe* **43**, No. 11, 454–61 (1953).
1287.	Jenckel, E., Teege, E., and Hinrichs, W.	*Kolloid-Z.* **129**, 19–24 (1952).
1288.	Karrer, E.	*Rayon Textile Monthly* **26**, 20–1 (1945).
1289.	Keller, A.	*J. Polymer Sci.* **11**, 567–74 (1953).
1290.	Kern, W.	*Farben, Lacke, Anstrichstoffe* **4**, 242–9 (1952).
1291.	Kienle, R. H., and Petke, F. E.	*J. Am. Chem. Soc.* **62**, 1053–6 (1940).

Concerning

Resins produced from maleic anhydride and dihydric alcohols, glycerol, styrene, and other polymerizable compounds.

Theory of thermal expansion and second-order transition effects in high polymers.

Drying oils and resins. Mechanism of drying.

Drying oils and resins. Influence of molecular structure on oxygen and heat convertibility.

Drying oils and resins. Mechanism of addition polymerization.

Drying, nondrying, and convertibility characteristics of glycol polyesters of maleic and succinic acids.

Mechanism of cross-linked polymerization of styrene and divinyl compounds.

Review of relation of chemical structure to properties (particularly washability) of synthetic fibers.

Polyester resins for surface coatings from glycerol alpha-allyl ether and saturated acids, e.g., phthalic and succinic.

Formation of popcorn polymer from styrene. Effect of cross-linking agents discussed.

Thermal stability of polyester-styrene resin systems.

Structure-property relationship in polyethylene terephthalate copolyesters.

The para-phenylene linkages in linear high polymers. Structure-property relationships.

Comparison of rates of polyesterification and alcoholysis of polyesters.

Mixed crystal formation in linear copolyesters.

Crystallization of high polymers and its effect on their mechanical properties.

Oxygen-hardening "polyglycolester" (linear polyester from glycols and unsaturated dibasic acids).

Effect of polymer structure on certain properties of polymers, particularly fiber formation.

Effect of orientation on ultimate strength of linear high polymers. Theory.

Addition of maleic anhydride and ethyl maleate to substituted styrene.

Review of chemical structure and properties, uses, and photoelasticimetric analysis of polyesters.

Crystallization effects in plastics. Relation to favorable properties (e.g., high strength toughness, high temperature resistance) of fiber-forming polymers.

Transcrystallization in high polymers. Spherulitic form of polyester crystals.

Nomenclature and classification of textile fibers.

Orientation process in synthetic crystalline polymers.

Steps in polymerization of unsaturated organic compounds, catalyzed by peroxides. Relation to drying of oils.

Polyhydric alcohol-polybasic acid reaction. Glyceryl succinate and maleate polyesters.

Polyesters (Continued)

	Author	Reference
1292.	Kienle, R. H., and Petke, F. E.	*J. Am. Chem. Soc.* **63**, 481–4 (1941).
1293.	Kolb, H. J., and Izard, E. F.	*J. Applied Phys.* **20**, 564–71 (1949).
1294.	Kolb, H. J., and Izard, E. F.	*J. Applied Phys.* **20**, 571–5 (1949).
1295.	Korshak, V. V., and Golubev, V. V.	*Izvest. Akad. Nauk S.S.S.R., Otdel Khim. Nauk* 1949, 379–85.
1296.	Korshak, V. V. and Vinogradova, S. V.	*Izvest. Akad. Nauk S.S.S.R., Otdel Khim. Nauk* 1952, 967–71 (Engl. translation).
1297.	Kropa, E. L.	*India Rubber World* **118**, 532–3 (1948).
1298.	Kropa, E. L., and Bradley, T. F.	*Ind. Eng. Chem.* **31**, 1512–6 (1939).
1299.	Kursanov, D. N., Korshak, V. V., and Vinogradova, S. V.	*Izvest. Akad. Nauk S.S.S.R., Otdel Khim. Nauk* 1953, 140–4.
1300.	Lepsius, R.	*Kunststoffe* **33**, 4–10 (1943).
1301.	Lepsius, R.	*Kunststoffe* **34**, 11–4 (1944).
1302.	Lombard, F.	*Bull. inst. textile France* No. 30, 177–82 (1952); *Makromol. Chem.* **8**, 187–207 (1952).
1303.	Lora Tomayo, M.	*Anales fis. quim.* (Madrid) **39**, 209–14 (1943).
1304.	Lora Tomayo, M., and Viguera, J. M.	*Anales fis. quim.* (Madrid) **37**, 397–402 (1941).
1305.	Mark, H. F.	*Textile Research J.* **16**, 361–8 (1946).
1306.	Mark, H. F.	*Ind. Eng. Chem.* **44**, 2110–4 (1952).
1307.	Mason, S. G.	*Tappi* **33**, 403–9 (1950); *Pulp Paper Mag. Can.* **51**, No. 9, 109–15 (1950).
1308.	Melville, H. W.	*Offic. Dig. Federation Paint & Varnish Production Clubs* No. 336, 24–44 (1953).
1309.	Okamura, I.	*Teijin Times* (Japan) **20**, No. 8, 3 (1950) (Engl. abstr.).
1310.	Patterson, D. G., and Robinson, J. D.	*India Rubber World* **118**, 811–5 (1948).
1311.	Pohl, H. A.	*J. Am. Chem. Soc.* **73**, 5660–1 (1951).
1312.	Point, J. J.	*Bull. classe sci., Acad. roy. Belg.,* **39**, 435–41 (1953).
1313.	Reynolds, R. J. W.	*Plastics Inst.* (London) *Trans.* **20**, No. 42, 81–93 (1952).
1314.	Rhys, J.	*Plastics* (London) **18**, 205–6 (1953).
1315.	Ridge, B. P.	*J. Textile Inst.* **44**, P48–65 (1953).
1316.	Ritchie, P. D.	*Chem. & Ind.* 1954, 37 (summary of paper).
1317.	Rowland, C. S.	*Interchem. Rev.* **5**, 83–94 (1946–1947).
1318.	Saccenti, G.	*Chimica e industrie* (Milan) **34**, 412–8 (1952).
1319.	Schuur, G.	*J. Polymer Sci.* **11**, 385–98 (1953).
1320.	Sippel, A.	*Kolloid-Z.* **127**, 79–82 (1952).

Concerning

Polyhydric alcohol-polybasic acid reaction. Glyceryl adipate and sebacate polyesters.

Relation between crystallinity and second-order transition temperatures and other dilatometric properties of polyesters.

Thermal crystallization behavior of polyesters. Minimum crystallization temperature.

Effect of varying proportions of reactants in polycondensation of glycol with adipic acid.

Interaction between polyester macromolecules.

Properties of polyester resins. Relation to ingredients and structure.

Insolubilization of maleic glycol polyesters by addition polymerization with vinyl derivatives, e.g., vinyl acetate and styrene.

Study of polyester exchange reactions by means of heavy hydrogen isotope.

Chemical basis for plastics industry—formulas and classification of plastics.

Chemical classification of polymers according to main chain.

Structure and properties of the polyester of 11-hydroxyundecanoic acid.

Addition of maleic anhydride to substituted styrene. Theoretical.

Condensation of styrene and derivatives of cinnamic series with maleic anhydride. Theoretical.

Resilience of textile materials. Relation of arrangement of chain molecules and mechanical properties of polymers to production of strong fibers.

Synthetic fibers. Influence of molecular structure on properties.

Review of measurement and application of specific surface of fibers.

Cross-linking reactions of resins.

Synthetic fibers made from polymers of cross-linked, long-chain molecules.

Review of catalysis and processing of polyester resins.

Thermal degradation of polyesters.

Investigations of crystal formation by glycol polyadipate. Two structural hypotheses proposed.

Review on fiber-forming polymers. Theory.

Review of basic chemistry of polyesters.

Review and classification of synthetic polymer fibers.

Thermal breakdown of linear polyesters.

Review on maleic and fumaric resins, including polyesters.

Review of chemistry and polymerization mechanics of polyester plastics.

Mechanism of crystallization of high polymers.

Photolysis of textile fibers. Fine structure of fibers.

Polyesters (Continued)

Author	Reference
1321. Smith, H. D.	*Rayon Textile Monthly* **22**, 508–10, 590–1 (1941).
1322. Stevens, W. H.	*India-Rubber J.* **104**, 385–6 (1945).
1323. Traill, D.	*Bull. inst. textile France* No. 30, 109–30 (1952).
1324. Vincent, H. L.	*Ind. Eng. Chem.* **29**, 1267–9 (1937).
1325. Whitehouse, A. A. K.	*Ann. Repts. Soc. Chem. Ind. Progress Applied Chem.* **33**, 5–36 (1948).
1326. Woods, H. J.	*J. Textile Inst.* **40**, P869–71 (1949).
1327. Woods, H. J.	*J. Textile Inst.* **44**, P39–47 (1953).
1328. Yarsley, V. E., and Goodchild, A. G.	*Glass Fibre Reinforced Plastics Conv.* (England) 1952, *Proc.* 7–32.

Concerning

Classification of man-made fibers.

Classification of plastics, including polyesters. Includes trade names.

Relation of composition and molecular arrangement of synthetic fibers to their physical properties.

Oxygen-induced gelation of unsaturated polyesters. Polyglycol maleates as drying oils.

Polycondensation products, e.g., polyesters. Theory, review, bibliography.

Structure of fibers.

Review on fundamental properties of fibers: length, fineness, density, crystal structure.

Chemical aspects of contact resins (polyesters and others).

Acids

	Author	Reference
1329.	Anon.	Allied Chemical & Dye Corp., National Aniline Div., New York, N. Y.
1330.	Anon.	Allied Chemical & Dye Corp., Barrett Div., New York, N. Y. 49-p. booklet.
1331.	Anon.	American Cyanamid Co., Manufacturers Chemicals Dept., New York, N. Y. Data Sheet.
1332.	Anon.	American Cyanamid Co., Manufacturers Chemicals Dept., New York, N. Y. 24-p. booklet.
1333.	Anon.	Carbide and Carbon Chemicals Co., New York, N. Y. 16-p. booklet.
1334.	Anon.	*Chem. Eng.* **59**, No. 9, 208–11 (1952).
1335.	Anon.	*Chem. Eng.* **60**, No. 7, 238–41 (1953).
1336.	Anon.	*Chem. Eng. News* **31**, 3630 (1953) (advertisement).
1337.	Anon.	*Chem. Week* **74**, No. 17, 94, 96 (1954).
1338.	Anon.	E. I. du Pont de Nemours & Co., Inc., Wilmington, Del. Information Bull. No. X-1 (1950).
1339.	Anon.	E. I. du Pont de Nemours & Co., Inc., Polychemicals Dept., Wilmington, Del. Bull. No. A-5073.
1340.	Anon.	E. I. du Pont de Nemours & Co., Inc., Polychemicals Dept., Wilmington, Del. Bull. No. A-7406.
1341.	Anon.	Emery Industries, Inc., Cincinnati, Ohio. Bull. No. 40.
1342.	Anon.	Hooker Electrochemical Co., Niagara Falls, N. Y. Bull. No. 40.
1343.	Anon.	*Modern Plastics* **31**, No. 1, 220 (1953).
1344.	Anon.	Monsanto Chemical Co., Organic Chemicals Div., St. Louis, Mo. Tech. Data Sheet (1953).
1345.	Anon.	Chas. Pfizer & Co., Inc., Brooklyn, N. Y. Tech. Bull. No. 46.
1346.	Anon.	*Plastics Ind.* **12**, No. 2, 4 (1954).
1347.	Anders, H.	*Ind. vernice* (Milan) **7**, 179–82 (1953).
1348.	Berthelot, C.	*Chimie & industrie* **45**, Special No., 38–41 (Mar. 1941); *Chem. Zentr.* 1942 I, 418.
1349.	Boath, N.	*Chem. & Ind.* 1952, 812–9.
1350.	Chowdhury, J. K., and Saboor, M. A.	*J. Indian Chem. Soc.* **14**, 633–7 (1937).
1351.	De Buigne, J.	*Rev. prod. chim.* **47**, 65–71 (1944); *Chimie & industrie* **53**, 334 (1945).
1352.	Doscher, C. K., *et al.*	*Ind. Eng. Chem.* **33**, 315–9 (1941).

I. RAW MATERIALS

Acids (Continued)

Author	Reference
1353. Ghatak, N.	*J. Sci. & Ind. Research* (India) **4**, 725–6 (1946).
1354. Gibello, H.	*Peintures, pigments, vernis* **22**, 245–52 (1946).
1355. Hamann, K.	*Angew. Chem.* **62A**, 325–34 (1950).
1356. Hodgman, C. D., editor	*Handbook of Chemistry and Physics.* 34th ed., Chemical Rubber Publishing Co., Cleveland, 1953, 2914 pp.
1357. Hovey, A. G., and Hodgins, T. S.	*Paint, Oil, & Chem. Rev.* **102**, No. 2, 9–12, 37–8, 42 (1940).
1358. Hovey, A. G., and Hodgins, T. S.	*Paint, Oil, & Chem. Rev.* **103**, No. 4, 10, 11, 33–4 (1941).
1359. Kinney, C. R., and Pincus, I.	*Ind. Eng. Chem.* **43**, 2880–4 (1951).
1360. Kiyama, R., and Minomura, S.	*Rev. Phys. Chem. Japan* **22**, 4–8 (1952).
1361. Morton, A. A., and Fallwell, F., Jr.	*J. Am. Chem. Soc.* **60**, 1924–7 (1938).
1362. Nystrom, R. F., Loo, Y. H., and Leak, J. C.	*J. Am. Chem. Soc.* **74**, 3434–5 (1952).
1363. Ono, K., and Hirayama, S.	*J. Chem. Soc. Japan* **58**, 1089–90 (1937).
1364. Peters, H.	*Textile Colorist* **65**, 96, 139 (1943).
1365. Radvinskii, M. B.	*Zhur. Priklad. Khim.* **12**, 1374–7 (1939).
1366. Robinson, R. S.	*Plastics Inst.* (London) *Trans.* **18**, 20–9 (1950).
1367. Shelmerdine, J., Popper, F., and McNeil, D.	*J. Appl. Chem.* (London) **3**, 513–2 (1953).
1368. Skeen, J. R.	*Chem. Eng. News* **26**, 3684 (1948).
1369. Takikawa, S.	*J. Soc. Chem. Ind. Japan* **48**, 37–9 (1945).
1370. Weiss, J. M.	*Chem. Eng. News* **32**, 1820–2 (1954).

Alcohols

Author	Reference
1371. Anon.	*Chem. Eng. News* **31**, 1344 (1953); **32**, 1669 (1954) (advertisement).
1372. Anon.	*Chem. Eng. News* **32**, back cover (1954) (advertisement).
1373. Anon.	*Chem. Eng. News* **32**, 567 (1954) (advertisement); *Chem. Week* **71**, No. 2, 47 (1952).
1374. Anon.	*Chem. Eng. News* **32**, 1466–7 (1954).
1375. Anon.	Dow Chemical Co., Midland, Mich. Tech. Data Bull., 56 pp.

Concerning

Plastics development in India. Phthalic anhydride as raw material for resins.
Review of patents on preparation of maleic anhydride, raw materials and prop-
    erties of maleic resins, French commercial maleic resins.
Development of polyesters for lacquer and paint fields; raw materials and their
    processing.

Unusual reactants for making alkyd resins: hydroxycarboxylic acids, carbohy-
    drates, polyhydric phenols, phthalic acid isomers and chlorinated derivatives,
    other polyfunctional compounds.
Review on use of maleic anhydride for production of alkyd resins; 43 references.

Production of phthalic anhydride by catalytic air oxidation of higher aromatics,
    e.g., naphthalene.
Isomerization of maleic acid to fumaric acid under pressure.

Production of phthalic acids in sodium exchange reactions between benzene and
    sodium amylate.
Synthesis of fumaric acid and maleic anhydride containing radioactive C.

Synthesis of cis-dicarboxylic acid anhydrides. Dehydration of maleic, fumaric,
    phthalic, and camphoric acids.
Preparation of adipic acid and its uses in textile industry.
Reactivation of vanadium oxide catalyst in oxidation of benzene to maleic
    anhydride.
Review, with 14 references, on formation of resinous polybasic acids from maleic
    anhydride.
Production of phthalic anhydride by oxidation of tar oils.

Review on maleic anhydride; history, uses, preparation, and production.
Methods for preparation of maleic acid from benzene by air oxidation.
Vapor-phase oxidation of aromatic hydrocarbons as production methods for
    phthalic anhydride, maleic anhydride, etc.

Commercial availability of unsaturated glycols, e.g. 2-butene-1,4-diol and 1,4-
    butanediol.
Propylene glycol for formulation of polyesters. Mentions properties and applica-
    tions of resins.
Commercial availability of unsaturated glycols, e.g., dimethyl octynediol and
    dimethyl hexynediol.
Commercial development of acetylenic compounds, e.g., tertiary acetylenic
    alcohols and glycols.
Dow glycols (ethylene, diethylene, triethylene, propyl, dipropylene).

Alcohols (Continued)

Author	Reference
1376. Anon.	Dow Chemical Co., Midland, Mich. 1-p. brochure.
1377. Anon.	General Aniline and Film Corp., Commercial Development Dept., New York, N. Y. Prelim. Data Sheet No. A-109 (1954).
1378. Anon.	Lummus Co., New York, N. Y. 8-p. booklet.
1379. Contardi, A., and Ciocca, B.	*Ricerca sci.* **16**, II, 9–16 (1938).
1380. Curme, G. O., Jr., and Johnson, F., editors	*Glycols* (Am. Chem. Soc. Monograph No. 114). Reinhold, New York, 1952, 389 pp.
1381. Dubois, J. F.	*Rusta-Rayonne* **14**, 231–5 (1939).
1382. Karimullah	*J. Sci. & Ind. Research* (India) **4**, 724–5 (1946).
1383. Kiddoo, G.	*Chem. Eng.* **59**, No. 9, 149–68 (1952).
1384. Lenth, C. W., and DuPuis, R. N.	*Ind. Eng. Chem.* **37**, 152–7 (1945).
1385. McClellan, P. P.	*Ind. Eng. Chem.* **42**, 2402–7 (1950).
1386. Milas, N. A., and Sussman, S.	*J. Am. Chem. Soc.* **59**, 2345–7 (1937).
1387. Pukirev, A. G.	*Trans. Inst. Pure Chem. Reagents* (Moscow) No. 15, 45–50 (1937).
1388. Tanno, T.	*J. Chem. Soc. Japan* **59**, 709–18 (1938).
1389. Valente, R.	*Ind. saccar. ital.* **34**, 155–63 (1941).
1390. Weidenhagen, R., and Wegner, H.	*Listy Cukrovar* **57**, 185–6 (1939).
1391. Williams, E. C., et al.	*Chem. & Met. Eng.* **47**, 834–8 (1940).
1392. Yosikawa, K., and Hanai, S.	*Bull. Inst. Phys. Chem. Research* (Tokyo) **17**, 1262–77 (1938).

Styrene and Other Vinyl Derivatives of Benzene

Author	Reference
1393. Anon.	American Monomer Corp., Leominster, Mass. Bull. No. M-13.
1394. Anon.	*Chem. Eng. News* **31**, 5355 (1953); *Materials & Methods* **38**, No. 5, 143 (1953); *Plastics World* **12**, No. 1, 24 (1954).
1395. Amos, J. L.	*Colloid Chemistry.* Vol. 6, Reinhold, New York, 1946, 992–1009.
1396. Armitage, F.	*Paint Manuf.* **19**, 341–2, 356 (1949); **20**, 8–10, 18, 313–9, 382 (1950).
1397. Armitage, F., and Kut, S.	*J. Oil & Colour Chemists' Assoc.* **35**, No. 383, 195–217 (1952).
1398. Balandin, A. A., and Marukyan, G. M.	*Zhur. Priklad Khim.* **19**, 623–31 (1946).
1399. Balandin, A. A., and Marukyan, G. M.	*Zhur. Priklad. Khim.* **19**, 1277–80 (1946).

Concerning

Glycols (as solvents, antifreeze agents, humectants, plasticizers).

Butenediol (2-butene-1,4-diol). Properties and reactions.

Process for producing ethylene oxide and ethylene glycol.
Industrial preparation of ethylene glycol from the chloride.

Production, properties, and applications of glycols.

Preparation of glycol and **properties and** uses in textile industry of glycol, di-
ethylene glycol, and glycol **ethers** and esters.
Plastics development in India. Polvhydric alcohols as raw materials for resins.
Petrochemical processes. Gives methods of preparation of glycols, including
flow sheets.
Production of polyhydric alcohols, e.g., propylene glycol, by catalytic hydro-
genolysis of sugars.
Manufacture and uses of ethylene oxide and ethylene glycol.
Catalytic hydroxylation of unsaturated hydrocarbons, e.g., styrene to phenyl
glycol, isobutylene to isobutylene glycol.
Physical constants, e.g., boiling point and index of refraction, of ethylene and
propylene glycols.
Catalytic hydrogenation of disaccharides, e.g., 1,2-propylene glycol from hydro-
genation of sucrose.
Industrial products from sucrose, e.g., 1,2-propylene glycol.
Cracking of carbohydrates during hydrogenation to yield polyhydric alcohols,
e.g., propylene glycol.
Synthesis of glycerol. Allyl alcohol, from hydrolysis of allyl chloride, as
intermediate.
Production of propylene glycol and other alcohols by hydrogenation of saccharides.

MPL (acrylic) monomer: Properties and uses, e.g., cross-linking of polyesters.

Vinyltoluene in full production; will compete with styrene in uses and price.

Manufacture, properties, and uses of styrene and polystyrene.

Historical survey on styrene, with 106 references. Manufacture, reactions,
polymerization.
Review, with 36 references, on copolymerization of styrene.

Production of styrene through catalytic dehydrogenation of ethylbenzene.

Separation of ethylbenzene from mixture with xylene by dehydrogenation to
styrene.

Styrene and Other Vinyl Derivatives of Benzene (Continued)

Author	Reference
1400. Berstein, I. A., Bennett, W., and Field, M.	*J. Am. Chem. Soc.* **74,** 5763 (1952).
1401. Bovey, P. A., and Kolthoff, I. M.	*Chem. Revs.* **42,** 491–525 (1948).
1402. Cermak, R. W.	*Instrumentation* **2,** No. 3, 7–10 (1946).
1403. Daletskii, G.	*J. Phys. Chem.* (U.S.S.R.) **21,** 231–2 (1947).
1404. Dow, W.	*Ind. Eng. Chem.* **34,** 1267–8 (1942).
1405. Eckert, H. K.	*Natl. Petroleum News* **35,** R 530 (1943); *Trans. Natl. Safety Congr.* **32,** I, 533–5 (1943).
1406. Everson, J. W.	*Styrene (Its Polymers, Copolymers, and Derivatives).* Reinhold, New York, 1952, 298–313.
1407. Foord, S. G.	*J. Chem. Soc.* (London), 1940, 48–56.
1408. Frank, R. L., and Adams, C. E.	*J. Am. Chem. Soc.* **68,** 908 (1946).
1409. Goldfinger, G., Skeist, I., and Mark, H. F.	*J. Phys. Chem.* **47,** 578–87 (1943).
1410. Hanai, S.	*J. Chem. Soc. Japan* **62,** 1208–15 (1941).
1411. Kern, W., and Feuerstein, K.	*J. prakt. Chem.* **158,** 186–99 (1941).
1412. Koerner, T.	*Kunststoffe* **42,** 318–21 (1950).
1413. LeFevre, J.	*Styrene (Its Polymers, Copolymers, and Derivatives).* Reinhold, New York, 1952, 960–1057.
1414. Lloyd, L. E.	*Styrene (Its Polymers, Copolymers, and Derivatives).* Reinhold, New York, 1952, 195–214.
1415. Mack, C. H., and Bickford, W. G.	*J. Am. Oil Chemists' Soc.* **29,** 428–30 (1952).
1416. McSweeney, E. E., and Kropa, E. L.	*Chem. Eng. News* **32,** 27–8 (1954).
1417. Mavity, J. M., Zetterholm, E. E., and Hervert, G. L.	*Ind. Eng. Chem.* **38,** 829–32 (1946).
1418. Melville, H. W., and Watson, W. F.	*Trans. Faraday Soc.* **44,** 886–905 (1948).
1419. Mitchell, J. E., Jr.	*Trans. Am. Inst. Chem. Engrs.* **42,** 293–308 (1946).
1420. Mitchell, J. E., Jr.	*Styrene (Its Polymers, Copolymers, and Derivatives).* Reinhold, New York, 1952, 28–46.
1421. Monsanto Chemical Co.	Letter communication.
1422. Nuckolls, A. H., *et al.*	*Natl. Board Fire Underwriters Research Rept.* No. 4, 31 pp. (1947).
1423. Panizo, F. M.	*Anales fis. y quim.* (Madrid) **42,** 843–53 (1946).
1424. Schildknecht, C. E.	*Vinyl and Related Polymers.* Wiley, New York, 1952.

Concerning

Preparation of tritium-labeled styrene.

Review of effects of inhibitors and retarders on vinyl polymerization.

Instrumentation for production of styrene by dehydrogenation of ethylbenzene.
Inhibitors for styrene polymerization: Cu, Ag, Au, and their compounds.
Review on styrene production. Mainly dehydrogenation of ethylbenzene.
Safety measures in production and handling of styrene.

Summary of uses for styrene monomer.

Thermal polymerization of styrene and its inhibition. 130 organic substances
    classified as inhibitors or retarders.
Relative efficiency of some polymerization inhibitors for styrene, etc.

Mechanism of inhibition of styrene polymerization (with benzoquinone).

Synthesis of styrene by dehydrochlorination of chloroethylbenzene and dehydra-
    tion of phenylethyl alcohol.
Chemical reaction underlying inhibition of styrene polymerization by quinone.

Auxiliaries in plastics processing, e.g., coloring agents, fillers, lubricants,
    stabilizers, foaming agents.
Survey of patent literature on styrene copolymers.

Handling styrene monomer.

Conidendrols as inhibitors of oxidation and polymerization, e.g., of vinyl-type
    monomers.
Review on progress in plastics in 1953, e.g., new styrene homologs, flame-
    resistant polyesters.
Styrene production by catalytic dehydrogenation of ethylbenzene.

Effect of quinone-type retarders on catalytic polymerization of styrene and methyl
    methacrylate.
Styrene production by dehydrogenation of ethylbenzene.

Manufacture of styrene monomer.

Availability of styrene for polyester manufacture.
Fire and explosion hazards in manufacture of synthetic rubber. Includes styrene
    production.
Ethylation of benzene in industrial synthesis of styrene.
Preparation, properties, and applications of vinyl polymers in rubbers, plastics,
    fibers, and in medical and industrial arts.

Styrene and Other Vinyl Derivatives of Benzene (Continued)

Author	Reference
1425. Schulz, G. V., Strassburger, M., and Glindemann, E.	*Makromol. Chem.* **1**, 94–105 (1947).
1426. Smith, H. H.	*Trans. Am. Inst. Chem. Engrs.* **43**, 152–4 (1947).
1427. Stanley, H. M.	*Chem. & Ind.* 1938, 93–8.
1428. Stedman, G. E.	*Plastics* (Chicago) **1**, No. 5, 70, 72–3, 94–6 (1944).
1429. Webb, G. A., and Corson, B. B.	*Ind. Eng. Chem.* **39**, 1153–6 (1947).

Other Cross-Linking Agents

Author	Reference
1430. Anon.	American Cyanamid Co. New Product Bull., Collective Vol. III, 116.
1431. Anon.	American Monomer Corp., Leominster, Mass. Bull. M-11.
1432. Anon.	*Modern Plastics* **24**, No. 12, 226, 228 (1947).
1433. Anon	Food Machinery & Chemical Corp., Ohio-Apex Div., Nitro, W. Va. 4-p. bulletin.
1434. Anon.	Shell Chem. Corp., New York, N. Y. Tech. Pub. SC-46-32 (1946).
1435. Anon.	Shell Chemical Corp., New York, N. Y. Tech. Pub. SC-49-28R (1949).
1436. Bright, R. D.	*Pacific Plastics Mag.* **3**, No. 8, 35–6 (1945).
1437. Castro, A. J., and Elwell, W. E.	*J. Am. Chem. Soc.* **72**, 2275–6 (1950).
1438. Day, H. M.	*India Rubber World* **127**, 230–2 (1952).
1439. Day, H. M., and Affleck, J. G.	*SPE J.* **9**, No. 21, 22–5 (1953).
1440. Day, H. M., and Patterson, D. C.	*Modern Plastics* **29**, No. 11, 116, 120, 122 (1952).
1441. Iwakura, Y., et al.	*Chem. High Polymers* (Japan) **8**, 306–14 (1951).
1442. Powers, P. O.	*Chem. Eng. News* **26**, 20–1 (1948).
1443. Toy, A. D. F.	*J. Am. Chem. Soc.* **70**, 186–8 (1948).
1444. Toy, A. D. F., and Brown, L. V.	*Ind. Eng. Chem.* **40**, 2276–9 (1948).
1445. Underwood, J. W.	*India Rubber World* **117**, 621–3 (1948).
1446. Warren, D. E.	*Plastics* (Chicago) **7**, No. 1, 39, 71 (1947).

Economics and General

Author	Reference
1447. Anon.	*Brit. Plastics* **26**, 446 (1953).
1448. Anon.	*Brit. Plastics* **27**, 30 (1954).

Concerning

Mechanism of polymerization inhibitors. Classification of inhibitors of styrene production.

Production of styrene by catalytic dehydrogenation of ethylbenzene.
Review on styrene and its polymers.
Manufacture, molding, and properties of polystyrene.

Pyrolytic dehydrogenation of ethylbenzene to styrene.

Physical and chemical properties, applications, and toxicity of triallyl cyanurate.

Properties and uses of diallyl maleate monomer.

Diallyl phenyl phosphonate as cross-linking agent for unsaturated alkyd resins.
Increases flame resistance, index of refraction, hardness; decreases solubility.
Properties and applications of diallyl phthalate, e.g., molding and laminating.

Allyl esters of acrylic, crotonic, maleic, and phthalic acids, e.g., diallyl diglycolyl carbonate (cross-linking agents).
Diallyl phthalate.

Survey of uses of allyl chemicals in plastics, e.g., as cross-linking agents for unsaturated alkyd resins.
Preparation of diallylcyclohexane phosphonate and polymerization to form fire-resistant allyl resins.
Heat-resistant polyester resins containing triallyl cyanurate.
Triallyl cyanurate resins for heat-resistant laminates.

Polyester resins containing triallyl cyanurate for high heat resistance.

Synthesis of heptamethylene, trimethylene, and pentamethylene di-isothiocyanates.
Review on plastics. Mentions copolymers of diallylbenzene phosphonate with same refractive index as glass fibers.
Preparation of allyl and methallyl esters of aryl phosphonic acids (e.g., benzene, para-toluene, para-chlorobenzene phosphonic acids). Impart flame resistance when cross-linked with unsaturated polyesters.
Diallylbenzene phosphonate as cross-linking agent for unsaturated polyesters and other compounds.
Review of advances in plastics in 1947, with 72 references.
Diallylbenzene phosphonate cross-linking agent. Improves flame resistance and optical properties.

Export of phthalic anhydride to Norway by Western Germany.
Increase in maleic acid——anhydride production by French firm.

Economics and General (Continued)

Author	Reference
1449. Anon.	*Chem. Eng. News* **31**, 1318–9 (1953).
1450. Anon.	*Chem. Eng. News* **31**, 2974–5 (1953).
1451. Anon.	*Chem. Eng. News* **31**, 3245 (1953).
1452. Anon.	*Chem. Eng. News* **31**, 4835 (1953).
1453. Anon.	*Chem. Eng. News* **31**, 5402–3 (1953).
1454. Anon.	*Chem. Eng. News* **32**, 190 (1954).
1455. Anon.	*Chem. Eng. News* **32**, 1870–1 (1954).
1456. Anon.	*Chem. Week* **74**, No. 8, 87–8, 90 (1954).
1457. Anon.	*Ind. Eng. Chem.* **46**, No. 1, 41A, 43A, 45A, 47A, 49A, 51A, 53A, 55A (1954).
1458. Anon.	*Ind. Eng. Chem.* **46**, No. 5, 7A (1954).
1459. Anon.	*Oil, Paint, & Drug Reporter* **165**, No. 12, 5 (1954).
1460. Anon.	*Plastics* (London) **19**, 235 (1954).
1461. Cruse, W. T.	*Reinforced Plastics Div., Soc. Plastics Ind. Confer., 6th Annual,* 1951, Sect. 14.
1462. Esselen, G. J., and Bacon, F. S.	*Ind. Eng. Chem.* **30**, 125–30 (1938).
1463. Fuson, R. H.	*Advanced Organic Chemistry.* Wiley, New York, 1950, 679 pp.
1464. Gilliland, E. R., and Lavender, H. M.	*India Rubber World* **111**, 67–72 (1944).
1465. Hibben, J. H., *et al.*	*U. S. Tariff Comm. Rept.* No. 173, Second Ser., 170 pp. (1951).
1466. Hibben, J. H., *et al.*	*U. S. Tariff Comm. Rept.* No. 175, Second Ser., 179 pp. (1952).
1467. Hibben, J. H., *et al.*	*U. S. Tariff Comm. Rept.* No. 190, Second Ser., 178 pp. (1953).
1468. Lichtenberg, C.	*Pacific Plastics Mag.* **2**, No. 3, 15 (1944).
1469. Powers, P. O.	*Chem. Eng. News* **24**, 2784–8 (1946).
1470. Raynolds, J. W.	*Chem. & Met. Eng.* **51**, No. 3, 109–13 (1944).
1471. Reuter, F. H.	*Austral. Plastics* **1**, No. 5, 24–7 (1945).
1472. Sayre, J. E.	*Chem. Eng. News* **30**, 5138–42 (1952).
1473. Sayre, J. E.	*Chem. Eng. News* **32**, 2052–4, 2056, 2058, 2060 (1954).
1474. Scott, W. D.	*Chem. & Ind.* 1944, 274–8.
1475. Sollenberger, G. H.	*Modern Plastics* **22**, No. 8, 101–2, 200–2 (1945).
1476. Vale, C. P.	*Brit. Plastics* **26**, 327–32 (1953).
1477. Webb, W.	*Reinforced Plastics Div., Soc. Plastics Ind. Confer., 7th Annual,* 1952, Sect. 7.

Concerning

Ethylene glycol production estimates.

Resins and plastics production figures; prediction of expansion in polyesters.

Estimate of phthalic anhydride production in 1954.

Reduction in price of maleic anhydride.

Market report, e.g., price reductions for ethylene glycol, propylene glycol, and phthalic anhydride.

Benzene end-use figures.

Use of styrene output from new plant directly in manufacturer's own plastics molding operations.

Production data on ethylene glycol, styrene, and other ethylene derivatives.

Report on plant construction and expansion in 1953, e.g., plants for phthalic anhydride, vinyltoluene, styrene, fumaric acid, adipic acid, polyester resins, polyester film.

New phthalic anhydride plant to increase major producers output to 80 million pounds a year.

New plant for production of phthalic anhydride.

British plant for production of maleic anhydride by benzene oxidation process.

Supply of raw materials for reinforced plastics.

Review of raw materials of plastics industry, production volumes, and uses.

Plant investment and production costs for synthetic rubber plants. Includes costs for styrene.

Synthetic organic chemicals. United States production and sales, 1950.

Synthetic organic chemicals. United States production and sales, 1951.

Synthetic organic chemicals. United States production and sales, 1952.

New plastics. Gives capacity for styrene production.

Plastics, resins, rubber. Tables list structures, raw materials, and reactions for manufacture.

Interrelation of plastics and chemicals. Styrene production figures.

Review on raw materials of plastics.

Survey of production and consumption of phthalic anhydride.

Production data and potentials for naphthalene and phthalic anhydride.

Raw material potential for synthetic resin development.

Material analysis. Brief mention of polyester resins, e.g., raw materials and applications.

A review, with 58 references, on the chemistry of unsaturated polyester resins. Includes raw materials, manufacture, and applications.

Availability and conservation of raw materials for polyesters.

Economics and General (Continued)

Author	Reference
1478. Worboys, W. J.	*India-Rubber J.* **106**, 633–5 (1944).
1479. Yarsley, V. E.	*Trade & Eng. Suppl. to "The Times"* (London) **56**, No. 973, 44 (1945).

Concerning

Raw materials for plastics industry.
Outlook for basic raw materials for plastics.

Author	Reference
1480. Anon.	*Can. Plastics* May–June 1954, 110.
1481. Anon.	Carbide and Carbon Chemicals Co., New York, N. Y. Tech. Information Sheets F8113 and F8117.
1482. Anon.	Dow Chemical Co., Midland, Mich. 16-p. booklet.
1483. Anon.	*Ind. Eng. Chem.* **44**, No. 3, 11A, 13A (1952).
1484. Anon.	*Plastics News Letter* **14**, No. 28, 3 (1954).
1485. Anon.	*Plastics World* **12**, No. 5, 37 (1954).
1486. Anon.	*SPE J.* **10**, No. 5, 4 (1954).
1487. Brinkman, W. H.	*Plastica* (Holland) **6**, No. 10, 436–40 (1953).
1488. Chin Chu J., Brown, F., and Burridge, K. G.	*Ind. Eng. Chem.* **45**, 1686–96 (1953).
1489. Goldberg, A. L	*Ind. Eng. Chem.* **39**, 1570–3 (1947).
1490. Hovey, A. G.	*Ind. Eng. Chem.* **41**, 730–37 (1949).
1491. Waeser, B.	*Chem. Tech.* (Japan) **16**, 237–9 (1943).
1492. Winding, C. C.	*Ind. Eng. Chem.* **42**, 1724–31 (1950).
1493. Winding, C. C., and Wiegandt, H. F.	*Ind. Eng. Chem.* **44**, 2052–64 (1952).
1494. Woods, D. T.	*Offic. Dig. Federation Paint and Varnish Production Clubs* No. 334, 769–82 (1952).

II. RESIN MANUFACTURE

Automatic equipment for manufacture of resins.

Properties of glycol maleates for use in polyester resin manufacture.

Dowtherm heat-transfer medium.

Report on polyesters: uses, production capacity, manufacture (in detail), and fabrication of laminates.

Machine for handling two-component plastics, e.g., polyesters, epoxies.

Automatic equipment for processing and dispensing polyesters on production-line basis.

Automatic equipment for production-line processing of polyesters. Performs functions of deaeration, proportioning of resin and hardener components, mixing, and meter dispensing.

Reinforced plastics: preparation of polyester resins; treatment of glass fiber to improve adhesion; properties of laminates; important molding methods, applications.

Design of heat exchangers for pseudo-plastic liquids.

Laboratory methods and equipment for bulk, solution, suspension, and emulsion polymerization.

Development of equipment for alkyd resin manufacture. A review with 34 references.

Pump for kneading and conveying plastics, etc.

Review with 264 references, on polymerization as chemical engineering unit operation.

Review on unit process of polymerization. Polyester use in coatings included.

Instrumentation for continuously recording viscosity of polymers and resins during processing.

Catalysts, Accelerators, Promoters

Author	Reference
1495. Anon.	American Cyanamid Co., Plastics and Resins Div., New York, N. Y. Booklet.
1496. Anon.	Bakelite Co., New York, N. Y. 18-p. booklet (1953).
1497. Anon.	Cadet Chemical Corp., Buffalo, N. Y. Tech. Data Bulls. Nos. 2–11.
1498. Anon.	General Electric Co., Chemical Div., Pittsfield, Mass. 23-p. bulletin.
1499. Anon.	Hercules Powder Co., Naval Stores Dept., Wilmington, Del. 13-p. booklet.
1500. Anon.	Hercules Powder Co., Naval Stores Dept., Wilmington, Del. 11-p. booklet.
1501. Anon.	Hooker Electrochemical Co., Niagara Falls, N. Y. Prelim. Bull. No. 51.
1502. Anon.	Interchemical Corp., Finishes Div., Cincinnati, Ohio. Bull. No. 40-1.
1503. Anon.	Nuodex Products Co., Inc. Elizabeth, N. J.
1504. Anon.	*Plastics Ind.* **12**, No. 4, 3 (1954) (advertisement).
1505. Anon.	*Plastics News Letter* **14**, No. 5, 3 (1954).
1506. Anon.	Rohm & Haas Co., Philadelphia, Pa. Bull. No. M-7-50.
1507. Anon.	U. S. Rubber Co., Naugatuck Chemical Div., Naugatuck, Conn. Tech. Bull.
1508. Anon.	Wallace & Tiernan Inc., Lucidol Div., Data Sheets and Bulls.
1509. Blomquist, A. T., and Berstein, I. A.	*J. Am. Chem. Soc.* **73**, 5546–50 (1951).
1510. Cohen, S. G., *et al.*	*J. Polymer Sci.* **3**, 264–82 (1948).
1511. Day, H. M., Dugliss, C. H., and Killeffer, R. A.	*Reinforced Plastics Div., Soc. Plastics Ind. Confer., 7th Annual*, 1952, Sect. 21.
1512. Delmonte, J.	*Modern Plastics* **24**, No. 6, 123 (1947).
1513. Delmonte, J.	*Plastics* (Chicago) **6**, No. 4, 39–40 (1947).
1514. Dickey, F. H., *et al.*	*Ind. Eng. Chem.* **41**, 1673–9 (1949).
1515. Franklin, P. J., French, D. M., and Nyberg, W. C.	*Natl. Bur. Standards Circ.* No. 493, 7 (1950).
1516. French, D. M.	*Paint, Oil, & Chem. Rev.* **112**, No. 20, 15, 26, 28, 30, 32 (1949).
1517. Gabriel, A. E.	*Modern Plastics* **25**, No. 8, 145–7, 200, 202, 204, 206, 208, 210, 212, 214, 216 (1948).
1518. Goggin, W. C., and Boyer, R. F.	*Ind. Eng. Chem.* **38**, 1090–6 (1946).

III. CATALYSIS AND INHIBITION

Concerning

Polyester resins: properties, casting procedures.

Polyester resins for reinforced plastics: properties, fabrication.

Organic peroxide catalysts.

Polyester resins: applications, properties, fabrication.

Cumene hydroperoxide: catalytic, physical, and chemical properties.

Properties and uses of organic hydroperoxides; cumene hydroperoxide, di-iso-propylbenzene hydroperoxide, and para-menthane hydroperoxide.
Curing of fire-resistant polyester resins.

Questions and answers on effect of promoters and activators on cure characteristics of polyester resins.
Cobalt naphthenate in mineral spirits—polymerization accelerator.
Low-temperature peroxide catalyst for polyesters.
Cobalt promoters for use with peroxide catalysts in curing polyester resins.
Polyester resins: properties, fabrication, uses.

Promoters and cold gelation of polyester resins.

Organic peroxide catalysts.

Effect of para substitutes on unimolecular decomposition of tertiary-butyl perbenzoates.
Light-induced polymerization of allyl and methacrylate monomers.
Control of gel and cure of polyester resins at room temperature.

Effect of catalysts on polyester coatings.
Effect of polymerization catalysts on properties of polyester resins.
Preparation, analysis, and properties of ditertiary-butyl peroxide and 2,2-bis-(tertiary-butylperoxy)butane (polymerization catalysts).
Development of NBS casting resin. Includes order of activity of various peroxide catalysts in this resin and comparison with order in polyester resins.

Organic reducing agents, e.g., mercaptans, as promoters for polymerization of unsaturated polyester resins.
Diethylene glycol maleate polyester as binder for sawdust in low-pressure molding compositions.
Plastic compositions for dielectric application, e.g., styrene monomer-unsaturated alkyd resin combination as potting compound for transformers.

417

Catalysts, Accelerators, Promoters (Continued)

Author	Reference
1519. Katchalsky, A., and Wechsler, H.	*J. Polymer Sci.* **1**, 229–30 (1946).
1520. Kern, W.	*Angew. Chem.* **61**, 471 (1949).
1521. Kern, W.	*Kunststoffe* **39**, 45 (1949).
1522. Muskat, I. E.	*Kunststoffe* **40**, 257 (1950); *Chem. Zentr.* 1950, II, 2257.
1523. Nichols, F. S., and Bliss, C.	*Modern Plastics* **29**, No. 9, 124, 194, 197, 199–200, 203–4 (1952).
1524. Nozaki, K., and Bartlett, P. D.	*J. Am. Chem. Soc.* **68**, 1686–92 (1946).
1525. Patterson, D. G., and Robinson, J. D.	*Modern Plastics* **25**, No. 6, 86 (1947). (Rept. on Soc. Plastics Ind. Confer.)
1526. Perry, R. P., and Seltzer, K. P.	*Modern Plastics* **25**, No. 3, 134–6, 216, 218, 220, 222 (1947).
1527. Perry, R. P., and Seltzer, K. P.	*Modern Plastics* **25**, No. 9, 169 (1948). (Abst. from West Coast Soc. Plastics Ind. Confer.)
1528. Proell, W. A., and Adams, C. E.	*Ind. Eng. Chem.* **41**, 2217–21 (1949).
1529. Razuvaev, G. A., Ol'dekop, Y. A., and Fedotova, E. I.	*Uspekhi Khim* **21**, 379–421 (1952).
1530. Rybolt, C. H., and Swigert, T. C.	*Reinforced Plastics Div., Soc. Plastics Ind. Confer., 4th Annual,* 1949; *Modern Plastics* **26**, No. 8, 97, 101–3, 150–4, 157 (1949).
1531. Steegmuller, M.	*Plastiques* **1**, 11–5, 47–52 (1943).
1532. Uehara, R.	*Kagaku no Ryoiki* (*J. Japan. Chem.*) **7**, 286–98 (1953).
1533. Van Boskirk, R. L.	*Modern Plastics* **27**, No. 6, 148 (1950) ("The Plastiscope").
1534. Wiles, Q. T., *et al.*	*Ind. Eng. Chem.* **41**, 1679–82 (1949).
1535. Zeigler, K.	*Brennstoff-Chem.* **30**, 181-4 (1949).

Inhibitors

1535a. Anon.	*Chem. Eng. News* **31**, No. 24, 2506 (1953).
1536. Anon.	*Ind. Eng. Chem.* **44**, 1730–5 (1952).
1537. Anon.	Interchemical Corp., Finishes Div., Cincinnati, Ohio. Bull. No. 35-1.
1538. Antlfinger, G. J., and Lufter, C. H.	*Ind. Eng. Chem.* **45**, 182–6 (1953).
1539. Cass, W. E., and Burnett, R. E.	Paper presented at Am. Chem. Soc. Meeting, Div. Paint, Plastics, and Printing Ink Chem., Chicago, September 1953.

Concerning

Determination of catalyst fragments in polymers by ultraviolet absorption.

Redox-systems for altering speed and temperature of catalyzed polymerization of unsaturated polyesters.

Oxidation-reduction systems for acceleration of polymerization of unsaturated compounds.

Definition of contact resins. Regulation of hardening rate and temperature.

Exotherm curves for cold-setting polyesters.

Kinetics of decomposition of benzoyl peroxide in solvents, e.g., styrene, maleic anhydride.

Developments in catalysis and processing of polyester resins.

Manufacture and properties of organic peroxides containing tertiary-butyl groups. Tables given on effect of peroxides on gel time of polyesters.

Behavior of alkyl hydroperoxides and peresters in polyester resins.

Alkanesulfonic acids as catalysts in polymerization of alkanes and alkylation of aromatics.

Review with 105 references, on polymerization initiators.

Organic peroxides as catalysts for polyester-type resins.

Catalysis of polymerization of unsaturated compounds.

Initiators for radical polymerization. A review with 108 references.

Catalyst for polyester resins.

Applications of ditertiary-butyl peroxide and 2,2-bis(tertiary-butylperoxy)butane, e.g., polymerization catalysts.

Azodi-isobutyronitrile and dimethyl azodi-isobutyrate as polymerization catalysts.

Nonexclusive licensing of General Electric patent on stabilizer for thixotropic compositions.

Manufacture of hydroquinone from aniline.

Inhibitor for polyester resins.

Polymerization-stopping agents, e.g., sulfur and sodium dimethyl dithiocarbamate.

Experiments on inhibition of unsaturated polyesters at room temperature. Activation effect of reaction of some inhibitors with peroxides.

Inhibitors (Continued)

Author	Reference
1540. Cohen, S. G., and Sparrow, D. B.	*J. Polymer Sci.* 693–703 (1948).
1541. Gerhart, H. L.	*Modern Plastics* **25**, No. 6, 86 (1947). (Report on Soc. Plastics Industry Low-Pressure Confer.)
1542. Hammond, G. S., and Bartlett, P. D.	*J. Polymer Sci.* **6**, 617–24 (1951).
1543. Moore, S. A., and Weber, A.	*Reinforced Plastics Div., Soc. Plastics Ind. Confer., 8th Annual*, 1953, Sect. 24G.
1544. Price, C. C., and Read, D. H.	*J. Polymer Res.* **1**, No. 1, 44–8 (1946).
1545. Zhurkov, S. N., and Lerman, R. I.	*Compt. rend. acad. sci. U. R. S. S.* **47**, 106–9; *Doklady Akad. Nauk S.S.S.R.* **47**, 109–12 (1945).

Concerning

Action of inhibitors, retarders, and chain-transfer agents on polymerization of allyl and methacrylate monomers.

New developments in polyester resins, including inhibition.

Inhibition by nitro compounds of polymerization of allyl compounds.

Gelation inhibitors for polyester resins.

Factors affecting polymerization and copolymerization: retarders, chain-transfer agents, foreign end groups, polarity of monomer double bonds.

Effect of sorption of organic vapors on solidification temperature of polymers. Relation to action of plasticizers.

Reinforcing Fillers

Author	Reference
1546. Anon.	Bee-lyte Fiberglass Co., Chicago, Ill. Brochure.
1547. Anon.	Bigelow-Sanford Carpet Co., Inc., Fiber Glass Products Div., New York, N. Y. 3-p. brochure; Fiber Glass News Letter, May 1954.
1548. Anon.	Bigelow-Sanford Carpet Co., Inc., Fiber Glass Products Div., New York, N. Y. Fiber Glass Tech. Bull. No. 1.
1549. Anon.	Bigelow-Sanford Carpet Co., Inc., Fiber Glass Products Div., New York, N. Y. Fiber Glass News Letter, June 15, 1954.
1550. Anon.	*Ceram. Age* **60**, No. 1, 26–7 (1952).
1551. Anon.	W. R. Chance Corp., Designers & Consultants, Arlington, Va.
1552. Anon.	E. I. du Pont de Nemours & Co., Inc., Grasselli Chemicals Dept., Wilmington, Del. Bull. No. A-360-b.
1553. Anon.	Ferro Corp., Fiber Glass Div., Nashville, Tenn. Brochure.
1554. Anon.	Glass Fibers, Inc., Textile Div., Toledo, Ohio. Tech. Bulls. Nos. 1, 2.
1555. Anon.	*Glass Fibre Reinforced Plastics Conv.* (England), 1952, *Proc.*, 74–8.
1556. Anon.	Hess, Goldsmith and Co., Inc., New York, N. Y.
1557. Anon.	Libbey-Owens-Ford Glass Co., Toledo, Ohio. Form No. F-5 (1953).
1558. Anon.	Linde Air Products Co., New York. Data Bull. (1952).
1559. Anon.	*Materials & Methods* **39**, No. 5, 4 (1954).
1560. Anon.	*Modern Plastics* **30**, No. 6, 137; **31**, No. 4, 188–9 (1953) (advertisements).
1561. Anon.	*Modern Plastics* **30**, No. 8, 244 (1953).
1562. Anon.	*Modern Plastics* **30**, No. 10, 236 (1953).
1563. Anon.	*Modern Plastics* **31**, No. 7, 10 (1954) (advertisement).
1564. Anon.	Modigliani Glass Fibers, Inc., Lancaster, Ohio. Brochure.
1565. Anon.	Modigliani Glass Fibers, Inc., Lancaster, Ohio.

IV. FILLERS AND REINFORCEMENTS

Concerning

Awnings from glass fiber-polyester resin sheeting.

Glass reinforcing mat for plastics (without chemical binder).

Weight variation of chopped glass roving mat.

Woven roving reinforcing material and "textured" glass fiber mats; will not "wash" in matched metal die molding.

Manufacture of paper from glass fibers.
Weight of polyester glass laminates as related to thickness and glass content (graphs).
Volan finish (methacrylate chromic chloride) for glass fabric.

Chopped strand reinforcing mats.

Glass fiber material for reinforcing plastics.

General questions and answers on glass fiber reinforced plastics.

Glass fabric specifications.

Properties of Garan finish glass fabric-polyester laminates.

Application of Linde sizing, GS-1, for production of moisture resistant polyester laminates.
New forms of reinforcement: (1) preimpregnated material with glass reinforcement made by superimposing warp threads in a staggered pattern; (2) glass cloth woven from rovings and sized with high-quality finish.
Glass fiber mats without chemical binder.

Volan finish (methacrylate chromic chloride) for glass fibers.
Glass cloth finishers licensed for use of Garan finish by Libbey-Owens-Ford Glass Co.
Glass fiber rovings with silane sizing.

Glass fiber types available for reinforced plastics and other applications.

New approach to glass fiber reinforcements—"grain" formation in plastics.

Reinforcing Fillers (Continued)

Author	Reference
1566. Anon.	Owens-Corning Fiberglas Corp., Toledo, Ohio. Fiberglas Standards PR6.C1.
1567. Anon.	Owens-Corning Fiberglas Corp., Toledo, Ohio. 4-p. brochure.
1568. Anon.	Pittsburgh Plate Glass Co., Pittsburgh, Pa. Reprint of advertisement.
1569. Anon.	*Plastics* (London) **18**, 3–5 (1953).
1570. Anon.	*Plastics News Letter* **14**, No. 24, 3 (1954).
1571. Anon.	*Plastics World* **11**, No. 1, 32 (1953).
1572. Anon.	*Plastics World* **11**, No. 2, 21 (1953).
1573. Anon.	*Plastics World* **12**, No. 6, 29 (1954); *Plastics News Letter* **14**, No. 20, 1 (1954).
1574. Anon.	St. George Textile Corp., Industrial Fabrics Div., New York, N. Y.
1575. Anon.	J. P. Schwebel & Co., New York, N. Y. 2-p. chart.
1576. Anon.	Soule Mill, New Bedford, Mass. 4-p. brochure.
1577. Anon.	J. P. Stevens & Co., Inc., New York, N. Y. 4-p. brochure.
1578. Anon.	Strandcote Corp., Hawthorne, Calif. Data Sheets Nos. 1, 1A (1953).
1579. Arend, A. G.	*Fibres, Fabrics, & Cordage* **13**, 330, 337, 371 (1946).
1580. Bacon, C. E.	*Plastics* (London) **17**, 178 (1952).
1581. Bacon, C. E.	*Modern Plastics* **29**, No. 11, 126 (1952).
1582. Barber, R. W.	*Plastics* (Chicago) **4**, No. 1, 66, 68, 86, 88 (1946).
1583. Biefeld, L. P., and Philipps, T. E.	*Reinforced Plastics Div., Soc. Plastics Ind. Confer.*, 7th Annual, 1952, Sect. 18.
1584. Biefeld, L. P., and Philipps, T. E.	*Am. Dyestuff Reptr.* **41**, No. 17, 501–6 (1952).
1585. Biefeld, L. P., and Philipps, T. E.	*Ind. Eng. Chem.* **45**, 1281–6 (1953).
1586. Bjorksten, J. A.	*Reinforced Plastics Div., Soc. Plastics Ind. Confer.*, 7th Annual, 1952, Sect. 15.
1587. Bjorksten, J. A., and Yaeger, L. L.	*Modern Plastics* **29**, No. 11, 124, 188 (1952).
1588. Bjorksten, J. A., Yaeger, L. L., and Henning, J. E.	Paper presented at Am. Chem. Soc. Meeting, Div. Paint, Plastics, and Printing Ink Chem., Chicago, September 1953.
1589. Bobeth, W.	*Silikattech* **1**, No. 3, 66–75 (1950).
1590. Braithwaite, K. H.	*Can. Mining Met. Bull.* No. 363, 277–80 (1942).
1591. Broun, G.	*Textile Bull.* **64**, No. 12, 35–6 (1943).
1592. Brown, B. J.	*Rubber Age & Synthetics* **34**, 314–5, 359–61 (1953).

Concerning

Glass fiber reinforcing materials for plastics.

Greater precision control of weight of rovings; also silane-sized rovings and glass fiber overlay (surfacing) mats.
Announcement of manufacture of glass fiber materials.

Production of glass fiber preforms.
Paper-base polyester laminate for use as electrical insulation.
Glass fabric for molding curved shapes.
Glass fiber reinforcings.
Paper-base electrical grade laminate made with melamine-polyester resin combination.
Glass fiber fabrics. Physical properties and specifications guide.

Glass fabric specifications.

Physical properties of glass fabrics.

Properties of industrial fabrics (glass).

Specifications for glass fabrics and plastic laminates.

Review on production and characteristics of glass fiber fabrics.

Methods of manufacturing reinforced plastics in the United States.
Finish 136 for high wet strength laminates. Data given for laminates made with 6 different polyester resins.
Selection of paper for resin-impregnated laminates.

Surface treatments for glass fibers.

Sizes for glass textiles for reinforcing polyester plastics.

Review, with 36 references, on finishes for glass fabrics for reinforcing polyester plastics.
Vinyl silane size for glass fabric.

Vinyl silane size for glass fabric.

Factors affecting adhesion in unsaturated polyester resin-glass fiber laminates. Theory.

Survey of production, properties, and applications of glass threads and fibers.
Review on glass fiber forms and uses.

Review of properties of protein and glass fibers.
Glass fabrics for use in plastics industry: constructions and weaves, relation between fabric structure and service.

Reinforcing Fillers (Continued)

Author	Reference
1593. Bushman, E. F.	*Modern Plastics* **30**, No. 4, 98–9 (1952).
1594. Calhoun, L. M.	*Modern Plastics* **30**, No. 6, 84–6, 189–90, 192–3 (1953).
1595. Callinan, T. D., and Lucas, R. T.	*Elec. Manuf.* **50**, No. 6, 242 (1952).
1596. Chernyak, M. G.	*Legkaya Prom.* **4**, Nos. 1/2, 6–10 (1944).
1597. Clark, G. A.	*Modern Plastics* **30**, No. 3, 142–4, 218–9 (1952).
1598. Clark, G. A.	*PB Rept.* No. 112387 (available from Library of Congress, Publication Board Project).
1599. Clark, R. F., and Dangelmajer, C. F.	*Modern Plastics* **30**, No. 6, 86–7, 195, 197, 198 (1953).
1600. Cole, H.	*Glass Fibre Reinforced Plastics Conv.* (England) 1952, *Proc.* 33–42.
1601. Darling, W. B.	*Ind. Plastics* **1**, No. 6, 22–5 (1945).
1602. Decker, E. H.	*Reinforced Plastics Div., Soc. Plastics Ind. Confer., 8th Annual,* 1953, Sect. 27B.
1603. Dennen, F. W.	*Reinforced Plastics Div., Soc. Plastics Ind. Confer., 8th Annual,* 1953, Sect. 27E.
1604. Dobson, A. M.	*Glass Fibre Reinforced Plastics Conv.* (England) 1952, *Proc.* 43–55.
1605. Dobson, A. M.	*Brit. Plastics* **27**, 103–5 (1954).
1606. Erickson, P., and Silver, J.	*Reinforced Plastics Div., Soc. Plastics Ind. Confer., 8th Annual,* 1953, Sect. 14.
1607. Evans, R. C., and Jones, C. L., Jr.	*Modern Packaging* **19**, No. 5, 140–2 (1946).
1608. Francis, R. J., and Bacon, C. E.	*Plastics* (Chicago) **5**, No. 6, 13–6, 97–8 (1946).
1609. Freytag, H.	*Melliand Textilber.* **25**, 37–9 (1944).
1610. Gallagher, M., and Seymour, R. B.	*Modern Plastics* **25**, No. 12, 117–8, 171–3 (1948).
1611. Gallagher, M., Goslen, H. H., and Seymour, R. B.	*Modern Plastics* **27**, No. 7, 111–4, 116, 118, 172 (1950).
1612. Gangloff, W. C.	*Chem. Ind.* (New York) **53**, 512–4 (1943).
1613. Godol.	*Rusta-Rayonne* **14**, 517–8 (1939).
1614. Gordon, J. E.	*Plastics* (London) **17**, 344–5, 362 (1952).
1615. Griffith, P.	*Pacific Plastics Mag.* **2**, No. 4, 18–9, 45 (1944).
1616. Hauserman, F. B., and Robb, R. M.	*Reinforced Plastics Div., Soc. Plastics Ind. Confer., 8th Annual,* 1953, Sect. 27H.
1617. Henning, A. R.	*Plastics* (London) **19**, 16–7 (1954) (summary of paper presented at 8th Swedish Plastics Conference).
1618. Hyde, K.	*Plastics* (London) **17**, 215 (1952).

Concerning

Reinforcing glass fiber-polyester resin for preformed products.
Selection of glass fabrics for plastics reinforcement. How fabric properties are obtained.
Characteristics of electrical insulation made from ceramic-fiber paper impregnated with various plastics.
Review of properties and uses of glass fiber.
Wet strength of polyester laminates reinforced with glass fibers having different finishes.
Developments concerning aircraft glass fiber plastic laminates: properties of heat-resistant laminates (polyester, silicone, phenolic); new sizings for glass fibers; mechanical properties of laminates.
Selection of glass fabrics for plastics reinforcement. Properties of finished moldings.
Relationships between composition, structure, and physical properties of glass.

Protective and decorative surfacings for paper, e.g., use of thermosetting resins.
Woven glass fiber for reinforcing plastics.

New developments in resin field. Describes glass mats for laminating.

Manufacture and properties of glass fibers.

Forms of glass fiber for reinforcing plastics. Review.
Chemical finishes for glass fibers in reinforced plastics.

Low-pressure resins (probably polyesters). Properties, fillers, molding, applications in packaging.
Fabrication of low-pressure resins, including polyesters.

Review on glass fiber.
Laminates from purified cotton linters sheet.

Reinforcement of polyester laminates with fabrics.

Properties and uses for fillers in the plastics industry.
Review of new patents and processes for production of glass fibers.
Plastics in engineering. Mentions various fillers, including glass fibers.
Review on thermosetting resins. Uses, properties, casting, and application in laminated (paper) products.
Volan finish (methacrylate chromic chloride) for glass fabric.

Use of glass fiber for reinforcing plastics.

Glass fiber-based laminates for electrical applications.

Reinforcing Fillers (Continued)

Author	Reference
1619. Jellinek, M. H.	*Reinforced Plastics Div., Soc. Plastics Ind. Confer.*, 7th Annual, 1952, Sect. 17; *Modern Plastics* **30**, No. 3, 150 (1952).
1620. Koch, P. A., and Bobeth, W.	*Glastech. Ber.* **25**, 396–405 (1952).
1621. Kreiser, H. D.	*Am. Inst. Mining Met. Engrs., Tech. Pub.* No. 1598, 14 pp. (1943).
1622. Krotova, N.	*J. Tech. Phys.* (U.S.S.R.) **14**, 455–61 (1944).
1623. Marschner, C. F.	*Pacific Pulp Paper Ind.* **18**, No. 8, 22–6 (1944).
1624. Meteer, C. L., and Layton, P. L.	*Wire and Wire Products* **26**, 302, 304–6, 338–9, 340, 341 (1951).
1625. Miller, H. S.	*Reinforced Plastics Div., Soc. Plastics Ind. Confer.*, 8th Annual, 1953, Sect. 27F.
1626. Moore, A. S.	*Fibres, Fabrics, & Cordage* **12**, 400 (1945).
1627. Murgatroyd, J. B.	*J. Soc. Glass Tech.* **28**, 368–87 (1944).
1628. Murphy, E. A.	*Instrumentation* **6**, No. 3, 10–12 (1952).
1629. Oburger, W.	*Elektrotech. u. Maschinenbau* **66**, 192–95 (1949); *Ceram. Abstracts* 1950, 5 (in *J. Am. Ceram. Soc.* **33**, No. 1).
1630. O'Leary, M. J., *et al.*	*Tappi* **35**, 289–93 (1952).
1631. Owens-Corning Fiberglas Corp., Research Laboratory staff.	*Modern Plastics* **21**, No. 9, 100–103 (1944).
1632. Page, W. H.	*Science Counselor* **8**, No. 4, 109–11, 124 (1942).
1633. Page, W. H.	*Textile Colorist* **65**, 13–4, 46 (1943).
1634. Page, W. H.	*Compressed Air Mag.* **50**, 200–5 (1945).
1635. Pazsiczky, G. V.	*Glass Ind.* **18**, 17–20 (1937).
1636. Perry, H. A., Jr., *et al.*	*Reinforced Plastics Div., Soc. Plastics Ind. Confer.*, 9th Annual, 1954, Sect. 1C.
1637. Plummer, J. H., and Neumeyer, C. F.	*Reinforced Plastics Div., Soc. Plastics Ind. Confer.*, 9th Annual, 1954, Sect 28.
1638. Preston, F. W.	*Glass Ind.* **25**, 266–7, 284, 287 (1944).
1639. Quarendon, R.	*Textile Recorder* **56**, 35–6 (1939).
1640. Richardson, R.	*J. Can. Ceram. Soc.* **14**, 30–6 (1945).
1641. Robertson, I. A. M.	*Chem. & Ind.* 1946, 138–9, 146–7; *Brit. Rayon & Silk J.* **27**, No. 319, 63 (1950).
1642. Rogers, T. S.	*Modern Plastics* **18**, No. 11, 69–70, 96, 98 (1941).
1643. Rogers, T. S.	*Trans. Electrochem. Soc.* **81**, 41 (1942).
1644. Rosato, D.	*Reinforced Plastics Div., Soc. Plastics Ind. Confer.*, 7th Annual, 1952, Sect. 10.
1645. Sargent, E. H. G.	*Ind. Chemist* **22**, 665–70 (1946).
1646. Schlitt, W.	*Gummi u. Asbest* **6**, 330–2, 380–1 (1953).

Concerning

Vinyl silicone size for glass fibers.

Properties of glass fiber textiles.

Description of manufacturing processes, raw materials, products, and uses of glass fibers.
Change of mechanical properties of glass fibers by coating with film-forming substance, e.g., alkyd resin.
High-strength, low-pressure molded paper-base laminates.   Disadvantages of glass fibers as fillers.
Dimensions and weight of glass fiber yarn applied to wires and cables.

Glass fabrics for reinforcing plastics.

Manufacture of glass yarns and fabrics.
Elastic properties of glass fibers and effect of heat treatment on strength.
Characteristics of glass fibers.   Interview with Owens-Corning Fiberglas Corp. executive.
Glass fiber insulation for electrical equipment.   Manufacture and properties.

Manufacture from glass fibers of paper suitable for reinforcing plastic laminates.
Forms, properties, and handling of glass reinforcements.

Review on history, manufacture, and uses of glass fibers.
History, manufacture, and uses of glass fiber textiles.
Manufacture and applications of glass fibers.
Manufacture, processing, and use of glass fibers.
Improvements in flexural properties of reinforced plastics by use of chlorosilane finishes.
New coupling agent for glass fiber roving-polyester products—vinyl ethoxy-silane applied as additive in impregnating resin.
Properties and uses of glass fiber fillers in plastic laminates.
Manufacture of glass fibers. Historical and latest methods.
Manufacture of glass fiber reinforced plastics.
Review on manufacture and uses of glass fibers.

Review of uses of glass fiber—synthetic resin combinations.

General review on glass fibers: forms, thermal insulation and other uses.
Plastics in aircraft. Sizes, foams, coatings.

Review on glass reinforced plastics, with 18 references.
Review on polyesters and glass fibers.

Reinforcing Fillers (Continued)

Author	Reference
1647. Shah, N. H.	*Indian Textile J.* **56**, 1113–5 (1946).
1648. Silverman, A.	*J. Chem. Educ.* **30**, 32–4 (1953).
1649. Slayter, G.	*Ind. Eng. Chem.* **32**, 1568–71 (1940).
1650. Slayter, G.	*Fibre and Fabric* **94**, No. 2920, 10–11 (1941).
1651. Slayter, G.	*Ohio State Univ. Eng. Expt. Sta. News* **16**, No. 4, 3–8 (1944).
1652. Slayter, G.	*Am. Dyestuff Reptr.* **34**, 189–90, 193 (1945).
1653. Slayter, G.	*Am. Ceram. Soc. Bull.* **31**, 2768 (1952).
1654. Smith, G. S.	*Metallurgia* **33**, 55–8 (1945).
1655. Smith, H. D.	*Am. Wool Cotton Reptr.* **55**, No. 30, 7–8, 42 (1941); *Textile Bull.* **60**, No. 11, 10, 12, 31, 34–7, 40–1 (1941).
1656. Smith, L.	*Textile Age* **10**, No. 1, 60, 62 (1946).
1657. Steinman, R.	*Modern Plastics* **29**, No. 3, 116–8, 184 (1951); *Reinforced Plastics Div., Soc. Plastics Ind. Confer.,* 7th Annual, 1952, Sect. 16.
1658. Thomas, J. H.	*Glass Ind.* **18**, 201, 211 (1937).
1659. Thomas, J. H.	*Textile Bull.* **70**, No. 2, 122, 124, 126, 128 (1946).
1660. Tooley, F. V.	*Bull. Am. Ceram. Soc.* **22**, 60–4 (1943).
1661. Torrey, J. V. P.	*Reinforced Plastics Div., Soc. Plastics Ind. Confer.,* 7th Annual, 1952, Sect. 19; *Modern Plastics* **30**, No. 3, 154 (1952).
1662. Tripathi, I. L.	*Indian Textile J.* **62**, 353–60 (1952).
1663. Tucker, J. L.	*Am. Dyestuff Reptr.* **26**, P182-5 (1937).
1664. Tucker, J. L.	*Ceram. Age* **31**, 9–10 (1938).
1665. Ulrich, H. M.	*Melliand Textilber.* **33**, 188–90, 281–2 (1952).
1666. Van Boskirk, R. L.	*Modern Plastics* **30**, No. 12, 206 (1953) ("The Plastiscope").
1667. Williams, S., Alfers, J. B., and Furgason, C. M.	*Modern Plastics* **24**, No. 7, 151–3, 190 (1947).
1668. Wolochow, D.	*Can. Chem. Process Inds.* **24**, 333–5 (1940).
1669. Yaeger, L. L.	*Reinforced Plastics Div., Soc. Plastics Ind. Confer.,* 6th Annual, 1951, Sect. 12.
1670. Yaeger, L. L., et al.	*U. S. Air Force Tech. Rept.* No. 6220, U. S. Air Force, Materiel Command, Wright-Patterson Air Force Base, Ohio (1951).

Bulk Fillers

1671. Anon.	*Brit. Plastics* **27**, 184 (1954).
1672. Anon.	Diamond Alkali Co., Cleveland, Ohio. Bull. No. 8.

Concerning

Review on glass fabric. Early production methods, properties.
Historical notes on glass, 1900–1950.
Review of production, properties, and uses of glass fibers.
Uses and manufacture of glass fibers.
Heat treatment to improve adhesion of resin to glass fibers in glass fiber reinforced plastics.
Manufacture, properties, and uses of glass fiber textiles.
Strength of solid glass and glass fibers.
Mechanism of fracture in brittle substances such as glass and plastics.
Properties and uses of glass fibers and other synthetic fibers.

Investigations of plastic laminates reinforced with cotton fiber.
Improvement of wet strength of glass fiber reinforced polyester plastics by Garan finish.

Properties and uses of textiles made from glass fibers.
Production and uses of glass fibers. Best weaves for reinforced plastics.

Forms, properties, and uses of glass fibers.
Volan finish for glass cloth.

History and manufacture of glass wool, continuous and staple fibers, yarns, and cloths.
Glass fiber products in textile industry.
General article on manufacture and uses of textile glass fibers and other glass products.
Review of properties of asbestos and methods of testing, spinning, and dyeing asbestos fibers.
Lightweight glass cloth made from very thin yarn. Permits reduction in space factor requirements.
Flameproofing of cotton fillers in plastic laminates.

Review of inorganic fibers. Properties and uses of glass fibers are discussed.
Glass fiber-polyester laminates with high moisture resistance. Sizing.

Development of sizings for glass fabric in polyester resin laminates.

Calcium carbonate coated with resin or stearate as filler for polyesters.
Applications of calcium carbonate (filler) with polyesters.

Bulk Fillers (Continued)

Author	Reference
1673. Anon.	Godfrey L. Cabot, Inc., Boston, Mass. 4-p. brochure.
1674. Anon.	Godfrey L. Cabot, Inc., Boston, Mass. Data Sheet.
1675. Anon.	Witco Chemical Co., New York, N. Y. Tech. Bull. No. W-1.
1676. Levenhagen, A. W.	*Reinforced Plastics Div., Soc. Plastics Ind. Confer.*, 6th Annual, 1951, Sect. 4.
1677. Linzmeyer, L. G.	*Reinforced Plastics Div., Soc. Plastics Ind. Confer.*, 7th Annual, 1952, Sect. 4.
1678. Linzmeyer, L. G.	*Reinforced Plastics Div., Soc. Plastics Ind. Confer.*, 8th Annual, 1953, Sect. 3.
1679. Moore, S. A.	*Reinforced Plastics Div., Soc. Plastics Ind. Confer.*, 8th Annual, 1953, Sect. 24G.
1680. Parker, R. C., and Whittaker, E. J. W.	*Proc. Phys. Soc.* (London) **64B**, 126–34 (1951).
1681. Shannon, R. F., and Biefeld, L. F.	*Modern Plastics* **31**, No. 4, 125–32, 215, 219 (1953).
1682. Wilcox, J. R.	*Reinforced Plastics Div., Soc. Plastics Ind. Confer.*, 9th Annual, 1954, Sect. 27.
1683. Witt, R. K., and Cizek, E. P.	Paper presented at Am. Chem. Soc. Meeting, Div. Paint, Plastics, and Printing Ink Chem., Chicago, September 1953.

Special Fillers

Author	Reference
1684. Anon.	American Cyanamid Co., Plastics and Resins Div., New York, N. Y.
1685. Anon.	Claremont Pigment Dispersion Corp., Brooklyn, N. Y. Data Sheets.
1686. Anon.	Ferro Corp., Color Div., Cleveland, Ohio.
1687. Anon.	Ferro Corp., Color Div., Cleveland, Ohio. 2-p. brochure.
1688. Anon.	Ferro Corp., Color Div., Cleveland, Ohio.
1689. Anon.	Imperial Chemical Industries, Ltd., Dyestuff Div., Manchester, England. Leaflet.
1690. Anon.	Interchemical Corp., Finishes Div., Cincinnati, Ohio. Bull. No. 35-1.
1691. Anon.	*Plastics News Letter* **14**, No. 8, 4 (1954).
1692. Ab, E. A.	*Bull. acad. sci. U.R.S.S.*, Ser. phys. **9**, 551–4 (1945).
1693. Fram, P., Dunne, T. F., and Leonard, F.	*Ind. Eng. Chem.* **46**, No. 2, 493–6 (1954).
1694. Musgrave, C.	*Plastics Inst.* (London) *Trans.* **21**, No. 43, 80–95 (1953).
1695. Oehlcke, C. R. M.	*J. Soc. Dyers Colourists* **61**, 306–10 (1945).

Concerning

Properties and uses of silica filler for polyesters.

Properties and uses of silicate filler for polyesters.

Properties of calcium carbonate fillers for polyesters.

Bulk fillers for reinforced plastics: types, advantages, and disadvantages.

Evaluation of fillers for reinforced plastics.

Evaluation of bulk fillers for reinforced plastics.

New developments in polyester resins. Bulk fillers.

Mechanical properties of powders bonded by synthetic resins.

Effects of high inorganic filler concentration on properties of polyester-glass fiber products.
Effect of mineral fillers on flow properties and thixotropy of resins.

Effect of particle size of filler and filler concentration on strength of parts made from polyester and melamine-formaldehyde resins and silica filler.

Color pastes for polyester resins.

Color paste concentrates for coloring polyesters.

Special color pastes for polyesters.
Technique of dry coloring polyester resins.

Chart of inorganic pigments.
Compound suitable for coloring of acrylic and polyester plastics.

Polyester color concentrates for polyester resins.

Colored glass fiber for coloring of mat, fabric, or molding compound for reinforced plastics.
Properties of luminescent methacrylate type of plastic.

Color uniformity in low-pressure laminates for artificial limbs. Procedure given for coloring laminates.

Review on pigments and colors used in plastics.

Coloring of plastics, including cast resins.

Special Fillers (Continued)

Author	Reference
1696. Van Boskirk, R. L.	*Modern Plastics* **25**, No. 12, 176 (1948) ("The Plastiscope").
1697. Vygodskaya, M.	*Bull. acad. sci. U.R.S.S. Ser. phys.* **9**, 547–50 (1945).
1698. Weeks, W.	*Plastics* (London) **11**, 588–92 (1947).
1699. Weeks, W.	*Modern Plastics* **25**, No. 12, 103–10 (1948).

General

Author	Reference
1700. Anon.	Glass Fibers, Inc., Toledo, Ohio.
1701. Anon.	Libbey-Owens-Ford Glass Co., Toledo, Ohio. Brochure.
1702. Anon.	*Modern Plastics* **30**, No. 9, 212 (1953); *SPE J.* **9**, No. 4, 30 (1953).
1703. Anon.	Owens-Corning Fiberglas Corp., Toledo, Ohio. Brochure.
1704. Anon.	Owens-Illinois Glass Co., Toledo, Ohio. Brochure.
1705. Fischer, M. H., *et al.*	*Modern Plastics* **14**, No. 2, 50 (1936).

Concerning

Colors for polyester resins.

Preparation and properties of luminescent methacrylate type of plastic.

Review on polyesters as casting resins. Pigments for coloring.
Casting techniques for polyesters. Metallic fillers.

Organization of subsidiaries.
Organization of company.

Purchase of Perrault Glass Fiber Corp. plant by International Glass Corp.

Organization of company and subdivisions.

Organization of company as related to subsidiaries.

Review articles on coloring, filling, molding, laminating, and finishing plastics.
   (Part of series of articles in special issue).

Molds and Mold Making

	Author	Reference
1706.	Anon.	American Wheelebrator & Equipment Co., Mishawaka, Ind. Bull. 633.
1707.	Anon.	*Chem. Eng. News* **32,** 905 (1954) ("Concentrates").
1708.	Anon.	Metallizing Engineering Co., Inc., Long Island City, N. Y. 4-p. brochure.
1709.	Anon.	*Modern Plastics* **30,** No. 10, 107–10 (1953).
1710.	Anon.	*Modern Plastics* **31,** No. 1, 109–14 (1953).
1711.	Anon.	*Plastics* (London) **17,** 253–4 (1952).
1712.	Anon.	*Plastics* (London) **19,** 126 (1954).
1713.	Anon.	*Rubber Age* **73,** 648 (1953).
1714.	Azarian, G. J.	*SPE J.* **9,** No. 5, 14–5, 42 (1953).
1715.	Brenner, W., and Hase, L.	*Modern Plastics* **30,** No. 1, 105–9, 112, 114, 116 (1952).
1716.	Brinkema, R. J., and Wilkins, W. B.	*Reinforced Plastics Div., Soc. Plastics Ind. Confer., 8th Annual,* 1953, Sect. 26A.
1717.	Butzko, R. L.	*Modern Plastics* **30,** No. 9, 103–4, 106–8 (1953).
1718.	Coleman, J. J.	*Reinforced Plastics Div., Soc. Plastics Ind. Confer., 7th Annual,* 1952, Sect. 6F.
1719.	Cuming, J.	*Reinforced Plastics Div., Soc. Plastics Ind. Confer., 9th Annual,* 1954, Sect. 6B.
1720.	Dearle, D. A.	*Plastics & Resins* **3,** No. 12, 8–10, 28, 32 (1944).
1721.	Dickinson, T. A.	*Ceramic Age* **60,** No. 3, 21–2 (1953).
1722.	Erbe, P. E., and Grey, J. T.	*Modern Plastics* **24,** No. 3, 153–6, 196, 198, 200, 202, 204 (1946).
1723.	Goldsworthy, W. B.	*Reinforced Plastics Div., Soc. Plastics Ind. Confer., 5th Annual,* 1950, Sect. 6F.
1724.	Green, I.	*Reinforced Plastics Div., Soc. Plastics Ind. Confer., 8th Annual,* 1953, Sect. 26H.
1725.	Hastings, N. M.	*Reinforced Plastics Div., Soc. Plastics Ind. Confer. 9th Annual,* 1954, Sect. 29.
1726.	Lyijynen, F.	*Reinforced Plastics Div., Soc. Plastics Ind. Confer., 9th Annual,* 1954, Sect. 18.
1727.	Marks, B. H.	*Modern Plastics* **28,** No. 10, 115–6, 121–2 (1951).
1728.	Merrill, A. M.	*SPE J.* **10,** No. 4, 35 (1954).
1729.	Miller, L. R.	*Plastics* (Chicago) **1,** No. 6, 60–1, 103 (1944).

V. SHAPING

Molds and Mold Making (Continued)

	Author	Reference
1730.	Mirt, O.	*Mitt. Chem. Forsch. Inst. Ind. Österr.* **5**, 11–7 (1951).
1731.	Morrison, R. S.	*Reinforced Plastics Div., Soc. Plastics Ind. Confer.*, 5th Annual, 1950, Sect. 6D.
1732.	Muskat, I.	*Reinforced Plastics Div., Soc. Plastics Ind. Confer.*, 5th Annual, 1950, Sect. 6B.
1733.	Orbaugh, M. H.	*Reinforced Plastics Div., Soc. Plastics Ind. Confer.*, 5th Annual, 1950, Sect 6E.
1734.	Prince, W. V.	*Ind. Plastics* **1**, No. 1, 30–4, 48, 53–4 (1945).
1735.	Prince, W. V.	*Ind. Plastics* **1**, No. 5, 24–8, 40 (1945).
1736.	Reib, J. C.	*Reinforced Plastics Div., Soc. Plastics Ind. Confer.*, 8th Annual, 1953, Sect. 26D.
1737.	Sachs, C. C.	*Modern Plastics* **21**, No. 9, 124–8, 178, 180 (1944).
1738.	Shailer, L. L.	*Reinforced Plastics Div., Soc. Plastics Ind. Confer.*, 5th Annual, 1950, Sect. 6A.
1739.	Thayer, G. B.	*Ind. Plastics* **1**, No. 4, 19; No. 5, 17–21 (1945).
1740.	Wiltshire, A. J.	*Reinforced Plastics Div., Soc. Plastics Ind. Confer.*, 6th Annual, 1951, Sect. 3.
1741.	Young, M. K.	*Reinforced Plastics Div., Soc. Plastics Ind. Confer.*, 5th Annual, 1950, Sect. 3.

Heating Methods for Molding

1742.	Anon.	Edwin L. Wiegand Co., Pittsburgh, Pa. Application Repts. Nos. 102, R123.
1743.	Anon.	Edwin L. Wiegand Co., Pittsburgh, Pa. 22-p. booklet; Application Repts. No. 144, RP201, RP202; Data Sheet W2-3.
1744.	Ahlgren, L.	*Industritidning. Norden* **74**, 213–5 (1946); *Chimie & industrie* **57**, 160 (1947).
1745.	Cable, J. W.	*Induction and Dielectric Heating.* Reinhold, New York, 1954, 576 pp. Chap. XVII.
1746.	Dubois, P.	*Inds. plastiques* **1**, 196–202 (1945).
1747.	Duryee, L. M.	*Elec. World* **124**, No. 9, 84–7 (1945).
1748.	Freund, M.	*Brit. Plastics* **17**, 251–4, 254a, 262a (1945).
1749.	Geirenger, P. L., and Hasselrus, F.	*Mech. Eng.* **75**, 957–62 (1953).
1750.	Giles, R.	*Austral. Plastics* **1**, No. 1, 16–21 (1945).
1751.	Hazen, T.	*Trans. Electrochem. Soc.* **90**, 12 pp. (1946).
1752.	Kreiser, C. F.	*Reinforced Plastics Div., Soc. Plastics Ind. Confer.*, 8th Annual, 1953, Sect. 26F.

Concerning

Corrosion-resistant steels for use in plastics manufacture.

Metal positive-pressure molds for glass fiber reinforced polyester resins.

Fabrication of molds for large-area moldings.

Molds for low-pressure laminates by electrodeposition of metals.

Control of imperfections in molding plastics. Mold design.

Types of molds for plastics.
Positive-pressure molds for large-scale production of reinforced polyester products.

Economical tooling for aircraft parts. Use of zinc-base alloy for making molds.

Flexible molds for reinforced plastics products.

Materials for plastic molds.

Mold design for reinforced plastics products.

Mold making. Use of plaster.

Electric radiant heaters for drying plastic powders and laminates.

Electric radiant heating method for plastics processing.

Methods and applications of high-frequency heating in plastics industry.

Applications of dielectric heating to various production processes in plastics field.

Review of use of heat in molding plastics and effect of heat on molded products.
High-frequency heating in manufacture of plastics. Electrical details, uses.
Efficiency and economy of various heating methods in molding plastics.
New developments in liquid heating and cooling of plastics processing machinery, e.g., calendering, extruding, molding, and pressing equipment.
High-frequency heating for the plastics industry.
Dielectric properties vs. temperature of thermosetting plastics at radio frequencies. Relation to success of high-frequency heating in commercial molding.
Use of electric heat in reinforced plastics production.

Heating Methods for Molding (Continued)

Author	Reference
1753. Meharg, V. E.	*Modern Plastics* **20**, No. 7, 87–90 (1943).
1754. Meharg, V. E., and Mazzucchelli, A. P.	*Modern Plastics* **21**, No. 10, 108–13, 160, 162 (1944).
1755. Rappolt, H. G.	*Ind. Gas* **25**, No. 2, 20–2, 24 (1946).
1756. Roberts, T. A., and Happerfield, G. J.	*Brit. Plastics* **17**, 302–5 (1945).
1757. Venable, D.	*Electronics* **18**, No. 11, 120–4 (1945).
1758. Yarsley, V. E.	*Trade & Eng. Suppl.* to *"The Times"* (London) **54**, No. 968, 44 (1944).

Presses for Molding

1759. Anon.	*Brit. Plastics* **26**, 388–91 (1954).
1760. Anon.	*Brit. Plastics* **26**, 407–40 (1954).
1761. Anon.	*SPE J.* **10**, No. 4, 30 (1954).
1762. Anon.	*Plastics Ind.* **11**, No. 12, 37 (1953).
1763. Anon.	R. D. Wood Co., Philadelphia, Pa. Brochure.
1764. Brinkema, R. J., and Wilkins, W. B.	*Reinforced Plastics Div., Soc. Plastics Ind. Confer., 7th Annual*, 1952, Sect. 22A.
1765. Hastings, D. A.	*Reinforced Plastics Div., Soc. Plastics Ind. Confer., 7th Annual*, 1952, Sect. 22C.
1766. Muller, J. A.	*Reinforced Plastics Div., Soc. Plastics Ind. Confer., 7th Annual*, 1952, Sect. 22E.
1767. Powell, R. W.	*Reinforced Plastics Div., Soc. Plastics Ind. Confer., 7th Annual*, 1952, Sect. 22D.
1768. Praël, C.	*Kautschuk u. Gummi* **5**, 133–4, 136, 160, 162 (1952).

Molding and Laminating Methods

1769. Anon.	Allied Chemical & Dye Corp., Barrett Div., New York, N. Y. Bull. A-14.
1770. * Anon.	Allied Chemical & Dye Corp., National Aniline Div., New York, N. Y. 52-p. booklet.
1771. Anon.	Atlas Powder Co., Industrial Chemicals Dept., Wilmington, Del. 8-p. booklet.
1772. Anon.	*Austral. Plastics* **8**, No. 87, 24–7 (1952); *Brit. Plastics* **25**, 218 (1952).

Concerning

"Heatronic" molding. Technical discussion.

Technique and applications of high-frequency preheating of thermosetting molding materials.

Heat applications in plastic molding, extrusion, casting, laminating, coating, etc.

Infrared heating for preheating of molding powders and preforms.

Fundamentals and uses, e.g., drying and curing plastics, of high-frequency heating.

High-frequency heating in plastics industry.

Developments in molding equipment, including special low-pressure presses for glass reinforced moldings.

Illustrated guide to fabrication plant equipment, including presses, extruders, preformers, etc.

Inexpensive hydraulic presses for reinforced plastic moldings.

Low-pressure press for molding reinforced plastic; uses combination of air and hydraulic pressures.

Hydraulic presses and equipment for the plastics industry.

Presses for reinforced plastics molding.

Design of hydraulic presses for reinforced plastics molding.

Presses for reinforced plastics molding.

Presses for reinforced plastics molding.

New machinery for processing of rubber and plastics.

Molding with glass fiber reinforced alkyd resin.

Chemistry, uses, and preparation of polyesters. Includes bibliography.

Industrial chemicals. Fabrication process for polyester resin illustrated.

Plastics for automobile bodies.

Molding and Laminating Methods (Continued)

	Author	Reference
1773.	Anon.	*Brit. Plastics* **25**, 263 (1952).
1774.	Anon.	*Can. Plastics* July–Aug. 1953.
1775.	Anon.	*Can. Plastics* Mar.–April 1954, 69.
1776.	Anon.	Celanese Corp. of America, Marco Products Dept., Newark, N. J. Customer Service Bull. No. M2.
1777.	Anon.	Celanese Corp. of America, Marco Products Dept., Newark, N. J. Customer Service Bull. No. M4.
1778.	Anon.	Celanese Corp. of America, Marco Products Dept., Newark, N. J. Customer Service Bull. No. M5.
1779.	Anon.	*Chem. Eng. News* **32**, 1474 (1954).
1780.	Anon.	Cordo Molding Products, Inc., New York, N. Y. Bull. CMP-MI.
1781.	Anon.	Flexifirm Products, El Monte, Calif. Brochures Nos. 2, 3.
1782.	Anon.	Flexifirm Products, El Monte, Calif. Tech. Bull. No. 112.
1783.	Anon.	Interchemical Corp., Finishes Div., Cincinnati, Ohio, Bull. No. 44-1.
1784.	Anon.	*Materials & Methods Manual No. 1.* Reinhold Publishing Corp., New York.
1785.	Anon.	*Modern Plastics* **23**, No. 1, 132A–H (1945).
1786.	Anon.	*Modern Plastics* **27**, No. 1, 103–7 (1949).
1787.	Anon.	*Modern Plastics* **28**, No. 4, 85–6 (1950).
1788.	Anon.	*Modern Plastics* **29**, No. 6, 84–5 (1952).
1789.	Anon.	*Modern Plastics* **29**, No. 8, 94 (1953).
1790.	Anon.	*Modern Plastics* **29**, No. 9, 75–82 (1952).
1791.	Anon.	*Modern Plastics* **29**, No. 10, 95–8, 100 (1952).
1792.	Anon.	*Modern Plastics* **30**, No. 5, 89 (1953).
1793.	Anon.	*Modern Plastics* **30**, No. 5, 97 (1953) (advertisement).
1794.	Anon.	*Modern Plastics* **30**, No. 7, 60 (1953) (advertisement).
1795.	Anon.	*Modern Plastics* **31**, No. 4, 105–7 (1953).
1796.	Anon.	*Plastics* (London) **17**, 202 (1950); *Machinery* April, 1952, 187.
1797.	Anon.	*Plastics* (London) **17**, 253–4 (1952).
1798.	Anon.	*Plastics* (London) **19**, 169 (1954).
1799.	Anon.	*Plastics Ind.* **10**, No. 8, 6–8 (1952).
1800.	Anon.	*Plastics Ind.* **10**, No. 12, 16 (1952).

Concerning

Glass fiber-polyester tanks for transporting oil across desert.
Production of high-strength, dimensionally stable reinforced polyester radomes.
Continuous production of glass fiber-polyester corrugated sheeting.
Marco method for producing molded laminates.

Directions for spraying mold separating film.

Hand lay-up of molded laminates with thixotropic resin.

Brief note on use of modified bag molding technique for assembly-line production of reinforced plastic bathtubs.
Molding processes for preimpregnated material.

Selection of molds and tooling and methods of forming and molding for preimpregnated laminating material.
Molding of glass fiber reinforced polyester molding compound.

Parting agents for polyester resins.

Low-pressure laminates.

Production of glass reinforced polyester radomes by mandrel wrapping method.
No-pressure, "open-air," single-mold (male) process for "mass" production of glass fiber-polyester boats. Comparison made with 2-mold, (low) pressure process.
Molding recommendations for mineral-filled alkyd.
Glass fiber reinforcement of molding material with good electrical properties.
Puttylike polyester containing glass fibers, for molding, electrical applications.
Review on progress in plastic pipes. Methods of fabricating.
Fabrication process for continuous production of polyester pipe.

Production of polyester-glass reinforced pipe.
Rotocure process for continuous laminating of plastics.

Mold release agent for direct addition to polyester resin.

Machine for extruding reinforced plastic rods, tubes, and bars in continuous lengths.
Preimpregnated glass fabric for molds.

Boats molded from glass fiber laminates in glass reinforced polyester molds.
Machine for continuous extrusion of glass fiber reinforced plastics in any shape.
Fiber reinforced alkyd molding compound.
Uses and production capacity for glass fiber-polyester laminates.

Molding and Laminating Methods (Continued)

	Author	Reference
1801.	Anon.	*Plastics Ind.* **11**, No. 2, 24 (1953); *Plastics World* **11**, No. 2, 13 (1953).
1802.	Anon.	*Plastics Ind.* **11**, No. 12, 6 (1953); *Plastics News Letter* **13**, No. 41, 4 (1953).
1803.	Anon.	*Plastics Ind.* **12**, No. 2, 16 (1954).
1804.	Anon.	*Plastics Ind.* **12**, No. 2, 18-21, 29 (1954).
1805.	Anon.	*Plastics Ind.* **12**, No. 4, 31 (1954).
1806.	Anon.	*Plastics News Letter* **14**, No. 1, 1 (1954); *Plastics World* **12**, No. 2, 11 (1954).
1807.	Anon.	*Plastics News Letter* **14**, No. 24, 1 (1954).
1808.	Anon.	*Plastics News Letter* **14**, No. 25, 1 (1954).
1809.	Anon.	*Plastics World* **10**, No. 8, 11 (1952).
1810.	Anon.	*Plastics World* **12**, No. 1, 40 (1954).
1811.	Anon.	*Plastics World* **12**, No. 5, 12 (1954).
1812.	Anon.	*Reinforced Plastics Div., Soc. Plastics Ind. Confer., 9th Annual*, 1954, Sect. 20.
1813.	Anon.	*Reinforced Plastics Div., Soc. Plastics Ind. Confer., 9th Annual*, 1954, Sect. 3.
1814.	Anon.	*Reinforced Plastics Div., Soc. Plastics Ind. Confer., 9th Annual*, 1954, Sect. 4.
1815.	Anon.	Roberts Industries, Salisbury, Md. 4-p. booklet.
1816.	Anon.	Russell Reinforced Plastics Corp., Lindenhurst, N. Y. Brochure.
1817.	Anon.	*SPE J.* **5**, No. 5, 9-28 (1949).
1818.	Anon.	*SPE J.* **9**, No. 4, 36 (1953).
1819.	Anon.	*SPE J.* **10**, No. 2, 10 (1954).
1820.	Anon.	Tempil Corp., New York, N. Y. Brochure.
1821.	Anon.	Thermaflow Chemical Corp., Tunkhannock, Pa. Bull. No. 2C6.
1822.	Alfers, J. B.	*Modern Plastics* **30**, No. 3, 102-6 (1952).
1823.	Armstrong, C. W.	*Iron Age* **152**, No. 4, 51-4 (1943).
1824.	Barron, H.	*Modern Plastics*, 2d ed., revised, Chapman & Hill, London, 1949.
1825.	Bigelow, M. H.	*Modern Plastics* **26**, No. 2, 85-7 (1948).
1826.	Borro, E.	*SPE J.* **9**, No. 4, 10-6 (1953).
1827.	Brush, C. E.	*Reinforced Plastics Div., Soc. Plastics Ind. Confer., 8th Annual*, 1953, Sect. 12.
1828.	Bucksch, W.	*Kunststoffe* **43**, No. 12, 558-61 (1953).

Concerning

Reconditioning of wooden boats with resin and glass fiber cloth.

Mold release method for polyester, epoxy, and other materials.

Continuous production system for glass fiber building panels.
Laminating techniques for production of radomes.
Quick-drying parting agent for polyesters and other resins.
Liquid mold release for compression molding, laminating, casting, and lay-up molding.
Pigmented polyvinyl alcohol parting agent for polyester molding.
Glass fiber-alkyd molding compound for heavy-duty electrical applications.
Process for making glass fiber-polyester pipe.
Polyester tubing produced by centrifugal casting process.
Special bag-molding process used in making reinforced plastic bathtubs.
Glossary for reinforced plastics industry.

Technical discussion on premix (preimpregnated molding materials).

Technical discussion on parting agents.

Dual-welt (a laminating method).

Products from matched die molding of reinforced plastics; also uses of sandwich construction.
Bibliography of laminating procedure and practice: resins, applications, fabrication and finishing, fillers, testing and properties, manufacturing, reviews.
Economics of production of large parts, e.g., automobile bodies, from polyester plastics.
Mold release agent for polyesters and other resins; intended for use on porous and semiporous molds.
Crayons for telling temperature, e.g., as in molding of plastics.
Molding conditions and techniques for glass reinforced polyester molding compounds.
Review of 4 ways of molding reinforced plastic boat hulls: hand lay-up method, bag method, injection method (Marco process), matched metal die high-pressure method.
Physical properties of glass fiber laminated plastics.

Polyester molding compound for hot molding. Combination with filler gives maximum strength and desirable electrical properties.
Closed-mold molding technique.
Use of reinforced plastics for molded boat hulls by U. S. Coast Guard.

Transfer molding tools for thermosetting resins.

Molding and Laminating Methods (Continued)

Author	Reference
1829. Bushey, A. C., *et al.*	*Laminated Glass Construction with Special Reference to Boats.* U. S. Navy Bureau of Ships, 1952, 84 pp.
1830. Carswell, T. S.	*Plastics & Resins* **3**, No. 10, 10–4, 29–31, 36 (1944); *Pacific Plastics Mag.* **2**, No. 9, 26–7, 39 (1944).
1831. Cash, S. M.	*SPE J.* **6**, No. 1, 21–4 (1950).
1832. Crawford, R. W., and Nathanson, I. B.	*Modern Plastics* **23**, No. 8, 161–4 (1946).
1833. Curl, B. B.	*Reinforced Plastics Div., Soc. Plastics Ind. Confer., 9th Annual,* 1954, Sect. 2N.
1834. Currie, C. C., and May, W. C.	*Reinforced Plastics Div., Soc. Plastics Ind. Confer., 9th Annual,* 1954, Sect. 26.
1835. Daniels, J. L.	*Inst. Mech. Engrs.* (London) *Proc.* **152**, 44–62.
1836. Day, H. M.	*Reinforced Plastics Div., Soc. Plastics Ind. Confer., 8th Annual,* 1953, Sect. 24A.
1837. DeVore, H. W.	*Modern Plastics* **27**, No. 3, 81–3 (1949).
1838. Dietz, A. G. H.	*Reinforced Plastics Div., Soc. Plastics Ind. Confer., 8th Annual,* 1953, Sect. 6.
1839. Donohue, F. J.	*SPE J.* **9**, No. 4, 18–9, 42 (1953).
1840. Douglas, H. T.	*Modern Plastics* **31**, No. 6, 84–6 (1954).
1841. Duflos, J.	*Materie plastiche* **20**, No. 1, 1953.
1842. Elliott, P. M.	*Reinforced Plastics Div., Soc. Plastics Ind. Confer., 7th Annual,* 1952, Sect. 6G.
1843. Estevez, J. M. J.	*Plastics Inst.* (London) *Trans.* **17**, 32 (Feb. 1949).
1844. Fingerhut, S., and Oleesky, S. S.	*Reinforced Plastics Div., Soc. Plastics Ind. Confer., 9th Annual,* 1954, Sect. 11C.
1845. Forelich, O. E. H.	*Reinforced Plastics Div., Soc. Plastics Ind. Confer., 6th Annual,* 1951, Sect. 5.
1846. Friedman, H. J.	*Reinforced Plastics Div., Soc. Plastics Ind. Confer., 8th Annual,* 1953, Sect. 7.
1847. Goldsworthy, B.	*Reinforced Plastics Div., Soc. Plastics Ind. Confer., 9th Annual,* 1954, Sect. 13.
1848. Hantz, B. F.	*Ind. Plastics* **1**, No. 10, 14–8 (1946).
1849. Hatch, D. M., Jr.	*Reinforced Plastics Div., Soc. Plastics Ind. Confer., 8th Annual,* 1953, Sect. 34.
1850. Heebink, B. G., Werren, F., and Mohaupt, A. A.	*U. S. Dept. Agriculture, Forest Products Lab. Rept.* No. 1843 (1953).
1851. Hemming, C. B.	*Modern Plastics* **23**, No. 2, 129–33 (1945).

Concerning

A complete description of Marco, Beetle, and Winner methods of producing poly-ester-glass fiber boats.

Large molding techniques; resin-pulp molding, low-pressure laminates, post-forming.

Continuous laminating of reinforced plastics: principles, equipment required, techniques, end uses of products.
Applications and future of impression molding (low pressure).

Standard nomenclature for defects in fabricated parts.

Silicone mold release agents.

Molding plant for plastics.

New developments in resins (American Cyanamid), e.g., promoters, glass filled polyester molding compounds.

Alkyd (polyester) molding compound: properties, molding procedures, uses in electrical field.
Glass fiber–polyester molding compounds. Formulations given.

Basic factors in transfer molding.
Continuous-production-line molding of bathtubs.
Reinforced plastics from glass and resin molded at low pressures.
New developments in resin field, e.g., new resins, molding processes.

Recent advances in use of contact resins.

Use of preforms and mat materials in matched metal die molding.

Glass fiber reinforced bread tray. Method of fabricating.

Use of polyester resin preimpregnated cloth in mated die and vacuum bag molding.

New continuous "extrusion" machine for production of tubing, bar stock, and other structural shapes.
General review on molding machines, with 11 photos. Compression and injection molding.
Fabrication techniques for high-temperature-resistant reinforced plastics.

Effect of fabricating variables on plastic laminates and plastic honeycomb sand-wich construction.

Low-pressure molding. Mentions polyesters for no-pressure radomes.

Molding and Laminating Methods (Continued)

Author	Reference
1852. Hulbert, G. C.	*Plastics* (London) **17**, 325 (1952); *Brit. Plastics* **25**, 103 (1952); *Glass Fibre Reinforced Plastics Conv.* (England) 1952, Proc. 103–20; *Austral. Plastics* **8**, No. 92, 40–5 (1953).
1853. Jarrijon, A.	*Ind. plastiques modernes* **3**, No. 1, 35–5; No. 2, 3–5 (1951).
1854. Kawai, R., and Koda, T.	*J. Inst. Elec. Eng. Japan* **64**, 82–3 (1944).
1855. Lubin, G.	*Reinforced Plastics Div., Soc. Plastics Ind. Confer., 9th Annual*, 1954, Sect. 11A.
1856. Lunn, J. S.	*Reinforced Plastics Div., Soc. Plastics Ind. Confer., 5th Annual*, 1950, Sect. 9.
1857. Lunn, J. S., and Barnett, R. E.	*Reinforced Plastics Div., Soc. Plastics Ind. Confer., 8th Annual*, 1953, Sect. 4.
1858. Lunn, J. S., and Scott, I. M.	*Reinforced Plastics Div., Soc. Plastics Ind. Confer., 9th Annual*, 1954, Sect. 9.
1859. Mack, B.	*Materials & Methods* **28**, No. 3, 91–104 (1948).
1860. McCann, H.,	*Modern Plastics Encyclopedia 1952.* Plastics Catalogue Corp., New York, 462.
1861. McGill, C. A.	*Reinforced Plastics Div., Soc. Plastics Ind. Confer., 9th Annual*, 1954, Sect. 8.
1862. Meyer, L. S.	*Reinforced Plastics Div., Soc. Plastics Ind. Confer., 7th Annual*, 1952, Sect. 3.
1863. Meyer, L. S.	*Reinforced Plastics Div., Soc. Plastics Ind. Confer., 9th Annual*, 1954, Sect. 12.
1864. Mills, J. F.	*Reinforced Plastics Div., Soc. Plastics Ind. Confer., 7th Annual*, 1952, Sect. 13.
1865. Moffett, E. W.	*Reinforced Plastics Div., Soc. Plastics Ind. Confer., 8th Annual*, 1953, Sect. 24K.
1866. Morgan, P., editor.	*Plastics Progress: Papers and Discussion at the British Plastics Convention, 1951.* Iliff & Sons, Ltd., London, 1951, 317 pp.
1867. Morgan, P., editor.	*Plastics Progress: Papers and Discussion at the British Plastics Convention, 1953.* Iliff & Sons, Ltd., London, 1953, 439 pp.
1868. Nelson, J. D.	*Tech. Assoc. Papers* **27**, 173–6 (1944); *Paper Trade J.* **120**, No. 1, 33–6 (1945).
1869. Nelson, J. D., and D'Alelio, G. F.	*Modern Plastics* **20**, No. 1, 45–7, 122–3 (1942).
1870. Noble, T. W.	*ASTM Bull.* No. 151, 77–9 (TP85–7) (1948).
1871. Otero, J. F.	*Ingenieria* (Mexico) **19**, 252–5 (1945).

Concerning

Glass reinforced plastics in aircraft: uses, properties, fabrication.

No-pressure polyester resins. Review of properties, uses, fabrication, analysis.

Deterioration of high-frequency dielectric characteristics of synthetic resin caused by hygroscopicity.

Vacuum injection method for making large parts with complex contours from reinforced plastics.

Mold release agents.

Release of parts from molds. Special mold equipment.

Bag molding techniques for reinforced plastics.

Properties and applications of 45 types of plastics.

Polyester-glass fiber molding putty.

Advantages and disadvantages of contact molding in the reinforced plastics field.

Progress report on cooperative effort between Fort Belvoir (Army Corps of Engineers) and SPI (fabrication of preforms, matched metal molds, etc.).

Continuous laminating of reinforced polyester sheet material.

Reinforced plastic landing craft for U. S. Navy.

Properties and applications of low-exotherm resin.

Applications and processing of plastics.

Applications and processing of plastics; 23 papers.

Low-pressure laminating. Techniques and properties of products.

Review on low-pressure laminating.

Low-pressure molding field—lay-up and pressing of plastic laminates.

Equipment and methods for molding and machining of plastics.

Molding and Laminating Methods (Continued)

Author	Reference
1872. Parkyn, B.	*Plastics* (London) **19**, 16–7 (1954) (summary of paper presented at 8th Swedish Plastics Conference).
1873. Perdue, L. M.	*Plastics* (Chicago) **3**, No. 3, 38, 40, 132–3 (1945).
1874. Premo, E. J.	*Reinforced Plastics Div., Soc. Plastics Ind. Confer., 9th Annual*, 1954, Sect. 15.
1875. Redfarn, C. A.	*A Guide to Plastics.* Iliff & Sons, London, 1951, 112 pp.
1876. Redfarn, C. A.	*Brit. Plastics* **27**, 131–3 (1954).
1877. Rehacek, J.	*Chem. Prumysl* **1**(26), 198–201 (1951).
1878. Reiling, V. G.	*Reinforced Plastics Div., Soc. Plastics Ind. Confer., 9th Annual*, 1954, Sect. 11E.
1879. Reinsmith, G., and Pebly, H. E.	*Reinforced Plastics Div., Soc. Plastics Ind. Confer., 8th Annual*, 1953, Sect. 22.
1880. Rose, K.	*Materials & Methods* **29**, No. 5, 71–8 (1949).
1881. Sabin, N. W.	*Plastics Inst.* (London) *Trans.* **20**, 43 (April 1952).
1882. Sachs, C. C.	*Modern Plastics* **21**, No. 11, 80–2, 172, 174 (1944).
1883. Shepard, H. R.	*Modern Plastics* **31**, No. 8, 121–2, 124, 126, 128, 130, 135, 227 (1954).
1884. Shobert, S. M.	*Ind. Plastics* **2**, No. 11, 13–6, 30 (1947).
1885. Sigtermans, A. A. J.	*Plastica* (Dutch) **3**, 8–12 (1950).
1886. Simonds, H. R., and Bigelow, M. H.	*The New Plastics.* 3d printing, Van Nostrand, New York, 1946.
1887. Simonds, H. R., and Ellis, C.	*Handbook of Plastics.* Van Nostrand, New York, 1943.
1888. Simonds and Weith	*Extrusion of Plastics, Rubber, and Metals.* Reinhold, 1952, New York, 463 pp.
1889. Smith, A. L.	*Reinforced Plastics Div., Soc. Plastics Ind. Confer., 8th Annual*, 1953, Sect. 1.
1890. Stanley, F. B.	*Modern Plastics* **27**, No. 1, 103–7 (1949).
1891. Stratton, J. D.	*Plastics* (Chicago) **5**, No. 4, 21–4, 100 (1946).
1892. Swedlow, D.	*Modern Plastics* **21**, No. 9, 112, 184, 186 (1944).
1893. Toyota, K.	*Plastic Trends* **7**, No. 11, 5–6 (1947).
1894. Townsend, J. J.	*Plastics & Resins* **5**, No. 7, 5–6, 36 (1946).
1895. Van Boskirk, R. L.	*Modern Plastics* **27**, No. 10, 162 (1950). ("The Plastiscope").
1896. Van Boskirk, R. L.	*Modern Plastics* **30**, No. 10, 230 (1953) ("The Plastiscope").

Concerning

Single mold process for molding polyesters.

Use of low pressures in manufacture of plastic laminates. Mentions addition-polymerization resins (including allyls).

Details of fabrication, with photographs, of plastic body for Chevrolet Corvette sports car.

Raw materials and applications for chief commercial plastics. Manufacture and fabrication outlined.

Alkyd molding materials: composition, molding techniques, properties of moldings, applications.

A review of technical methods for low-pressure laminating of plastics.

Use of premix glass fiber-polyester molding compounds in transfer molding.

Glass reinforced plastics in Ordinance Corps applications.

Methods of production and properties of thermosetting plastics (includes polyesters).

Fabrication of laminated material (polyesters).

Review on high-, low-, and no-pressure laminates.

Manufacture of polyester-glass molding compounds.

Fabrication techniques for polyester resins.

Fabrication of low-pressure polyester and phenolic resins.

Discussion of materials, equipment, techniques, and economics of extrusion.

Standard terminology for defects in fabricated parts.

Mass-production boat molding (with polyester resins).

Progress in injection molding of plastics.

Versatility of low-pressure molding.

Evaluation of various mold release agents for polyester casting.

Tooling and production methods for low-pressure reinforced plastics.

Dry laminate——cloth impregnated with polyester resin and catalyst and shipped dry.

Low-pressure laminating material——glass cloth impregnated with polyester resin and catalyst.

Molding and Laminating Methods (Continued)

	Author	Reference
1897.	Verman, L. C.	*J. Sci. & Ind. Research* (India) **4**, 744–5 (1946).
1898.	Wahl, N. E.	*Reinforced Plastics Div., Soc. Plastics Ind. Confer., 6th Annual,* 1951, Sect. 17.
1899.	White, R. B.	*Modern Plastics* **26**, No. 4, 105–8 (1948).
1900.	White, R. B.	*Reinforced Plastics Div., Soc. Plastics Ind. Confer., 9th Annual,* 1954, Sect. 11D.
1901.	Whitlock, C. H.	*Tool & Die J.* **10**, No. 10, 124–6 (1945).
1902.	Wier, J. E.	*Reinforced Plastics Div., Soc. Plastics Ind. Confer., 8th Annual,* 1953, Sect. 19.
1903.	Wier, J. E.	*Reinforced Plastics Div., Soc. Plastics Ind. Confer., 7th Annual,* 1952, Sect. 9.
1904.	Wier, J. E., Pons, D. C., and Axilrod, B. M.	*SPE J.* **8**, No. 9, 8–13, 27 (1952).
1905.	Wilkins, W. B.	*Plastics* (Chicago) **3**, No. 1, 102, 104, 106, 146–8 (1945).
1906.	Wilson, F. P., and Hanson, N. D.	*Modern Plastics* **20**, No. 12, 57–60, 144 (1943).
1907.	Wittman, L.	*Reinforced Plastics Div., Soc. Plastics Ind. Confer., 9th Annual,* 1954, Sect. 11F.
1908.	Yarsley, V. E.	*Trade & Eng. Suppl.* to "*The Times*" (London) **54**, No. 970, 44 (1944).
1909.	Ziegler, E. E.	*India Rubber World* **114**, 826–9 (1946).

Preforming

1910.	Anon.	Atlas Powder Co., Wilmington, Del. Tech. Bull.
1911.	Anon.	*Brit. Plastics* **26**, 20–3 (1953).
1912.	Anon.	*Modern Plastics* **29**, No. 9, 210 (1952); *Plastics Ind.* **10**, No. 4, 25 (1952).
1913.	Anon.	*Modern Plastics* **31**, No. 4, 116–8, 212 (1953).
1914.	Anon.	Turner Machine Co., Inc., Danbury, Conn. 2-p. brochure.
1915.	Brucker, M. L.	*Reinforced Plastics Div., Soc. Plastics Ind. Confer., 6th Annual,* 1951, Sect. 2.
1916.	Chase, H.	*Brit. Plastics* **25**, 46–9 (1952).
1917.	Darling, W. B.	*Ind. Plastics* **2**, No. 2, 28–30, 36 (1946).
1918.	Day, H. M.	*Reinforced Plastics Div., Soc. Plastics Ind. Confer., 7th Annual,* 1952, Sect. 6A.
1919.	Goldsworthy, W. B.	*Reinforced Plastics Div., Soc. Plastics Ind. Confer., 7th Annual,* 1952, Sect. 5B.
1920.	Jones, C. D.	*Reinforced Plastics Div., Soc. Plastics Ind. Confer., 5th Annual,* 1950, Sect. 2.

Concerning

Plastics developments in India. Laminated plastic containers without use of
hydraulic process.
Design and fabrication of glass reinforced helicopter rotor blades.

Molding polyester-glass fiber laminates. Adaptation of bag molding techniques.
Glass reinforced premix polyester molding compounds: manufacture, uses,
advantages.

Review on molding processes and equipment.
Effects of laminating pressure on properties of glass fiber laminates.

Effect of humidity during fabrication on properties of glass fabric-polyester
laminates.
Effects of humidity during fabrication on polyester laminates.

Molding by low pressure.

Low-pressure molding of laminates. Mentions use of thermosetting ester type of
resin.
Molding with prepreg materials (preimpregnated glass cloth or mat).

High-strength moldings.

Test for release of plastic resins from mold.

Methods for preform binding.

Review on processes in glass reinforced plastics. Includes preforming.
Research by Pittsburgh Plate Glass Co. on polyester preform molding.

Molding process for swivel chair bases. Special preforming machine used.

Preform machines.

Variables in molding glass fiber preforms.

Discussion of use of preforming machine in United States, plus 8 photographs.
Pulp molding and postforming of laminates.
New developments in resins, e.g., preform binder.

Hand and machine forming of reinforced plastics.

Advantages and manufacture of glass fiber preforms.

Preforming (Continued)

Author	Reference
1921. Jones, C. D.	*Reinforced Plastics Div., Soc. Plastics Ind. Confer., 8th Annual,* 1953, Sect. 26E.
1922. Levenhagen, A. W.	*Reinforced Plastics Div., Soc. Plastics Ind. Confer., 7th Annual,* 1952, Sect. 5A.
1923. Moffett, E. W.	*Reinforced Plastics Div., Soc. Plastics Ind. Confer., 7th Annual,* 1952, Sect. 6H.
1924. Moss, F. J.	*Ind. Plastics* **1**, No. 5, 29–30, 46 (1945).
1925. Penn, W. S.	*Plastics* (London) **10**, 456–63, 518–21 (1946).
1926. Robinson, J. D., and Case, J. W.	*Reinforced Plastics Div., Soc. Plastics Ind. Confer., 9th Annual,* 1954, Sect. 25.
1927. Vaill, E. W.	*SPE J.* **9**, No. 4, 7–9, 42 (1953).

Casting

Author	Reference
1928. Anon.	*Brit. Plastics* **26**, 444 (1953).
1929. Anon.	*Can. Plastics* Jan.–Feb. 1953, 49–75.
1930. Anon.	Castolite Co., Woodstock, Ill. 8-p. booklet.
1931. Anon.	Technicraft Co., Boston, Mass. Tech. Bull. No. 3, Sect. 1.
1932. Anon.	Ward's Natural Science Establishment, Inc., Rochester, N. Y. 20-p. booklet.
1933. Anon.	*Modern Plastics* **23**, No. 3, 102–3 (1945).
1934. Anon.	*Plastics* (London) **16**, 249 (Sept. 1951).
1935. Apley, M.	*Plastics Inst.* (London), *Trans.* **20**, No. 40, 7–28 (1952).
1936. Firth, G.	*Reinforced Plastics Div., Soc. Plastics Ind. Confer., 9th Annual,* 1954, Sect. 14.
1937. Javitz, A. E.	*Elect. Manuf.* **48**, No. 3, 103–8 (1951).
1938. Mahon, D. S.	*Plastics* (London) **19**, 16–7 (1954) (summary of paper presented at 8th Swedish Plastics Conference).
1939. Müller, A.	*Kunststoffe* **43**, 440–1 (1953).
1940. Quillery, H.	*Assoc. tech. fonderie* (Paris), *Conf.* Dec. 18, 1942, 14 pp.
1941. Weeks, W.	*Modern Plastics* **25**, No. 11, 115–9 (1948).
1941a. Anon.	*Elec. Manuf.* **51**, No. 1, 146 (1953).
1942. Knewstubb, N. W.	*Plastics Inst.* (London), *Trans.* **16**, 43–60 (Oct. 1948).
1943. Nash, B.	*Modern Plastics* **23**, No. 1, 129–31 (1945).
1943a. Beach, W. I.	*Machinery* **57**, No. 6, 163–6; No. 7, 170–2 (1951).

Concerning

Preforming equipment.

Automatic preforming of reinforced plastics.

New developments in resins, *e.g.*, preform binder.

Pulp preforms for compression molding. Description of method.
Preparation of resin-containing pulp preforms for molding. Allyl ester resins may be suitable.
New method for applying binders to glass fibers as formed and effect on strength of parallel glass fiber laminates.
Preheating of preforms.

Summary of papers at German Plastics Convention: *e.g.*, potting of metal parts in polyesters, fabrication of laminates.
Review on polyesters. Casting, compression molding.
Directions for casting and embedding with liquid polyester plastic.

Directions for casting and embedding with polyester resin.

Directions for casting and embedding with polyester resin.

Casting of unsaturated polyester resins.
Embedding in cast polyesters.
Review on cast resins, including polyesters.

Review on electrical potting and encapsulation, including resins and methods used.
Cast resin embedment of electrical circuit subunits.
Use of polyesters for reinforced castings and low-pressure molding.

Potting of metal parts in unsaturated polyester resins.
Review on cast plastics materials.

Mold techniques for polyester casting.
Systematic method for selecting and evaluating casting resins; uses numerical scoring system.
Postforming laminates (shaping after curing of resin).

Postforming and its applications (phenolic laminates). Types of molds and general forming procedure.
Postforming of thermosetting laminated plastics: (1) effects; (2) methods of heating.

Foamed Plastics and Honeycomb Structures

	Author	Reference
1944.	Anon.	*Chem. Eng. News.* **30**, 4964–5 (1952).
1945.	Anon.	Dow Chemical Co., Midland, Mich. Booklet.
1946.	Anon.	*Electronics* **25**, No. 9, 166, 168 (1952).
1947.	Anon.	Hexcel Products Co., Oakland, Calif. Brochure C.
1948.	Anon.	U. S. Rubber Co., Naugatuck, Conn. Compounding Res. Rept. No. 16.
1949.	Anon.	*Plastics World* **11**, No. 1, 10 (1953).
1950.	Aita, A.	*Materie plastiche* **14**, 45–9 (1948).
1951.	Axilrod, B. M., and Koenig, E.	*Natl. Advisory Comm. Aeronaut. Tech. Note* No. 991, 26 pp. (1945).
1952.	Benkendorff, G. W.	*Austral. Plastics* **8**, No. 96, 6–14 (1953).
1953.	Clark, R. A., McCuistion, T. J., and Cheyney, L. E.	*India Rubber World* **117**, 361–3 (1947).
1954.	DeBell, J. M., and Richardson, H. M.	*Ind. Eng. Chem.* **40**, 651–4 (1948).
1955.	Dietz, A. G. H., and Wilkins, W. G.	*Reinforced Plastics Div., Soc. Plastics Ind. Confer., 7th Annual,* 1952, Sect. 20.
1956.	Estevez, J. M. J.	*Plastics Inst.* (London), *Trans.* **16**, 79–95 (April 1948).
1957.	Goggin, W. C., and McIntire, O. R.	*Brit. Plastics* **19**, 528–36 (1937).
1958.	Hall, H. W.	*Glass Fibre Reinforced Plastics Conv.* (England) 1952, *Proc.* 80–91; *Plastics* (London) **17**, 198 (1952).
1959.	Herbst, A. H.	*SPE J.* **8**, No. 1, 13 (1952).
1960.	Hoppe, P.	*Kunststoffe* **42**, 450–9 (1952).
1961.	Hunter, D. N.	*Plastics* (London) **19**, 58–59 (1954).
1962.	Lever, A. E.	*Plastics* (London) **18**, No. 193, 274–7 (1953).
1963.	May, G.	*Plastics* (London) **14**, 64–6 (Oct. 1949).
1964.	May, G.	*Plastics* (London) **15**, 265 (Oct.–Dec. 1950).
1965.	May, G.	*Brit. Plastics* **25**, 201–5 (1952); *Plastics* (London) **17**, 92–4 (1952).
1966.	McCann, H., editor.	*Modern Plastics Encyclopedia 1953.* Plastics Catalogue Corp., New York, p. 314.
1967.	Oleesky, S. S.	*Reinforced Plastics Div., Soc. Plastics Ind. Confer., 7th Annual,* 1952, Sect. 14; *Modern Plastics* **29**, No. 6, 99 (1954).

Pictorial record of radome making from glass reinforced plastic.
Properties and uses of foamed resin product.

Fabrication techniques for solid-wall, glass honeycomb sandwich, and foam sandwich (alkyd-isocyanate) types of radomes.
Structural honeycomb for sandwich construction.

Nitrogen blowing agent for plastics.

Reinforced polyester resin radomes. Brief description of manufacture.
Review of German, British, and American developments in cellular plastic materials.
Properties of expanded plastics and other low-density materials.

Review of all types of expanded plastics and their principal uses. Specific instructions are given for producing most important commercial types of foams.
Review of advantages, types, properties, and uses of products with sponge or cellular structures, e.g., foamed resins, honeycomb structures.

German advances in plastics technology, e.g., foaming agents such as isocyanate-modified alkyds, azoisobutyric dinitrile.
Structural sandwich constructions with "dog-bone" (honeycomb) cores.

Review on contact-pressure laminating resin. Molding, properties, uses.

Review on foamed plastics, with 8 references. Gives methods of foaming.

Application of glass fiber laminates. Honeycomb fabrication.

Compounded curved honeycomb core for sandwich panels. Manufacture and properties.
Survey of expanded (foamed) plastics and their utilization.
Expanded resins—thermosetting resins with expanding agent which liberates nitrogen by actual combination with the resin during the curing process.
Review of various expanded and foamed materials, including polyesters.

Honeycomb sandwich construction—a review.
Radome construction with low-pressure resins (polyesters).

Applications of honeycomb structure.

Methods for making honeycomb core.

Repair and maintenance of reinforced plastics.

Foamed Plastics and Honeycomb Structure (Continued)

Author	Reference
1968. Rose, K.	*Materials & Methods* **39**, No. 3, 116–32 (1954).
1969. Sachs, C. C.	*Mech. Eng.* **68**, 233–6 (1946).
1970. Scherr, H., Gottfurcht, A., and Stenzel, R. W.	*Plastics* (New York) **9**, No. 2, 8–9 (1949).
1971. Schlitt, W.	*Gummi u. Asbest.* **5**, 408–9, 440, 442, 444 (1952).
1972. Scogland, C. A.	*Ind. Plastics* **1**, No. 4, 14–8 (1945).
1973. Scogland, C. A.	*Plastics* (Chicago) **3**, No. 1, 74–6 (1945).
1974. Seidl, R. J.	*Paper Ind.* **34**, 1112–5 (1952).
1975. Seidl, R. J., *et al.*	*Natl. Advisory Comm. Aeronaut. Tech. Note* No. 2504 (1951).
1976. Steele, R. C.	*Modern Plastics* **31**, No. 6, 101–4, 193 (1954).
1977. Wahl, N. E., and Reilly, A. S.	Cornell Aeronautical Laboratory, Inc. Rept. No. UD-691-M-1 (1950).

General

1978. Anon.	*Fortune* **49**, No. 4, 152–5, 170, 172, 174, 178 (1954).
1979. Anon.	*Modern Plastics* **27**, No. 2, 69–76, 158–60 (1949).
1980. Anon.	*Modern Plastics* **28**, No. 4, 89–92 (1950).
1981. Brown, W. J.	*Fabric-Reinforced Plastics.* Interscience, New York, 1949.
1982. Dammer, O.	*Chem.-Ing.-Tech.* **24**, 546–54 (1952).
1983. Davies, B. L.	*Technology of Plastics: Manufacture, Structure, Design.* Pitman, New York, 1949, about 400 pp.
1984. Draeger, H.	*Kunststoffe* **42**, 327–9 (1952).
1985. Dubois, J. H.	*Plastics*, 2nd ed., Am. Tech. Soc., Chicago, 1943, 435 pp.
1986. Estabrook, F. R., Jr.	*Reinforced Plastics Div., Soc. Plastics Ind. Confer., 8th Annual*, 1953, Sect. 29.
1987. Francis, R. J.	*Product Eng.* **22**, No. 2, 85–108 (1951).
1988. Hicks, J. S.	*Low Pressure Laminating of Plastics.* Reinhold, New York, 1947, 162 pp.
1989. Kaye, S. L.	*Production and Properties of Plastics.* International Textbook Co., Scranton, Pa., 1947, 612 pp.
1990. Khan, C. A. R.	*J. Sci. & Ind. Research* (India) **4**, 754–5 (1946).

Concerning

Survey of sandwich materials. Includes brief discussion of honeycomb and foamed plastics as cores and glass-reinforced polyester laminates as facings.

Application of cellular plastics in aircraft. Methods of foaming synthetic resin polymers, e.g., styrene polyesters.

Structure and uses of plastic foams.

Manufacture and uses of cellular and foam synthetic products, including artificial resins.

New plastics—low-density laminates, foamed cores, cores of resin-impregnated fibers.

Low-density laminates. Use of sand-filled tubes in making early types of honeycomb structure.

Resin-treated paper honeycomb cores for structural sandwich panels.

Properties of honeycomb cores as affected by fiber type, orientation, resin type and amount.

New methods for fabrication of honeycomb structures.

Development of foamed core materials for radomes.

Review of technology and economics of reinforced plastics industry.

Review of fabricating procedures for and economics of reinforced polyesters.

New fabricating techniques in reinforced plastics.

Processing of plastics in equipment construction and for use in chemical industry.

Discussion of plastics fabrication.

Equipment for processing plastics.

Simplified presentation of manufacture and use of important plastics. Includes property tables.

Economics of custom molding.

General-information article on reinforced plastics. List of manufacturers.

Fabrication and preparation of plastics.

Plastics development in India. Plastic laminates.

General (Continued)

Author	Reference
1991. Lategan, P. N.	*J. Chem. Met. Mining Soc. S. Africa* **44**, 138–53 (1944).
1992. Learmonth, G. S.	*Laminated Plastics.* Leonard Hill, London, 1951.
1993. Morrison, R. S.	*Modern Plastics* **30**, No. 6, 109 (1953).
1994. Morse, A. R.	*SPE J.* **8**, No. 9, 7 (1952).
1995. Nauth, R.	*Chemistry and Technology of Plastics.* Reinhold, New York, 1947, 500 pp.
1996. Schack, W.	*Prod. Eng.* **23**, No. 10, 128–33 (1952).
1997. Simonds, H. R.	*Industrial Plastics*, 3d ed., Pitman, New York, 1945, 360 pp.
1998. Smith, P. I.	*Plastics for Production.* Chapman and Hall, London, 1946, 200 pp.
1999. Smith, P. L, editor	*Practical Plastics.* Odhams Press, London, 1947, 320 pp.
2000. Warring, R. H.	*Austral. Plastics* **8**, No. 90, 26–8 (1953).

Concerning

Review of theory, production, testing, and application of plastics.

Setting up a plant for custom molding reinforced plastics.
Economics of low pressure laminating.

Status of plastics in industry. Uses, testing, economics.

Review from point of view of industrial applications.

Technology of plastics production.

Summary of processes used in reinforced plastics field.

Machining

Author	Reference
2001. Anon.	*Am. Mach.* **92**, 83 (Feb. 26, 1948).
2002. Anon.	Kett Tool Co., Cincinnati, Ohio. Bulls. Nos. K-52-278 G.P. and 4931-GP-5M-1-50.
2003. Anon.	*Plastics Engineering Handbook* of the Society of the Plastics Industry. Reinhold, New York, 1954, 852 pp.
2004. Anon.	Tumb-L-Matic, Inc., New York, N. Y. Bull. No. PG-52
2005. Allen, F. E.	*Modern Plastics* **21**, No. 9, 107–9 (1944).
2006. Allen, F. E.	*Ind. Plastics* **1**, No. 2, 10–15 (1945).
2007. Argy, R. T.	*Reinforced Plastics Div., Soc. Plastics Ind. Confer., 9th Annual,* 1954, Sect. 24.
2008. Barberis, N.	*Materie plastiche* **12**, 5–9 (1946).
2009. Chambers, D. W.	*Modern Plastics* **27**, No. 9, 91, 94 (1950).
2010. White, R. B.	*Modern Plastics* **28**, No. 8, 103–6, 111–4 (1951).
2011. White, R. B.	*Reinforced Plastics Div., Soc. Plastics Ind. Confer., 6th Annual,* 1951, Sect. 15.
2012. Williams, A. E.	*Plastics in Industry.* Mechanical World Monograph No. 35. Mott, Manchester, England, 1947, 41 pp. Chap. 2.
2013. Wiltshire, A. J.	*Reinforced Plastics Div., Soc. Plastics Ind. Confer., 5th Annual,* 1950, Sect. 10.

Surface Treatments

Author	Reference
2014. Anon.	Bradford Novelty Co., Inc., Cambridge, Mass. 2-p. mimeographed letter.
2015. Anon.	Chemical Development Corp., Danvers, Mass. New Product Bull.
2016. Anon.	Logo, Inc., Chicago, Ill. Technical literature.
2017. Anon.	*Monsanto Mag.,* April–May 1953.
2018. Anon.	*Plastics* (London) **14**, 67 (1949).
2019. Anon.	*Plastics Ind.* **11**, No. 10, 6 (1953).
2020. Anon.	*Plastics News Letter* **13**, No. 36, 1 (1953).
2021. Anon.	*Plastics World* **11**, No. 11, 6 (1953).
2022. Angelino, L.	*Ind. vernice* (Milan) **6**, 65–8 (1952).
2023. Bancroft, G. H.	*Modern Plastics* **31**, No. 4, 122–3, 210 (1953).
2024. Brown, R. W.	*Can. Chem. Processing* **36**, No. 12, 38–40 (1952).

VI. FINISHING

Surface Treatments (Continued)

	Author	Reference
2025.	Bushman, E. F.	*Reinforced Plastics Div., Soc. Plastics Ind. Confer., 9th Annual*, 1954, Sect. 17.
2026.	Carr, G. W.	*Plastics Ind.* **11**, No. 12, 18 (1953).
2027.	Dickinson, T. A.	*Plastics* (New York) **9**, No. 1, 12–4 (1949).
2028.	Escales, E.	*Kunststoffe* **42**, 61–4 (1952).
2029.	Gale, P. T., and Sagar, H.	*Textile Mfr.* **78**, 430 (1952).
2030.	Moore, S. A.	*Reinforced Plastics Div., Soc. Plastics Ind. Confer., 5th Annual*, 1950, Sect. 12.
2031.	Narcus, H.	*Proc. Am. Electroplaters' Soc.* June 1944, 76–92.
2032.	Narcus, H.	*Trans. Electrochem. Soc.* **88**, 17 pp. (preprint) (1945).
2033.	Narcus, H.	*Metal Finishing* **44**, 240–2 (1946).
2034.	Narcus, H.	*SPE J.* **9**, No. 3, 26–9 (1953).
2035.	Nelson, B. W.	*Reinforced Plastics Div., Soc. Plastics Ind. Confer., 9th Annual*, 1954, Sect. 5.
2036.	Nelson, B. W., and Munton, C. B.	*Reinforced Plastics Div., Soc. Plastics Ind. Confer., 8th Annual*, 1953, Sect. 5.
2037.	Pocock, B. W.	*Products Finishing* **9**, No. 11, 48–50, 52, 54, 56, 58, 62, 64 (1945).
2038.	Seiter, J. G.	*India Rubber World* **128**, 493–6 (1953).
2039.	Self, M. A.	*Org. Finishing* **13**, No. 7, 19–23 (1952).
2040.	Wandersleben, A. J., et al.	*Offic. Dig. Federation Paint & Varnish Production Clubs* No. 334, 718–25 (1952).
2041.	Zimmerman, A.	*Plastics & Resins* **4**, No. 1, 9–12, 20–33 (1945).

Concerning

Special fiber treatments for reinforced plastics, e.g., fiber-coloring methods.

Vacuum metalizing of plastic, glass, and metal surfaces.
Electrostatic method for applying coatings to plastics.
Electrostatic flocking (e.g., with textile fibers, powdered metal) of plastic surfaces for special effects.
Antistatic agents for synthetic fibers.

Design reproductions on flat sheets and irregular shapes of reinforced plastics.

Suitable resins for applications in plating industry and methods of metal-plating plastics.
Electrodeposition of metals on plastics. Advantages and methods.

Chemical reduction method for silvering of plastics.
Methods of metalizing plastics.
As-molded and post-mold finishing systems for reinforced polyesters.

Finishes for and surface qualities of glass fiber reinforced moldings.

Metal plating on plastics—uses and processes.

Vacuum metalizing of plastics. Illustrated review.
Review of coating methods and materials for finishing plastic products.
Painting of plastic surfaces.

Uses and manufacture of cast resin products.

Author	Reference
2042. Anon.	Alkydol Laboratories, Inc., Cicero, Ill. 6-p. booklet.
2043. Anon.	Alkydol Laboratories, Inc., Cicero, Ill. Tech. Service Bull.
2044. Anon.	Allied Chemical & Dye Corp., Barrett Div., New York, N. Y. Tech. Data Repts. 54-8-54-17.
2045. Anon.	Allied Chemical & Dye Corp., Barrett Div., New York, N. Y. Bull. A-13.
2046. Anon.	American Cyanamid Co., Plastics and Resins Div., New York, N. Y.
2047. Anon.	American Cyanamid Co., Plastics and Resins Div., New York, N. Y.
2048. Anon.	American Cyanamid Co., Plastics & Resins Div., New York, N. Y. Catalog.
2049. Anon.	American Insulator Corp., New Freedom, Pa.
2050. Anon.	Archer-Daniels-Midland Co., Minneapolis, Minn. Data Sheets.
2051. Anon.	Armstrong Products Co., Warsaw, Ind. Bull. No. 650.
2052. Anon.	Atlas Powder Co., Industrial Chemicals Dept., Wilmington, Del.
2053. Anon.	*Australian Plastics Yearbook.* 1952–53 ed., Australian Trade Publications Pty. Ltd., Sydney, Australia.
2054. Anon.	Bakelite Co., New York, N. Y. Tech. Bulls. Nos. 1–10.
2055. Anon.	*British Plastics Yearbook.* 23rd ed., Iliff & Sons, Ltd., London, 1953, 562 pp.
2056. Anon.	*Buyer's Guide to Plastic Materials.* British Plastics Federation, 1953, London, 44 pp.
2057. Anon.	*Can. Plastics* Mar.–April 1954, 32.
2058. Anon.	Celanese Corp. of America, Marco Products Dept., Newark, N. J. Customer Service Bull. No. M1 and Data Sheet DL-75.
2059. Anon.	Celanese Corp. of America, Marco Products Dept., Newark, N. J. Customer Service Bull. No. M7-(354).
2060. Anon.	Celanese Corp. of America, Marco Products Dept., Newark, N. J. Customer Service Bull.
2061. Anon.	*Chem. Eng. News* **31**, 5172 (1953).
2062. Anon.	*Chem. Eng. News* **32**, 893 (1954).
2063. Anon.	Chemical Process Co., Redwood City, Calif. Data Leaflets Nos. 900, 901, 902, 903–364, 903–364L.

VII. COMMERCIAL RESINS

Concerning

Alkydol S-1700 polyester resin for baking finishes.

Properties, compounding, and uses of Alkydol S-452 polyester.

Properties of Plaskon polyester resins.

Physical properties of Plaskon glass fiber reinforced molding compound.

Property charts for Laminac resins.

Guide to applications for Laminac polyester resins.

Properties and uses of plastic products, including chart of polyester properties.

Applicator for selecting plastics for specific applications.
Properties of Aropol polyester resins.

Adhesive for rigid materials difficult to bond.

Specifications and properties of polyester resins for laminating.

Manufacturers' data, trade names, products, equipment.

Bakelite polyesters for reinforced plastics.

Manufacturers' data, trade names, products, equipment.

Listing of uses, suppliers, and trade names of important plastics materials produced in Great Britain.
Canadian production of polyester resins by Glidden Co.
Marco polyester resins: properties and fabrication.

Chemical resistance of Marco MR-28C resin.

Chemical resistance of Marcothix resin-glass cloth laminate.

Self-extinguishing, flame-resistant polyester plastics containing chlorendic acid (Atlas Powder).

Polyester resin (Laminac 4147, American Cyanamid) for use in fabrication of translucent panels with both light stability and self-extinguishing properties.

Duolite polyester resins.

Author	Reference
2064. Anon.	Cordo Molding Products, Inc., New York, N. Y. General Bulls. Nos. CMP-G1, CMP-MF-1, CMP-RF-5, CMP-57-2.
2065. Anon.	Fiberfil Corp., Warsaw, Ind. Data Sheet.
2066. Anon.	Flexifirm Products, El Monte, Calif. Tech. Bull. No. 105 and Brochure No. 1.
2067. Anon.	Flexifirm Products, El Monte, Calif. Tech. Bull. No. 111.
2068. Anon.	*Furniture Manuf.* **74**, No. 12, back cover (1953) (advertisement).
2069. Anon.	General Electric Co., Chemical Div., Pittsfield, Mass. Booklet.
2070. Anon.	General Tire & Rubber Co., Chemical Div., Akron, Ohio. Tech. Bulls.
2071. Anon.	Glaskyd, Inc., Perrysburg, Ohio. Tech. literature.
2072. Anon.	Glidden Co., Reading, Pa. Brochure and Data Sheets.
2073. Anon.	Hooker Electrochemical Co., Niagara Falls, N. Y. Prelim. Tech. Data Sheets Nos. 386, 387.
2074. Anon.	Interchemical Corp., Finishes Div., Cincinnati, Ohio. Tech. Bulls.
2075. Anon.	Lunn Laminates, Inc., Long Island, N. Y. Booklet.
2076. Anon.	*Modern Plastics* **20**, No. 2, 88–90, 120, 122 (1942).
2077. Anon.	*Modern Plastics* **25**, No. 2, 111–5 (1947).
2078. Anon.	*Modern Plastics* **27**, No. 11, 111 (1950); No. 8, 129 (1950) (advertisements).
2079. Anon.	*Modern Plastics* **30**, No. 5, 204 (1953).
2080. Anon.	*Modern Plastics* **31**, No. 1, 212 (1953).
2081. Anon.	*Modern Plastics* **31**, No. 1, 216 (1953).
2082. Anon.	Narmco Resins & Coatings Co., Costa Mesa, Calif. Data Sheets.
2083. Anon.	Pittsburgh Plate Glass Co., Pittsburgh, Pa. 23-p. booklet.
2084. Anon.	Pittsburgh Plate Glass Co., Pittsburgh, Pa. Tech. Data Sheets.
2085. Anon.	*Plastics* (London) **17**, 349–50 (1952).
2086. Anon.	*Plastics* (London) **19**, 169 (1954); *Machinery* March 1954, 198.
2087. Anon.	*Plastics Ind.* **11**, No. 10, 5 (1953) (advertisement).
2088. Anon.	*Plastics Ind.* **12**, No. 2, 9–10 (1954).
2089. Anon.	*Plastics Ind.* **12**, No. 3, 31 (1954).

Concerning

Cordopreg—impregnated materials and resins for reinforced plastic molding.

Fiberfil Styrene-G—glass fiber filled injection molding compound.
Properties of Dryply—low-pressure preimpregnated laminating material.

Properties of Pre-imp—glass fiber reinforced polyester molding compound.

Properties and application of Plaskon polyester resin.

Polyester resins for matched die molding, wet lay-up, and laminating.

General information and technical data on Glykon polyester resins.

Properties of Glaskyd glass reinforced alkyd molding compounds.

General information and technical data on Glidpol polyester resins.

Hetron fire-resistant polyester resins.

Polyester resins: properties and fabrication.

Description of company's activities in production and design of reinforced plastics.
Thermosetting resins (allyl) for casting and laminating (Columbia).

Tailor-made polyester resins; properties of Selectron 5000 series of resins (Pittsburgh Plate Glass Co.).
Vibrin polyester resins (Naugatuck Chemical).

New low-temperature-curing polyester resin, Atlac LV, suitable for fibrous glass reinforced products.
Glaskyd—a new molding compound containing fibrous glass and alkyd resins.
New fast-curing polyester resin for use in reinforced plastics.
Properties of Narmco resin 3117 and Narmco putty 3118 (polyester resins).

Selectron polyester reinforcing resins (5000 series).

Properties of Selectron heat-resistant, preform-binding, and potting resins.

German plastics exhibition. Manufacture of polyesters by Badische Anilin.
Chemical- and heat-resistant polyester for ducting, storing of chemicals, etc. (General Electric).
Polyester impregnated glass fabrics and mat.
Heat- and chemical-resistant polyester resin (General Electric).
Glass fiber chopped strand reinforcing mat for plastics (Ferro Corp.).

Author	Reference
2090. Anon.	*Plastics Ind.* **12**, No. 5, 4 (1954).
2091. Anon.	*Plastics Ind.* **12**, No. 5, 15 (1954).
2092. Anon.	Reichhold Chemicals, Inc., New York, N. Y. Tech. Bulls. PR-1–Pr-11.
2093. Anon.	H. H. Robertson Co., Pittsburgh, Pa. Tech. Data Sheets.
2094. Anon.	Rohm & Haas Co., Philadelphia, Pa. Prelim. Notes L-1-53, L-2-53.
2095. Anon.	*Polyester Handbook.* Scott Bader & Co., Ltd.
2096. Anon.	*Retailers Plastics Manual.* Society of the Plastics Industry, Inc., New York, N. Y., and Manufacturing Chemists Association, Washington, D. C., 1954, 40-p. booklet.
2097. Anon.	Sun Chemical Corp., Electro-Technical Products Div., Nutley, N. J. Tech. Data Sheet.
2098. Anon.	Synvar Corp., Wilmington, Del.
2099. Anon.	*Technical Data on Plastics.* Manufacturing Chemists Association, Inc., Washington, D. C., 1952, 183 pp.
2100. Anon.	Thermaflow Chemical Corp., Tunkhannoch, Pa. Bull. No. 2C5.
2101. Anon.	U. S. Rubber Co., Naugatuck Chemical Div., Naugatuck, Conn. Series of Tech. Bulls.
2102. Anon.	U. S. Rubber Co., Naugatuck Chemical Div., Naugatuck, Conn. Form No. NC-51-8.
2103. Bennett, F.	*Reinforced Plastics Div., Soc. Plastics Ind. Confer.*, 6th Annual, 1951, Sect. 13C.
2104. Bennett, F	*Reinforced Plastics Div., Soc. Plastics Ind. Confer.*, 7th Annual, 1952, Sect. 6C.
2105. Bigelow, M. H., and Nowicki, P. E.	*Reinforced Plastics Div., Soc. Plastics Ind. Confer.*, 7th Annual, 1952, Sect. 6I.
2106. Curtis, F. J.	*Chimie & industrie* **55**, 436–8 (1946).
2107. Day, H. M.	*Reinforced Plastics Div., Soc. Plastics Ind. Confer.*, 9th Annual, 1954, Sect. 7F.
2108. Dauphine, T. C.	*Reinforced Plastics Div., Soc. Plastics Ind. Confer.*, 9th Annual, 1954, Sect. 7E.
2109. Elliott, P. M.	*Reinforced Plastics Div., Soc. Plastics Ind. Confer.*, 5th Annual, 1951, Sect. 13G.
2110. Elliott, P. M.	*Reinforced Plastics Div., Soc. Plastics Ind. Confer.*, 8th Annual, 1953, Sect. 24J.
2111. Erickson, W. O., Case, J. C., and Hoppens, H. A.	*Reinforced Plastics Div., Soc. Plastics Ind. Confer.*, 8th Annual, 1953, Sect. 24L.
2112. Gerhart, H. L.	*Modern Plastics* **25**, No. 6, 86 (1947). (Report on Soc. Plastics Ind. Confer.).

Concerning

Low-viscosity resin for low-temperature curing (American Cyanamid).

Chemical-resistant polyester resin (American Cyanamid).

Polylite resins (liquid copolymers of styrene and unsaturated alkyd resins).

Properties and uses of Stypol polyester resins.

Unsaturated polyester-styrene resins for matched die molding (Paraplex P-47 and P-49).

Fabrication, chemistry, and general characteristics of polyester resins.

How to buy and sell plastics. Listings of trademarks, trade names, generic terms.

Sunform preimpregnated glass for low-pressure laminating.

Specifications of Synvar low-pressure polyester resins.

Properties and fabrication of plastics. Includes allyl and polyester resins, laminated thermoset products.

Physical properties of Thermaflow glass reinforced polyester molding compounds.

Vibrin polyester resin—properties, fabrication.

Chemicals for industry and agriculture, including brief discussion of properties and uses of Vibrin polyester resins.

Polyester resins (Bakelite).

New developments in resin field (Bakelite).

Reinforced alkyd plastic molding compound (Libbey-Owens-Ford; now Allied Chemical & Dye).

New German plastics, e.g., Desmophen 1100 (polyester of adipic acid, 1,3-butanediol, and trimethylpropane.)

New Laminac resins for various applications, e.g., fire resistance, electrical applications, preimpregnating, low-temperature curing, exposure to hot liquids, foaming (American Cyanamid).

Hetron fire-resistant polyester resins (Hooker Electrochemical).

Vibrin polyester resins (Naugatuck Chemical).

New Vibrin polyester resins (Naugatuck Chemical).

Review of developments in Plaskon polyester resins (Libbey-Owens-Ford; now Allied Chemical & Dye).

New developments in polyester resins (Pittsburgh Plate Glass).

Author	Reference
2113. Goss, W.	*Reinforced Plastics Div., Soc. Plastics Ind. Confer., 8th Annual*, 1953, Sect. 24F.
2114. Greenfield, J.	*Reinforced Plastics Div., Soc. Plastics Ind. Confer., 9th Annual*, 1954, Sect. 7B.
2115. Hoppens, H. A.	*Reinforced Plastics Div., Soc. Plastics Ind. Confer., 9th Annual*, 1954, Sect. 7M.
2116. Husen, W. R.	*Am. Ink Maker* **30**, No. 6, 63–5, 67, 69, 71, 73, 111 (1952).
2117. Jefferson, G. D.	*Reinforced Plastics Div., Soc. Plastics Ind. Confer., 6th Annual*, 1951, Sect. 13B.
2118. Kropa, E. L.	*Modern Plastics* **25**, No. 9, 182 (1948). (Abst. from West Coast Soc. Plastics Ind. Confer.)
2119. Loritsch, J. A.	*Reinforced Plastics Div., Soc. Plastics Ind. Confer., 6th Annual*, 1951, Sect. 13D.
2120. Maker, W. J.	*Reinforced Plastics Div., Soc. Plastics Ind. Confer., 9th Annual*, 1954, Sect. 7D.
2121. McCann, H., editor.	*Modern Plastics Encyclopedia 1953*. Plastics Catalogue Corp., New York, plastics properties chart.
2122. Miller, J. V.	*Reinforced Plastics Div., Soc. Plastics Ind. Confer., 7th Annual*, 1952, Sect. 6B.
2123. Moffett, E. W.	*Reinforced Plastics Div., Soc. Plastics Ind. Confer., 6th Annual*, 1951, Sect. 13H.
2124. Moffett, E. W.	*Reinforced Plastics Div., Soc. Plastics Ind. Confer., 9th Annual*, 1954, Sect. 7A.
2125. Moore, S. A.	*Reinforced Plastics Div., Soc. Plastics Ind. Confer., 6th Annual*, 1951, Sect. 13E.
2126. Moore, S. A.	*Reinforced Plastics Div., Soc. Plastics Ind. Confer., 7th Annual*, 1952, Sect. 6E.
2127. Moore, S. A.	*Reinforced Plastics Div., Soc. Plastics Ind. Confer., 9th Annual*, 1954, Sect. 7P.
2128. Muskat, I. E., and Hort, E. V.	*Reinforced Plastics Div., Soc. Plastics Ind. Confer., 8th Annual*, 1953, Sect. 24H.
2129. Nelb, R. G.	*Reinforced Plastics Div., Soc. Plastics Ind. Confer., 9th Annual*, 1954, Sect. 7K.
2130. Patterson, D. G.	*Reinforced Plastics Div., Soc. Plastics Ind. Confer., 6th Annual*, 1951, Sect. 13A.
2131. Patterson, D. G.	*Reinforced Plastics Div., Soc. Plastics Ind. Confer., 9th Annual*, 1954, Sect. 7J.
2132. Savage, R. J.	*Reinforced Plastics Div., Soc. Plastics Ind. Confer., 9th Annual*, 1954, Sect. 7Q.
2133. Steenstrup, P. V.	*Reinforced Plastics Div., Soc. Plastics Ind. Confer., 9th Annual*, 1954, Sect. 7H.
2134. Van Boskirk, R. L.	*Modern Plastics* **26**, No. 8, 170 (1949) ("The Plastiscope").
2135. Van Boskirk, R. L.	*Modern Plastics* **27**, No. 1, 176 (1949) ("The Plastiscope").

Concerning

New developments in resin field (General Electric), e.g., new series of polyester resins.

Light-stable, self-extinguishing resin; low-cost resin; and flexible resin (U. S. Industrial Chemicals; now Archer-Daniels-Midland).

New Plaskon light-stable, resilient, and flexible resins (Allied Chemical & Dye).

Tabulation of 300 resins giving type, trade name, manufacturer, and properties.

Atlac polyester resins (Atlas Powder).

Polyester resins (American Cyanamid).

General Electric resins (polyesters, phenolics, silicones) for laminating.

New Glidpol resins: air-uninhibited resin with good impregnating values and gel-coat resin.

Properties of cast rigid and flexible polyester resins.

Atlac polyester resins and molding compound (Atlas Powder).

New developments in Selectron 5000 resins (Pittsburgh Plate Glass).

New Selectron resins for matched metal die molding, low-temperature curing, light-stable and fire-retardant applications (Pittsburgh Plate Glass).

Polyester resins (Interchemical).

Developments in resin field (Interchemical).

Resins for room-temperature tack-free cure, preform binding, light-stable, and fire-retardant applications (Interchemical).

Marco thixotropic resins.

Vibrin resins for automotive and light-stable applications (Naugatuck Chemical).

Developments in resin field (American Cyanamid). Resins for special needs.

New Polylite polyester resins for light-stable, fire-resistant, and air-curing applications (Reichhold Chemicals).

Marco thixotropic, fire-resistant, and light-stable resins (Celanese Corp.).

Developments in General Electric resins, e.g., heat-resistant polyester.

Low-pressure polyester-styrene resin products (Paraplex, Rohm & Haas).

Properties of new stable polyester casting resin.

	Author	Reference
2136.	Van Boskirk, R. L.	*Modern Plastics* **27**, No. 4, 168 (1949) ("The Plastiscope").
2137.	Van Boskirk, R. L.	*Modern Plastics* **28**, No. 6, 174 (1950) ("The Plastiscope").
2138.	Van Boskirk, R. L.	*Modern Plastics* **30**, No. 9, 214 (1953) ("The Plastiscope").
2139.	Van Boskirk, R. L.	*Modern Plastics* **31**, No. 7, 206 (1954).
2140.	Van Boskirk, R. L.	*Modern Plastics* **31**, No. 9, 216–7 (1954).
2141.	Wirsch, W. E.	*Reinforced Plastics Div., Soc. Plastics Ind. Confer.*, 6th Annual, 1951, Sect. 13L.
2142.	Wirsch, W. E.	*Reinforced Plastics Div., Soc. Plastics Ind. Confer.*, 8th Annual, 1953, Sect. 24N.
2143.	Wirsch, W. E.	*Reinforced Plastics Div., Soc. Plastics Ind. Confer.*, 9th Annual, 1954, Sect. 7C.

Concerning

Flexible polyester for casting and laminating (General Tire & Rubber).

Solid alkyd (polyester) resin with long shelf life (Atlas Powder).

New Marco resin that will not drain from smooth, vertical surfaces.

Polyester resin with superior chemical and heat resistance (General Electric).
Light-stable and fire-resistant Hetron resin (Hooker Electrochemical Co.).
Developments in polyester resins (Rohm & Haas).

Molding resins with high strength at elevated temperatures and easy handling characteristics.
Paraplex resins for molding, light-stable applications, preform binding (Rohm & Haas).

Author	Reference
2144. Anon.	*Chem. Eng. News* **31**, 2771–2 (1953).
2145. Anon.	*Chem. Eng. News* **32**, 873, 893 (1954).
2146. Anon.	*Materials and Methods* **39**, No. 2, 98–100 (1954).
2147. Anon.	*Plastics* (London) **18**, 446 (1953).
2148. Anon.	*Plastics* (London) **19**, 14 (1954).
2149. Abe, S.	*Rept. Osaka Municipal Inst. Ind. Research* No. 12, 56–60 (1948).
2150. Alfrey, T., Jr., and Lavin, E.	*J. Am. Chem. Soc.* **64**, 2044–5 (1945).
2151. Azumi, T., and Havashi, M.	*J. Chem. Soc. Japan, Ind. Chem. Sect.* **55**, 475–6 (1952).
2152. Bartlett, P. D., and Altschul, R.	*J. Am. Chem. Soc.* **67**, 812–22 (1945).
2153. Batzer, H.	*Makromol. Chem.* **10**, 13–29 (1953).
2154. Batzer, H., and Mohr, B.	*Makromol. Chem.* **8**, 217–33 (1952).
2155. Bennitt, J. H.	*Brit. Plastics* **25**, 416–7 (1952).
2156. Bevan, E. A.	*Vernici* **18**, 309–11 (1942); *Z. ges. Schiess. u. Sprengstoffw. Nitrocellulose* **38**, 187 (1943).
2157. Biggs, B. S., Erickson, R. H., and Fuller, C. S.	*Ind. Eng. Chem.* **39**, 1090–97 (1947); *Modern Plastics* **25**, No. 5, 124 (1948).
2158. Blakey, W.	*Ann. Repts. Soc. Chem. Ind. Progress Applied Chem.* **26**, 298–305 (1941).
2159. Blom, A. V.	*Verfkronick* **21**, 87–8 (1948).
2160. Blom, A. V.	*Kunststoffe* **42**, 433–6 (1952).
2161. Bourry, J.	*Alkyd Resins. Polyesters.* Dunod, Paris, 1952.
2162. Bunn, C. W.	*J. Chem. Soc.* (London) 1947, 297–306.
2163. Burgess, A. R.	*Chem. & Ind.* **4**, 78–81 (1952).
2164. Chamberlain, N. H.	*Plastics* (London) **9**, 622 (1945).
2165. Cummings, W., and Botwick, M.	Paper presented at Am. Chem. Soc. Meeting, Div. Paint, Plastics, and Printing Ink Chem., Chicago, September 1953.
2166. Dmitriev, P. I.	*Zhur. Priklad. Khim.* **12**, 1848–55 (1939).
2167. Dmitriev, P. I., and Dogadkina, L. A.	*Zhur. Priklad. Khim.* **14**, 110–9 (1941).

VIII. TAILOR-MAKING POLYESTERS

Concerning

Relation of properties of polymer to structure.

Properties and uses, *e.g.*, flame-retardant polyester resins, of chlorendic acid and anhydride.

Properties and uses of fire-resistant polyesters containing HET acid ($C_6H_4O_4Cl_6$).

Copolymerization of preformed unsaturated polyesters with styrene.

Nonflammable polyester-glass laminates made from resins with chlorinated compounds as bases.

Copolymerization of vinyl chloride and dimethyl maleate. Properties of copolymers.

Copolymerization of styrene and maleic anhydride. Relation of polymer composition to monomer composition.

Polyester condensation product of para-xylene glycol.

Peroxide-induced polymerization of allyl acetate.

Physical properties of linear polyesters. Preparation of various types of polyesters.

Linear polyesters with sterically equivalent double bonds.

Synthesis and properties of alkyd molding materials.

A review of maleic acid resins, largely from patents.

Elastomeric linear polyesters from dibasic acids and propylene glycol: preparation, vulcanization (cross-linking), relation of structure to strength and useful life.

Thermosetting resins.

Synthetic resins for lacquer industry. Versatility of polyesters as film-forming materials.

Relation between structure and mechanical properties of macromolecular substances.

Study of high-polymer structure by x-ray diffraction. Relation between chemical structure and flexibility of polyesters.

Relation of degradation and weathering of plastics to structural considerations.

Allyl polyesters: properties, polymerization stages, preparation of laminate.

Heat-resistant polyesters. Effect of various cross-linking monomers, *e.g.*, triallyl cyanurate.

Glyptaladipic resins from glycerol, phthalic anhydride, and adipic acid.

Alkyd resins with a base of polyglycols and polyglycerols.

Author	Reference
2168. Doscher, C. K.	*Colloid Chemistry.* Vol. 6, Reinhold, New York, 1946, 1068–1176.
2169. Drinberg, A. Y., and Zhebrovskii, V. V.	*Zhur. Priklad. Khim.* **13**, 1442–8 (1940).
2170. Ebers, E. S. *et al.*	U. S. Rubber Co., Naugatuck Chemical Div., Naugatuck, Conn. (1949).
2171. Elliott, P. M.	*Modern Plastics* **29**, No. 11, 113 (1952).
2172. Evans, E. M.	*Brit. Plastics* **27**, No. 3, 100–3 (1954).
2173. Goggin, W. C., and Boyer, R. F.	*Plastics & Resins* **3**, No. 11, 6–12, 29–33, 36 (1944).
2174. Grassie, N., and Melville, H. W.	*Proc. Royal Soc.* A199, 24 (1949).
2175. Hurd, C. D., and Blunck, S. H.	*J. Am. Chem. Soc.* **60**, 2419 (1938).
2176. Jones, G. D.	*Styrene (Its Polymers, Copolymers, and Derivatives).* Reinhold, New York, 1952, 674.
2177. Kardashev, D. A., Leznov, N. S., and Nuzhdina, V. P.	*Khimicheskaya Prom.* 1945, No. 2, 5–6.
2178. Kargin, V. A.	*Chem. Průmysl* **1**, No. 26, 167–70 (1952).
2179. Klimenkov, V. S., Kargin, V. A., and Kitaigorodskii, A. I.	*Khim i. Fiz. Khim. Vysokomolekul. Soedinenii, Doklady 7-oi Konf. Vysokomolekul Soedineniyam* 1952, 231–41.
2180. Korshak, V. V., and Soboleva, T. A.	*Bull. Acad. Sci. U.S.S.R., Div. Chem. Sci.* 1952, 505–8 (Engl. translation).
2181. Kropa, E. L.	*Trans. Electrochem. Soc.* **90**, 247 (1946).
2182. Lawton, E. J., Bueche, A. M., and Baleirt, J. S.	*Nature* **172**, 76–7 (1953).
2183. Lazarev, A. I., and Sorokin, M. F.	*Khim. Prom.* 1947, No. 5, 20–5.
2184. Linke, R.	*Oesterreiche Plastic Rundschau* (Oct. 1953).
2185. Liquori, A. M., and Mele, A.	*Chimica i industria* (Milan) **35**, 799–809 (1953).
2186. Lombard, F.	*Makromol. Chem.* **8**, 187–207 (1952).
2187. Mark, H. F.	*Am. J. Phys.* **13**, 207–14 (1945).
2188. Mark, H. F., *et al.*	*Advancing Fronts in Chemistry* **1**, 1–182 (1945).
2189. Marvel, C. S., and Young, C. H.	*J. Am. Chem. Soc.* **73**, 1066–9 (1951).
2190. Massey, L.	*Trans. Inst. Rubber Ind.* **16**, 325–54 (1941).
2191. Melville, H. W.	*Proc. Intern. Congr. Pure and Applied Chem.* (London) **11**, 551 (1947).

Concerning

Preparation and properties of fumaric and maleic acid resins. Patent abstracts, 22 references.

Glycerol polyester of maleic acid; preparation, properties, and structure.

Final report on flame- and heat-resistant resins for naval construction.

Heat-resistant copolymers of triallyl cyanurate and a maleic alkyd.

Preparation and properties of polyester resins. Review.

Effect of chemical structure of plastics on electrical, mechanical, and chemical properties.

Effect of inhibitors and end groups on the degradation of polymethyl methacrylate.

Pyrolysis of esters.

Chemical alternation of styrene polymers.

Characteristics of allyl esters of dibasic acids, e.g., fumaric and maleic, and their polymers.

Structure and physico-chemical properties of macromolecular materials.

Data on packing coefficient (volume change after polymerization) of various polymers. Relation to flexibility of chains.

Polyesters of aromatic dicarboxylic acids.

Thermosetting vinyl polymers as laminating and low-pressure molding resins. Effect of constituents on properties of resin.

Irradiation of polymers by high-energy electrons; causes cross-linking.

Survey of synthetic resins, including patents.

Chemistry of polyester resin forming components, preparation and fabrication of resins, properties of end products, fields of application.

Relation between molecular structure and physical properties of linear high polymers.

Polycondensation products of 11-hydroxyundecylic acid.

Review of molecular structure and mechanical properties of high polymers.

Review lectures on relation between structure and properties of polymers, mechanism of polymerization, textile fibers, etc.

Effect of cis and trans olefinic groups on the properties of polyurethanes and polyesters.

Properties of dielectric materials. Theoretical aspects of polymers as dielectrics.

Highly branched superester molecules from adipic acid, ethylene glycol, and pentaerythritol or other polyfunctional alcohols.

Author	Reference
2192. Morgan, P. W.	*Ind. Eng. Chem.* **45**, 2296–306 (1953).
2193. Nichols, P. L., Jr., and Yanovsky, E.	*J. Am. Chem. Soc.* **67**, 46–9 (1945).
2194. Nordlander, B. W., and Cass, W. E.	*J. Am. Chem. Soc.* **69**, 2679 (1947).
2195. Parker, E. E., and Moffett, E. W.	Paper presented at Am. Chem. Soc. Meeting, Div. Paint, Plastics, and Printing Ink Chem., Chicago, September 1953.
2196. Pechukas, A.	*Colloid Chemistry.* Vol. 6. Reinhold, New York, 1946, 1063–7.
2197. Pechukas, A., Strain, F., and Dial, W. R.	*Plastics & Resin Ind.* **1**, No. 5, 21 (1947).
2198. Penn, W. S.	*Plastics* (London) **10**, 33–42 (1946).
2199. Pyle, J. J.	*Pacific Plastics Mag.* **2**, No. 7, 18–21 (1944).
2200. Pyle, J. J.	*Pulp & Paper Ind.* **19**, No. 10, 62–3 (1945).
2201. Robinson, H. W., *et al.*	U. S. Rubber Co., Naugatuck Chemical Div., Naugatuck, Conn. (1950).
2202. Robitschek, P.	*Plastics Ind.* **11**, No. 10, 7 (1953) (summary of paper).
2203. Robitschek, P., and Bean, C. T.	Paper presented at Am. Chem. Soc. Meeting, Div. Paint, Plastics, and Printing Ink Chem., Chicago, September 1953.
2204. Rowland, J. S.	*Interchem. Rev.* **5**, No. 4, 83–94 (1946–47).
2205. Rust, J. B.	*Ind. Eng. Chem.* **32**, 64–7 (1940).
2206. Ruzicka, F. C. I.	*Oil Colour Trades J.* **114**, 442, 444, 446, 500, 502, 504, 556, 558, 615–6, 618 (1948).
2207. Ryan, J. W.	*SPE J.* **10**, No. 4, 11, 40–1 (1954).
2208. Senda, H., and Oda, R.	*Chem. High Polymers* (Japan) **8**, 150–3 (1951).
2209. Simpson, W.	*J. Soc. Chem. Ind.* **65**, 105–11 (1946).
2210. Singleton, F. G.	*Modern Plastics* **30**, 152 (1952).
2211. Strain, F.	*Am. Soc. Testing Materials Symposium on Plastics*, Feb. 22–3, 1944, 136–9.
2212. Tobolsky, A. V.	*Faraday Soc. Discussions* No. 2, 384 (1947).
2213. Turner, P. S.	*J. Research Natl. Bur. Standards* **37**, 239–50 (1946); *Modern Plastics* **24**, No. 4, 153–7, 214, 216, 218, 220 (1946).
2214. Ushakov, S. N., and Mitsengendler, S. P.	*Zhur. Priklad. Khim.* **20**, 1261–9 (1947).

Concerning

Relation of moisture permeability of film-forming polymers to their structure. Structural requirements for low permeability given.

Preparation of polyallyl ethers, by allylation of polyhydric alcohols, and polymerization of the ethers.

Esterification of tetrachlorophthalic anhydride.

Relationship between properties of a cured polyester resin and the chemical composition of the uncured resin, e.g., unsaturation, proportion of styrene, chemical components.

Allyl resins—preparation, properties, and applications.

Allyl alcohol resins.

Relation of molecular structure to properties of plastics. Review of theory.

Recent developments in plastics, e.g., unsaturated alkyd-styrene resins for low-pressure laminations.

Review of new types of resins (mentions polyester) and other plastics developments of interest to pulp and paper industry.

Final summary report on low-pressure heat-resistant laminated resins.

Heat- and flame-resistant polyesters containing chlorine and pentane ingredients.

Properties of polyesters from hexachlorocyclopentadiene, particularly flame resistance.

Review on maleic and fumaric resins.

Copolymerization of maleic polyesters with vinyl derivatives, e.g., styrene and vinyl acetate.

Review on alkyd resins. Mentions modification of ethylene glycol-maleic acid ester with styrene.

Theory of changes in physical characteristics of plastics (includes linear polyesters) caused by radiation.

Synthesis of diallyl esters of butyric, caproic, benzoic, succinic, adipic, and phthalic acids and copolymerization of these esters with vinyl acetate or methyl methacrylate.

Catalytic polymerization of allyl esters e.g., diallyl phthalate.

High-temperature properties of Stypol 16B glass cloth laminate.

Properties and uses of allyl plastics (allymers).

Oxidative degradation of polymeric materials.

Thermal-expansion stresses in reinforced plastics. Equation given for coefficient of thermal expansion of mixtures.

Copolymerization of ethylene glycol maleate with vinyl formate.

	Author	Reference
2215.	Wickert, K.	*Korrosion u. Metallschutz* **19**, 125–30 (1943).
2216.	Wicks, Z. W.	*Interchem. Rev.* **6**, No. 3, 63–77 (1947).
2217.	Wiley, R. H.	*Ind. Eng. Chem.* **38**, 959–60 (1946).
2218.	Wiloth, F.	*Makromol. Chem.* **8**, 111–23 (1952).
2218a.	Richardson, H. M.	*Elect. Manuf.* **51**, No. 4, 114 (1953).
2219.	Worner, H. K.	*Austral. Plastics* **1**, No. 4, 21–6, No. 6, 19 (1945).
2220.	Yager, W. A., and Baker, W. O.	*J. Am. Chem. Soc.* **64**, 2164–71 (1942).

Concerning

Relation of electron shifts to corrosion of various materials, including plastics.

Chemistry of alkyd resins.   Effect of variation in ingredients on properties.

Relation between specific refractivity of polymers and atomic structure of the polymer unit.   Theoretical.

Influence of chemical constitution on the molecular configuration of polyesters.

Effect of chemical structure on dielectric properties of plastics.

Review of chemistry, structure, and properties of commercial plastics.   Comparison with properties of metals.

Relation of dielectric properties to structure of polyesters.

Properties of Polyester Plastics

	Author	Reference
2221.	Anon.	*Brit. Plastics* **25**, 382–5 (1952).
2222.	Anon.	*Can. Chem. Processing* **36**, No. 11, 78–9 (1952).
2223.	Anon.	*Chem. Eng. News* **32**, 373, 1310 (1954) ("Concentrates").
2224.	Anon.	*Can. Plastics* Jan.-Feb. 1954, 72.
2225.	Anon.	*Modern Plastics* **23**, No. 10, 144–5; No. 11, 146 (1946).
2226.	Anon.	*Modern Plastics* **24**, No. 7, 122–3 (1947). (Rept. of Soc. Plastics Ind. meeting).
2227.	Anon.	*Modern Plastics* **29**, No. 1, 75–8 (1951).
2228.	Anon.	*Modern Plastics* **31**, No. 1, 83–9, 176–9 (1953).
2229.	Anon.	*Plastics* (London) **19**, 169 (1954).
2230.	Anon.	*Plastics Ind.* **11**, No. 11, 22 (1953).
2231.	Anon.	*Prod. Eng.* **18**, No. 3, 160–5 (1947).
2232.	Axilrod, B. M., and Sherman, M. A.	*J. Res. Natl. Bur. Standards* **44**, 65 (1950).
2233.	Bigelow, M. H., and Nowicki, P. E.	*Elect. Mfg.* **49**, No. 4, 110–3 (1952).
2234.	Bigelow, M. H., and Nowicki, P. E.	*J. Electrochem. Soc.* **100**, No. 2, 60–2 (1953).
2235.	Carswell, T. S., and Nason, H. K.	*Modern Plastics* **21**, No. 9, 41–6, 55–6 (1944).
2236.	Clauser, H. R.	*Materials & Methods* **39**, No. 4, 117–32 (1954).
2237.	Crouse, W. A., Caudill, D. C., and Reinhart, F. W.	*Natl. Advisory Comm. Aeronaut. Tech. Note* No. 1240, 21 pp. (1947).
2238.	Crouse, W. A., Carickhoff, M., and Fisher, M. A.	*Trans. Am. Soc. Mech. Engrs.* **72**, 175–88 (1950).
2239.	Dale, M., and Faller, I. L.	*J. Am. Chem. Soc.* **72**, 414–9 (1950).
2240.	Duflos, J.	*Materie plastiche* **20**, No. 1 (1954).
2241.	Field, P. M.	*Modern Plastics* **21**, No. 8, 47–9, 61 (1944).
2242.	Findley, W. M., and Worley, W. J.	*SPE J.* **7**, No. 4 (1951).
2243.	Francis, R. J.	*Prod. Eng.* **22**, No. 2, 85–108 (1951).
2244.	Franck and Nagel	*German Tekh.* **20**, Sonderheft No. 2, 18–21 (1941); *Chem. Zentr.* 1941, II, 1800.

IX. FINAL PRODUCTS

Concerning

Electrical and other properties of glass reinforced plastics; includes polyester laminates.

Review of properties of plastics and comparison with metals.

Resistance of structural materials including glass fiber reinforced polyesters to agricultural chemicals.

Review of properties and applications of polyesters.

Data on low-pressure laminating resins relating to properties, manufacture, and fabrication.

Review of general characteristics of polyesters.

Properties of new textile fibers, including polyester fiber.

Plastics vs. corrosion; includes polyester-glass reinforced plastics.

Classification table with mechanical, physical, and electrical properties of laminated fabric plastics.

Review on fabrication and properties of polyester-glass fiber laminates.

Properties and applications of glass fibers and of glass-plastic laminates.

Strength of heat-resistant laminated plastics up to 300° C.

Glass reinforced alkyd plastics.

Effect of humidity upon insulation resistance of alkyd molding compounds.

Review, with 157 references, on effect of environment, especially temperature, on mechanical properties of organic plastics.

Materials for high-temperature service, including resistant polyesters.

Effect of simulated service conditions on laminated plastics, including glass fabric-unsaturated polyester laminate.

Effect of immersion in fuels on laminated plastics, including glass fabric-unsaturated polyester laminate.

Water sorption by synthetic high polymers. Sorption very small on polyesters.

Properties of glass fibers and glass cloth-resin plastics.

Effect of elevated and reduced temperatures on impact strength of reinforced plastics.

Elevated temperature creep and fatigue properties of a polyester glass fabric laminate.

Properties, manufacture, and design factors of reinforced plastics.

Review of properties and applications of laminated plastics, impregnated paper, and impregnated fabrics.

Properties of Polyester Plastics (Continued)

	Author	Reference
2245.	Fried, N., Winans, R. R., and Sieffert, L. E.	*Proc. Am. Soc. Testing Materials* **50**, 1383–98 (1950).
2246.	Fried, N., Stenstrom, A., and Winans, R. R.	*Reinforced Plastics Div., Soc. Plastics Ind. Confer., 9th Annual*, 1954, Sect. 1F.
2247.	Hammond, A.	*Selected Govt. Research Repts.* (Gt. Brit.) Vol. 1, *Plastics*, Rept. No. 4, 169–98 (1952).
2248.	Hatch, D. M., Jr., and Steinman, J.	*Modern Plastics* **30**, No. 12, 89–90, 188 (1953).
2249.	Hausman, E. E., Parkinson, A. E., and Mains, G. H.	*Modern Plastics* **22**, No. 3, 151 (1944).
2250.	Haward, R. N.	*Strength of Plastics and Glass.* Interscience, New York, 1949, 253 pp.
2251.	King, R.	*Machine Design* **25**, No. 3, 112–22 (1953).
2252.	Kline, G. M.	*Reinforced Plastics Div., Soc. Plastics Ind. Confer., 5th Annual*, 1950, Sect. 5.
2253.	Kline, G. M.	*Natl. Advisory Comm. Aeronaut. Research Mem.* No. 51B23, 9 pp. (1951).
2254.	Kline, G. M.	*Modern Plastics* **28**, No. 12, 113–24, 182–6, 189 (1951).
2255.	Lamb, J. J., Albrecht, I., and Axilrod, B. M.	*Natl. Advisory Comm. Aeronaut. Tech. Note* No. 1550, 57 pp. (1948).
2256.	Lamb, J. L. *et al.*	*J. Research Natl. Bur. Standards* **43**, 257–89 (1949).
2257.	Lincoln, J. D.	*Modern Plastics* **21**, No. 9, 110–11 (1944).
2258.	Long, J. K.	*Modern Plastics* **27**, No. 3, 107–8, 110, 152–6 (1949).
2259.	Lubin, G., and Martin, M.	*Prod. Eng.* **25**, No. 5, 165–9 (1954).
2260.	McCann, H., editor.	*Modern Plastics Encyclopedia 1953.* Plastics Catalogue Corp., New York, 768.
2261.	Moore, R. J.	*India Rubber World* **113**, 674–8 (1946).
2262.	Norelli, P.	*Modern Plastics* **26**, 119 (1948).
2263.	Norelli, P., and Gard, W. H.	*Ind. Eng. Chem.* **37**, 580 (1945).
2264.	Parsons, G. B.	*Modern Plastics* **29**, No. 2, 129–40, 210 (1952).
2265.	Preston, F. W.	*Soc. Plastics Ind. Rept.* No. 44-05b (1944).
2266.	Rector, C.	*Chem. Eng. News* **23**, 150–2 (1945).

Concerning

Effects of elevated temperatures on strength of thermosetting plastic laminates.

Pull-out strength of fasteners in polyester glass laminates; compressibility of dry and resin-impregnated glass mat and glass cloth.

Sorption of water by high-polymeric materials.

Design criteria for efficient plastic components in missiles.

Heat resistance of laminated plastics.

Review on low-pressure laminates: fabrication, reinforcing materials, resins, properties, cost, design.
Properties of reinforced laminates as related to type of reinforcement, e.g., glass fiber, asbestos, etc.
Physical properties of cast polyester resins (tables).

Mechanical and permanence properties of various laminates, including polyesters.

Tensile and compressive strength of laminated plastics. Includes polyester laminates reinforced with glass fabric.

Mechanical properties of laminated plastics at -70°, 77°, and 200° F.

Desirable handling properties of low-pressure resins.
Effect of outdoor exposure on physical properties of glass fiber-polyester laminates and other plastics.
Advances in reinforced plastics (including polyesters). A review covering choice of resin and reinforcement, methods of fabrication, and design considerations.
Properties of glass cloth and glass mat polyester laminates.

Survey, with 36 references, on developments in plastics. Table compares properties of reinforced polyester laminates, aluminum, and steel.
Thermal effects on flexural strength of laminates.
Effect of temperature on strength of laminates.

Properties of glass fiber laminates.

Significance of new data on combinations of plastic and glass fiber.
Review of plastics developments in 1944, e.g., unsaturated polyester-glass fiber combinations with very high strength-weight ratios.

Properties of Polyester Plastics (Continued)

Author	Reference
2267.	Reinhart, F. W., and Williams, H. C., Jr.	*Amer. Soc. Testing Materials Bull.* No. 167, 60–2 (1950).
2268.	Renwick, W. C.	*Naval Air Exp. Station Rept.* TED NAM 25217.0 (1944).
2269.	Rice, R. B., Fiedler, E. F., and Pyle, J. J.	*Modern Plastics* **24**, No. 9, 156 (1947).
2270.	Rose, K.	*Materials & Methods* **37**, No. 1, 87–9 (1953).
2271.	Schliekelman, R. J.	*Plastics* **6**, 484–7 (1953).
2272.	Schoenborn, E. M., Armstrong, A. A., Jr., and Beatty, K. O., Jr.	*ASTM Bull.* No. 174, 54–9 (1951).
2273.	Schwartz, R. T., and Dugger, E., Jr.	*Modern Plastics* **21**, No. 7, 39–43, 60–1 (1944).
2274.	Schwartz, R. T., and Dugger, E.,	*Modern Plastics* **21**, No. 9, 49–53, 69–71 (1944).
2275.	Scofield, F.	*Natl. Paint. Varnish Lacquer Assoc. Sci. Sect. Circ.* No. 738, 150 pp.
2276.	Sebrell, L. B.	*India Rubber World* **114**, 388–90 (1946).
2277.	Seymour, R. B.	*SPE J.* **10**, No. 1, 14–5 (1954).
2278.	Seymour, R. B., and Steiner, R. H.	*Chem. Eng.* **59**, No. 12, 278, 280, 282, 284, 286 (1952).
2279.	Seymour, R. B., and Steiner, R. H.	*Reinforced Plastics Div., Soc. Plastics Ind. Confer., 9th Annual,* 1954, Sect. 7L.
2280.	Sieffert, L. E., and Schoenborn, E. M.	*Ind. Eng. Chem.* **42**, 496 (1950).
2281.	Slayter, G., and Collins, H. W.	*Plastics & Resins* **5**, No. 3, 8–12, 31–4, 36 (1946).
2282.	Terp, G.	*Plastic* (Denmark) **3**, No. 1, 4–5 (1953).
2283.	Von Hippel, A.	*Mass. Inst. Tech. Lab. Insulation Res., Tech. Rept.* No. 57 (Tables of Dielectric Materials, Vol. IV), 1953, 138 pp.
2284.	Weir, C. E.	*J. Research Natl. Bur. Standards* **46**, 207–12 (1951). Research Paper No. 2192.
2285.	Welch, L.	*Brit. Plastics* **27**, 105–6 (1954).
2286.	Worner, H. R.	*Australasian Engr.* **44**, No. 348, 34–42 (1945).
2287.	Wyroteck, E. J., and Koch, W. R.	*U. S. Air Force Memo* Ex. PM-56-606-3280 (June 22, 1940).
2287a.	Bettridge, R. A.	*J. Textile Inst.* **37**, No. 7, 226 (1946).
2287b.	Hoffman, K. R., and Elliott, E. C.	*Elect. Manuf.* **52**, No. 5, 64 (1953).

Concerning

Resistance of plastic materials to hydrofluoric acid. Unsaturated polyester-glass fabric laminates markedly affected.
Properties of plastic laminates.

Spectral transmission of transparent plastics, including polyesters.

Properties of glass fiber filled molding resins.
Polyester-glass fiber products: specifications, choice of materials, factors to be considered when used as substitute for wood or metal.
Thermal properties (thermal diffusivity, thermal conductivity, heat capacity) of laminated plastics (including glass fiber-polyester).

Shear strength of thermosetting and thermoplastic plastics.

Bearing strength of thermosetting laminates and thermoplastic sheets.

Resin index of 1950. Lists properties of two polyesters.

Review on plastics as materials of construction. Mentions properties of some polyester resins.
Practical indices for chemical-resistant plastics (including polyesters), based on relative values for physical and chemical properties.
Corrosion resistance of polyester-glass plastics.

Resins for chemical-resistant construction.

Heat resistance of laminated plastics.

Survey of developments in glass-resin combinations.

Proper use of plastics. Based on physical, chemical, and electrical properties.
Dielectric constants and tangents of loss angle for many materials, including polyesters.

Compressibility of natural and synthetic high polymers at high pressures.

Properties and design of glass fiber reinforced plastic structures.
Comparison of chemical and physical properties of plastics and metals.

Effect of exposure on physical properties of transparent plastics.

Fundamentals of plastic laminate construction; manufacture; properties.
Evaluation of high-temperature laminates, including polyester laminates.

Transportation

	Author	Reference
2288.	Anon.	*Automotive Ind.* September 1953, 15, 42.
2289.	Anon.	*Brit. Plastics* **24**, 415–20 (1951).
2290.	Anon.	*Brit. Plastics* **26**, 172–3 (1953).
2291.	Anon.	*Brit. Plastics* **26**, 362 (1953).
2292.	Anon.	*Brit. Plastics* **26**, 362 (1953).
2293.	Anon.	*Brit. Plastics* **26**, 446 (1953).
2294.	Anon.	*Brit. Plastics* **26**, 450–2 (1953).
2295.	Anon.	*Brit. Plastics* **26**, 472 (1953).
2296.	Anon.	*Brit. Plastics* **27**, 154 (1954).
2297.	Anon.	*Brit. Plastics* **27**, 161 (1954).
2298.	Anon.	*Can. Plastics* Mar.–April 1954, 63.
2299.	Anon.	*Can. Plastics* Mar.–April 1954, 73.
2300.	Anon.	Castolite Co., Woodstock, Ill. 32-p. booklet.
2301.	Anon.	*Chem. Eng. News* **31**, 2810 (1953).
2302.	Anon.	*Chem. Eng. News* **31**, 3122 (1953).
2303.	Anon.	*Chem. Eng. News* **31**, 3946 (1953).
2304.	Anon.	*Chem. Eng. News* **32**, 128 (1954).
2305.	Anon.	*Chem. Eng. News* **32**, 373 (1954) ("Concentrates").
2306.	Anon.	*Chem. Eng. News* **32**, 378 (1954) (advertisement).
2307.	Anon.	*Chem. Eng. News* **32**, 1939 (1954).
2308.	Anon.	*Chem. Eng. News* **32**, 2180–3 (1954).
2309.	Anon.	*Chem. Week* **73**, No. 14, 62, 64, 66 (1953); *Plastics World* **11**, No. 11, 11 (1953).
2310.	Anon.	*Chem. Week* **73**, No. 23, 62 (1953); *Modern Plastics* **31**, No. 7, 172 (1954); *Plastics World* **12**, No. 2, 1 (1954).
2311.	Anon.	*Chem. Week* **74**, No. 4, 72 (1954).
2312.	Anon.	*Chem. Week* **74**, No. 8, 90 (1954).
2313.	Anon.	*Ind. des plastiques modernes* **5**, No. 8, 2–3 (1953).
2314.	Anon.	*Ind. des plastiques modernes* **6**, No. 2, 20 (1954).
2315.	Anon.	Glass Plastics Supply Co., Linden, N. J. Data Sheets.
2316.	Anon.	Goodyear Aircraft Corp., Akron, Ohio. 4-p. brochure.

Concerning

Survey of plastics components in modern motor cars.
Low-pressure laminates for aircraft.
Boats molded from polyester resin and glass.
Refitting of ketch with plastic materials.
Wing section of airplane: glass reinforced plastic ribs, asbestos reinforced plastic covering.
Reinforced plastic yacht.
Reinforced polyester side panels for buses.
Glass-polyester fuselage for sailplane.
Developments in glass-polyester boats: properties of boats, economics.
Glass-polyester bodywork for commercial vehicles.
Commercial plane galley equipment of reinforced polyester.
Aircraft radio-compass housing from polyester, acetylene black, and cotton duck.
Directions for building glass fiber boats.

Glass fiber reinforced plastic storage tanks for minesweepers.
Reinforced plastic car bodies.
Polyester resin-glass fiber reinforced plastics in trailer truck and sports car production.
Contract awarded Lunn Laminates for production of reinforced plastic bodies for Chevrolet Corvette sports car.
Prediction of foothold for plastic auto bodies in 1954.

Photographs of some of 225 glass fiber reinforced polyester parts in F-84 Thunderjets.
Experimental sports car body from glass fiber and polyester resin. Use of reinforced polyester may permit molding of major body sections in 1 piece.
Review on glass reinforced plastic cars: materials used, assembly process, repair, economics.
Use of reinforced polyester in truck and trailer body production.

Reinforced polyester doors for insulated trucks; save weight and do not freeze shut.

Belly radome for Air Force picket plane made from glass fiber-polyester laminate over nylon-phenolic resin honeycomb.
All plastic (glass fiber-resin) body, including bumpers, structural members, and body-attaching brackets, for Dodge Granada.
Rebuilding of wooden boat hulls by application of glass mat and polyester.

Glass-polyester trailer tank.

Polyester-glass fiber boat repair kit. Methods of application.

Reinforced plastic transparent enclosure, e.g., radomes.

Transportation (Continued)

	Author	Reference
2317.	Anon.	*Chem. Week* **74**, No. 11, 94 (1954); *Materials & Methods* **39**, No. 3, 7, 222 (1954).
2318.	Anon.	*Materials & Methods* **38**, No. 2, 100–1 (1953).
2319.	Anon.	*Materials & Methods* **38**, No. 4, 133 (1953); *Plastics World* **11**, No. 11, 30 (1953).
2320.	Anon.	*Materials & Methods* **38**, No. 5, 7 (1953).
2321.	Anon.	*Materials & Methods* **39**, No. 3, 81 (1954).
2322.	Anon.	*Materies, Plastiques, et Resins*, May–June 1953.
2323.	Anon.	*Modern Plastics* **25**, No. 7, 54 (1948) (advertisement).
2324.	Anon.	*Modern Plastics* **25**, No. 12, 77 (1948).
2325.	Anon.	*Modern Plastics* **26**, No. 2, 166 (1948).
2326.	Anon.	*Modern Plastics* **28**, No. 4, 75 (1950).
2327.	Anon.	*Modern Plastics* **28**, No. 5, 58 (1951).
2328.	Anon.	*Modern Plastics* **28**, No. 7, 78 (1951).
2329.	Anon.	*Modern Plastics* **28**, No. 8, 73–7, 177 (1951).
2330.	Anon.	*Modern Plastics* **28**, No. 10, 102–3 (1951).
2331.	Anon.	*Modern Plastics* **28**, No. 12, 92–3 (1951).
2332.	Anon.	*Modern Plastics* **29**, No. 3, 80–1 (1951).
2333.	Anon.	*Modern Plastics* **29**, No. 8, 96–9 (1952).
2334.	Anon.	*Modern Plastics* **30**, No. 3, 125–6, 128, 130 (1952).
2335.	Anon.	*Modern Plastics* **30**, No. 5, 98 (1953).
2336.	Anon.	*Modern Plastics* **30**, No. 6, 54 (1953) (advertisement).
2337.	Anon.	*Modern Plastics* **30**, No. 6, 75–82 (1953).
2338.	Anon.	*Modern Plastics* **30**, No. 9, 95–7 (1953).
2339.	Anon.	*Modern Plastics* **30**, No. 10, 69 (1953) (advertisement).
2340.	Anon.	*Modern Plastics* **30**, No. 12, 116–8 (1953).
2341.	Anon.	*Modern Plastics* **31**, No. 2, 99–102 (1953); *Chem. Eng. News* **32**, 2144 (1954); *Prod. Eng.* **25**, No. 5, 209 (1954).
2342.	Anon.	*Modern Plastics* **31**, No. 2, 202 (1953).
2343.	Anon.	*Modern Plastics* **31**, No. 3, 98 (1953).
2344.	Anon.	*Modern Plastics* **31**, No. 4, 83–91, 201 (1953).

Concerning

Reinforced polyester laminates as facings for sandwich construction of tailcone of Navy patrol plane (polyester-glass honeycomb core) and wings of Air Force trainer (cellular cellulose acetate core).

Use of plastics in passenger air liners, e.g., polyester laminates for cargo compartment liners, battery containers, wing trailing edge strips, power distribution boxes, oil drip pans.

Repair of fishing cruisers with glass fiber reinforced plastic.

Production of glass reinforced bodies for Chevrolet Corvette sports car: economics, switch to matched metal die process.

Plastic boats with nondenting, seamless, resilient hulls made from glass reinforced polyester resin.

A short outline of the history, advantages, and disadvantages of glass fiber-plastic automobile bodies.

Polyester-glass fiber mat for parts of railroad coach seats (Owens-Corning).

Use of plastics by armed forces (storm boat made of polyester-glass fiber plastic).

Navy plastic personnel boat made from glass fiber and polyester resin.

Reinforcement of race boat hull with glass fiber-polyester material.

Coast Guard lifeboats from glass fiber reinforced polyesters. Timbers molded hollow and filled with expanded cellulose acetate.

Use of polyester resins and glass cloth for 1-piece hull of sports boat.

Uses of plastics in aircraft. Includes polyester resins, e.g., for radomes, ballast tanks.

Small Navy boats molded from polyester-glass material.

Reinforced plastic boat.

Polyester-glass mat for railroad tie plate.

Fabrication procedures for plastic car body.

Ship and plane testing models from glass reinforced polyesters.

Test models of boats, airplanes, etc., from polyester-glass fiber reinforced plastics.

Droppable fuel tanks for U. S. Air Force (from polyesters).

Reinforced plastics for automobile bodies.

Polyester-glass fiber repair kits for old, wooden boats.

Taxi seat panel molded from polyester resins.

Use of sandwich construction (cellular cellulose acetate core, polyester-impregnated glass cloth skins) to save weight in aircraft construction.

Reinforced polyesters for molding of large truck trailers.

Sports car body made from glass fiber reinforced polyester laminates.

Molded reinforced polyester chassis for aircraft control panel.

Chevrolet Corvette sports car with glass fiber reinforced polyester body: description, fabrication, economics.

Transportation (Continued)

	Author	Reference
2345.	Anon.	*Modern Plastics* **31**, No. 4, 186 (1953); *Plastics World* **11**, No. 10, 5 (1953).
2346.	Anon.	*Modern Plastics* **31**, No. 6, 100 (1954).
2347.	Anon.	*Modern Plastics* **31**, No. 9, 138–9 (1954) (advertisement).
2348.	Anon.	Naugatuck Chemical Co., Naugatuck, Conn. 15-p. booklet.
2349.	Anon.	Owens-Corning Fiberglas Corp., Toledo, Ohio. 4-p. brochure.
2350.	Anon.	Palmer Scott & Co., Inc., New Bedford, Mass. 4-p. brochure.
2351.	Anon.	*Plastics* (London) **18**, 297 (1953).
2352.	Anon.	*Plastics* (London) **18**, 347 (1953).
2353.	Anon.	*Plastics* (London) **18**, 392 (1953).
2354.	Anon.	*Plastics* (London) **18**, 369 (1953).
2355.	Anon.	*Plastics* (London) **19**, 24 (1954).
2356.	Anon.	*Plastics* (London) **19**, 25 (1954).
2357.	Anon.	*Plastics* (London) **19**, 126 (1954).
2358.	Anon.	*Plastics* (London) **19**, 126 (1954).
2359.	Anon.	*Plastics* (London) **19**, 173–4 (1954).
2360.	Anon.	*Plastics* (London) **19**, 174 (1954).
2361.	Anon.	*Plastics Ind.* **10**, No. 5, 7–8, 10 (1952).
2362.	Anon.	*Plastics Ind.* **10**, No. 7, 6 (1952).
2363.	Anon.	*Plastics Ind.* **10**, No. 8, 3 (1952).
2364.	Anon.	*Plastics Ind.* **11**, No. 10, 14 (1953).
2365.	Anon.	*Plastics Ind.* **11**, No. 11, 8 (1953).
2366.	Anon.	*Plastics Ind.* **11**, No. 11, 12 (1953).
2367.	Anon.	*Plastics Ind.* **11**, No. 12, 7 (1953).
2368.	Anon.	*Plastics Ind.* **12**, No. 1, 18–23 (1954).
2369.	Anon.	*Plastics Ind.* **12**, No. 3, 4 (1954).
2370.	Anon.	*Plastics Ind.* **12**, No. 4, 12 (1954).
2371.	Anon.	*Plastics Ind.* **12**, No. 4, 27 (1954).
2372.	Anon.	*Plastics Ind.* **12**, No. 5, 4 (1954).
2373.	Anon.	*Plastics Ind.* **12**, No. 5, 12 (1954).
2374.	Anon.	*Plastics Ind.* **12**, No. 5, 26 (1954).
2375.	Anon.	*Plastics World* **10**, No. 7, 3 (1952); *Glass Ind.* **33**, No. 7, 366 (1952).
2376.	Anon.	*Plastics World* **10**, No. 8, 1 (1952).
2377.	Anon.	*Plastics World* **11**, No. 10, 1, 49 (1953).
2378.	Anon.	*Plastics World* **11**, No. 11, 35 (1954).
2379.	Anon.	*Plastics World* **12**, No. 1, 31 (1954).
2380.	Anon.	*Plastics World* **12**, No. 5, 10 (1954).
2381.	Anon.	*Plastics World* **12**, No. 8, 8 (1954).
2382.	Anon.	*Prod. Eng.* **25**, No. 2, 162–5 (1954).

Concerning

Lightweight reinforced plastic cabinets for food storage on airplanes.

Safety helmet for pilots of aircraft traveling at supersonic speeds.
Body of experimental Packard Panther Daytona made from polyester resin and glass fiber.
Story of glass fiber-polyester car body.

Applications of glass fiber materials in aircraft.

Glass fiber-reinforced plastic boat.

Bicycle with tubular frame made of glass fiber-polyester material.
Uses of reinforced plastics, i.e., glass reinforced polyesters, asbestos reinforced polyesters, in structural parts of airplanes.
Reinforced plastic sailing yacht.
Use of reinforced polyesters in sports cars and motor scooters.
Production of glass-polyester car bodies in East Germany.
Use of reinforced plastics in 45-foot motor yacht.
Manufacture by Dutch firm of plastic bodies for American cars.
Reinforced plastic fenders as replacement for damaged steel fenders.
All-plastics body for 5-ton truck; roof of polyester laminate.
Production of Corvette plastic cars.
End uses of reinforced polyesters. Discussion of sports-car body manufacture.
Custom-built sports car with one-piece glass reinforced plastic body.
Glass reinforced polyester boat for Army.
Plastic materials, including polyester laminates, in Convair liners.
Reinforced polyester food carriers for airplanes.
Truck and trailer bodies made from glass reinforced polyester.
Reinforced polyester doors for insulated trucks.
Volume production of Chevrolet Corvette automobile with one-piece reinforced polyester body.
Camping trailer made of glass fiber reinforced polyester.
Giant radomes with nylon-phenolic resin honeycomb cores and polyester-glass cloth skins.
Plastic glass laminate aircraft wings and fuselage sections.
Formation of Aircraft Division by Zenith Plastics.
Reinforced polyester fuselage structures for Navy patrol bombers.
Reinforced plastic panels for car trailers.
Glass fiber-polyester reinforced plastic body for sports car.

Reinforced plastics boat. Contains polyester resin.
Glass reinforced polyester tail for record-setting speedboat.
Reinforced plastic boat with lightweight, seamless, leakproof 1-piece hull.
Sloops, launches, and tenders made of glass fiber reinforced polyester resin.
Glass fiber-polyester yacht tender.
Glass turbine test car with reinforced polyester body.
Picture description of Chevrolet Corvette sports car with glass fiber reinforced polyester body.

Transportation (Continued)

	Author	Reference
2383.	Anon.	*Rohm & Haas Reporter* **11**, 6 (Sept.–Oct. 1953).
2384.	Anon.	Wilking Co., Pasadena, Calif. 28-p. manual.
2385.	Alfers, J. B.	*Reinforced Plastics Div., Soc. Plastics Ind. Confer., 6th Annual,* 1951, Sect. 9.
2386.	Braham, W. E.	*Reinforced Plastics Div., Soc. Plastics Ind. Confer., 8th Annual,* 1953, Sect. 27G; *Plastics* (London) **18**, 350–2 (1953).
2387.	Braham, W. E.	*Plastics* (London) **19**, 83 (1954).
2388.	Bushey, A. C., *et al.*	*Trans. Soc. Naval Architect. Marine Engrs.* **60**, 595–637, discussion, 638–44 (1952).
2389.	Campbell, D., *et al.*	*Fiber Glass Reinforced Plastics in the Polyester Laminating Field.* Fiber Glass Reinforced Plastics Associates, Boston, 1953.
2390.	Corelli, R. M.	*Aerotecnica* **32**, 8–19 (1952).
2391.	Costanza, L. J.	*Modern Plastics* **31**, No. 1, 93–5, 180 (1953).
2392.	De Bell, G. W.	*J. Aeronaut. Sci.* **9**, 341–9 (1942).
2393.	Graner, W. R.	*Reinforced Plastics Div., Soc. Plastics Ind. Confer., 8th Annual,* 1953, Sect. 16.
2394.	Graner, W. R., and Alfers, J. B.	*Reinforced Plastics Div., Soc. Plastics Ind. Confer., 9th Annual,* 1954, Sect. 1G.
2395.	Harris, M., and Krasny, J.	*Chem. Eng. News* **32**, 38–40 (1954).
2396.	Haut, H. N.	*India-Rubber J.* **101**, 147–8, 152, 158 (1941).
2397.	Holmes, C. E.	*Modern Plastics* **29**, No. 8, 115–8 (1952).
2398.	Hughes, G. E.	*SAE J.* **61**, No. 1, 38 (1953).
2399.	Jones, J. A., and Niswander, R. V.	*Aircraft Eng.* **22**, No. 254, 109–12 (1950).
2400.	Kemmer, P. H.	*Modern Plastics* **21**, No. 9, 89–93 (1944).
2401.	Marshall, K. T.	*Reinforced Plastics Div., Soc. Plastics Ind. Confer., 8th Annual,* 1953, Sect. 10.
2402.	Marshall, K. T.	*Reinforced Plastics Div., Soc. Plastics Ind. Confer., 9th Annual,* 1954, Sect. 1I.
2403.	McCann, H., editor.	*Modern Plastics Encyclopedia 1952.* Plastics Catalogue Corp., New York, 465.
2404.	O'Keefe, P.	*Materials & Methods* **37**, No. 2, 119–34 (1953).
2405.	Ramke, W. G.	*Reinforced Plastics Div., Soc. Plastics Ind. Confer., 8th Annual,* 1953, Sect. 11.
2406.	Rheinfrank, G. B., Jr., and Norman, W. A.	*Modern Plastics* **21**, No. 9, 94–9 (1944).

Concerning

Reinforced polyester radomes.

Polyester-glass fiber reinforced plastics for automobile bodies.

Low-pressure reinforced plastics. Uses and properties from Navy standpoint.

Reinforced plastics in aircraft and guided missiles. Table compares properties of plastics (including glass reinforced polyester) and metals at room and elevated temperatures.

Reinforced polyester fuselages for aircraft.
Discussion of chemistry of polyester resins and methods of laminated glass-plastic construction, with special reference to boats.
Raw materials, molding methods and machining characteristics, engineering properties, and applications of glass fiber reinforced plastics.

Synthetic resin glues. Properties and uses in aircraft fabrication.
Plastic armor for aircraft. Polyester-glass tested with good results.

Review of use of plastics in aircraft. Properties required by an "airplane plastic."
Uses and testing of reinforced plastics (Navy Bureau of Ships).

Naval applications of reinforced plastics, e.g., boats, tanks, pipes, minesweeper floats.
Review on progress in textiles in 1953, e.g., mentions polyester fiber production, use of glass fibers in car bodies.
Synthetic resins in airplane construction.

Army sleds for Arctic use, molded from reinforced plastics.
Transparent plastics, e.g., polyesters, for aircraft enclosures.
Fire-resistant finishes for aircraft.

Review on development of glass reinforced low-pressure plastics for aircraft.
Use of reinforced plastics in transportation equipment, e.g., boats.

Use of sandwich construction with reinforced polyester facings for a self-propelled barge.
Cast polyester sheets for windows in civilian airplanes.

Properties, fabrication, and uses of glass-reinforced polyesters.

Air Force use of reinforced plastics in aircraft. Properties required.

Application of glass laminates to aircraft.

Transportation (Continued)

Author	Reference
2407. Reiley, C. R.	*Modern Plastics* **30**, No. 11, 71 (1953).
2408. Rosenbaum, H. H.	*Modern Plastics* **30**, No. 11, 71 (1953).
2409. Schwartz, R. T.	*Reinforced Plastics Div., Soc. Plastics Ind. Confer., 6th Annual*, 1951, Sect. 11.
2410. Stanley, F. B.	*Modern Plastics* **23**, No. 1, 132A–132H (1945).
2411. Stevens, J. M.	*Reinforced Plastics Div., Soc. Plastics Ind. Confer., 8th Annual*, 1953, Sect. 15.
2412. Swallow, J. C.	*J. Sci. Instruments* **23**, 44–8 (1946).
2413. Temple, R.	*Reinforced Plastics Div., Soc. Plastics Ind. Confer., 6th Annual*, 1951, Sect. 8.
2414. Temple, R.	*Reinforced Plastics Div., Soc. Plastics Ind. Confer., 7th Annual*, 1952, Sect. 8.
2415. Van Boskirk, R. L.	*Modern Plastics* **29**, No. 9, 212 (1952) ("The Plastiscope").
2416. Wood, W. C.	*Technol. Review* No. 6 (1951).

Electrical Applications

Author	Reference
2417. Anon.	*Brit. Plastics* **26**, 362 (1953).
2418. Anon.	*Brit. Plastics* **27**, 65 (1954).
2419. Anon.	*Brit. Plastics* **27**, 148 (1954); *Plastics World* **12**, No. 5, 13 (1954).
2420. Anon.	*Can. Plastics* Mar.–April 1954, 66.
2421. Anon.	Celanese Corp. of America, Marco Products Dept., Newark, N. J. Customer Service Bull.
2422. Anon.	*Elect. Manuf.* **51**, No. 2, 150 (1953).
2423. Anon.	*Elect. Manuf.* **53**, No. 5, 9 (1954) (advertisement).
2424. Anon.	*Elect. Manuf.* **53**, No. 5, 95 (1954).
2425. Anon.	Glastic Corp., Cleveland, Ohio. 8-p. booklet.
2426. Anon.	*Materials & Methods* **39**, No. 4, 3 (1954).
2427. Anon.	Mitchell-Rand Insulation Co., Inc., New York, N. Y.
2428. Anon.	*Modern Plastics* **24**, No. 10, 200–1 (1947).
2429. Anon.	*Modern Plastics* **26**, No. 6, 138 (1949).
2430. Anon.	*Modern Plastics* **28**, No. 4, 59–63 (1950).
2431. Anon.	*Modern Plastics* **28**, No. 5, 78–9 (1951).
2432. Anon.	*Modern Plastics* **28**, No. 8, 213 (1953) (advertisement).
2433. Anon.	*Modern Plastics* **29**, No. 2, 196 (1951).

Concerning

Forming of polyester canopies for aircraft.
Polyester parts for commercial aircraft.
Use of reinforced plastics in aircraft.

Radio detection and ranging. Mentions styrene alkyd composition plus glass cloth for radomes.
Application of reinforced plastics in naval aircraft.

Applications of plastics in scientific instruments, e.g., glass reinforced plastic for radomes.
Reinforced plastics in naval aircraft.

Reinforced plastics in naval aircraft.

Cast polyester sheet for airplane windows, etc.

Sailing at M. I. T. Mentions glass fiber boats.

Embedding of transformer in polyester resin.
Glass fiber-polyester electric heating apparatus, e.g., for drying shoes; heating aquariums and seed boxes.
Copper-glass-polyester laminate for electrical use.

Electrostatic shield of woven copper and cotton bound in polyester resin.
Applications of polyester resins in electrical field.

Glass-reinforced polyester for switch gear parts.
Polyester glass rods for structural parts, shafts for electronic components, color for decoration, identification, or coding.
Chart showing safe operating temperatures for insulating materials, including glass-alkyd.
Properties and uses of glass fiber reinforced laminate for electrical insulation.

New family of reinforced plastics for electrical applications: diallyl phthalate polyester resins reinforced with cotton, glass, nylon, or Orlon.
Polyester-glass mat laminate especially designed for transformer sticks.

Cast polyester dielectric plate for determining x-ray intensity.
Polyester-glass fiber laminate for electrical uses, e.g., insulating panel stock, electric motor armature end laminations and slot sticks, switch washers, etc.
Uses for polyester casting resins, e.g., "potting" electrical circuits.
Polyester resin for potting of amplifier in hearing aid.
Polyester as insulator in television aerial.

Use of polyester resins in impregnating armatures of electric motors.

Electrical Applications (Continued)

	Author	Reference
2434.	Anon.	*Modern Plastics* **30**, No. 8, 183 (1953).
2435.	Anon.	Owens-Corning Fiberglas Corp., Textile Products Div., New York, N. Y. 34-p. catalog.
2436.	Anon.	*Plastics Ind.* **12**, No. 1, 12 (1954).
2437.	Anon.	*Plastics News Letter* **13**, No. 46, 4 (1953).
2438.	Anon.	*Plastics News Letter* **14**, No. 18, 3 (1954).
2439.	Anon.	*Plastics World* **12**, No. 6, 49 (1954).
2440.	Anon.	*Prod. Eng.* **24**, No. 12, 22–3 (1953) (advertisement).
2441.	Anon.	Russel Reinforced Plastics Corp., Lindenhurst, N. Y. Data Sheet.
2442.	Astin, A. V., *et al.*	*Elect. Eng.* **60**, 22–6 (1941).
2443.	Custis, R. L.	*Materials & Methods* **33**, No. 3, 74–5 (1951).
2444.	Delmonte, J.	*Modern Plastics* **28**, No. 7, 64–7, 159 (1951).
2445.	DeVore, H. W., and Murray, H. C.	*Modern Plastics* **28**, No. 8, 88–90 (1951).
2446.	Foster, N. C.	*Trans. Electrochem. Soc.* **90**, Preprint 24, 307–14 (1946).
2447.	Heitest, D. H., and Nieman, H. W.	*Elect. Manuf.* **49**, No. 5, 113–7 (1952).
2448.	Hill, C. F., and Foster, N. F.	*Elect. Manuf.* **42**, No. 6, 83–5, 164 (1948).
2449.	Hyde, K.	*Glass Fibre Reinforced Plastics Conv.* (England) 1952, *Proc.* 93–102.
2450.	Martin, T. J., and Hauter, R. L.	*Elect. Manuf.* **53**, No. 4, 102–7 (1954); *SPE J.* **10**, No. 2, 13–5, 39, 42 (1954).
2451.	McCann, H., editor.	*Modern Plastics Encyclopedia 1952.* Plastics Catalogue Corp., New York, 465.
2452.	McIntosh, R. O.	*Elect Manuf.* **49**, No. 4, 120–3 (1952).
2453.	Parkyn, B.	*Brit. Plastics* **24**, 47–9 (1951).
2454.	Schreiner, S. A., Jr.	*Parade Mag.*, May 24, 1953, 8–9 (Sunday Washington Post and other newspapers).
2455.	Shaw, E. N., *et al.*	*Plastics* (London) **16**, 336–7 (1951).
2456.	Van Boskirk, R. L.	*Modern Plastics* **31**, No. 9, 216 (1954).
2457.	White, R. B.	*Elect. Manuf.* **47**, No. 1, 84–7 (1951).
2458.	White, R. B.	*Reinforced Plastics Div., Soc. Plastics Ind. Confer., 5th Annual,* 1950, Sect. 11.
2458a.	Anon.	*Brit. Plastics* **24**, 302–7 (1951).

Concerning

Use of molded alkyd insulation in electrical plugs and receptacles.

Glass fiber base electrical insulating materials, including laminates and plastics parts.

Mineral-filled alkyd for heavy-duty electrical jobs in automotive field.

High-strength electrical tape with polyester film backing.

Flexible, loop-type cable clamps made of glass cloth-polyester laminate.

Small electrical connectors made from alkyd molding compound.

Replacement of complex parts assemblies, with 1-piece molded parts of glass reinforced alkyd, e.g., circuit breaker, commutator, electrode holder with threaded section, centralized electrical control panel.

Properties of electrical insulation sheet made from glass fiber laminate impregnated with special polyester for superior electrical properties and self-extinguishing features.

Review of electrical insulation research, including dielectric constants of polyesters.

New insulating materials (glass fiber-polyester laminate) and coatings for extending electric motor life.

Potting with plastics (encasing electrical and mechanical instruments in solid mass of plastic).

Case histories of successful use of polyester molding compound in electrical field, e.g., motor parts, television tuners, light switches, watt-hour meters, etc.

Varnishes for electrical windings containing copolymers of styrene with maleic anhydride-castor oil half-esters.

Selecting an embedment system for electronic components.

Solvent-reacted polyester resin approaching ideal requirements for an insulating varnish.

Electrical properties of various types of glass fiber laminates.

Arcing performance of plastic insulation, including mineral and glass filled alkyd resins.

Polyester encasing for germanium junction transistor.

Resins for potting.

Uses of polyester resins in the electrical industry.

Use of plastics and germanium for transistors.

Potted electronic circuit.

Laminate of copper-to-polyester-glass-mat sheet; low power factor makes it valuable as base for etched circuits in television and radio applications.

Polyester-glass laminates for motor parts.

Applications for glass fibers and polyesters in electrical field.

Use of polyester resins for embedding electrical equipment.

Electrical Applications (Continued)

	Author	Reference
2458b.	Dummer, G. W. A.	*Elect. Manuf.* **51**, No. 5, 84 (1953).
2458c.	Poirot, R.	*Elect. Manuf.* **50**, No. 3, 280 (1952).
2458d.	Wulfert, O.	*Elect. Manuf.* **51**, No. 6, 107 (1953).

Industrial Uses

2459.	Anon.	*Brit. Plastics* **24**, 206–9 (1951).
2460.	Anon.	*Brit. Plastics* **26**, 14–8 (1953).
2461.	Anon.	*Brit. Plastics* **26**, 51–5 (1953).
2462.	Anon.	*Brit. Plastics* **26**, 366 (1953).
2463.	Anon.	*Brit. Plastics* **27**, 13 (1954).
2464.	Anon.	*Can. Plastics* Mar.–April. 1954, 63.
2465.	Anon.	*Chem. Eng.* **59**, No. 12, 218 (1952).
2466.	Anon.	*Chem. Eng. News* **31**, 1883 (1953).
2467.	Anon.	*Chem. Eng. News* **32**, 181 (1954).
2468.	Anon.	*Chem. Eng. News* **32**, 578 (1954).
2469.	Anon.	*Chem. Eng. News* **32**, 671 (1954).
2470.	Anon.	*Chem. Eng. News* **32**, 2002–3 (1954); *Plastics World* **12**, No. 1, 27 (1954).
2471.	Anon.	*Chem. Week* **74**, No. 14, 52–4 (1954).
2472.	Anon.	*Chem. Week* **74**, No. 20, 62 (1954) (advertisement).
2473.	Anon.	*Chem. Week* **74**, No. 20, 63 (1954) (advertisement).
2474.	Anon.	Hooker Electrochemical Co., Niagara Falls, N. Y. Diagram and descriptive page.
2475.	Anon.	*Ind. Bull. of Arthur D. Little* No. 293 (1952).
2476.	Anon.	*Ind. des plastiques modernes* **6**, No. 1, 13 (1954).
2477.	Anon.	Laminex Corp., Fall River, Mass. Information Sheets.
2478.	Anon.	Machlett & Son, New York, N. Y. Leaflet.
2479.	Anon.	*Materials & Methods* **38**, No. 5, 92–5 (1953).
2480.	Anon.	*Modern Plastics* **23**, No. 11, 142–5 (1946).
2481.	Anon.	*Modern Plastics* **25**, No. 5, 137–46 (1948).
2482.	Anon.	*Modern Plastics* **27**, No. 5, 118–9 (1950).
2483.	Anon.	*Modern Plastics* **27**, No. 7, 74–5 (1950).
2484.	Anon.	*Modern Plastics* **29**, No. 1, 87–91 (1951).
2485.	Anon.	*Modern Plastics* **29**, No. 4, 108–9 (1951).
2486.	Anon.	*Modern Plastics* **29**, No. 10, 76–8 (1952).
2487.	Anon.	*Modern Plastics* **30**, No. 6, 100–3 (1953).

Concerning

Review on resin-embedded and printed electrical circuits.
Case histories of use of polyester-epoxy compound for potting applications in coal mining equipment and precision instruments.
Uses of plastics in electric motors.

Manufacture of various types of gears from plastic laminates.
"Shell" molding process for making molds from sand-resin mixtures.
Polyester pipe for liquid handling.
Applications of plastics, e.g., reinforced polyester trays, tanks, insulation.
Acid-pouring funnels made of reinforced polyester.
Self-stacking tote box in glass reinforced polyester.
Storage tank for crude oil made from glass fiber and polyester resin.
Process for impregnating porous sintered metal parts with polyester resin.
Chemical-resistant crocks from glass fiber reinforced polyester laminate.
High-strength, corrosion-resistant plastic pipe for petroleum industry; made from polyester resins and glass fiber mat.
Molded trays from polyester resins for use in chemical, pharmaceutical, and food-handling industries.
Threaded plastic pipe fittings molded from glass reinforced polyester resin.

Future for plastic pipe.
Polyester glass laminated plant equipment: cooling towers, fume ducts, tanks, covers, linings, pipe.
Use of polyester glass fiber laminates for water cooling towers, chemical storage tanks, sports car bodies, building panels, air conditioning towers, etc.
Use of glass reinforced polyester pipe in brine wells at levels where steel would corrode faster and where plastic pipe is easier to withdraw and repair.
Plastic pipe and plastic-coated pipe.

Reinforced polyester molds for cold stainless steel sheet stamping.

Molded glass fiber tanks, trucks, containers. Chemical resistance table.

Electrothermal heating tape from glass fibers.
Die materials for limited production runs. Polyester laminates suitable as blanking and forming dies, short- or moderate-run dies, and for patching cast phenolic dies.
Glass fiber reinforced plastic molds for electronic vulcanizing of rubber products.
Review on plastics engineering. Mentions use of glass fibers-polyester combinations, e.g., honeycomb cores, molds for rubber vulcanization.
Polyester-glass fiber housing for power scythe.
Plastic pipes from polyester resins and glass cloth.
Industrial applications of plastic laminates.
Polyester-glass fiber driers and boxes for foundry cores.
Reinforced plastic tanks for transporting oil across desert.
Tanks for various uses from reinforced plastics.

Industrial Uses (Continued)

	Author	Reference
2488.	Anon.	*Modern Plastics* **30**, No. 7, 156 (1953).
2489.	Anon.	*Modern Plastics* **31**, No. 2, 185 (1953).
2490.	Anon.	*Modern Plastics* **31**, No. 2, 198 (1953).
2491.	Anon.	*Modern Plastics* **31**, No. 4, 110 (1953).
2492.	Anon.	*Modern Plastics* **31**, No. 5, 91 (1954).
2493.	Anon.	*Modern Plastics* **31**, No. 6, 87, 190 (1954); *Plastics World* **11**, No. 11, 6 (1953).
2494.	Anon.	*Modern Plastics* **31**, No. 6, 96–7 (1954).
2495.	Anon.	*Modern Plastics* **31**, No. 6, 98–9, 192 (1954).
2496.	Anon.	*Modern Plastics* **31**, No. 7, 73–81, 181–7 (1954).
2497.	Anon.	*Modern Plastics* **31**, No. 7, 87 (1954).
2498.	Anon.	*Modern Plastics* **31**, No. 9, 9 (1954) (advertisement).
2499.	Anon.	*Paper Ind.* Nov. 1952, 1022.
2500.	Anon.	*Plastics* (London) **19**, 25 (1954).
2501.	Anon.	*Plastics* (London) **19**, 42 (1954).
2502.	Anon.	*Plastics* (London) **19**, 46 (1954).
2503.	Anon.	*Plastics* (London) **19**, 118 (1954).
2504.	Anon.	*Plastics Ind.* **11**, No. 2, 7 (1953).
2505.	Anon.	*Plastics Ind.* **11**, No. 10, 25 (1953).
2506.	Anon.	*Plastics Ind.* **11**, No. 11, 4 (1953).
2507.	Anon.	*Plastics Ind.* **11**, No. 12, 4 (1953).
2508.	Anon.	*Plastics Ind.* **11**, No. 12, 23 (1953).
2509.	Anon.	*Plastics Ind.* **12**, No. 1, 6 (1954).
2510.	Anon.	*Plastics Ind.* **12**, No. 3, 6 (1954).
2511.	Anon.	*Plastics Ind.* **12**, No. 4, 18 (1954).
2512.	Anon.	*Plastics News Letter* **13**, No. 41, 3 (1953).
2513.	Anon.	*Plastics News Letter* **13**, No. 52, 1 (1953); **14**, No. 4, 3 (1954).
2514.	Anon.	*Plastics News Letter* **14**, No. 1, 4 (1954).
2515.	Anon.	*Plastics News Letter* **14**, No. 4, 2 (1954).
2516.	Anon.	*Plastics News Letter* **14**, No. 21, 3 (1954).
2517.	Anon.	*Plastics World* **10**, No. 7, 5 (1952).
2518.	Anon.	*Plastics World* **10**, No. 9, 8 (1952).
2519.	Anon.	*Plastics World* **10**, No. 11, 22 (1952).
2520.	Anon.	*Plastics World* **11**, No. 11, 15 (1954).
2521.	Anon.	*Plastics World* **12**, No. 1, 4 (1954).
2522.	Anon.	*Plastics World* **12**, No. 1, 16 (1954).
2523.	Anon.	*Plastics World* **12**, No. 1, 35; No. 2, 14 (1954).

Concerning

Observation window for mechanical equipment made from an allyl diglycol carbonate resin.

One-piece molded polyester-glass reinforced tank for truck transportation of chemicals.

Reinforced polyester core driers for foundry use.

Lightweight, chemical-resistant crocks from glass fibers and polyester resins.

Engineering progress in 1953. Mentions increase in use of reinforced polyesters, e.g., for tanks, structural purposes, dies.

One-piece molded milk tank with sandwich walls, i.e., reinforced polyester skins and balsa wood core.

Protective hoods for turbine pump motors; made from glass reinforced polyesters.

Polyester-glass laminate tray used for drying gelatin capsules.

Future for plastic pipe; includes brief mention of reinforced polyester pipe.

Glass cloth-polyester laminate as drafting medium for industrial full-scale drawings.

Reinforced polyester tank trailer for liquid transportation; permits increased loads.

Glass fiber reinforced plastic as chemical "porcelain."

Glass reinforced plastic tank for truck trailers.

Glass fiber-polyester cast tools for beating of metal parts.

One-piece tank molded from glass fiber-polyester.

Reinforced plastics rollers for mine conveyors.

Glass fiber-polyester tanks as replacement for lead- and brick-lined tanks in alum manufacture.

Reinforced polyester tank for transporting chemicals.

One-piece reinforced polyester milk tank truck.

Reinforced polyester valves of plug gate type.

Reinforced polyester pipe as replacement for steel pipe in corrosion service.

Concentrator stack for corrosive fumes made from glass reinforced polyester.

Polyester-glass fiber phototemplate for drafting and reproduction work.

Polyester-glass fiber corrosion-resistant pipe for oil industry.

Rigid reinforced polyester pipe.

Centrifugal cast reinforced polyester pipe and tubing.

Glass fiber-polyester concentrator stack for chemical plant.

Glass fiber-polyester template for drafting and reproduction operations.

Vent pipes, ducts, and fittings made of glass fiber-polyester.

Glass fiber-polyester tanks for transporting oil across desert.

Reinforced polyester for molded welder's helmet.

Glass fiber-reinforced plastic pipe.

Use of reinforced polyester pipe in City of Los Angeles steam-generating plant.

Large tanks for industrial plating made from reinforced polyester.

Polyester welding lens with long use life.

Glass fiber reinforced polyester tote tray for handling food, confections, pharmaceutical chemicals, and small parts.

Industrial Uses (Continued)

Author	Reference
2524. Anon.	*Plastics World* **12**, No. 2, 10 (1954).
2525. Anon.	*Plastics World* **12**, No. 4, 14 (1954).
2526. Anon.	*Prod. Eng.* **24**, No. 10, 203 (1953); *SPE J.* **9**, No. 9, cover picture (1953).
2527. Anon.	U. S. Safety Service, Kansas City, Mo. 2-p. advertisement.
2528. Barnet, F. R., and Atkinson, H. B., Jr.	*Reinforced Plastics Div., Soc. Plastics Ind. Confer., 7th Annual,* 1952, Sect. 12.
2529. Barnet, F. R., and Atkinson, H. B., Jr.	*SPE J.* **9**, No. 8, 22–4, 32 (1953).
2530. Bruner, W. M., and Wayne, P. J.	*Chem. Eng.* **60**, No. 7, 193–204 (1953).
2531. Buttrey, D. N.	*Brit. Plastics* **25**, 410 (1952).
2532. Déribérél, M.	*Mecanique* **25**, 41–2 (1941); *Chimie & Industrie* **47**, 95 (1942).
2533. Dick, G. M.	Canadian Ingersoll-Rand Co., Ltd., Montreal, Que., Canada (1952).
2534. Elliot, E. M.	*J. Inst. Production Engrs.* **24**, 163–79 (1945).
2535. Evans, V.	*Ind. Finishing* (London) **5**, 176, 178–80, 182–4, 276, 278, 280, 282 (1952).
2536. Fagan, C. P.	*Plastics* (London) **18**, 323 (1953).
2537. Foulks, D. G.	*Proc. Am. Electroplaters' Soc.* **39**, 127–40 (1952).
2538. Gallay, W.	*Eng. J.* (Canada) **27**, 72–7, 103 (1944).
2539. Hausen, J., and Söhngen, R.	*Chem.-Ing.-Tech.* **24**, 654–6 (1952).
2540. Huscher, J. L.	*Chem. Eng. News,* **31**, 860–3 (1953).
2541. Ing, C. V.	*Water Works and Sewage* **100**, No. 1, 40–1 (1953).
2542. Kline, G. M.	*Plastics & Resins* **4**, No. 9, 11–3, 27–34, (1945); *Chem. Eng. News* **23**, 1615 (1945).
2543. Kline, G. M., and Seymour, R. B.	*Ind. Eng. Chem.* **44**, 2339–43 (1952).
2544. Martin, F. A.	*SPE J.* **9**, No. 5, 36 (1953).
2545. McKenzie, A. M., and Stark, H. J.	*J. Am. Soc. Naval Eng.* **65**, No. 2, 57–70 (1953).
2546. Muskat, I. E.	*SPE J.* **10**, No. 4, 28–9, 44–6 (1954).
2547. Muller, A.	*Kunststoffe* **43**, No. 10 (1953).
2548. Repsher, L.	*Reinforced Plastics Div., Soc. Plastics Ind. Confer., 9th Annual,* 1954, Sect. 30.
2549. Seymour, R. B.	*Ind. Eng. Chem.* **45**, 2237–41 (1953).
2550. Seymour, R. B.	*Modern Plastics* **27**, No. 12, 91–2, 94, 96, 98, 148, 150 (1950).
2551. Seymour, R. B., and Steiner, R. H.	*Chem. Eng. Progress* **48**, No. 8, 430 (1952).

Concerning

Use of glass fiber reinforced polyester in molding large carrying trays for bread.
Heat-resistant glass fiber-polyester laminate for chemical applications.
Glass fiber-polyester tank for liquid hauling.

Safety helmet made of glass reinforced polyesters.

Reinforced plastics tubing for naval ordnance: uses, testing, fabrication.

Review on methods of producing and testing of reinforced tubing.

Review on use of plastics in industry. Includes polyester-glass fiber laminates
  and polyethylene terephthalate.
Polyester-glass fiber driers and boxes for foundry cores.
Applications of plastics as substitutes for metals.

Reinforced plastic housing for a portable air compressor.

Review on plastics in engineering.

Application of plastics, e.g., glass fibers impregnated with synthetic resins,
  polyurethanes, etc., in industrial fabrication, linings, and castings.
Manufacture of magnetic tapes; includes polyester resins as bases.
Plastics as plating-room engineering materials, e.g., glass fiber-polyester tank
  linings and ductwork.
Plastics in engineering, including laminated resins.
Synthetics in chemical equipment.

Applications and limitations of plastics in chemical and allied industries.
Glass fiber-polyester orifice plates for rotary filter distributors in sewage plants.

Review of plastics manufacture and application in Germany. Mentions polyesters
  of adipic acid and glycols for gasoline tank linings.
Review on use of plastics in chemical engineering field, e.g., glass fiber-poly-
  ester resin material for tanks, pipe.
Report on speeches on plastic pipe, alkyd isocyanate resins for radomes, poly-
  ester rubber.
Summary of Naval development and use of reinforced polyester pipe up to April
  1952.
Review on polyester resins and their industrial applications.
Potting of metal parts in unsaturated polyesters.
Outlook for reinforced polyester pipe.

Review on plastics as materials of construction; includes polyesters.
Review on use of plastics as protective coatings, linings, and cements in chemical construction.
Properties of chemical engineering equipment of polyester-glass laminated
  plastics. Corrosion resistance data.

Industrial Uses (Continued)

Author	Reference
2552. Shepard, S. W.	*Reinforced Plastics Div., Soc. Plastics Ind. Confer.*, *9th Annual*, 1954, Sect. 19.
2553. Stanley, F. B.	*Modern Plastics* **30**, No. 5, 87–108, 186 (1953).
2554. Stein, G. A.	*Reinforced Plastics Div., Soc. Plastics Ind. Confer.*, *9th Annual*, 1954, Sect. 2H.
2555. Wittman, L.	*Modern Plastics* **24**, No. 10, 132–7 (1947).

Coatings, Adhesives, Plasticizers, Lubricants

Author	Reference
2556. Anon.	*Brit. Plastics* **26**, 17 (1953) (advertisement).
2557. Anon.	*Brit. Plastics* **27**, 76 (1954).
2558. Anon.	Carboline Co., St. Louis, Mo. (letter communication).
2559. Anon.	Celanese Corp. of America, Marco Products Dept., Newark, N. J. Customer Service Bull. No. M3.
2560. Anon.	Celanese Corp. of America, Marco Products Dept., Newark, N. J. Customer Service Bull. No. M12 (1053).
2561. Anon.	*Chem. Eng. News* **31**, 3730–5 (1953).
2562. Anon.	*Chem. Eng. News* **32**, 2228 (1954).
2563. Anon.	E. F. Drew & Co., Inc., New York, N. Y. 4-p. brochure.
2564. Anon.	Interchemical Corp., Finishes Div., Cincinnati, Ohio. 10-p. manual.
2565. Anon.	*Ind. des plastique modernes* **5**, No. 9, 15–20 (1953).
2566. Anon.	*Plastics Ind.* **12**, No. 2, 22 (1954).
2567. Anon.	*Plastics Ind.* **12**, No. 5, 11 (1954); *Can. Plastics* Jan.–Feb. 1954, 108.
2568. Beavers, E. M.	*Ind. Eng. Chem.* **41**, 738–40 (1949).
2569. Clermont, J.	*Chem.-Ztg.* **66**, 537–41 (1942); *Chem. Zentr.* 1943, II, 957.
2570. Eickner, H. W., Olson, W. Z., and Blomquist, R. F.	*Natl. Advisory Comm. Aeronaut. Tech. Note* No. 2717, 26 pp. (1952).
2571. Fischer, W. V.	*Finish.* **9**, No. 7, 29–32, 64–6 (1952).
2572. Fligor, K. K., and Sumner, J. K.	*Ind. Eng. Chem.* **37**, 504–8 (1945).
2573. Holm, V. C. F.	*J. Research Natl. Bur. Standards* **37**, 177–82 (1946).
2574. Hönel, H.	*Farbe u. Lack* **59**, 174–80 (1953).
2575. Koroly, J. E., and Beavers, E. M.	*Ind. Eng. Chem.* **45**, 1060–3 (1953).
2576. Lynn, J. E., and Nyquist, A. S.	*Textile Chemicals and Auxiliaries.* Reinhold, New York, 1952, 362–82.
2577. Micksch, K.	*Nitrocellulose* **14**, 45–7 (1943).

Concerning

Limitations of plastic materials used in the chemical industry.

Review of engineering progress in plastics in 1952. Mentions polyester pipe.

Report of Standards Committee. Important properties for reinforced pipe.

Better tools from molded laminates.

Polyester plasticizers for polyvinyl chloride.
Triethylene glycol dicaprylate as plasticizer.
Concrete floor coating and paint based on polyester resins.

Spray coating with polyester resins.

Impregnation and coating with polyester resins.

Condensation of 9 papers from symposium on fire-retardant paints.
Polyester cement for laying-up corrosion-resistant masonry.
Properties and applications of polyester plasticizer for polyvinyl chloride type
    compositions.
Impregnating metal and other porous materials with polyester resins.

Classification of adhesive tapes, including polyester-base tapes.

Use of polyesters as plasticizers for polyvinyl chloride plastics.
Production of plasticizers by Reichold Chemicals.

Applications for alkyds and polyesters, e.g., in coating field and as plasticizers.
Synthetic resins, e.g., maleic-alkyd types, as metal lacquer raw materials.

Effect of temperatures from -70° to 600°F. on strength of adhesive-bonded
    specimens of aluminum alloy and cotton and glass fabric-plastic laminates.
    Polyester resins one of 14 types of adhesives tested.
Finishes containing polyesters and other resins.
Sebacic acid polyester as plasticizer in polyvinyl chloride, synthetic rubber,
    etc.
Resinous sealing agents for porous metal casting. Styrene-polyester resin ef-
    fective for limited service.
Coating resins made from polyesters and resols (alkyl phenol-formaldehyde) or
    dimethylol-urea.
Polyester plasticizers.

Review on synthetic resins in the textile industry.

Review on cements and sizes of synthetic resins.

Coatings, Adhesives, Plasticizers, Lubricants (Continued)

Author	Reference
2578. Mori, S.	*Plastics Kogyo (Plastics Ind.)* (Osaka) **9**, No. 1, 11–4 (1940).
2579. Perry, H. A., Jr.	*Prod. Eng.* **24**, 288 (1953).
2580. Perry, H. A., Jr., and Mathews, H. E., Jr.	*Reinforced Plastics Div., Soc. Plastics Ind. Confer., 8th Annual*, 1953, Sect. 13.
2581. Schwarz, E. W. K., and Bennett, J. A.	*Textile Chemicals and Auxiliaries.* Reinhold, New York, 1952, 143–59.
2582. Thinius, K.	*Farbe u. Lack* **54**, 227–31, 275–7, 302–6 (1948).
2583. Trimborn, W.	*Chem.-Ing.-Tech.* **24**, 564–71 (1952).
2584. Walker, F. T., and Mackay, T.	*J. Oil & Colour Chemists' Assoc.* **34**, 311–36 (1951).
2585. Walker, F. T., and Mackay, T.	*J. Oil & Colour Chemists' Assoc.* **35**, 218–26 (1952).
2586. Walter	*Farbe u. Lack* 1940, 198.

Building Industry

Author	Reference
2587. Anon.	*Aminco Laboratory News*, March 1952, 7. American Instrument Co., Inc., Silver Spring, Md.
2588. Anon.	*Austral. Plastics* **8**, No. 89 (1952).
2589. Anon.	Cast Optics Corp., Riverside, Conn. 12-p. booklet.
2590. Anon.	*Chem. Eng. News* **32**, No. 22, 2192 (1954).
2591. Anon.	*Chem. Week* **74**, No. 12, 78 (1954).
2592. Anon.	Chemold Co., Santa Monica, Calif.
2593. Anon.	Homalite Corp., Wilmington, Del. 10-p. booklet.
2594. Anon.	*Ind. Eng. Chem.* **46**, No. 1, 39A, 41A (1954).
2595. Anon.	*Modern Plastics* **25**, No. 1, 5 (1947).
2596. Anon.	*Modern Plastics* **25**, No. 11, 92 (1948).
2597. Anon.	*Modern Plastics* **26**, No. 9, 128 (1949).
2598. Anon.	*Modern Plastics* **27**, No. 1, 82–3 (1949).
2599. Anon.	*Modern Plastics* **27**, No. 1, 88–91, 156, 159–60 (1949).
2600. Anon.	*Modern Plastics* **28**, No. 2, 77 (1950).
2601. Anon.	*Modern Plastics* **28**, No. 8, 87 (1951).
2602. Anon.	*Modern Plastics* **28**, No. 9, 67 (1951).
2603. Anon.	*Modern Plastics* **28**, No. 12, 81–3 (1951).
2604. Anon.	*Modern Plastics* **29**, No. 10, 174 (1952).
2605. Anon.	*Modern Plastics* **29**, No. 11, 80–1 (1952).
2606. Anon.	*Modern Plastics* **30**, No. 4, 162 (1952).

Concerning

Maleic acid resins, e.g., from maleic acid and glycerol. Suitable for paint.

Adhesives for reinforced plastics.
Adhesives for reinforced plastics.

Review on coated fabrics.

Review of linear polycondensation products, e.g., polyesters, their preparation, and coating applications.
Synthetic lacquer resins: preparation, properties, and applications. Includes polyaddition resins and polymerizates.
Polyester binder as substitute for linoleum binder made from linseed oil; disadvantage is susceptibility to attack by mild alkalies.
Use of polyesters as linoleum binders. Improvement of product by cross-linked polymers.
Mixed polymers of vinyl chloride, e.g., with methyl maleate, as lacquer ingredients.

Concrete wall panel with center layer of glass fibers.

Plastics as a structural material.
Properties and uses of optically clear rigid plastic (allyl-based) sheets.

Reinforced polyester sheet for building: 2 layers of reinforced resin become workable for construction through "expander" (dowel-like piece) in center.
Curved-surface skylights and windows made of glass reinforced polyester.
Glass fiber reinforced polyester building panels: properties and uses.
Properties and uses of transparent plastic sheets.

Largest volume application of polyester resins—translucent panels for architectural use.
Cinder building bricks coated with polyester resin.
Laminate of polyester-impregnated paper as fabric for wall or furniture covering.
Ribbed polyester plastic shield for fluorescent lights.
Glass fiber-polyester windows for corrugated-metal buildings.
Plastic wall coverings; brief discussion of polyester laminates included.

Polyester bonded to plywood as decorative laminate.
Corrugated sheets of glass mat and polyester for porch roof.
Glass fiber-polyester domes for Civil Aeronautics Administration omnirange stations; provide protection for equipment without disturbing signal transmission.
Polyester decorative laminate as replacement for linoleum on sink cabinet.
Reinforced-polyester awnings.
Polyester-glass reinforced plastic for shelters in Arctic regions.
Translucent door of resin-impregnated wall covered with glass reinforced polyester sheets.

Building Industry (Continued)

	Author	Reference
2607.	Anon.	*Modern Plastics* **31**, No. 1, 162 (1953); *Materials and Methods* **38**, No. 4, 129 (1953).
2608.	Anon.	*Modern Plastics* **31**, No. 3, 87–92, 193, 196, 198–200, 203 (1953).
2609.	Anon.	*Modern Plastics* **31**, No. 6, 83 (1954).
2610.	Anon.	*Modern Plastics* **31**, No. 6, 88–90 (1954).
2611.	Anon.	*Modern Plastics* **31**, No. 7, 171 (1954).
2612.	Anon.	*Modern Plastics* **31**, No. 9, 181 (1954).
2613.	Anon.	*Modern Plastics* **31**, No. 9, 183 (1954); *Plastics World* **11**, No. 11, 11 (1954).
2614.	Anon.	*Plastics* (London) **17**, 191–2 (1952).
2615.	Anon.	*Plastics Ind.* **11**, No. 10, 27 (1953).
2616.	Anon.	*Plastics Ind.* **11**, No. 11, 18 (1953).
2617.	Anon.	*Plastics Ind.* **12**, No. 4, 4, 6 (1954).
2618.	Anon.	*Plastics Ind.* **12**, No. 4, 16 (1954).
2619.	Anon.	*Plastics Ind.* **12**, No. 4, 27 (1954).
2620.	Anon.	*Plastics Ind.* **12**, No. 5, 4 (1954).
2621.	Anon.	*Plastics Ind.* **12**, No. 5, 14 (1954).
2622.	Anon.	*Plastics Newsfront* 2nd Quarter 1954, 12–7.
2623.	Anon.	*Plastics News Letter* **14**, No. 6, 4 (1954); *Plastics Newsfront* 2nd Quarter 1954.
2624.	Anon.	*Plastics World* **10**, No. 10, 56 (1952).
2625.	Anon.	*Plastics World* **10**, No. 11, 1 (1952).
2626.	Anon.	*Plastics World* **10**, No. 11, 23 (1952); *Modern Plastics* **30**, No. 6, 178 (1953).
2627.	Anon.	*Plastics World* **11**, No. 1, 33 (1953).
2628.	Anon.	*Plastics World* **11**, No. 2, 1 (1953).
2629.	Anon.	*Plastics World* **11**, No. 2, 29 (1953).
2630.	Anon.	*Plastics World* **12**, No. 1, 1 (1954).
2631.	Anon.	Strick Co., Plastics Div., Philadelphia, Pa. Forms PD-2, PD-4.
2632.	Anon.	*U. S. I. Chemical News* (U. S. Industrial Chemicals Co.), November 1953.
2633.	Engel, H. C., Hemming, C. B., and Merriman, H. R.	*Structural Plastics*. McGraw-Hill, New York, 1950.
2634.	Flemming, H.	*Silikattech.* **2**, No. 11, 327–30 (1951).
2635.	Formo, J.	*SPE J.* **9**, No. 1, 10–12, 23 (1953).
2636.	Patterson, D. G.	*Plastics Ind.* **12**, No. 2, 14 (1954).
2637.	Singer, J. B.	*Plastics* (London) **16**, 31, (Feb. 1951).
2638.	Singer, J. B.	*Plastics* (London) **18**, 371–4 (1953).

Concerning

Dome of Ford Rotunda (Detroit) made from polyester-glass plastic.

Use of reinforced plastics in building, e.g., walls, partitions, glazing, awnings, etc.

Glass reinforced polyester panels for windows; identical in color but with range in light transmission to permit light control.

Properties, uses, and fabrication of translucent, corrugated, glass reinforced polyester sheets.

Translucent glass fiber-polyester dome for phone booth.

Shatterproof polyester-glass fiber windows for industrial plants.

Polyester "marble" surfacing material—combination of polyester resin, glass mat, white paper laminate, and marble dust.

Light-diffusing panels of polyester-glass mat laminate for roof lighting.

Building plan for reinforced plastic greenhouses.

Self-extinguishing, fire-resistant, translucent glass fiber-polyester building panels.

Polyester resin for awnings, skylight sheets, canopies, greenhouses, etc.

Self-extinguishing translucent polyester panels.

Polyester-glass fiber dome for telephone booth.

Translucent glass fiber-polyester windows; curve outward for increased strength and light transmission.

Reinforced polyester panels for architectural use; light transmission varies with density.

Production and applications of glass fiber-polyester structural sheeting.

Glass fiber-polyester illuminated dome for telephone booths.

Manufacture and properties of glass fiber reinforced polyester wall.

Glass fiber-polyester forms for precasting concrete roofing slabs.

Hurricane panels of glass fiber reinforced plastic for installation over windows.

Translucent panels of reinforced plastic for greenhouses.

Polyester resin-glass cloth (or mat) sheets.

Properties of structural panels of reinforced plastic.

Large corrugated building panels for unbroken spans in, e.g., awnings, industrial side-lighting, and sky-lighting.

Specification for glass fiber reinforced plastic (polyester) sheets, shapes, rods.

Use of polyester-glass fiber panels in greenhouses. Have low heat transmission, high light transmission, and other advantages.

Compressive strength of glass fiber tile.

Future for plastics: improved properties, new materials and fabricated products.

Use of translucent polyester-glass fiber sheet for structural purposes.

Plastics (including reinforced polyesters) in modern school construction.

Plastics in prefabricated buildings (includes reinforced polyesters).

Building Industry (Continued)

Author	Reference
2639. Wennerholm, B.	*Swedish Plastics Fed. Tech. Bull.* 8, No. 45 (1952).

Military Uses

Author	Reference
2640. Anon.	*Ind. des plastique modernes* 6, No. 2, 5–7 (1954).
2641. Anon.	*Modern Plastics* 28, No. 1, 88D (1950).
2642. Anon.	*Modern Plastics* 28, No. 7, 55; No. 8, 91; No. 9, 64 (1951).
2643. Anon.	*Modern Plastics* 30, No. 12, 96–7, 182, 183, 185, 187 (1953).
2644. Anon.	*Modern Plastics* 31, No. 4, 108–9 (1953).
2645. Anon.	*Plastics World* 11, No. 2, 1 (1953).
2646. Anon.	*SPE J.* 8, No. 5, 23–5 (1952).
2647. Beekman, E. M., and Rusch, A.	*Reinforced Plastics Div., Soc. Plastics Ind. Confer., 8th Annual*, 1953, Sect. 21.
2648. Case, J. W.	*Reinforced Plastics Div., Soc. Plastics Ind. Confer., 9th Annual*, 1954. Sect. 1A.
2649. Cramsie, K. J.	*Reinforced Plastics Div., Soc. Plastics Ind. Confer., 6th Annual*, 1951, Sect. 10.
2650. Dobert, M.	*Plastics* (Chicago) 4, No. 1, 55–6, 129–30 (1946).
2651. Donaldson, C.	*Reinforced Plastics Div., Soc. Plastics Ind. Confer., 8th Annual*, 1953, Sect. 30.
2652. Donaldson, W. E.	*Modern Plastics* 31, No. 1, 95–6, 180.
2653. Ehlers, R. W.	*Reinforced Plastics Div., Soc. Plastics Ind. Confer., 5th Annual*, 1950, Sect. 4.
2654. Gallay, W.	*Can. Chem. Process Inds.* 25, 635–8 (1941).
2655. Gold, M. H.	*Modern Plastics* 30, No. 12, 90, 189, 191 (1953).
2656. Howard, G. W.	*Reinforced Plastics Div., Soc. Plastics Ind. Confer., 8th Annual*, 1953, Sect. 20.
2657. Huddle, F. P.	*Reinforced Plastics Div., Soc. Plastics Ind. Confer., 8th Annual*, 1953, Sect. 18.
2658. Hunter, N. D.	*Plastics* (London) 18, 387–8 (1953).
2659. Van Boskirk, R. L.	*Modern Plastics* 27, No. 3, 172 (1949) ("The Plastiscope").
2660. Weiss, A. C.	*Reinforced Plastics Div., Soc. Plastics Ind. Confer., 6th Annual*, 1951, Sect. 7.
2661. Weiss, A. C.	*Reinforced Plastics Div., Soc. Plastics Ind. Confer., 9th Annual*, 1954, Sect. 1K.

Scientific Uses

Author	Reference
2662. Anon.	*Brit. Plastics* 26, 384 (1953).
2663. Anon.	Castolite Co., Woodstock, Ill. 4-p. brochure.

Concerning

Use of reinforced low-pressure plastics, *e.g.*, glass reinforced polyester, for construction material.

Description of armored vests and body armor, including glass reinforced type.

Prediction of boom in polyesters for defense.   Mentions uses of polyester-glass combinations.
Reinforced plastics in defense.

Body armor for military use made from polyester-glass plates in nylon cover.

Two-man submarine from reinforced polyesters.
Resin-glass body armors for stopping low-velocity missiles.
Panel on military applications (of reinforced plastics).
Signal Corps applications of low-pressure reinforced plastics.

Development of Navy reinforced plastic ammunition cases: manufacture and testing.
Reinforced plastics in Engineer Research and Development (Army Corps of Engineers). Requirements for specialized uses.
Plastic armor, including glass fabric reinforced thermosetting resins.

Application of reinforced plastics to military items.

Pottings and adhesives in rockets and missiles.
Reinforced plastics for Quartermaster items.

Plastic developments in defense and other fields, *e.g.*, metal replacement, aircraft, high-impact molded plastics.
Advantages and disadvantages of reinforced plastics as housings for motors for rockets and guided missiles.
Work of Corps of Engineers' Industry Advisory Committee on Plastics.

Reinforced plastics in the spot materials conservation program of the Department of Defense.
Experimental liquid-fueled rocket made of glass fiber reinforced polyester.
Army foot lockers from polyester resin and glass cloth.

Design and development of reinforced plastic Quartermaster items.

Use of reinforced plastics by Quartermaster Corps, *e.g.*, containers, sleds, furniture.

Glass-polyester container for breathing study equipment in Mt. Everest expedition.
Uses of liquid casting plastic in crafts and science classes.

Scientific Uses (Continued)

Author	Reference
2664. Anon.	*Modern Plastics* **24**, No. 11, 91 (1947).
2665. Anon.	*Modern Plastics* **28**, No. 8, 96–5 (1951).
2666. Anon.	*Modern Plastics* **30**, No. 4, 166 (1952).
2667. Anon.	*Modern Plastics* **30**, No. 7, 90 (1953).
2668. Anon.	*Modern Plastics* **30**, No. 8, 168 (1953).
2669. Anon.	*Modern Plastics* **31**, No. 7, 93, 195–6 (1954); *Plastics World* **12**, No. 2, 17 (1954).
2670. Anon.	*Plastics* (London) **18**, 343 (1953).
2671. Anon.	*Plastics World* **10**, No. 11, 4 (1952).
2672. Albrecht, R.	*Der Plastverarbeiter* **4**, No. 10, 294.
2673. Foppl, L.	*Kunststoffe* **43**, No. 9, 346–9 (1953).
2674. Gurtowski, J. J.	*SPE J.* **9**, No. 4, 28–9 (1953).
2675. Jackson, E. W.	*Brit. Plastics* **22**, 272–80 (1950).
2676. Lightbody, A.	*SPE J.* **9**, No. 3, 23–5, 55 (1953).
2677. Löffler, K.	*Geologie* **1**, 384–9 (1952).
2678. Schwab, H. A.	*Kunststoffe* **43**, 8 (1953).
2679. Sugarman, B., Moxley, G. O., and Marshall, I. A.	*Brit. J. Appl. Phys.* **3**, 233–7 (1952).
2680. Van Boskirk, R. L.	*Modern Plastics* **25**, No. 11, 182 (1948) ("The Plastiscope").
2681. Wright, C. E.	*Modern Plastics* **29**, No. 2, 113–21 (1951).
2682. Zastrow, K., and Pessler, E.	*Geologie* **1**, 390–2 (1952).
2682a. Anon.	*Plastics* (London) **16**, 249–50 (1951).
2682b. Mede, J. J.	*Elect. Manuf.* **52**, No. 4, 146 (1953).

Consumer Items

2683. Anon.	Bakelite Company, New York, N. Y.
2684. Anon.	*Brit. Plastics* **26**, No. 2, (1953) (editorial).
2685. Anon.	*Brit. Plastics* **26**, 320 (1953).
2686. Anon.	*Brit. Plastics* **27**, 91 (1954).
2687. Anon.	*Brit Plastics* **27**, 162–3 (1954).
2688. Anon.	*Can. Plastics*, Jan.–Feb. 1953, 37, 43 (advertisement).
2689. Anon.	*Can. Plastics* Mar.–April 1954, 70.
2690. Anon.	*Can. Plastics* Mar.–April 1954, 78.
2691. Anon.	*Can. Plastics* May–June 1954, 43.
2692. Anon.	*Can. Plastics* May–June 1954, 44.
2693. Anon.	*Chem. Week* **74**, No. 20, 18 (1954).

Concerning

Polyester-glass fiber parts for atom smasher.
Aerial camera with glass fiber-polyester magazine cover.
Dome for small movable planetarium made from polyester impregnated glass fiber.
Polyester resin for impregnating anatomical models.
Polyester coating for concrete blocks in radiation shield.
"Wounded" mannequin that "bleeds" for use in first-aid courses.

Protective coating of polyester resin for cosmotron.
Polyester-allyl diglycol carbonate copolymer as replacement for lacquered gel-
atin in photoprinting filters.
Hard, rubberlike polyester resin for construction of models for photoelastic
studies.
Polyester resin plates for use in stress optical research.
Use of plastics (including polyesters) for relief map making.
Glass fiber laminates in cartography.
Reinforced plastics for artificial limbs.
Properties of Phthalopal G (phthalic acid-polyhydric alcohol condensation prod-
uct) synthetic embedding medium.
Foamed plastics, e.g., polyurethane, as replacement for plaster casts for injuries.
Polyester resins for photoelastic work. Properties required.

Polyester resin for casting lenses, flat sheets, small mirrors, etc.

Specific directions for embedment of flowers in polyester resin.
Directions for use of Phthalopal G (phthalic acid-polyhydric alcohol condensa-
tion product) for embedding coal sections.
Use of polyester resins for embedding biological and archeological specimens.
Use of polyester resins for embedment of cyclotron coil magnet.

1954 guide to improved packaging with plastics and resins.
Mentions percentage of U. S. plastics industry devoted to packaging uses (25%).
Manufacture and uses of reinforced plastic safety helmets.
Use of plastic laminates for display of artwork (woodcuts, engravings)
reproductions.
Plastics materials in refrigerators, e.g., polyester-fiber laminate for door liners.
Glass fiber-polyester blade for hockey stick.

Glass fiber-polyester archery bow.
Polyester-glass fiber chair.
Reinforced polyester bowling alley score stand.
Reinforced polyester chair seat made by hand lay-up.
Glass-polyester helmet liners as toppers for Japanese coal miners, policemen,
sportsmen, band members, etc.

Consumer Items (Continued)

	Author	Reference
2694.	Anon.	*Chem. Week* **74**, No. 20, 37 (1954) (advertisement).
2695.	Anon.	*Furniture Manuf.* **74**, No. 10, 42 (1953).
2696.	Anon.	*Ind. des plastiques modernes* **6**, No. 2, 1 (1954).
2697.	Anon.	*Modern Plastics* **24**, No. 6, 110–2 (1947).
2698.	Anon.	*Modern Plastics* **24**, No. 7, 100–1 (1947).
2699.	Anon.	*Modern Plastics* **24**, No. 11, 112–4 (1947).
2700.	Anon.	*Modern Plastics* **24**, No. 12, 162 (1947).
2701.	Anon.	*Modern Plastics* **25**, No. 1, 93 (1947).
2702.	Anon.	*Modern Plastics* **25**, No. 3, 77 (1947).
2703.	Anon.	*Modern Plastics* **25**, No. 8, 106 (1948).
2704.	Anon.	*Modern Plastics* **26**, No. 3, 39 (1948). (advertisement).
2705.	Anon.	*Modern Plastics* **26**, No. 6, 77–9 (1949).
2706.	Anon.	*Modern Plastics* **26**, No. 11, 126 (1949).
2707.	Anon.	*Modern Plastics* **26**, No. 11, 138 (1949).
2708.	Anon.	*Modern Plastics* **27**, No. 8, 92–3 (1950).
2709.	Anon.	*Modern Plastics* **27**, No. 8, 93–4 (1950).
2710.	Anon.	*Modern Plastics* **27**, No. 9, 57, 60 (1950).
2711.	Anon.	*Modern Plastics* **27**, No. 12, 67-8, 147 (1950).
2712.	Anon.	*Modern Plastics* **28**, No. 7, 74–5 (1951).
2713.	Anon.	*Modern Plastics* **28**, No. 8, 171 (1951).
2714.	Anon.	*Modern Plastics* **29**, No. 2, 103–6; No. 4, 123–5 (1951).
2715.	Anon.	*Modern Plastics* **29**, No. 2, 122–3 (1951) (advertisement).
2716.	Anon.	*Modern Plastics* **29**, No. 3, 88 (1951).
2717.	Anon.	*Modern Plastics* **29**, No. 4, 123–5 (1951).
2718.	Anon.	*Modern Plastics* **29**, No. 5, 96–7 (1952).
2719.	Anon.	*Modern Plastics* **30**, No. 4, 96–7 (1952).
2720.	Anon.	*Modern Plastics* **30**, No. 6, 88–9 (1953).
2721.	Anon.	*Modern Plastics* **30**, No. 6, 96 (1953).
2722.	Anon.	*Modern Plastics* **30**, No. 9, 69 (1953).
2723.	Anon.	*Modern Plastics* **30**, No. 10, 178 (1953).
2724.	Anon.	*Modern Plastics* **30**, No. 10, 239 (1953) (advertisement).
2725.	Anon.	*Modern Plastics* **30**, No. 12, 75 (1953).
2726.	Anon.	*Modern Plastics* **30**, No. 12, 84–7 (1953).
2727.	Anon.	*Modern Plastics* **30**, No. 12, 81–3, 192–3 (1953).
2728.	Anon.	*Modern Plastics* **30**, No. 12, 177 (1954).

Concerning

Bathtub (colored) made of glass fiber reinforced polyester.

Eames chair with polyester-glass fiber upholstery and chrome bases.
Glass-polyester base for office revolving chairs.

Use of polyester resins and cotton cloth to make model racing sloop.
Polyester-glass laminates for outdoor displays.
Polyester impregnated glass mat minnow bucket.
Sheet materials for use in lampshades, screens, and wall paneling from glass mat impregnated with polyester or vinyl resins.
Polyester replicas of piano keyboard for students.
Washing machine parts of glass fiber-polyester material.
Reinforced polyester for skating rink "bang board," orchestra stand, stage props.
Edge board for skating rink of glass fiber mat and polyester.

Glass fiber-polyester mannequins.
Glass fiber reinforced laminate as replacement for metal in washing machine parts.
Polyester molded novelties, e.g., figures, ash trays, cigarette boxes.
Polyester-glass fiber material for tub and lid of low-cost dishwasher.
Polyester-glass fiber liner as replacement for aluminum liner in automatic washer.
Glass fiber-polyester luggage.
Fabrication of polyester-glass fiber chair.

Boxes from glass fiber reinforced polyester plastic.
Glass fiber-polyester lamp shades.
Polyester-glass fiber material for dust bowl and other parts of vacuum cleaner.

Molded polyester-glass fiber chair, shower stall, lamp shade.

Harp with glass fiber plastic shell and sounding board and nylon strings.
Reinforced polyester dust bowl for vacuum cleaner; process for making described.
Lightweight, leakproof shower stall made of reinforced polyester resin.
Reinforced polyester for speaker unit in public-address system.
Polyesters for file drawers.
Reinforced plastic bathtubs.
Polyester-glass fiber table and chairs.
Advertising display made of polyester—"Fisk boy" of U. S. Rubber Co.
Chair and other products from polyester resin.

Plastic parts in computing machines, e.g., polyester film in capacitors, polyester backing for magnetic tape.
Juice dispenser molded of polyester-glass laminate.
Plastic components, including reinforced polyesters, in new automatic ice maker.

Glass fiber reinforced plastic fishing rod for children.

Consumer Items (Continued)

Author	Reference
2729. Anon.	*Modern Plastics* **31**, No. 1, 77 (1953) (advertisement).
2730. Anon.	*Modern Plastics* **31**, No. 1, 102 (1953).
2731. Anon.	*Modern Plastics* **31**, No. 1, 107 (1953).
2732. Anon.	*Modern Plastics* **31**, No. 6, 80–82, 191 (1954).
2733. Anon.	*Modern Plastics* **31**, No. 6, 115 (1954).
2734. Anon.	*Pittsburgh Plate Glass Products* **61**, No. 3 (1953).
2735. Anon.	*Plastics* (London) **17**, 259 (1952); *Materials & Methods* **35**, No. 5, 109 (1952).
2736. Anon.	*Plastics* (London) **19**, 172 (1954).
2737. Anon.	*Plastics Ind.* **10**, No. 5, 23, 25 (1952).
2738. Anon.	*Plastics Ind.* **12**, No. 2, 4 (1954).
2739. Anon.	*Plastics Ind.* **12**, No. 3, 19 (1954).
2740. Anon.	*Plastics Ind.* **12**, No. 5, 20 (1954).
2741. Anon.	*Plastics Newsfront* Oct. 1953, 24.
2742. Anon.	*Plastics News Letter* **14**, No. 25, 3 (1954).
2743. Anon.	*Plastics News Letter* **14**, No. 25, 4 (1954).
2744. Anon.	*Plastics News Letter* **14**, No. 28, 4 (1954).
2745. Anon.	*Plastics World* **10**, No. 7, 27 (1952).
2746. Anon.	*Plastics World* **10**, No. 12, 27 (1952); *Modern Plastics* No. 8, 179 (1953).
2747. Anon.	*Plastics World* **11**, No. 1, 35 (1953).
2748. Anon.	*Plastics World* **11**, No. 2, 6 (1953).
2749. Anon.	*Plastics World* **11**, No. 2, 9 (1953).
2750. Anon.	*Plastics World* **11**, No. 10, 10 (1953).
2751. Anon.	*Plastics World* **12**, No. 1, 5 (1954).
2752. Anon.	*Plastics World* **12**, No. 1, 26 (1954).
2753. Anon.	*Plastics World* **12**, No. 1, 30 (1954).
2754. Anon.	*SPE J.* **9**, No. 4, cover picture (1953).
2755. Anon.	*Washington* (D. C.) *Post*, Nov. 7, 1953, 22.
2756. Bacon, C. E.	*Plastics* (London) **17**, 198 (1952); *Glass Fibre Reinforced Plastics Conv.* (England) 1952, *Proc.* 125–44.
2757. Bushman, E. K.	*Modern Plastics* **30**, No. 7, 82–5 (1953).
2758. De Bell, G. W.	*Modern Plastics* **24**, No. 8, 143 (1947).
2759. Gillis, M. D.	*Plastics Ind.* **11**, No. 10, 20–1 (1953).
2760. Greutert, H.	*Plastics Newsfront* Oct. 1953, 3–9.
2761. Howald, A. M.	*Modern Plastics* **23**, No. 6, 124–5 (1946).
2762. Kränzlein, P.	*Kunststoffe* **43**, 305–8 (1953).
2763. McCann, H.	*Reinforced Plastics Div., Soc. Plastics Ind. Confer., 5th Annual*, 1950, Sect. 8B.

Concerning

Luggage from polyester resin and glass fibers.

Glass fiber-polyester plastics for advertising displays.
Polyester-glass chair (photograph).
Description, with illustrations, of reinforced plastic air conditioners.

Portable insulated beverage case; outer shell of glass reinforced polyester.
Yearly investment of fishermen in new "glass" rods.

Glass reinforced plastic seats.

Radio components; includes use of polyesters for potting and insulating and for
    structural parts.
Glass fiber-polyester bucket seat.
Glass fiber-polyester luggage.
Glass reinforced polyester luggage.
Consumer products, e.g., containers, lampshades, blackboards, etc., from rein-
    forced polyesters.
Traffic control signs molded of glass reinforced polyester resin.
Pearl polyester button blanks.
Reinforced polyester utility hampers.
Molded glass fiber-polyester liner for refrigerator-freezer.
Polyester-glass fiber sheets for highway signs.
Swimming pool ladder steps of reinforced polyester.

Reinforced polyester 2-piece unit as replacement for 22 metal parts in washing
    machine.
Glass fiber-polyester blade for hockey stick.
Glass fiber reinforced polyester for props and scenery in movie studios.
Caps for protection of baseball players from glass fiber reinforced polyester.
Portable insulated food chest made of glass fiber reinforced polyester.
Lightweight long-lasting luggage molded of glass fiber reinforced polyester.
Cabinet parts of room air conditioner cast from polyester resin.
Dinette set of glass fiber reinforced plastic.
Installation of highway markers made from plastic reinforced with glass fibers in
    Virginia.
Applications of reinforced plastics in United States.

"Jet-age luggage" of glass fiber reinforced plastics.
Polyester-glass fiber molded mutes for trumpets.
Living-dining area furnished with plastic materials, including polyesters.
Use of polyester resins and reinforced plastics in motion picture set making.
Polyester bonded glass fiber flyrod.
Manufacture and applications of floor coverings, including polyester-base covering.
Markets for molded reinforced plastics products.

Consumer Items (Continued)

Author	Reference
2764. Reynolds, F. W.	*SPE J.* **9**, No. 5, 23–7 (1953).

Miscellaneous

2765. Anon.	American Insulator Corp., New Freedom, Pa. 8-p. booklet.
2766. Anon.	*Austral. Plastics* **18**, No. 87, 36–41 (1952).
2767. Anon.	Bassons Industries Corp., New York, N. Y., 12-p. booklet.
2768. Anon.	*Brit. Plastics* **25**, 282–5 (1952).
2769. Anon.	*Brit. Plastics* **26**, No. 9, 58 (1953) (advertisement).
2770. Anon.	Brunswick-Balke-Collender Co., Chicago, Ill. 14-p. booklet.
2771. Anon.	Canadian Ingersoll-Rand Co., Montreal, Que., Canada.
2772. Anon.	*Chem. Eng.* **61**, No. 3, 202–4 (1954).
2773. Anon.	*Chem. Eng. News* **31**, 2776 (1953).
2774. Anon.	Lunn Laminates, Inc., Huntington Station, N. Y. Brochure G-313.
2775. Anon.	*Modern Plastics* **24**, No. 5, 153–8, 192 (1947).
2776. Anon.	*Modern Plastics* **26**, No. 9, 88–9 (1949) (advertisement).
2777. Anon.	*Modern Plastics* **29**, No. 5, 87–92 (1952).
2778. Anon.	*Modern Plastics* **29**, No. 7, 128–31 (1952).
2779. Anon.	*Modern Plastics* **30**, No. 10, 10 (1953) (advertisement).
2780. Anon.	*Natl. Bur. Standards, Letter Circ.* LC-782, 5 pp. (1945).
2781. Ackerman, E.	*SPE J.* **9**, No. 3, 48 (1953).
2782. Appleton, E. V.	*J. Inst. Civil Engrs.* (London) No. 8, 448–68 (1939–40).
2783. Beavers, E. M.	*Am. Paint J.* **33**, No. 29, 38, 42, 44, 46 (1949).
2784. Beguin, C.	*Schweiz. Apoth.-Ztg.* **90**, 525–9, 545–52 (1952).
2785. Brother, G. H.	*Plastics* (Chicago) **3**, No. 1, 82, 84, 86, 150–54 (1945).
2786. Day, H. M.	*SPE J.* **9**, No. 4, 38 (1953).
2787. De Marco, T. A., and Mills, C. R.	*Reinforced Plastics Div., Soc. Plastics Ind. Confer., 6th Annual,* 1951, Sect. 13F.
2788. Ebers, E. X.	*SPE J.* **7**, No. 2, 31–3 (1951).

Concerning

Plastics applications in business machines, *e.g.*, polyester-glass dust covers for clocks.

Molded reinforced plastics: uses and properties.

Symposium on reinforced plastics: applications, raw materials, fabrication, testing, properties, economics.
Reinforced plastics products.

Publications on production and application of plastics in Great Britain.
Applications of reinforced polyester plastics.

Polyester reinforced plastics.

Glass reinforced plastic laminate.

Review of developments in plastics in 1953.
Report on British Plastics Exhibition. Mentions some polyester products.
Origin of company and products, including reinforced polyesters.

Review, with 411 references, on advances in plastics during 1946.

Use of polyester resins, with suitable fillers, for various objects.

Review on plastics applications trends in 1951. Mentions uses for polyesters.
Present and future applications of plastics, including reinforced polyesters.
Uses (about 50) for polyester resins.

Bibliography of 36 references on plastics.

Report on speech by I. E. Muskat on fabrication and applications of polyester resins.
Survey of new solid materials, including plastics.

Review on alkyd resins. Mentions unsaturated linear polyesters in "laminating resins."
Review on plastics.

Review on polyesters (actually alkyd resins), polyamides, nylon, protein plastics, and shellacs.
Future developments in polyester products.
Lustrex styrene-glass fiber combinations. Products, properties, processes.

Historical review on polyesters; also discussion of applications in molding, laminating, and potting.

Miscellaneous (Continued)

Author	Reference
2789. Finger, J. S.	*Reinforced Plastics Div., Soc. Plastics. Ind. Confer., 7th Annual*, 1952, Sect. 2.
2790. Hodgson, D. G., and Ader, G.	*Plastics* (London) **18**, 202–4 (June 1953).
2791. Kline, G. M.	*India Rubber World* **111**, 694–9; *Mech. Eng.* **67**, 255–61 (1945).
2792. Kline, G. M.	*Modern Plastics* **19**, No. 5, Tech. Sect., 57–9 (1942).
2793. Kline, G. M.	*Modern Plastics* **27**, No. 5, 205–8, 210, 212, 262, 265, 266, 268, 270, 272, 274, 276, 278, 280 (1950).
2794. Kline, G. M.	*Modern Plastics* **30**, No. 5, 111–24, 187–99 (1953).
2795. Kline, G. M.	*Modern Plastics* **31**, No. 5, 117–8, 120, 122, 124, 126, 128, 130, 133, 189–92, 195–6, 198, 201 (1954).
2796. McSweeney, E. E.	*Chem. Eng. News* **31**, 37–8 (1953).
2797. Muskat, I. E.	*Schweiz. Ver. Lack- u. Farben.-Chem. u. -Tech., Bull.* No. 8, 19–27 (1950).
2798. Parkyn, B.	*Plastics* (London) **15**, 66 (March 1950).
2799. Parkyn, B.	*Plastics Inst.* (London), *Trans.* **20**, No. 41, 36–56 (1952).
2800. Phillips, S. M.	*Domestic Commerce* **35**, No. 9, 55–60 (1947).
2801. Schick, J.	*Ind. des plastiques modernes* **6**, No. 3, 56 (1954).
2802. Schlitt, W.	*Gummi u. Asbest.* **6**, 330–2, 380–1, 430–2 (1953).
2803. Smet, J. D.	*Plastiques* **1**, 41–6 (1943).
	Economics
2804. Anon.	*Austral. Plastics* **8**, No. 93, 25 (1953).
2805. Anon.	*Brit. Plastics* **25**, 314–39 (1952).
2806. Anon.	*Brit. Plastics* **26**, 1–5, (1953).
2807. Anon.	*Brit. Plastics* **26**, No. 2, 65 (1953).
2808. Anon.	*Brit. Plastics* **26**, 373 (1953).
2809. Anon.	*Brit. Plastics* **27**, 1–5 (1954).
2810. Anon.	*Brit. Plastics* **27**, 69 (1954).
2811. Anon.	*Can. Plastics* Jan.-Feb. 1953, 33.
2812. Anon.	*Can. Plastics* Jan.-Feb. 1954, 40.
2813. Anon.	*Chem. Eng.* **61**, No. 1, 170–86 (1954).
2814. Anon.	*Chem. Eng.* **61**, No. 2, 175–206 (1953).
2815. Anon.	*Chem. Eng. News* **30**, 3256 (1952).

Concerning

Annual report of Committee on Preparedness.

Recent developments in glass reinforced polyesters.

A review on plastics with 250 references.   Mentions polyesters for reinforced plastics.
General review of advances in plastics in 1941.

Review of plastic materials and their applications for 1949.

Review, with 404 references, of plastics developments in 1952.

Review of plastic materials and their applications for 1953.

Review of plastics developments in 1952.
Cure, properties, and application of copolymers of unsaturated alkyd-type polyester resins with styrene.
Low-pressure resins (polyesters).
Unsaturated polyester resins.   Review, uses.

Survey of new types of plastics, including polyester resins.   Some production data.
Review of applications of polyesters.

Applications of polyester-glass fiber materials.

Properties and applications of transparent plastics.

First commercial production of polyesters in Australia.
Imports, exports, and trends in British plastics business.
British production of plastics 1943–51 and sales trends.
Estimate for 1953 United States plastics production.
Statistics on United Kingdom, German, and United States exports of plastic materials.
Review of plastic developments in 1953, e.g., Terylene film, mass production of plastic auto bodies.
Production statistics for U. S. plastics industry.
New British producers of polyesters.
Reduction in price of polyester resins.
New plants and facilities under way in 1953.
New plants and facilities under way and new processes and technology adapted in 1952. Includes some applying to polyesters.
Statistics on synthetic resin production.

Economics (Continued)

Author	Reference
2816.	Anon.	*Chem. Eng. News* **31**, 1872 (1953).
2817.	Anon.	*Chem. Eng. News* **31**, 2043 (1953).
2818.	Anon.	*Chem. Eng. News* **31**, 2043 (1953).
2819.	Anon.	*Chem. Eng. News* **31**, 3042 (1953).
2820.	Anon.	*Chem. Eng. News* **31**, 3771 (1953).
2821.	Anon.	*Chem. Eng. News* **32**, 126–7 (1954).
2822.	Anon.	*Chem. Eng. News* **32**, 591–2 (1954).
2823.	Anon.	*Chem. Week* **71**, No. 25, 32–6 (1952).
2824.	Anon.	*Chem. Week* **72**, No. 10, 65 (1953).
2825.	Anon.	*Kunststoffe* **43**, No. 8 (1953).
2826.	Anon.	*Materials & Methods* **39**, No. 5, 70–116 (1954).
2827.	Anon.	*Modern Plastics* **24**, No. 8, 95–104 (1947).
2828.	Anon.	*Modern Plastics* **27**, No. 2, 69–76, 158–60 (1949).
2829.	Anon.	*Modern Plastics* **28**, No. 5, 59 (1950).
2830.	Anon.	*Modern Plastics* **30**, No. 8, 5 (1953).
2831.	Anon.	*Modern Plastics* **31**, No. 5, 63–4 (1954).
2832.	Anon.	*Modern Plastics* **31**, No. 6, 5 (1954) (editorial).
2833.	Anon.	*Modern Plastics* **31**, No. 6, 79 (1954).
2834.	Anon.	*Plastics Ind.* **12**, No. 2, 26 (1954).
2835.	Anon.	*Plastics Ind.* **12**, No. 3, 7 (1954).
2836.	Anon.	*Plastics Ind.* **12**, No. 3, 9 (1954).
2837.	Anon.	*Plastics. The Story of An Industry.* 6th ed., Soc. Plastics Ind., Inc., New York, N. Y., 1953.
2838.	Anon.	Research Institute of America, Inc. New York, N. Y.
2839.	Brinkema, R. L.	*Reinforced Plastics Div., Soc. Plastics Ind. Confer., 8th Annual*, 1953, Sect. 31.
2840.	Brown, E. A.	*Reinforced Plastics Div., Soc. Plastics Ind. Confer., 6th Annual*, 1951, Sect. 18.
2841.	Cone, W. L.	*Reinforced Plastics Div., Soc. Plastics Ind. Confer., 8th Annual*, 1953, Sect. 28.
2842.	Darling, W.	*Reinforced Plastics Div., Soc. Plastics Ind. Confer., 5th Annual*, 1950, Sect. 8A.
2843.	Dring, G.	*Repts. Progress Applied Chem.* **24**, 395–403.
2844.	Ellis, C.	*Plastics Ind.* **12**, No. 2, 15 (1954).
2845.	Fabel, K., editor.	*Deutsches Jahrbuch fuer die Industrie der plastichen Massen 1951/1952.* Wilhelm Pansegrau Verlag, Berlin, 1953, 646 pp.
2846.	Finger, J. S.	*Reinforced Plastics Div., Soc. Plastics Ind. Confer., 6th Annual*, 1951, Sect. 6.

Concerning

Purchase of Sierra Products Co., polyester fabricator, by Swedlow Plastics Co.

Purchase of Marco Chemicals firm by Celanese Corp.

Addition of plastics division to Los Angeles building and safety codes.

Sales statistics for plastics.

Firms producing polyesters in Britain.

Plastics production may reach record.

Report on meeting of Reinforced Plastics Division, Society of the Plastics Industry. Statistics on production of reinforced plastics and polyester resins given.

Survey of production of expanded plastics.

Production of polyester resins 1951, 1952, 1953 (estimated).

Production of polyesters for casting and low-pressure molding in Germany.

Case histories of how proper materials selection and use reduces costs. Polyesters included in several examples.

Economics of low-pressure plastics.

Review of fabricating procedures and economic situation for reinforced polyesters.

Production volume and prospects for polyesters.

Polyester consumption in reinforced plastics. (Prediction in editorial).

Review of growth of plastic production from 1934 to 1954. (No data given specifically for polyesters.)

Comments on growth of reinforced plastics industry.

Summary of inherent advantages of reinforced plastics and some negative factors, also problems still to be overcome by the industry.

Expansion of plant for production of reinforced plastics.

Reduction in prices of glass reinforced alkyd molding compounds.

Reduction in prices of polyester resins.

Plastics industry statistics, products, processes.

Analysis of market trends in the United States.

Development contract sales of reinforced plastics.

Survey of Canadian reinforced plastics industry.

Selling proprietary reinforced plastics products.

Market outlook for low pressure, reinforced flat laminates.

Progress in thermosetting resins.

Prediction of expansion in plastics and resins.

Worldwide developments in plastics from 1950 to 1952.

Business aspects of reinforced plastics.

Economics (Continued)

	Author	Reference
2847.	Huddle, F. P.	*Reinforced Plastics Div., Soc. Plastics Ind. Confer. 9th Annual*, 1954, Sect. 1B.
2848.	McCann, H. C.	*Reinforced Plastics Div., Soc. Plastics Ind. Confer., 9th Annual*, 1954, Sect. 22.
2849.	Potter, H. V.	*Chem. & Ind.* 1938, 503–6.
2850.	Randolph, A. F.	*Chem. & Met. Eng.* **44**, 25–8 (1937).
2851.	Renfrew, A.	*SPE J.* **10**, No. 4, 22–3, 41–2 (1954).
2852.	Slayter, G.	*Reinforced Plastics Div., Soc. Plastics Ind. Confer., 7th Annual*, 1952, Sect. 23.
2853.	Smythe, W. J.	*Reinforced Plastics Div., Soc. Plastics Ind. Confer., 8th Annual*, 1953, Sect. 24I.
2854.	Van Boskirk, R. L.	*Modern Plastics* **25**, No. 1, 196 (1947) ("The Plastiscope").
2855.	Van Boskirk, R. L.	*Modern Plastics* **31**, No. 4, 224 (1953).
2856.	Weith, A. J.	*Ind. Eng. Chem.* **31**, 557–62 (1937).
2857.	White, R. B.	*Reinforced Plastics Div., Soc. Plastics Ind. Confer., 8th Annual*, 1953, Sect. 33.

Concerning

Relationship of reinforced plastics industry to long-range materials conservation policy of Department of Defense.
Future of reinforced plastics; economics.

Economics of the plastics industry.
Economic and engineering trends in plastics, 1933–37.
Review of progress and future of plastics industry in general.
Future of reinforced plastics. Uses and economics.

Summary of problems facing polyester-glass laminate industry.

Future for polyesters.

Purchase of Libbey-Owens-Ford Glass Co.'s Plaskon Division by Allied Chemical & Dye Corp.
Development of American plastics industry. Economics.
Effective selling of reinforced plastics.

Manufacture of Fiber-Forming Polymers

Author	Reference
2858. Anon.	*Chem. Eng.* **58**, No. 8, 125–32 (1951).
2859. Anon.	*Chem. Eng.* **61**, No. 4, 106 (1954).
2860. Anon.	*Chem. Eng. News* **31**, 1611 (1953).
2861. Anon.	*Chem. Eng. News* **31**, 1754 (1953).
2862. Anon.	*Chem. Eng. News* **32**, 128 (1954); *Modern Plastics* **31**, No. 7, 214, 216 (1954); *Plastics World* **12**, No. 2, 24 (1954).
2863. Anon.	*Chem. Eng. News* **32**, 500 (1954).
2864. Anon.	*Chem. Eng. News* **32**, 712 (1954).
2865. Anon.	*Chem. Eng. News* **32**, 1995 (1954).
2866. Anon.	Hercules Powder Co., Wilmington, Del. Synthetics Dept. Bull. No. 30, 26 pp. (1953).
2867. Akiyoshi, S., and Shizunobu, H.	*Kogaku Iho Kyushu Univ.* **24**, 75–7 (1951).
2868. Coke, C. E.	*Can. Chem. Proc.* **36**, No. 11, 74, 76–7 (1952).
2869. Gilman, H., Langham, W., and Moore, F. W.	*J. Am. Chem. Soc.* **62**, 2327–35 (1940).
2870. Hall, A. J.	*Fibres, Nat. and Synthetic* **14**, 393–4 (1953).
2871. Hardy, D. V. N.	*J. Soc. Chem. Ind.* (London) **67**, 426–32 (1948).
2872. Heckert, W. W.	*Ind. Eng. Chem.* **44**, 2103–9 (1952).
2873. Hill, R.	*Chem. & Ind.* No. 15, April 10, 1954, 419 (summary of paper).
2874. Hill, R., editor.	*Fibres from Synthetic Polymers.* Elsevier, Houston, 569 pp.
2875. Hudson, R. A.	*Brit. Plastics* **26**, 6–9 (1953).
2876. Infiesta, J. L., and Vega, J. A.	*Anales real soc. espan. fis. y quim.* (Madrid) **44B**, 153–60 (1953).
2877. Law, P. B.	*Textile J. Australia* **22**, 68–74 (1947).
2878. Lum, F. G., and Carlston, E. F.	*Ind. Eng. Chem.* **44**, 1595–600 (1952).
2879. Miller, R. N., Crooke, J. O., and Rietz, E. G.	*J. Am. Chem. Soc.* **74**, 4214 (1952).
2880. Moncrieff, R. W.	*Fibres* **14**, 86–9 (1953).
2881. Profft, E.	*Chem. Tech.* (Berlin) **5**, 503–7 (1953).
2882. Reynolds, R. J. W.	*Textile Mfr.* No. 941, 264 (1953).

I. LINEAR FIBER-FORMING POLYESTERS

Concerning

Review on production of man-made fibers. Equipment flowsheet for polyester fiber production.

Plant for production of dimethyl terephthalate by air oxidation of xylenes.

Plants for production of para-xylene.

Work of E. F. Izard leading to development of Dacron.

Manufacture of dimethyl terephthalate by Hercules Powder Co. for use in Canadian production of Terylene.

Liquid-phase oxidation process for production of dimethyl terephthalate from para-xylene.

Sinclair Chemicals to supply para-xylene for Hercules dimethyl terephthalate plant.

New plants for production of isophthalic acid.

Dimethyl isophthalate. Properties and uses, *e.g.*, in polyester resins.

Synthesis of terephthalic acid by oxidation of para-cymene.

Structure, raw materials, properties of man-made fibers, including polyethylene terephthalate.

Reactions of halo derivatives of benzene compounds with organolithium compounds to give acids, *e.g.*, terephthalic acid from dibromobenzene.

Chemicals for use in synthetic fiber manufacture. A review covering Terylene and Perlon U.

Polyethylene terephthalate and its early development. Review on preparation during 1942–44.

Synthetic fibers. Selection of fiber monomers.

Chemistry of fibers; includes polyesters.

Basic aspects of linear polymers; preparation, properties, and applications of fibers.

Production, properties, and applications of polyethylene terephthalate film.

Catalytic oxidation of para-cymene to terephthalic acid.

Review on textile applications of synthetic resins. Includes Terylene fibers.

Applications of isophthalic acid in condensation polymers. Comparison with phthalic anhydride and terephthalic acid polymers.

Preparation of alkyl esters of terephthalic acid.

Review of synthesis of fibrous "superpolymers."

Methods of manufacture and laboratory preparation of terephthalic acid.

Chemistry of synthetic fibers, including polyester fiber.

Manufacture of Fiber-Forming Polymers (Continued)

Author	Reference
2883. Ridge, B. P.	*Review of Textile Progress, 1952.* Textile Institute and Society of Dyers and Colourists, England, 1953, 90–111.
2884. Ross, S. D., *et al.*	*J. Polymer Sci.* **8**, No. 70, 406–7 (1954).
2885. Scheurer, P. G., and Le Fave, G. M.	*J. Am. Chem. Soc.* **72**, 3308–9 (1950).
2886. Sherwood, P. W.	*Can. Chem. Processing* **37**, No. 7, 56–8 (1953).
2887. Smith, R. C., Tomarelli, R. C. and Howard, H. C.	*J. Am. Chem. Soc.* **61**, 2398–2402 (1939).
2888. Vega, J. A.	*Revista de Plasticos* **4**, No. 9 (1953).
2889. Whinfield, J. R.	*Nature* **158**, 930–1 (1946).
2890. Whinfield, J. R.	*Endeavour* **11**, 29–32 (1952).
2891. Xavier, M. L., Verghese, J., and Yeddanapalli, L. M.	*Current Sci.* (India) **22**, 112–3 (1953).

Manufacture of Fibers and Films

Author	Reference
2892. Anon.	*Plastics* (London) **18**, 17 (1953); *Chem. Age* **68**, 8 (1953).
2893. Abramov, S. A.	*Legkaya Prom.* **9**, No. 6, 23–5 (1949).
2894. Borghetty, H. C.	*Colloid Chem.* **7**, 599–617 (1950).
2895. Brass, K.	*Kolloid-Z.* **113**, 110–20, 114, 174–80 (1949); **116**, 33–46 (1950).
2896. Cobbold, A., *et al.*	*Compt. rend.* **236**, 369 (1953).
2897. Fourné, F.	*Melliand Textilber.* **33**, 639–43 (1952).
2898. Fourné, F.	*Melliand Textilber.* **33**, 753–7 (1952).
2899. Grove, C. S., Jr., Vodonik, J. L., and Casey, R. S.	*Ind. Eng. Chem.* **44**, 2318–24, 2371–5 (1952).
2900. Hadfield, H. R.	*Textile Mfr.* No. 937, 39 (1953).
2901. Hadfield, H. R.	*Textile Mfr.* No. 941, 265 (1953).
2902. Kamrisch, B.	*Dyer* **108**, 709–13 (1952).
2903. Kamrisch, B., and Grainger, F.	*Dyer* **110**, 751–7 (1953).
2904. Loasby, G., and Munden, A. R.	*Review of Textile Progress, 1952.* Textile Institute and Society of Dyers and Colourists, England, 1953, 172–85.
2905. Marshall, I., and Thompson, A. B.	*Chem. & Ind.* No. 15, April 10, 1954, 419 (summary of paper).

Concerning

Chemistry of synthetic polymer fibers.

Isolation of a cyclic trimer from polyethylene terephthalate film.
Preparation of isophthalic and terephthalic acids by the reaction of $ClSO_3H_2$, H_2SO_4, and $C_6H_4(CF_3)_2$.
Terephthalic acid for the Terylene process—a review.

Oxidation of carbonaceous materials, e.g., coal, to organic acids, e.g., terephthalic acid.

Derivation of Terylene (polyethylene terephthalate), Buna, and Plexiglass from turpentine.
Chemistry of Terylene (polyethylene terephthalate).
Review of development of Terylene (polyethylene terephthalate).
Estimation of para-cymene by oxidation to terephthalic acid. Rapid oxidation increases yield of acid.

Terylene (polyethylene terephthalate) film, sheets, and fabric.

Review, with 14 references, of technical and patent literature on polyester synthetic fibers.
Modification of chemical, physical, and dyeing properties of textile fibers (including synthetic fibers).
Review on fibers, chemical textile improvements, and dyes. Many references.

Fine structure of polyethylene terephthalate monofilaments.
High-temperature setting of synthetic fibers. Relation of conditions to properties of fibers.
Review of heat setting of synthetic fibers.
Review, with 179 references, on developments in fiber field.

Dyeing of polyethylene terephthalate fiber. Use of "carrier" swelling agents to accelerate process.
Recent advances in dyeing of polyester fiber.
Techniques for dyeing modern synthetic fibers, e.g., Terylene (polyethylene terephthalate).
Dyeing of garments containing man-made fibers, including polyester fiber.

Production of synthetic fibers.

Analysis of continuous drawing processes in terms of basic load/extension properties of polymer, e.g., polyethylene terephthalate.

Manufacture of Fibers and Films (Continued)

Author	Reference
2906. Marshall, I., and Thompson, A. B.	*Nature* **171**, 38–9 (1953).
2907. Marshall, I., and Thompson, A. B.	*Proc. Roy. Soc.* (London) **A221**, 541–57 (1953).
2908. Marvin, D. N.	*Textile Mfr.* No. 941, 268 (1953).
2909. Mitchie, A. G. H.	*J. Soc. Dyers Colourists* **70**, 13–5 (1954).
2910. Mitchie, A. G. H.	*Textile Mfr.* No. 941, 265 (1953).
2911. Moncrieff, R. W.	*Fibres* **14**, 19–21, 62–5 (1953).
2912. Moncrieff, R. W.	*Artificial Fibers* 2nd ed., Wiley, New York, 1954, 462 pp.
2913. Morgan, L. B.	*Chem. & Ind.* No. 15, April 10, 1954, 419 (summary of paper).
2914. Niederhauser, J. P.	*De Tex* **8**, 557, *et seq.* (1949).
2915. Penn, W. S.	*India-Rubber J.* **110**, 501–2, 505, 533–4, 537 (1946).
2916. Remington, W. R.	*Am. Dyestuff Reptr.* **41**, 859–60 (1952).
2917. Scarlott, C. A.	*Nucelo* **7**, 409–16 (1952).
2918. Speel, H. C., editor.	*Textile Chemicals and Auxiliaries.* Reinhold, New York, 1952, 493 pp.
2919. Somers, J. A.	*Brit. Rayon Silk J.* **26**, No. 308, 59–60 (1950).
2920. Turner, K.	*Textile Recorder* **64**, No. 765, 36–7 (1946).
2921. Whinfield, J. R.	*Rubber Age & Synthetics* **34**, 115, 119–20 (1953).
2922. Wojatschek, K.	*Deut. Textilgewerbe* 1950, 51–3; *Chem. Zentr.* 1950, I, 2180.

Elastomeric Terephthalates

2923. Fisher, H. L.	*India Rubber World* **127**, 641–5, 712 (1953).
2924. Hamburger, W. J., Platt, M. M., and Morgan, H. M.	*Textile Research J.* **22**, 695–729 (1952).
2925. Hayashi, S.	*Busseiron Kenkyu* No. 56, 49–54 (1952).
2926. Mark, H. F.	*Am. Dyestuff Reptr.* **36**, 323–6 (1947).
2927. Stevens, W. H.	*India-Rubber J.* **123**, 983–6, 992 (1952).

Properties and Uses

2928. Anon.	*Chem. Age* **67**, 533–5 (1952).
2929. Anon.	*Chem. & Ind.* No. 19, May 8, 1954, 547.
2930. Anon.	*Chem. Eng.* **61**, No. 3, 144 (1954).
2931. Anon.	*Chem. Eng. News* **31**, 2838 (1953) ("Concentrates").
2932. Anon.	*Chem. Eng. News* **31**, 3406 (1953) (advertisement).

Concerning

Drawing of synthetic fibers (polyethylene terephthalate).

Cold drawing of fine filaments of amorphous polyethylene terephthalate.

Heat setting of polyester fiber in relation to dyeing and finishing.
Printing of polyester fiber material.
Technique for printing polyester fiber material.
Fundamental structural features of fibers.
Structure and properties of fibers in general; regenerated cellulosic and alginic
    fibers; regenerated protein fibers; synthetic fibers; processing of fibers.
Crystallization phenomena in fiber-forming polymers.

Dyeing superpolyamide and polyvinyl fibers. Survey of structure and properties
    of Terylene and other synthetic fibers.
Method of coloring polymers by copolymerization with dyes.

Dyeing Dacron polyester fiber.
History, fabrication, and impact of artificial fibers on the textile industry.
Role of chemicals, dyes, finishing agents, and auxiliaries in textile industry.
    Includes chapters on properties and processing of synthetic fibers (e.g.,
    Dacron).
Progress in manufacture of synthetic fibers in 1949. New production methods for
    Terylene (polyethylene terephthalate).
Terylene (polyethylene terephthalate), a new synthetic fiber. Forms produced.
Chemistry, physics, and manufacture of textile fibers.

Review of production and properties of artificial fibers, including Terylene.

Review of developments in synthetic elastomers. 82 references.
Elastic behavior of fabrics at low tensile strains.

Viscoelasticity of linear polymers.
Structure of synthetic fibers, e.g., requirements for good elastomers.
Review on elastomers.

Progress report on Terylene (polyethylene terephthalate). Estimated production
    capacity.
Terylene high pressure hose for fighting forest fires.
Chemically resistant rope made from polyester film.
Polyethylene terephthalate base for photographic film.

Mylar polyester film for electrical insulation of dial telephone equipment.

Properties and Uses (Continued)

Author	Reference
2933. Anon.	*Chem. Eng. News* **32**, 928 (1954).
2934. Anon.	*Chem. Eng. News* **32**, 1719 (1954).
2935. Anon.	*Chem. Eng. News* **32**, 1998–9 (1954).
2936. Anon.	*Du Pont Mag.* **47**, No. 1, 16–7 (1953).
2937. Anon.	E. I. du Pont de Nemours & Co., Inc., Textile Fibers Dept. Wilmington, Del. Booklet A-5339.
2938. Anon.	E. I. du Pont de Nemours & Co., Inc., Film Dept., Wilmington, Del. Tech. Bull. No. 1-2-53.
2939. Anon.	*Elect. Manuf.* **53**, No. 3, 6, 8 (1954).
2940. Anon.	*Fortune* March, 1954 (advertisement).
2941. Anon.	*Industries des plastiques modernes* **5**, No. 2 (1953).
2942. Anon.	Irvington Varnish & Insulator Co., Irvington, N. J. 4-p. brochure.
2943. Anon.	*Modern Packaging* **26**, No. 5, 83–9 (1953).
2944. Anon.	*Modern Packaging* **29**, No. 1, 75–8 (1951).
2945. Anon.	*Modern Plastics* **30**, No. 5, 204 (1953); *Plastics World* **10**, No. 12, 2 (1952).
2946. Anon.	*Modern Plastics* **30**, No. 9, 74–5, 182–3 (1953).
2947. Anon.	*Modern Plastics* **31**, No. 9, 76 (1954) (advertisement).
2948. Anon.	*Plastics World* **10**, No. 12, 31 (1952).
2949. Anon.	*Plastics World* **11**, No. 2, 25 (1953).
2950. Anon.	*Plastics World* **11**, No. 11, 6 (1953).
2951. Anon.	Wellington Sears Co., New York, N. Y. 20-p. booklet (1952).
2952. Amborski, L. A., and Flierl, D. W.	*Ind. Eng. Chem.* **45**, 2290–5 (1953).
2953. Amborski, L. A., and Burton, R. L.	*Elect. Manuf.* **53**, No. 3, 124–8 (1954).
2954. Astbury, W. T., and Brown, C. J.	*Nature* **158**, 871 (1946).
2955. Bouvet, R.	*Ind. Eng. Chem.* **44**, 2125–8 (1952).
2956. Bright, N. F. H., Carson, T., and Duff, G. M.	*J. Textile Inst.* **44**, T587–95 (1953).
2957. Carpenter, A. S.	*J. Soc. Dyers Colourists* **65**, 469–78 (1949).
2958. Coke, C. E.	*Can. Chem. Processing* **36**, No. 11, 74–6 (1952).
2959. De Malde, M.	*Materie plastiche* **18**, 205–10 (1952).
2960. Dillon, J. H.	*Ind. Eng. Chem.* **44**, 2115–22 (1952).
2961. Fabel, K.	*Melliand Textilber.* **31**, 110–2 (1950).
2962. Grew, H. S., Jr.	*Ind. Eng. Chem.* **44**, 2140–4 (1952).

Concerning

Polyester film as insulating material in motor.
Dacron filter cloth with excellent resistance to acid and caustic.
Report on meeting of Electrochemical Society. Includes summary of paper by
   J. A. Ruby on properties of Mylar polyester film.
Properties and applications of polyethylene terephthalate film.
Textile fibers for modern living. Includes Dacron (polyethylene terephthalate).

Properties and applications of Mylar polyester film.

Specialty applications for polyester film.
Applications of Mylar polyester film.
Discussion of polyester film.

Electrical insulation composed of polyester film bonded to various papers.

Mylar polyester film for packaging.
New textile fibers, e.g., Dacron polyester fiber.
Electrical insulation of polyester film and asbestos paper.

Polyester and other films as backing material for pressure-sensitive tape.

Properties and uses of Mylar polyester film, e.g., for lamination, electrical in-
   sulation, metallic threads, recording and industrial tapes.
Properties of four types of polyester film.
New Du Pont polyester film plant. Lists applications of films.
Fabrics from Dacron polyester fiber: tricot and taffeta.
Textiles for industry, e.g., Dacron.

Physical properties of polyethylene terephthalate films.

High-temperature resistivity of polyester film.

Structure of Terylene (polyethylene terephthalate) from x-ray photographs.

Relation of properties of synthetic fibers to properties of fabric made from them.
Heats of wetting for fibers, including polyester fiber.

Review, with 47 references, on synthetic fiber developments. Includes Terylene
   (polyethylene tereththalate).
Review of man-made fibers.

Review, with 44 references, on Terylene (polyethylene terephthalate).
Tensile properties of synthetic fibers (e.g., Dacron).
A survey of synthetic fibers.
Synthetic fibers. Industrial applications.

Properties and Uses (Continued)

	Author	Reference
2963.	Hardy, D. V. N., and Wood, W. A.	*Nature* **159**, 673–4 (1947).
2964.	Howlett, F.	*J. Textile Inst.* **41**, P124–31 (1950).
2965.	Javitz, A. E.	*Elect. Manuf.* **52**, No. 3 (1953).
2966.	Javitz, A. E.	*Elect. Manuf.* **52**, No. 9, 123 (1953).
2967.	Javitz, A. E.	*Elect. Manuf.* **53**, No. 1, 88–94 (1954).
2968.	Koch, P. A.	*Kolloid-Z.* **108**, 225–33 (1944).
2969.	Kollek, L.	*Melliand Textilber.* **31**, 26–31 (1950).
2970.	Krueger, R. C.	*Materials & Methods* **39**, No. 3, 104–6 (1954).
2971.	Mark, H. F.	*Chem. Eng. News* **27**, 138–42 (1949).
2972.	Marshall, I., and Todd, A.	*Trans. Faraday Soc.* **49**, 67–78 (1953).
2973.	McCann, H., editor.	*Modern Plastics Encyclopedia 1953*. Plastics Catalogue Corp., New York, 756.
2974.	Morris, M. G.	*Am. Dyestuff Reptr.* **41**, *Proc. Am. Assoc. Textile Chemists & Colorists* P479–81 (1952).
2975.	Morris, J. R.	*Chemist & Druggist* **160**, 143–5 (1953).
2976.	Owen, W. W.	*Rubber Age* (New York) **66**, 52–4 (1949).
2977.	Potter, H. V.	*Chem. & Ind.* 1949, 879–85.
2978.	Quig, J. B., and Dennison, R. W.	*Ind. Eng. Chem.* **44**, 2176–83 (1952).
2979.	Reddish, W.	*Trans. Faraday Soc.* **46**, 459–75 (1950).
2980.	Renfrew, A.	*Plastics Inst.* (London), *Trans.* **20**, No. 41, 57–67 (1952).
2981.	Royer, G. L.	American Cyanamid Co., Calco Chemical Div., Bound Brook, N. J. Tech. Bull. No. 831, 12 pp. (1953).
2982.	Sassi, D.	*Interchem. Rev.* **10**, No. 1–3, 1–20 (1951).
2983.	Soulaz, M.	*Industrie textile* **69**, 673–6 (1952).
2984.	Susich, G.	*Textile Res. J.* **24**, 210–28 (1954).
2985.	Urquhart, A. R., et al.	*Development of Some Man Made Fibers*. Textile Institute, Manchester, England, 1952, 79 pp.
2986.	Van Boskirk, R. L.	*Modern Plastics* **28**, No. 1, 178 (1950) ("The Plastiscope").
2987.	Van Boskirk, R. L.	*Modern Plastics* **29**, No. 7, 280 (1952) ("The Plastiscope").
2988.	Van Boskirk, R. L.	*Modern Plastics* **31**, No. 9, 210, 212 (1954).
2989.	Weston, G. J.	*Chem. & Ind.* No. 21, May 22, 1954, 604.
2990.	Wiese, W. E.	*SPE J.* **9**, No. 6, 73 (1953).

Concerning

Structure of Terylene (polyethylene terephthalate) from x-ray photographs.

Structure of synthetic-polymer rayons, including Terylene (polyethylene terephthalate) fibers.

Nonrigid materials for functional design of electrical insulating systems. Includes Mylar polyester film.

Nonrigid materials, e.g., polyester film, for electrical insulating systems.

Research progress in dielectrics during 1953. Includes polyester film.

Tensile strength of textile fibers. Method for measuring brittleness.

Review of applications of synthetic resins and elastomers in the textile industry. 26 references.

Properties and applications of Mylar polyester film.

Trends in polymer chemistry. Mentions "terylenes" (polyethylene terephthalate) for formation of fibers.

Thermal degradation of polyethylene terephthalate. Kinetics and products.

Properties of Dacron polyester fiber.

Dyeing of auto fabrics. Dacron as unsatisfactory substitute for pile fabrics.

Properties and identification of artificial fibers, including polyester fiber.

Review of industrial uses of synthetic fibers.

Historical survey of development of synthetic fibers.

Synthetic fibers. Functional properties of synthetics.

Dielectric properties of polyethylene terephthalate (Terylene).

Fibers and plastics. Includes polyethylene terephthalate fibers.

Identification of synthetic fibers by microscopical and dye staining techniques. Includes Dacron polyester fiber.

General review of textile fibers. Dacron mentioned.

Trade names, manufacturer, properties, and uses of textile fibers, e.g., polyethylene terephthalates, polyurethanes.

Measurement of abrasion damage of fibers.

Three papers with many references.

Fiber V (Dacron)—a condensation polymer of ethylene glycol and terephthalic acid.

Brief note on properties and applications of Mylar polyester film.

Brief note on progress of new Mylar plant construction and available types, applications, and properties of Mylar polyester film.

Infrared spectrum of Terylene.

Progress in man-made fibers, e.g., Dacron polyester fiber.

Properties and Uses (Continued)

Author	Reference
2991. Wooley, M. C., Kohman, G. T., and McMahan, W.	*Elect. Eng.* **71**, 715–7 (1952).
2991a. Anon.	*Textile World* **101**, No. 7, 120 (1951).
2991b. Larson, L. L.	*Am. Assoc. Textile Technol.* **6**, No. 2, 125–34 (1951).

Economics

Author	Reference
2992. Anon.	*Brit. Plastics* **27**, No. 2, 67 (1954).
2993. Anon.	*Can. Plastics* May–June 1954, 33.
2994. Anon.	*Chem. & Ind.* No. 38, Sept. 1953, 1000; No. 40, Oct. 1953, 1065, 1154; *Chem. Eng. News* **31**, 4797 (1953).
2995. Anon.	*Chem. & Ind.* No. 6, Feb. 6, 1954, 154.
2996. Anon.	*Chem. & Ind.* No. 22, May 29, 1954, 622.
2997. Anon.	*Chem. Eng. News* **31**, 1326 (1953).
2998. Anon.	*Chem. Eng. News* **31**, 2655 (1953).
2999. Anon.	*Chem. Eng. News* **31**, 2998 (1953).
3000. Anon.	*Chem. Eng. News* **31**, 3830 (1953).
3001. Anon.	*Chem. Eng. News* **31**, 3830 (1953).
3002. Anon.	*Chem. Eng. News* **32**, 546–7 (1954).
3003. Anon.	*Chem. Eng. News* **32**, 550 (1954).
3004. Anon.	*Chem. Eng. News* **32**, 697 (1954).
3005. Anon.	*Chem. Week* **72**, No. 18, 44 (1953).
3006. Anon.	*Modern Plastics* **30**, No. 5, 204 (1953).
3007. Anon.	*Plastics* (London) **17**, 337 (1952).
3008. Bunn, H.	*Ind. Eng. Chem.* **44**, 2128–33 (1952).
3009. Grove, C. S., Jr., Vodonik, J. L., and Casey, R. S.	*Ind. Eng. Chem.* **45**, 2119–2204 (1953).
3010. Hover, C. O.	*Ind. Eng. Chem.* **44**, 2133–9 (1952).
3011. Penn, W. S.	*Austral. Plastics* **8**, No. 90, 30–1 (1953).

Concerning.

Polyethylene terephthalate (Mylar) as a dielectric in capacitors.

Dacron data sheet. Gives types of fibers and properties.
Properties of Dacron and its use in clothing.

Licensing of Dutch firm for production of Terylene fibers.
Licensing of foreign firms for production of Terylene.
Licensing of Italian, French, and German firms for production of Terylene fibers.

Progress on construction of Terylene plant.
Annual report of Imperial Chemical Industries; mentions pilot plant for polyester film (Melinex).
German production of terephthalic acid and synthetic fibers.
Increased production capacity for Terylene fiber (polyethylene terephthalate).
New Canadian plant for production of Terylene (polyethylene terephthalate fiber).
Terylene (polyethylene terephthalate fiber) production in Italy.
Commercial production of acrylic and polyester fibers by Japanese firms.
Price reductions for synthetic fibers: nylon, Orlon, and Dacron.
Expansion at Hercules Powder Co., e.g., full-scale production of dimethyl terephthalate.
Licensing of Dutch and Belgian firms to produce Terylene.
Dacron production.
New plant for manufacture of Mylar polyester film.
Terylene production capacity of Imperial Chemical Industries, Ltd.
Synthetic fibers. Cost and availability of raw materials.
Review, with 163 references, on developments in fibers. Mainly on expansion of existing facilities or construction of new production units.

Synthetic fibers. Choice of plant sites.
British plastics production, including Terylene.

SATURATED POLYESTERS

General

Author	Reference
3012. Bayer, O.	*Modern Plastics* **24**, No. 10, 149–52, 250–62 (1947).
3013. Bayer, O.	*Angew. Chem.* **59**, 257–72 (1947).
3014. Bjorksten, J. A., Tovey, H., and Dollard, H. L., Jr.	*Modern Plastics* **31**, No. 8, 143–4, 228–30, 233 (1954).
3015. Hoff, G. P., and Wicker, D. B.	*PB Rept.* No. 1122 (*FIAT Rept.* FR 37).
3016. Reinl, W.	*Farbe u. Lack* **60**, 69–72 (1954).

Elastomers

Author	Reference
3017. Anon.	*Modern Plastics* **31**, No. 2, 232, 234 (1953).
3018. Bayer, O., *et al.*	*Angew Chem.* **62**, 57–66 (1950).
3019. Bayer, O., *et al.*	*Rubber Chem. and Tech.* **23**, 812–35 (1950).
3020. Dinsmore, R. P.	Address before Washington, D. C., Rubber Group, Goodyear Rubber Co., March 18, 1953.
3021. Harper, D. A., Smith, W. F., and White, H. G.	*Proc. 2nd Rubber Technol. Conf.* (London) 1948, 61–8.
3022. Höchtlen, A.	*Kunststoffe* **42**, 302–10 (1952).
3023. Kline, G. M.	*Modern Plastics* **23**, No. 2, 152A–152B (1945).
3024. Kline, G. M.	*Plastics and Resins* **4**, No. 12, 13–4, 28–30, 32 (1946).
3025. Muller, E.	*Kunststoffe* **41**, 13–9 (1951).
3026. Muller, E., *et al.*	*Angew. Chem.* **64**, 523–31 (1952).
3027. Seeger, N. V., *et al.*	*Ind. Eng. Chem.* **45**, 2538–42 (1953).

Adhesives

Author	Reference
3028. Anon.	Monsanto Chemical Co., Phosphate Div., St. Louis, Mo. Tech. Bull. No. P-145, 6 pp. (1953).
3029. Anon.	Monsanto Chemical Co., Phosphate Div., St. Louis, Mo. Tech. Bull. No. P-151, 15 pp. (1953).

Foams

Author	Reference
3030. Anon.	American Latex Products Corp., Hawthorne, Calif. 12-p. booklet.
3031. Anon.	American Latex Products Corp., Hawthorne, Calif. Data Sheets.

II. DI-ISOCYANATE-MODIFIED POLYESTERS

Concerning

Comprehensive review on polyurethanes.

Detailed description of polyurethanes.
Applications of polyurethane resins: fibers, foamed plastics, adhesives, elastomers, coatings.

A report on German methods of preparation of polyurethanes (Perlon U).

Toxic effects of plastics and lacquers based on polyurethanes.

Polyester (polyurethane) rubber with high tensile strength and resistance to
abrasion and oxidation.
Elastomers based on polyurethanes. A detailed report.
New types of highly elastic substances.
Mechanical properties of polyurethane elastomer, Chemigum SL.

Preparation and applications of rubberlike linear polymers from condensation of
a dibasic acid with a di-reactive alcohol or amine, e.g., di-isocyanate-modified
polyesteramide (Vulcaprene-A).
Chemistry and applications of polyurethanes.
Review on German plastics, 1939–1945.
German I-gummi and I-rubber di-isocyanate-modified polyesters.

A review on German plastics with a polyester base.
Cross-linking agents for polyurethane elastomers (Vulcollan), e.g., diamines,
glycols.
Properties and uses of elastomers from glycol-adipic acid polyesters and
di-isocyanates.

Isocyanates in the adhesion of rubber.

Polyurethanes and their use as adhesives.

Properties and applications of thermosetting foamed plastics.

Properties of alkyd-di-isocyanate foams.

Foams (Continued)

Author	Reference
3032. Anon.	Armour & Co., Adhesive Div., Chicago, Ill. Tech. Bull.
3033. Anon.	*Brit. Plastics* **26**, 170–1 (1953).
3034. Anon.	*Chem. Eng. News* **32**, 1621, 1665 (1954).
3035. Anon.	*Chem. Eng. News* **32**, 1661, (1954); *Can. Plastics* May–June 1954, 119.
3036. Anon.	*Chem. Eng. News* **32**, 1712 (1954) (advertisement).
3037. Anon.	*Chem. Eng. News* **32**, 1998–9 (1954).
3038. Anon.	*Chem. Week* **74**, No. 20, 68, 70, 72 (1954).
3039. Anon.	Isocyanate Products, Inc. Wilmington, Del. 4-p. booklet.
3040. Anon.	*Modern Plastics* **30**, No. 8, 85–7 (1953).
3041. Anon.	Monsanto Chemical Co., Phosphate Div., St. Louis, Mo. Tech. Bull. No. P-144, 5 pp. (1953).
3042. Anon.	Monsanto Chemical Co., Phosphate Div., St. Louis, Mo. Tech. Bull. No. P-125, 10 pp. (1953).
3043. Anon.	Nopco Chemical Co., Inc., Harrison, N. J. 28-p. booklet.
3044. Fromardi, G.	*Rubber Age and Synthetics* **33**, 521 (1953).
3045. Gerschler, J. M.	*SAE J.* **61**, No. 2, 24–8 (1953).
3046. Goodyear Aircraft Co.	Reports on USAF Contract No. W 33-038-AC-15228, Wright-Patterson Air Force Base, Dayton, Ohio.
3047. Lever, A. E.	*Plastics* (London) **18**, 274–7 (1953).
3048. Moore, H. R.	*Reinforced Plastics Div., Soc. Plastics Ind. Confer., 9th Annual,* 1954, Sect. 1E.
3049. Stevens, J. M.	*Reinforced Plastics Div., Soc. Plastics Ind. Confer., 9th Annual,* 1954, Sect. 1H.

Molding Compounds

3050. Romanowski, A.	*Kunststoffe* April 1953.

Coatings

3051. Anon.	*Chem. Age* **54**, No. 1655, 481–4 (1951).
3052. Beck, G.	*Kunststoffe* **43**, 107–9 (1953).
3053. Eitel, F.	*Das Leder* **4**, 234–40 (1953).
3054. Kubitzky, K.	*Melliand Textilber.* **35**, 66–8 (1954).
3055. Petersen, S.	*Ann. Chem.* **562**, 205–29 (1949).
3056. Scheer, R. J.	*Farbe u. Lack* **59**, 54–5 (1953).

Concerning

Properties, applications, and handling of alkyd-di-isocyanate foams.

Foamed plastics (polyurethanes) in aircraft structures.
Two-component isocyanate foamed-in-place resins.
Joint production of isocyanates by Monsanto and German firm.

Brief mention of properties and applications of isocyanate rigid foams.
Report of Electrochemical Society meeting. Includes summary of paper by J. H. Saunders which mentions use of di-isocyanate-modified polyesters as foams in radomes and as electric wire coatings.
Properties and applications of polyester-isocyanate foams, also producer and future for product.
Properties, applications, and directions for use of isocyanate foamed-in-place resins.
New foamed plastics, including isocyanate-based foams: properties and applications.
Properties and uses of polyurethanes for foamed plastics.

Isocyanates: reactions, uses (e.g., foamed resins), toxicity, testing, bibliography, storage.

Applications and properties of alkyd-isocyanate foams.

Nontoxicity and moisture resistance of polyisocyanates.
Polyurethane filled-in-place (foamed) structures.
Foaming-in-place of alkyd resin for sandwich radomes.

Preparation and properties of expanded and foamed plastics; includes polyurethanes.
Low-temperature process, based on internal cooling with dry ice, for foaming of alkyd-di-isocyanate resins.
Uses of foamed plastics in aircraft.

Polyurethanes are listed among the plastics that can be blow-molded to give films. Methods and machines are described.

Evaluation of the properties of polyurethane coatings.
Use of polyamides and polyurethanes for bonding polyvinyl chloride coatings.
Use of isocyanate-polyester resins in leather industry.
Waterproofing of fabrics with isothiocyanate-polyester resins.
Relatively stable types of di-isocyanate reagents.
Properties of di-isocyanate-alkyd coatings for wires.

Raw Materials

Author	Reference
3057. Anon.	*Paint, Oil,* & *Chem. Rev.* **116**, No. 5, 12–21; No. 7, 12–3, 36–7; No. 8, 24, 26–9, 54–6; No. 10, 12–8, 20–1 (1953).

Resins and Plastics

3058. Anon.	*ASTM Bull.* No. 192, 10 (1953).
3059. Anon.	*ASTM Bull.* No. 192, 12 (1953).
3060. Anon.	*ASTM Bull.* No. 192, 13 (1953).
3061. Anon.	*ASTM Bull.* No. 192, 15 (1953).
3062. Anon.	*ASTM Index.* American Society for Testing Materials, Philadelphia, 1953, 216 pp.
3063. Anon.	*ASTM Standards on Plastics.* American Society for Testing Materials, Philadelphia, 1953, 705 pp.
3064. Anon.	*Plastics.* American Society for Testing Materials, Philadelphia, 1953, 680 pp.
3065. (Various authors)	*Plastics Symposium.* ASTM Tech. Pub. STP 59, Philadelphia, 1944, 200 pp.
3066. Anon.	American Standards Testing Bureau, New York, N. Y. 4-p. booklet.
3067. Anon.	*Elect. Manuf.* **53**, No. 4, 336, 338, 340 (1954).
3068. Anon.	*Federal Specification No. L-P-406.* Superintendent of Documents, Washington, D. C., 1951.
3069. Anon.	Manufacturing Chemists Association, New York, N. Y. Booklet.
3070. Anon.	*Modern Packaging* **26**, 137–40 (1952).
3071. Adams, W. H., and Lebach, H. H.	*Chem. Eng.* **56**, No. 7, 98–101 (1949).
3072. Albert, G. A.	*Plastics* (Chicago) **5**, No. 4, 56–7, 69–70 (1946).
3073. Barron, H.	*Brit. Plastics* **16**, 339–48 (1944).
3074. Barron, H.	*Plastics* (London) **8**, 258–6, 322–30 (1944).
3075. Berkson, J. S.	*Reinforced Plastics Div., Soc. Plastics Ind. Confer., 9th Annual,* 1954, Sect. 2C.
3076. Blom, A. V.	*Kunststoffe* **43**, No. 8, 294–6 (1953).

Concerning

Review of methods and criteria for examination of polyhydric alcohols.

Report of committee on structural sandwich construction on standardization of test methods.
Report of committee on electrical insulating materials, e.g., tests for polymerizable embedding materials.
Report of committee on plastics, e.g., tests for dynamic properties, flamability, heat distortion, and brittle temperature of plastics.
Report of committee on appearance, e.g., determination of color differences, measurement of gloss.
Author and subject guide to ASTM technical papers, 1898–1950.

Specifications, test methods, nomenclature, definitions.

Compilation of standards and methods of testing for plastics.

Properties and uses of various plastics families. 15 articles, including testing of plastics.
List of testing methods for 90 different products.

Proposed National Electrical Manufacturers' Association standard for general-purpose grade polyester-glass mat laminates.
General specifications and test methods for organic plastics.

Progress report on basic research project to define behavior of plastics. Reports new testing equipment.
Test methods for conditioning and accelerated-age setting of molded plastic products and plastic films.
Statistical method for determining chemical resistance of plastics, based on (1) changes of appearance of solution, (2) changes in appearance of sample, (3) changes in weight of sample, (4) changes in volume of sample.
Mechanical testing of plastics. Compressive, flexural, impact, and tensile strength.
Qualitative methods of identifying plastics.
British Standards Institution test methods for plastics.
Report of Standards Committee. Need for corrugated sheeting standard.

Method for comparison of test results by different scientists. Graphic characterization of plastics.

Resins and Plastics (Continued)

Author	Reference
3077. Boller, K. H.	*U. S. Dept. Agriculture, Forest Products Lab. Rept.* No. 1823, 66 pp. (1952).
3078. Boller, K. H.	*U. S. Dept. Agriculture, Forest Products Lab. Rept.* No. 1839 (1953).
3079. Boyer, R. F.	*J. Polymer Sci.* **9**, 289–94 (1952).
3080. Brinkema, R. J.	*Reinforced Plastics Div., Soc. Plastics Ind. Confer., 9th Annual,* 1954, Sect. 2F.
3081. Charlton, M. G., and Farmer, S. N.	*Brit. Plastics* **19**, 208–11 (1947).
3082. Curl, B. B.	*Reinforced Plastics Div., Soc. Plastics Ind. Confer., 9th Annual,* 1954, Sect. 2B.
3083. Dewar, W. J.	*Tool & Die J.* **10**, No. 10, 129–30 (1945).
3084. Dietz, A. G. H., Hauser, E. A., and Sofer, G. A.	*Ind. Eng. Chem.* **45**, 2743 (1953).
3085. Dobraczynski, A.	*Przemysl Chem.* **31**, No. 8, 408–11 (1952).
3086. Eckhaus, S., Wolock, I., and Harris, B. L.	*Ind. Eng. Chem.* **45**, 426–8 (1953).
3087. Epprecht, A. G.	*Ind. vernice* (Milan) **6**, 194–201 (1952).
3088. Esch, W., and Nitsche, R.	*Wiss. Abhandl. deut. Materialprüfungstalt* **2**, No. 1, 22–9 (1941); *Chem. Zentr.* 1941, II, 1687.
3089. Evans, C. G., and Hall, H. W.	*Chem. & Ind.* 1953, 229–34.
3090. Findley, W. N.	*Applied Mechanics Reviews* **6**, 49–53 (1953).
3091. Fineman, M. N., and Puddington, I. E.	*Can. J. Research* **25B**, 101–7 (1947).
3092. Frankel, L. P., and Radcliffe, C. W.	*ASTM Bull.* No. 175, 71–5 (1951).
3093. Fuller, C. S.	*Ind. Eng. Chem.* **30**, 472–7 (1938).
3094. Gordon, P. L., and Lerner, I.	*Am. Paint J.* **30**, No. 9, 51, 54 (1945).
3095. Hertel, O. R.	*India-Rubber J.* **109**, 657–61 (1945).
3096. Krassowsky, W.	*Kunststoffe* **33**, 78–9 (1943); *Chem. Zentr.* 1943, II, 477.
3097. Kraus, H. S.	*Reinforced Plastics Div., Soc. Plastics Ind. Confer., 9th Annual,* 1954, Sect. 20.
3098. Lamb, J. J., and Axilrod, B. M.	*ASTM Bull.* No. 151, 59–66 (TP67–74) (1948).
3099. Lappala, R. P.	Personal communication, Bjorksten Research Laboratories, Inc., Madison, Wis.
3100. Leonard, J. M.	*Elec. Manuf.* **50**, No. 3, 98–103, 316, 318, 320 (1952).

Concerning

Results and various methods of fatigue testing of glass fabric base laminates made with commercial polyesters.

Stress-rupture tests of glass fabric–polyester laminates. Methods and results.

Ratio of tensile strength to melt viscosity for high polymeric materials.

Report of Standards Committee. Need for standard for reinforced plastics for chemical resistance applications.

Falling-weight type of method for measuring impact strength of plastics.

Proposed standard for glass mat reinforced polyester flat sheet. (Report of Standards Committee.)

Review of testing of plastics.

Measurement of resin cure by ultrasonic waves.

Standardization of measurements and methods of investigating plastic materials.

Porosity of paint film. Water vapor adsorption and permeability.

Determination of viscosity in the laboratory and in the plant.

Chemical analysis and structure determination of thermosetting and thermoplastic resins. (Polyesters not specifically mentioned.)

Discussion of sources of error in common strength tests of plastics, value of tests to aircraft designers, and effect of resin content on strength of reinforced plastics.

Review, with 119 references, on mechanical behavior and testing of plastics.

Rate and extent of cure of thermosetting resins, including unsaturated polyester resins.

Comparison between conventional continuous load tests for determination of pin bearing strength of laminates and test based on repeated load-permanent set technique.

X-ray investigation of linear copolyesters and mechanical mixtures of linear polyesters.

Time-saving centrifuge method for determining phthalic anhydride in resins.

Commercial testing of plastics in United States.

Standards for laminated plastics. Includes properties, testing methods, and rating of finished products.

Quality control program for aircraft plastics; also brief description of quality control process for low-pressure laminating.

Tensile stress-strain relationships of laminated plastics for small strains. Includes glass fabric-unsaturated polyester laminates.

Method for determining gel time of resins.

Tests and improvement of resistance of plastics to fungi.

Resins and Plastics (Continued)

Author	Reference
3101. Mandelkern, L., Garrett, R., and Flory, P. J.	*J. Amer. Chem. Soc.* **74**, 3949–51 (1952).
3102. Manfield, H. G.	*Brit. Plastics* **26**, 230–1 (1953).
3103. Meyer, L. S.	*Reinforced Plastics Div., Soc. Plastics Ind. Confer., 5th Annual,* 1950, Sect. 7.
3104. Meysenburg, C. M. v.	*Kunststoffe* **43**, 214–20 (1953).
3105. Millane, J. J.	*Brit. Plastics* **25**, 367–73 (1952).
3106. Nijveld, W. J.	*Verfkroniek* **20**, 191–4 (1947).
3107. Nitsche, R.	*Kunststoffe* **42**, 427–33 (1952).
3108. Pallaud, R.	*Chim. anal.* **32**, 14–7 (1950).
3109. Peters, D.	*Angew. Chem.* **64**, 586–90 (1952).
3110. Rohde, L.	*Kunststoff-Tech. u. Kunststoff-Anwend.* **11**, 77–82 (1941); *Chem. Zentr.* 1941, II, 1686–7.
3111. Rosato, D.	*Reinforced Plastics Div., Soc. Plastics Ind. Confer., 9th Annual,* 1954, Sect. 1J.
3112. Schmieder, K., and Wolf, K.	*Kolloid-Z.* **127**, 65–78 (1952).
3113. Shaw, T. P. G.	*Ind. Eng. Chem., Anal. Ed.* **16**, 541–9 (1944).
3114. Shay, J. F., Skilling, S., and Stafford, R. W.	*Anal. Chem.* **26**, 652–6 (1954).
3115. Shepard, H. R.	*Reinforced Plastics Div., Soc. Plastics Ind. Confer., 9th Annual,* 1954, Sect. 2A.
3116. Simril, V. L., and Herschberger, A.	*Modern Plastics* **27**, No. 10, 97, 98, 100, 102, 150–2, 154, 156, 158 (1950).
3117. Sontag, L. A., and Borro, E. F.	*Modern Plastics* **23**, No. 8, 200–2, 250, 252 (1946).
3118. Speitmann, M.	*Chem.-Ztg.* **61**, 415–9 (1937).
3119. Stafford, R. W., Francel, R. J., and Shay, J. F.	*Anal. Chem.* **21**, 1454–7 (1949).
3120. Stafford, R. W., and Shay, J. F.	Paper presented at Amer. Chem. Soc. Meeting, Div. Paint, Plastics, and Printing Ink Chem., Chicago, September 1953.
3121. Stafford, R. W., Shay, J. F., and Skilling, S.	*Anal. Chem.* **26**, 656–61 (1951).
3122. Stock, C. R., *et al.*	*Plastics Testing—Present and Future.* ASTM Tech. Pub. STP 132, Philadelphia, 1953, 78 pp.
3123. Swann, M. H.	*Anal. Chem.* **25**, 1735–7 (1953).
3124. Thinius, K.	*Farben, Lacke, Anstrichstoffe* **4**, 113–20 (1950).

Concerning

Methods of determining heats of fusion of aliphatic polyesters.

Measurement of exotherms of casting and laminating resins.
Standards Committee report. Procedures for resins, paper, glass.

Method for determination of the heat distortion of plastics.
Review, with 27 references, on physical testing of thermoplastics.
Qualitative reactions for resins.
Review, with 22 references, of testing methods for plastics.
Qualitative analysis of plastics. Review of chemical and physical tests.
Method and apparatus for comparing foam-producing materials by "minimum bubble size."
Test methods for plastics to be used as insulating materials, condensers, or in other high-frequency applications.

Discussion of specifications for materials and process used in fabricating aircraft parts.
Mechanical properties of polymers (including polyester resin) as determined by free torsion indications.
Systematic procedure for identification of synthetic resins and plastics. Common resins classified by types and general reactions.
Identification of polyhydric alcohols in polymeric esters.

Proposed standard for general-purpose polyester-glass mat sheet laminate. (Report of Standards Committee.)
Permeability of polymeric films, e.g., vinyl chloride–diethyl fumarate, to organic vapors.
Measurement of ability of thermosetting plastics to flow during molding.

Molecular structure of plastics as indicated by graphs obtained with dynamometer type of viscosity-measuring apparatus.
Identification of dicarboxylic acids in polymeric esters by means of dibenzylamides.

Method for analysis of unsaturated polyester formulations containing fillers, dyes, etc.

Identification of dicarboxylic acids in polymeric esters.

Symposium on procedures used for testing plastics.

Determination of polystyrene in styrenated alkyd and epoxy resins.
Analytical chemistry of solvents, plasticizers, and resins compounded with high polymers. Includes determination of esters of phthalic, maleic, and adipic acids.

Resins and Plastics (Continued)

	Author	Reference
3125.	Tschudi	*Schweiz. Arch. angew. Wiss. Tech.* **9**, 360 (1943).
3126.	Tucker, J. R.	*Plastics* (Chicago) **2**, No. 1, 34–5, 78 (1945).
3127.	Veillon, E. A.	*Schweiz. Arch. angew. Wiss. Tech.* **9**, 184–5 (1943); *Chem. Zentr.* 1943, II, 1146–7.
3128.	Wandeberg, E.	*Kunststoffe* **43**, appendix Kunststoff-Praxis, 165–6 (1953).
3129.	Werner, W., and Nielsen, A.	*Kunststoffe* **34**, 122–6 (1944).
3130.	Whitnack, G. S.	*Anal. Chem.* **20**, 658–61 (1948).
3131.	Zinzow, W. A.	*ASTM Bull.* No. 134, 31–7 (1945).
3131a.	Brent, A.	*Elect. Manuf.* **51**, No. 5, 105 (1953).
3131b.	Coats, A. L., and Pomeroy, C.	*Elect. Manuf.* **51**, No. 1, 100 (1953).
3131c.	Wredden, J. H.	*Plastics* (London) **12**, 38–44, 90, 152, 208, 266, 323, 381, 436, 496, 551, 607, 662 (1948).
3131d.	Yustein, S. E., *et al.*	*Elect. Manuf.* **51**, No. 2, 110 (1953).
3131e.	Anon.	Translation of Testing Method of ASEA, Sweden (P Se 38).
3131f.	Anon.	Translation of Testing Method of ASEA, Sweden (P Se 120).

Equipment for Testing Plastics

	Author	Reference
3132.	Anon.	Baldwin-Lima-Hamilton Corp., Testing Equipment Dept., Philadelphia, Pa. Bull. No. 4202.
3133.	Anon.	*Chem. Eng. News* **30**, 5256 (1952).
3134.	Anon.	*Modern Plastics* **30**, No. 10, 160 (1953).
3135.	Anon.	*Natl. Bur. Standards Rept.* No. 4742.
3136.	Anon.	National Forge and Ordnance Co., Irvine, Pa. Brochure.
3137.	Anon.	*Plastics News Letter* **14**, No. 23, 1 (1954).
3138.	Anon.	United States Testing Co., Inc., Hoboken, N. J. 4-p. leaflet.
3139.	Agnew, W. B. R.	*Electronics* **18**, No. 12, 160–1 (1945).
3140.	Bailey, A. J., and Ward, O. W.	*ASTM Bull.* No. 140, 50–4 (1946).
3141.	Bashore, H. H.	*Ind. Plastics* **1**, No. 11, 19–21, 35 (1946).
3142.	Boor, L., *et al.*	*ASTM Bull.* 1947, 68–73.
3143.	Burns, R.	*ASTM Bull.* No. 195, 61–2 (1954).

Concerning

Testing of thermosetting plastics.

General discussion of laboratory testing of plastics.
Method for testing the flow of hardening plastics.

Methods of identifying type of resin and filler in laminated plastics.

Application of statistical methods in manufacture, testing, and use of plastics.

Polarographic determination of free monomer in heteropolymerization mixtures, e.g., maleic anhydride in mixtures with styrene and their copolymers.
Flexural properties of plastics.
Special temperature-humidity cycling tests for evaluating electrical performance of laminated and molded thermosetting plastics.
Evaluation tests for molded plastic materials; includes electrical, mechanical, chemical, and thermal tests.
Microscopic examination of plastics—identification of various filler materials.

Simple laboratory tests for shock resistance of molded thermosetting plastics.
Standard for determination of volume resistivity and surface resistivity in plastic materials. Electrode arrangement described.
Standard for determination of insulation resistance in plastic materials using bolt electrodes and stopper electrodes.

Machine for static, dynamic, impact, and torsion testing.

Tester of flammability of plastics.
Hand polariscope for detection of strains in glass and plastics.
Inexpensive, accurate laboratory accelerated weathering test for plastics; fluorescent sunlamps used.
Impact tester for Izod and Charpy tests.

Machine for testing fatigue properties of plastics.
Flammability tester.

Interference-free weatherometer for testing plastic and rubber materials.
Small-scale ball-impact test for laboratory testing of plastics.

Testing applications in the plastic industry and equipment for such testing.
Hardness and abrasion resistance of 25 commercial plastics (includes polyester canvas laminate).
New impact test machine for plastics. Eliminates source of error of Izod method, i.e., the toss factor, or energy consumed in tossing away broken specimen.

Equipment for Testing Plastics (Continued)

	Author	Reference
3144.	Gale, J. A., Stewart, R. W., and Alfers, J. B.	*ASTM Bull.* No. 131, 23–7 (1944).
3145.	Gordon, C. A.	*Selected Govt. Research Repts.* (Gt. Brit.) Vol. 1, Plastics, Rept. No. 16, 317–25 (1952).
3146.	Goss, A. E., and Ross, A. M., Jr.	*India Rubber World* **127**, 652–6 (1953).
3147.	Grodzenski, P.	*Plastics* (London) **18**, 312–4 (1953).
3148.	Grotlisch, V. E., and Burstein, H. N.	*Ind. Eng. Chem., Anal. Ed.* **17**, 476–80 (1945).
3149.	Higgenbotham, R. S., and Benhow, J. J.	*J. Sci. Instr.* **29**, 221–4 (1952).
3150.	Kepes, A.	*Inds. plastiques* **3**, 168–70 (1947).
3151.	Lidstone, F. M.	*Chem. & Ind.* 1952, 873–4.
3152.	Masson, D.	*Plastics & Resins* **4**, No. 4, 9–11 (1945).
3153.	Mehdorn, W.	*Kunststoffe* **34**, 133–6 (1944).
3154.	Mehnert, K.	*Dechema Monograph* **18**, 113–24 (1951).
3155.	Nielsen, L. E., and Buchdahl, R.	*SPE J.* **9**, No. 5, 16–9, 41 (1953).
3156.	Nitsche, R.	*Schweiz. Arch. Angew. Wiss. u. Tech.* **19**, 139–48 (1953).
3157.	Nowak, P.	*Kunststoffe* **34**, 120–1 (1944).
3158.	Rencker, E.	*Plastiques* **1**, 171–5 (1943).
3159.	Robertson, R. G., Lobisser, R. J., and Stein, R. E.	*Ind. Eng. Chem.* **38**, 590–1 (1946).
3160.	Setchkm, N. P.	*J. Research Natl. Bur. Standards* **43**, 591–608 (1949).
3161.	Sieffert, L. E., and Schoenborn, E. M.	*Ind. Eng. Chem.* **42**, 496–502 (1950).
3162.	Sofer, G. A., and Hauser, E. A.	*J. Polymer Sci.* **8**, 611–20 (1952).
3163.	Stark, H. J.	*ASTM Bull.* No. 162, 55–8 (1949).
3164.	Stock, C. R.	*ASTM Bull.* No. 130, 21–6 (1944).
3165.	Vieweg, R., and Gast, T.	*Kunststoffe* **34**, 117–9 (1944).
3166.	Ward, O. W., and Bailey, A.	*ASTM Bull.* No. 138, 33–6 (1936).

Concerning

Apparatus for measuring flame resistance of filled thermosetting plastics and
laminates.

Microscopic examination of fiber reinforced synthetic resins.

Shore type A Durometer for hardness testing of plastics (vinyl).

New instruments for hardness testing of plastics. Limitations of present methods
and equipment discussed.
Determination of softening points of resins by heating in an air bath immersed in
a constant-temperature liquid bath.
Viscometers for rapid measurements at definite shearing stresses.

Apparatus for flexibility and hardness tests on plastics.
Microviscometer of improved design.
Equipment for testing wear and abrasion resistance of plastics.
Abrasion tester for measuring abrasion of metals by plastics. Simulates wear on
molds.
Apparatus for determining the brittle point of synthetic films and laminated fiber
sheets.
Mechanical properties of plastics. Torsion pendulum shear modulus tester.

Methods and instruments for measuring the creep of plastics.

Titrimetric determination of the water-vapor permeability of plastics.
Methods for evaluating effect of heat on physical properties of thermosetting
materials.
Laboratory tests to determine resistance of glass-cloth laminates to rain abrasion.

Determination of flash and self-ignition temperatures of plastics, including polyester group.
Heat resistance of laminated plastics. Glass-base low-pressure polyester had
lowest critical thermal instability temperature.
Ultrasonic equipment for determination of stage of polymerization of thermosetting polymers. Data given for a polyester resin.
Ignition resistance and burning time of polyester, phenolic, and melamine fibrous
glass laminates. Polyesters had lowest values.
A ball-impact tester for plastics that is superior to pendulum and falling-weight
types.
Recording microbalance for the measurements of vapor diffusion through plastic
membranes.
Small-scale flexure test for laboratory testing of plastics.

Catalysts and Inhibitors

Author	Reference
3167. Banes, F. W., and Eby, L. T.	*Ind. Eng. Chem., Anal. Ed.* **18**, 535–8 (1946).
3168. Hermann, F. J., Talen, H. W., and Scheffer, G. J.	*Centraal Inst. Materiaal Onderzoek Afdel. Verf. Circ.* No. 68, 25 pp. (1950).
3169. Mohaupt, A. A., and Freas, A. D.	*U. S. Dept. Agr. Forest Service, Forest Products Lab. Rept.* No. 1825, 10 pp. (1952).
3170. Smith, A. L.	*Reinforced Plastics Div., Soc. Plastics Ind. Confer.*, 6th Annual, 1951, Sect. 1.

Glass Fillers

3171. Bainton, G. W., Jr., Guare, C. J., and Mathes, K. N.	*Reinforced Plastics Div., Soc. Plastics Ind. Confer.*, 9th Annual, 1954, Sect. 21.
3172. Collins, H. W.	*Modern Plastics* **21**, No. 9, 104–6 (1944).
3173. Fox, A.	*Reinforced Plastics Div., Soc. Plastics Ind. Confer.*, 8th Annual, 1953, Sect. 27C.
3174. Murgatroyd, J. B.	*J. Soc. Glass Tech.* **28**, 388–97 (1944).
3175. Smith, A. L.	*Reinforced Plastics Div., Soc. Plastics Ind. Confer.*, 7th Annual, 1952, Sect. 1.

Design Data and Nondestructive Tests

3176. Anon.	Research & Control Instruments Div., North American Philips Co., Inc., Mt. Vernon, N. Y. 8-p. booklet.
3177. Amidon, S. D.	*Ind. Radiography* **3**, 4, 21–3 (1945).
3178. Guinier, A.	*Chimie & industrie* **49**, 248–50 (1943).
3179. Howard, G. W.	*Reinforced Plastics Div., Soc. Plastics Ind. Confer.*, 7th Annual, 1952, Sect. 11.
3180. Kirkwood, W. A., and Richie, P. D.	*J. Inst. Production Engrs.* **23**, 91–153 (1944).
3181. Perry, H. A., Jr., et al.	*Reinforced Plastics Div., Soc. Plastics Ind. Confer.*, 9th Annual, 1954, Sect. 1D.
3182. Temple, R.	*Reinforced Plastics Div., Soc. Plastics Ind. Confer.*, 8th Annual, 1953, Sect. 17.
3182a. Dietz, A. G. H., Bockstruck, H. N., and Epstein, G.	*ASTM Spec. Pub.* No. 138, 1952.

Concerning

Determination of inhibitor concentration in polymers by ultraviolet-light absorption. Gives estimate of polymer stability.

Effect of ozone on properties of paint vehicles and other macromolecular products.

Effect of different catalysts and amounts of styrene monomer on strength and durability of glass cloth—plastic laminates.

Standards Committee report. Includes evaluation of catalysts.

Methods for evaluating effect of glass sizings on glass reinforced plastics, e.g., cyclic flexing of rod specimens.

Fabrication of experimental low-pressure laminates for test purposes.

Determination of effect of sizes on glass fibers for reinforced plastic laminates.

Apparatus for rapid determination of breaking strain of glass fibers. Effect of heat treatment on strength.

Standards Committee report. Glass fiber reinforcement, finished products.

Use of x-ray tools for nondestructive analysis.

X-ray control of plastics. Shows voids, distribution of filler, position of metal parts, impurities.

X-ray control of articles made of plastics. X-ray photographs show nature and distribution of fillers and uniformity of molding.

Review on testing, fabrication, and uses of reinforced plastics.

Testing of molded plastic products by x-rays. Uses of plastics in engineering.

Variations in preparation of resin-impregnated glass cloth test panels. Recommendations are given for standardization.

Interests of Research and Development Board in reinforced plastics, e.g., need for design data.

Nondestructive determination of mechanical properties and deterioration of adhesives.

Author	Reference
3183. Anon.	*Safety Manual for Operation of Copolymer Plant Laboratories.* Office of Rubber Reserve, Washington, D. C., 51 pp. (1946).
3184. Anon.	*Natl. Board Fire Underwriters, Research Rept.* No. 1, 53 pp. (1946).
3185. Anon.	Natl. Fire Protection Assoc., Boston, Mass. (1950).
3186. Anon.	Owens-Corning Fiberglas Corp., Toledo, Ohio. Fiberglas Standards PR6.A1, Sect. VIIIb (1950).
3187. Albisser, R. H.	*Chem. Eng. News* **31**, 2380 (1953).
3188. Baráil, L. C.	*SPE J.* **9**, No. 1, 14–5 (1953).
3189. Bradley, W. R.	*Reinforced Plastics Div., Soc. Plastics Ind. Confer., 6th Annual,* 1951, Sect. 16.
3190. Brown, A. E.	*Modern Plastics* **23**, No. 8, 189–95, 254, 256 (1946).
3191. Brown, H. R.	*Ind. Standardization* **17**, 53–5 (1946).
3192. Carpenter, C. P., *et al.*	*J. Ind. Hyg. Toxicol.* **26**, 69 (1944).
3193. Cranch, A. G.	*Ind. Med.* **15**, 168–70 (1946).
3194. Cummings, J. A.	*Penna. Dept. Labor Ind., Safe Practice Bull.* No. 88, 8 pp. (1942).
3195. Duverneuil, G., and Buisson, G.	*Arch. maladies profess. med. travail et securite sociale* **13**, 389–90 (1952).
3196. Erwin, J. R.	*Ind. Med.* **16**, 439–41 (1947).
3197. Gorbell, G. L., and Albisser, R. H.	*Chem. Eng. News* **31**, 2270 (1953).
3198. Gast, T.	*Deckema Monograph* **16**, 210–7 (1951).
3199. Hazard, W. G.	Rhode Island Ind. Health Inst. Transcript of speech (May 1943).
3200. Hopff, H.	*Kunststoffe* **42**, 423–6 (1952).
3201. Karel, L., Landing, B. H., and Harvey, T. S.	*J. Pharmacol. Exptl. Therapy* **90**, 338 (1947).
3202. Levey, S., *et al.*	*J. Am. Pharm. Assoc.* **35**, 298–304 (1946).
3203. Loeser, A., *et al.*	*Nauyn. Schmiedebergs Arch. exptl. Pathol. Pharmacol.* **221**, 14–33 (1954).
3204. McKinley, C. S.	*Ind. Med.* **16**, 432–4 (1947).
3205. McOmie, W. A., and Anderson, H. H.	*Univ. Calif.* (Berkeley) *Pub. Pharmacol.* **2**, 205 (1947).
3206. Meyer, G., and Stürmer, E.	*Arch. intern. pharmacodynamie* **90**, 193–202 (1952).
3207. Miller, O. G., and Blank, I. H.	*Leather and Shoes* **124**, No. 14, 8, 36–7 (1952).
3208. Moore, S. A., and Weber, A.	*Reinforced Plastics Div., Soc. Plastics Ind. Confer., 7th Annual,* 1952, Sect. 25.

HEALTH HAZARDS

Concerning

Handling instructions for flammable and explosive hydrocarbon mixtures.

Fire hazards of the plastics industry.

Code for prevention of dust explosions in the plastics industry.

How to handle glass fiber reinforced plastics: avoiding health hazards.

General rules for safety in manufacturing.
Biology of plastics. Health hazards, resistance of plastics to micro-organisms.
Industrial hygiene considerations in manufacture of reinforced plastics.

Resistance of synthetic resins and plasticizers to fungal growth. Recommended
    fungicides.
Bureau of Mines report on prevention of explosions of plastic dusts.
Health hazards connected with use of styrene.
Toxicity of plastics. General rules for protection of workers.
Causes and prevention of dermatitis in the plastics industry.

Dermatitis from hexamethylenediamine in nylon factory.

Health hazards of glass fiber plastics.
Organization of an industrial safety program.

Instrument for determining dust concentration in air.
Health aspects of glass fiber materials.

Thermal reduction of macromolecular compounds. Mentions health hazards
    involved.
Intraperitoneal toxicity of some glycols, glycol esters, and phthalates in mice.

Toxicity of fumaric acid.
Pharmacology and toxicology of diethylene glycol.

Health hazards from materials used in plastics manufacture and fabrication and
    basic principles for controlling them.
Toxicity of diallyl phthalate.

Pharmacology and toxicology of polyethylene glycols.

Dermatitis caused by shoe-adhesive ingredients, e.g., monobenzyl ether of hydro-
    quinone and mercaptobenzothiazole.
Effect of promoters and activators on cure characteristics of polyester resins.

	Author	Reference
3209.	Morris, G. E.	*Arch. Ind. Hyg. Occupational Med.* **5**, 37 (1952).
3210.	Rowe, V. K., *et al.*	*J. Ind. Hyg. Toxicol.* **25**, 348 (1943).
3211.	Schwalb, H. M.	*Ind. Labs.* **2**, No. 11, 7–11 (1951).
3212.	Schwartz, L.	*Plastics* (Chicago) **3**, No. 5, 48, 50, 52, 80, 82, 84 (1945).
3213.	Schwartz, L.	*J. Investigative Dermatol.* **6**, 239–55 (1945).
3214.	Schwartz, L.	*Penna. Med. J.* **53**, 593–8 (1950).
3215.	Siebert, W. J.	*Ind. Med.* **11**, 6–9 (1942).
3216.	Silverman, L., Schulte, H. F., and First, M. W.	*J. Ind. Hyg. Toxicol.* **28**, 262–6 (1946).
3217.	Smith, H. F., Jr., Carpenter, C. P., and Weil, C. S.	*J. Ind. Hyg. Toxicol.* **31**, 60–2 (1949).
3218.	Spence, H. D., *et al.*	*J. Ind. Hyg. Toxicol.* **24**, 295 (1942).

Concerning

Dermatological and chemical aspects of condensation plastics.

Health hazards connected with use of styrene.

General safety practices for laboratories.

Health hazards in manufacture and use of plastics, including modified alkyd resins.

Review on dermatitis from synthetic resins. Production of glass fiber reinforced plastic laminates outlined briefly.

Review of dermatitis caused by synthetic fibers and finishes.

Glass fiber health hazards investigations.

Studies of sensory response to certain industrial solvents, including diallyl phthalate. Values given for highest satisfactory concentrations for 8-hour exposure and for irritating concentration.

Toxicity data for various organic compounds, including allyl ether of propylene glycol and diallyl maleate.

Health hazards connected with use of styrene.

UNCLASSIFIED REFERENCES PUBLISHED AFTER JUNE 1, 1954

Author	Reference
3219. Anon.	*Chem. Eng. News* **32**, No. 46, 4614–5 (1954).
3220. Anon.	*Chem. Eng. News* **33**, No. 6, 512–3 (1955).
3221. Anon.	*Modern Plastics* **32**, No. 4, 121–5, 233 (1954).
3222. Bello, F.	*Fortune* **51**, No. 3, 110–3, 166, 169 (1955).
3223. Byars, E. F.	Paper presented at Am. Chem. Soc. Meeting, Div. Ind. and Eng. Chem., New York, September 1954.
3224. Calhoun, L. M.	*Modern Plastics* **32**, No. 2, 132–6 (1954).
3225. Carlson, E. F., Lum, F. G., and Johnson, G. B.	Paper presented at Am. Chem. Soc. Meeting, Div. Paint, Plastics, and Printing Ink Chem., New York, September 1954.
3226. Cummings, W., and Botwick, M.	Paper presented at Am. Chem. Soc. Meeting, Div. Ind. and Eng. Chem., New York, September 1954.
3227. Dean, R. T., and Manasia, J. P.	*Interchem. Rev.* **13**, No. 4, 91–9 (1954); *Modern Plastics* **32**, No. 6, 131–2, 134, 136, 138, 233 (1955).
3228. Dorst, R. W.	*Western Plastics* **2**, No. 2, 24–6 (1955).
3229. Goldfein, S.	*Reinforced Plastics Div., Soc. Plastics Ind. Confer., 10th Annual,* 1955, Section 7D.
3230. Izard, E. F.	*Chem. Eng. News* **32**, No. 38, 3724–8 (1954).
3231. Katz, I.	*Papers Presented at 11th Annual Nat. Tech. Conf., Soc. Plastics Eng., Inc.,* Vol. 1, 149–72 (1955).
3232. Rible, U. F.	*Reinforced Plastics Div., Soc. Plastics Ind. Confer., 10th Annual,* 1955.
3233. Sonneborn, R. H. *et al.*	*Fiberglas Reinforced Plastics.* Reinhold, New York, 1954, 350 pp.
3234. Stevens, J. N., and Goodwin, P. M.	*Reinforced Plastics Div., Soc. Plastics Ind. Confer., 10th Annual,* 1955, Section 7I.
3235. Sweitzer, C. W., Lyon, F., and Grabowski, T. S.	Paper presented at Am. Chem. Soc. Meeting, Div. of Paint, Plastics, and Printing Ink Chem., New York, September 1954.
3236. U. S. Forest Products Laboratory, Air Force, Civil Aeronautics Authority, and Navy Bureau of Aeronautics.	*ANC-17 Bulletin on Plastics for Aircraft* (Revised). To be published in 1955.
3237. Yaeger, L. L.	*Amer. Paint J.,* July 19, 1954.

UNCLASSIFIED REFERENCES

Concerning

Market trends in resins. Gives estimated consumption of major resins, including polyesters.

New ICI plant for production of Terylene polyester fiber (Wilton, England).

Preimpregnated moldable glass fiber reinforced plastic sheet; available with controlled directional strengths.

Foams and solid rubber based on polyurethanes: preparation, properties, applications.

Plastic reinforced with parallel glass fibers for structural use (deck truss); superior to steel and aluminum on strength-weight ratio basis but has greater deflections.

Comparison of glass fabric finishes and fiber sizings: properties and application.

Application of isophthalic acid in unsaturated polyesters. Comparison with phthalic anhydride: increases softening point, viscosity, flexural and impact strengths, heat distortion temperature.

Monomer synergism in heat resistant polyesters. Improvement of heat resistance by mixture of triallyl cyanurate and diallyl bicyclo[2,2,1]-hept-5-ene-2,3-dicarboxylate.

Use of stabilizers to retard darkening of cured polyester resins caused by exposure to ultraviolet light.

Comparison of three methods for determination of light transmission through reinforced plastic panels.

Prestressing of reinforced polyester laminates; increases flexural strength and average stiffness.

Review of development of polyethylene terephthalate.

Recent advances with isocyanate-base polymers: elastomers, adhesives, potting compounds, greases, rocket propellants, expanded plastics.

Possible applications of reinforced plastics in the building industry.

Materials, theory, design, fabrication, finishing, and properties of glass fiber reinforced plastics.

Review of work by Navy Bureau of Aeronautics to improve structural characteristics of glass fiber reinforced plastics.

Effect of carbon black on cure and hardness of unsaturated polyesters; retards cure with peroxide catalysts, accelerates cure with peroxide-promoter combinations; increases hardness.

Properties of plastics used in aircraft. Includes compilation of data on glass reinforced plastic laminates.

Polyesters as coating materials.

Author	Reference
3238. Herr, R.	*Reinforced Plastics Div., Soc. Plastics Ind. Confer., 10th Annual,* 1955, Section 15D.
3239. Hibben, J. H., *et al.*	*U. S. Tariff Comm. Rept.* No. 194, Second Ser. (1954).

Concerning

Formable reinforced plastic tapes for electrical insulation: electrical properties and molding possibilities.

Synthetic organic chemicals. United States production and sales, 1953.

SUPPLEMENT

Since the text of this book was completed, expansion of the polyester field has continued at a rapid rate. This section was therefore prepared to summarize briefly some of the trends in the development of polyesters and their applications from June 1, 1954 to the date of publication.

* * * *

The polyester field appears to have turned away from a race to introduce as many innovations as possible, toward entrenchment and broadening of already established markets. This is being accomplished by the development of materials with a specific range of properties for a given end use and by increased emphasis on better design and engineering.

UNSATURATED POLYESTERS

Resins

Keeping pace with the entire plastics industry, polyester resins had a big year in 1954 and their biggest year in 1955. In comparison with 1953, production was almost doubled in 1954 and more than doubled in 1955. Sales in 1954 and 1955 lagged somewhat behind production but still represented tremendous jumps over 1953. (The year 1954 was the first time that separate production and sales figures were reported for polyester resins by the U. S. Tariff Commission.) Reinforced plastics accounted for the largest volume use of polyester resins.

Year	Production Pounds	Sales Pounds
1955[1]		
For reinforced plastics	51,296,719	43,919,319
For all other uses	3,533,467	3,178,548
Total	54,830,186	47,097,867
1954[1]	49,019,000	43,443,000
1953[2]	26,000,000	27,000,000

[1]From statistics compiled by U. S. Tariff Commission.
[2]See p. 194 of text.

A recent trend in the resin field is for major suppliers to concentrate on the development of polyester resins for specific purposes (see chapter on Commercial Resins, p. 131) rather than continued over-extension of the use of general-purpose resins (1).

Raw Materials

From the standpoint of new raw materials for polyesters, perhaps the most important event was the starting up of Standard Oil of California's new isophthalic acid plant late in 1955 (2,3). This plant is expected to reach a production rate of 50 million pounds per year in 1956. The use of isophthalic acid in unsaturated polyesters could help relieve periodic shortages of phthalic anhydride due to fluctuating demand and scarcity of high-cost naphthalene. Isophthalic acid polyesters are similar and in some respects superior to phthalic anhydride polyesters (p. 165).

Alpha methyl styrene is now available in fairly large quantities (several million pounds per year) from Hercules Powder Co. (4). This compound is somewhat like styrene monomer but is slower in reaction and will not homopolymerize with peroxide catalysts. An ionic catalyst must be used to polymerize alpha methyl styrene. In polyester resins alpha methyl styrene reduces the peak exotherm or maximum temperature rise during polymerization.

Modification of polyesters with silicones is reported to greatly improve thermal stability (5). Silicone-modified polyesters showed decided superiority over unmodified polyesters (selected for their high thermal stability) in terms of flexural strength retention after 64 days of aging at 225°C.

Reinforcements

Much work is being done to adapt the unique qualities of various reinforcements to scientific engineering of reinforced polyester products. Glass is still far in front as the prime reinforcement for polyesters, but certain non-glass reinforcements are making a strong bid for use in specialized applications (6,7).

Nylon, Dacron[3] polyester, and Orlon[3] acrylic fibers, in particular, have advantages which provide a very sound basis for promoting their use with polyesters. These synthetic fibers possess high tensile strength but are less stiff and more tough than glass fiber and can be machined with less tool wear. Reinforcement of polyesters with them is advantageous in applications requiring greatly improved resistance to abrasion, surface erosion, and flexing, as well as outstanding surface finish and high strength. They also have excellent electrical properties, good chemical resistance, lighter weight than glass fiber, and good bonding properties with resins. They can be easily bonded together into uniform non-woven structures (needled batts) by mechanical means, thus eliminating the need for binders and lubricants which introduces problems with glass.

The following are general recommendations for choosing nylon, Dacron, or Orlon as reinforcement for polyesters:

(1) Where a high degree of translucency is desired, bright nylon fibers are best.

[3]Du Pont trade names.

(2) For exposure under alkaline conditions, nylon is best.

(3) For exposure under acid conditions, either Dacron or Orlon is preferred.

(4) All three fibers offer a marked advantage in abrasion resistance over glass. However, where exceptionally high abrasion resistance is desired, either nylon or Dacron is preferred.

(5) Dacron provides the best electrical properties over a wide range of frequencies and is particularly outstanding where high humidity or moist conditions prevail.

(6) For overlay applications, all three fibers in the form of needled batts provide excellent surfaces. However, if subsequent procedures involving sanding of the surface are to be used, Orlon is recommended. The sanded Orlon reinforced part can be wiped clean with a special solvent to create a smooth polished surface that is capable of accepting a high finish.

Asbestos also is making inroads into traditional glass fiber territory, especially in high temperature-high stress applications such as high-speed aircraft and guided missiles. Asbestos reinforcements are available in a variety of forms, including felts, mats, papers, fibers, cloth, and yarn (8).

A third type of non-glass reinforcement which has recently broadened its base of application in the polyester field is sisal fiber. This fiber is used to a considerable extent in premixes for molding small automotive parts, where it provides adequate strength at lower cost than glass fiber (9). (Synthetic fibers are also being considered for use in polyester premixes for compression and transfer molding because of their non-abrasiveness, flexibility, and easy flowability.)

It is not likely that any of the non-glass reinforcements will supersede glass as the principal reinforcement for polyesters, but instead, they will supplement it in opening new applications and expanding established ones. They will probably find one of their biggest outlets in reinforcements in which they will be used in conjunction with glass, for example, as surface overlays.

Despite its well established position, there are continuing efforts to improve the over-all performance of glass fiber reinforcement. With respect to improved mechanical properties for glass reinforced polyesters, there have been two main approaches: (1) stronger bonds between the glass fiber material and the resin and (2) better orientation of the glass filaments. Recent developments have provided several examples of these approaches.

Additional evidence has been obtained that the vinyl trichlorosilane finish developed by Yaeger (p. 86) gives the optimum properties in polyester laminates. In long-term tests (90 days and 1 year) on glass-reinforced laminates at the U. S. Forest Products Laboratory, laminates with this finish consistently had the highest wet flexural strength and the lowest percentage of moisture absorption (9a). In British tests, vinyl trichlorosilane has been found to be very effective for improving both the wet and dry strength of high-alkali glass fiber, which is a very poor reinforcement unless treated (9b).

Further refinement of the principle of the vinyl silane chemical bonding finish has led to a chemical finish which appears to be more versatile than any other glass finish now in commercial use (10). The NOL 24 finish, which was developed by Erickson and Silver at the Naval Ordnance Laboratory, is a reaction product of allyl trichlorosilane and resorcinol. In pilot plant tests, laminates made with 181 style cloth and polyester, epoxy, and phenolic resins all had ultimate flexural strengths of over 100,000 pounds per square inch (11).

Because of the unidirectional properties of glass fiber rovings, cloth woven from this type of reinforcement gives high strength to a laminate. Several weavers have developed weaves in which the warp is heavy woven rovings held together by very fine yarns which serve as the fillings (7).

Fabrics produced by another new type of weave are claimed to give a higher stiffness modulus and higher ultimate strengths in both directions of laminates than conventional weave fabrics (12). These new fabrics are composed of two separate systems of yarns. The heavy yarns, which constitute the load-carrying elements, are made to lie flat and never cross over and under each other as in conventional weaves. Very light binding yarns (only 7% of the fabric by weight) interlace with each other to hold these heavy yarns, but they are so light that they do not crimp the straight densely packed "structural" yarns.

Two other developments in glass fiber reinforcement are of interest from the standpoint of improved formability. One is a mat constructed of looped continuous strands rather than conventional chopped strands (7). This mat can be easily formed and does not need to be tailored accurately; a square placed in a mold will take the desired form without tailoring. The other is a knit elastic glass fiber fabric which is especially suited for use in curved or cylindrical surface laminations (13). The elasticity of the knit stitch allows full flexibility of stretch.

Fabrication

In the fabrication of reinforced polyesters, the trend continues toward increased use of hydraulic presses and matched metal dies for mass production of uniform-quality products. Even in such fields as the boat industry, which has almost completely relied on slow, no-pressure methods in the past, this trend is evident. One molder, using a set of molds weighing 65,000 pounds to produce a 15-foot one-piece boat hull, reported that he turns out 50 hulls a day instead of the five formerly possible (14).

Probably the most suitable alternate to matched metal dies is pressure bag molding, which can be used for shorter, continuous runs justifying a semi-permanent tool. A new development in this field is a glass fabric reinforced pressure membrane which is capable of producing 400 to 500 polyester resin-glass fabric laminated parts, in contrast to the "one-shot" polyvinyl alcohol bag now generally used (15).

The solubility of air in polyester resins has been advanced as a possible explanation for the formation of bubbles and other defects in reinforced polyesters (16). Under the conditions of molding and laminating, the capacity of the resin to hold dissolved air changes and the air reappears in the form of such defects as bubbles, surface pits, voids, and pinhole leaks. Degassing of the resin under reduced pressure is recommended as the most efficient method of reducing or eliminating these defects.

Late 1954 saw the design and construction of the first complete plant intended expressly for the fabrication of reinforced polyester automobile parts (17). This plant makes parts for the Chevrolet Corvette body. However, prospects have faded for the entry of plastics in a big way in structural parts of automobile bodies. Faster production techniques than the present and greatly reduced finishing costs are needed.

Applications and Properties

The range of applications of polyesters and reinforced polyesters is still much the same as when the text of this book was written (see chapter on Final Products, p. 174), but the list of individual products continually grows. No attempt will be made to enumerate them, since this would involve a full-scale review of the literature which is beyond the scope of this supplement.

A more important trend to be pointed out in the applications field is the recognition of fabricators and consumers alike that reinforced polyester products must be designed on the basis of the limitations of these materials as well as their strong points. This trend was emphasized by the fact that the largest portion of the papers presented at the 11th Annual Conference of the Reinforced Plastics Division of the Society of the Plastics Industry in February 1956 were concerned with the strength properties and design of reinforced plastics. In previous Conferences the emphasis was largely on new types of resins and new applications of reinforced plastics.

Major emphasis has been placed on the strength-time behavior of reinforced polyesters, particularly since short-time laboratory tests have frequently failed to predict accurately the performance of these materials in service (19–23). One long-term testing program is underway at the U. S. Forest Products Laboratory where the long-time (for periods up to 5 years) stress-rupture and creep characteristics of reinforced plastics are being investigated (24). A time-temperature dependent modulus test has been developed for polyester resins used in reinforced plastics (25), laboratory results have been compared with service performance for reinforced polyesters in automobiles (26), and an analysis has been made of the long-term structural strengths of reinforced plastic pipe (27).

SATURATED POLYESTERS

Polyester Film and Fiber

The applications of polyester film (Mylar and Terylene, p. 220) continue to increase as its superior properties are recognized. This high-strength film can be metalized or laminated and can thus be used in combinations of thin-gage film (down to ¼ mil) with low-cost materials (28). A method of sealing the film into tubular form has been developed which uses benzyl alcohol applied to the edges of the film strips as a solvent cement (29). Recent price reductions should give added impetus to adoption of this film by the packaging industry (30). Other applications include recording tapes, drum liners, electronic capacitors, building insulation, reproduction materials for map and drafting work, and metalized textiles. Continuous production of motion picture film base made from polyester film was begun in 1955 (31).

Recent developments in the use of polyester fiber (Dacron and Terylene, p. 217) include the previously mentioned reinforcement of polyester plastics and the production of experimental high-strength papers. Papers produced from this fiber have outstanding resistance to chemicals and to sunlight, heat, moisture, and bacteria (32). Their unusual stability makes them of interest in the manufacture of maps and tracing papers, as well as for documents where permanence is required. Electrical applications are also a potential use.

Di-Isocyanate-Modified Polyesters

The biggest use of di-isocyanate-modified polyesters at present and in the immediate future is foam, both flexible and rigid. One producer has predicted that the total market for isocyanate-polyester foams may reach 100 million pounds annually in the next 5 years (9), but this expansion will depend on the development of adequate processing machinery for mass production (32). An important outlet for these foams is likely to be cushioning applications in the automobile (seats, doors, "crashproof" dashboards) and furniture industries (14).

The di-isocyanate-modified polyesters are also bound to find increasing application in all types of coatings where exceptional adhesion, tenacity, water resistance, weathering resistance, chemical resistance, or electrical properties are important (33,34). One proposed coating application of particular interest (see p. 178) is as a coating for the leading edges of high-speed aircraft where resistance to rain erosion, elasticity, and abrasion resistance are required (35).

REFERENCES

1. R. B. Seymour, "Plastics—Chemical Engineering Review 1954," *Ind. Eng. Chem.* 47, No. 9, 2011–5 (1955).

2. R. L. Van Boskirk, "Oronite Isophthalic," *Modern Plastics* 33, No. 4, 243 (1955) ("The Plastiscope).

3. Anon., "Chemicals for Plastics Soar," *Chem. Eng. News* 34, 69–70 (1956).

4. R. L. Van Boskirk, "Alpha Methyl Styrene," *Modern Plastics* 33, No. 1, 246 (1955) ("The Plastiscope").

5. F. A. Yeoman and D. A. Rogers, "Thermal Evaluation of Some New Thermosetting Resins," *Reinforced Plastics Div., Soc. Plastics Ind. Confer., 11th Annual*, 1956, Section 14-D.

6. J. Bjorksten, "Non-Glass Reinforcement for Plastics," *SPE J.* 12, No. 3 (1956).

7. Anon., "What's New in Reinforcements," *Modern Plastics* 33, No. 6, 81–6, 210, 212, 214, 216, 218, 222, 224, 227 (1956).

8. D. V. Rosato, "Properties of Fibrous Asbestos in Reinforced Plastic Parts and Techniques of Fabrication," *Reinforced Plastics Div., Soc. Plastics Ind. Confer., 11th Annual*, 1956, Section 14-B.

9. Anon., "Automotive Plastics: 1956," *Modern Plastics* 33, No. 7, 89–94, 211–2, 214, 218–20 (1956).

9a. F. Werren, "Effects of Fabric Finish and Wet Exposure on Strength Properties of Glass-Cloth Polyester Laminates," *Wright Air Dev. Center Tech. Rept.* No. 53–483 (March 1955) (Air Res. Dev. Command, U. S. Air Force, Wright-Patterson Air Force Base, Ohio).

9b. R. B. King and E. W. Russel, "The Effect of Heat and Moisture on the Tensile Strength of Surface-Treated Glass Fibres," *Royal Aircraft Establishment Tech. Note* No. Chem. 1203 (Sept. 1953) (British Ministry of Supply, London).

10. E. L. Straus, "A Universal Glass Finish for Reinforced Plastics," *Materials and Methods* 43, No. 1, 106–7 (1956).

11. P. Erickson and I. Silver, "Improved Reinforced Plastics With the Universal Type Chemical Finish, NOL 24," *Reinforced Plastics Div., Soc. Plastics Ind. Confer., 10th Annual*, 1955, Section 7A.

12. J. Duflos, "A New Concept—High Modulus Fabrics for Improved Mechanical Properties of Reinforced Plastics," *Reinforced Plastics Div., Soc. Plastics Ind. Confer., 11th Annual*, 1956, Section 10-E.

13. R. L. Van Boskirk, "Knit Fabric Glass," *Modern Plastics* 33, No. 2, 268 (1955) ("The Plastiscope").

14. Anon., "Plastics Push Into Blue Chip Markets," *Modern Plastics* 33, No. 5, 97–113, 223 (1956).

15. H. S. Kraus, "Fibrous Glass Pressure Membrane," *Reinforced Plastics Div., Soc. Plastics Ind. Confer., 11th Annual*, 1956, Section 17-F.

16. A. L. Smith and J. R. Lowry, "Degassing—For Improved Quality," *Reinforced Plastics Div., Soc. Plastics Ind. Confer., 11th Annual*, 1956, Section 17-C.

17. Anon., "Application Progress: 1954," *Modern Plastics* 32, No. 5, 92 (1955).

18. G. M. Kline, "The Year 1955 in Review," *Modern Plastics* 33, No. 5, 135–6, 138, 140, 142, 144, 149, 150, 152, 154, 156, 234–7 (1956).

19. C. R. Stock, "Strength-Time Behavior of Reinforced Plastics," *Reinforced Plastics Div., Soc. Plastics Ind. Confer., 11th Annual*, 1956, Section 1.

20. B. J. Lazan, "Strength Properties, Design Requirements, and Service Performance, An Introduction to Engineering Concepts," *Reinforced Plastics Div., Soc. Plastics Ind. Confer., 11th Annual*, 1956, Section 1-A.

21. H. R. Sheppard, Jr. and E. H. Van Antwerp, "Creep Characteristics of Reinforced Plastics at Temperatures up to $600°F$," *Reinforced Plastics Div., Soc. Plastics Ind. Confer., 11th Annual*, 1956, Section 1-C.

22. A. Rufolo, "A Creep Test of Plastics Under Face Compression," *Reinforced Plastics Div., Soc. Plastics Ind. Confer., 11th Annual*, 1956, Section 1-E.

23. B. B. Pusey, "Effect of Time, Temperature, and Environment on the Mechanical Properties of Glass-Reinforced Thermosetting Plastics," *Reinforced Plastics Div., Soc. Plastics Ind. Confer., 11th Annual*, 1956, Section 8-A.

24. K. H. Boller, "Effect of Long-Term Loading on Glass-Fiber-Reinforced Plastic Laminates," *Reinforced Plastics Div., Soc. Plastics Ind. Confer., 11th Annual*, 1956, Section 1-B.

25. J. R. Lawrence, "A Time-Temperature Dependent Modulus Test for Polyester Resins Used in Reinforced Plastics," *Reinforced Plastics Div., Soc. Plastics Ind. Confer., 11th Annual*, 1956, Section 5-C.

26. J. G. Coffin, "Laboratory Results vs. Serviceability for Reinforced Plastics in Automobiles," *Reinforced Plastics Div., Soc. Plastics Ind. Confer., 11th Annual*, 1956, Section 6-B.

27. H. D. Boggs, "Analysis of the Long-Term Structural Strengths of Reinforced Plastic Pipe," *Reinforced Plastics Div., Soc. Plastics Ind. Confer., 11th Annual*, 1956, Section 8-C.

28. Anon., "Polyester Film Earns Its Title: Mighty Beauty," *Modern Plastics* 33, No. 3, 85–90, 218, 224 (1955).

29. R. L. Van Boskirk, "Packaging Laboratory," *Modern Plastics* 33, No. 4, 238 (1955) ("The Plastiscope").

30. R. L. Van Boskirk, "Mylar Prices Trimmed Again," *Modern Plastics* 33, No. 7, 35 (1956) ("The Plastiscope").

31. Anon., "Long-Playing Movie Film," *Chem. Eng. News* 33, 4392 (1955).

32. E. E. McSweeney and E. L. Kropa, "Plastics and Resins—Annual Review, 1955," *Ind. Eng. Chem.* 48, 22A–27A (1956).

33. J. Bjorksten and B. Harker, "Isocyanate Resins," *Modern Plastics Encyclopedia* 1955, 145–7.

34. Anon., "Isocyanate Resins for Coatings," *Paint Varnish Prod.* 45, No. 12, 25–31, 97; No. 13, 25–30, 70–1 (1955).

35. C. B. Reilly and M. Orchin, "Preparation and Properties of Polyurethane Coatings," *Ind. Eng. Chem.* 48, 59 (1956).

INDEXES

INDEX OF AUTHORS, COMPANIES, AND ORGANIZATIONS

INDEX OF SUBJECTS